ECONOMICS OF AGRICULTURAL PRODUCTION,
MARKETS, AND POLICY

THE IRWIN SERIES IN ECONOMICS

Consulting Editor
LLOYD G. REYNOLDS
YALE UNIVERSITY

ECONOMICS OF
AGRICULTURAL PRODUCTION,
MARKETS, AND POLICY

JOHN P. DOLL
Professor of Economics and Agricultural Economics

V. JAMES RHODES
Chairman, Department of Agricultural Economics

JERRY G. WEST
Professor of Agricultural Economics

All of the University of Missouri

1968
RICHARD D. IRWIN, INC.   Homewood, Illinois
IRWIN–DORSEY LIMITED   Nobleton, Ontario

First Printing, February, 1968

Library of Congress Catalog Card No. 67–29144
PRINTED IN THE UNITED STATES OF AMERICA

PREFACE

This book treats some of the more important parts of agricultural economics at the next level past principles. Because of our belief that the undergraduate curriculum in agricultural economics should (and will) increasingly emphasize the fundamentals of economic theory, we have deliberately kept the treatment theoretical. Because of our belief that theory can best be mastered when its uses are demonstrated, we have included liberal applications to current problems. While cognizant of the dangers of premature application of elementary theory, we believe that irrelevance is the greater threat to effective undergraduate learning.

The book contains three distinct parts: production economics, competition and market theory, and agricultural policy. Each part is reasonably self-contained and designed to be used as a text in each of the three areas. When one portion is selected as a text, readings from the other sections can be used to augment students' backgrounds or provide complementary knowledge. Teachers using nontheoretical texts in farm management, marketing, or prices may find a useful theoretical supplement in this book. Finally, the entire book is designed as a text for an intermediate course in agricultural economics, providing that interweaving of theory and application which is the hallmark of our profession.

The section on production economics was drafted by Doll, the theory of markets by Rhodes, and the agricultural policy by West. The subject matter was in large part taken from undergraduate courses we have taught at the University of Missouri. Each of us reviewed the chapters of the others. In addition, we gratefully acknowledge the reading of one or more chapters by Harold Breimyer, Darrell Fienup, Clyde Cunningham, Kenneth Boggs, J. C. Headley, Dale Colyer, Amir Khalili, Thomas Hall, and Angela Lancaster. We offer the usual caveat: errors of omission and commission are ours, not theirs.

Since a text is anything but original, we acknowledge our indebtedness to economists as far back as Adam Smith. We acknowledge gratefully the interest and support of Dean Elmer R. Kiehl of the University of Missouri, College of Agriculture.

University of Missouri

January, 1968

JOHN P. DOLL
V. JAMES RHODES
JERRY G. WEST

TABLE OF CONTENTS

versus Private Sorting. Problems of Grading: *Confusion of Ends and Means. Obtaining and Maintaining Accuracy. Differing Grade Requirements at Various Market Levels. Grade Boundaries and Names and Product Design. Interference with Merchandising and Product Differentiation.* Some Further Theoretical Considerations: *Competitive Relationships among Grades. Designing the Grade Standards.* Attempting to Maximize Consumer Expenditures through Design and Manipulation of Grades. The Political Economy of Grading Lambs: *Industry Conflict about the Fat Problem. Industry Disagreement and Congressional Intervention. How Many Working Grades? The Second Revision.* Summary.

PART IV. AGRICULTURAL POLICY

and the General Economy. Contributions of Agriculture to Economic Development: *Increased Food Supplies. Increased Exports. Increased Capital. Release of Labor. Increased Demand for Nonfarm Inputs.* Future Contributions of Agriculture: *Provision for Food and Fiber Needs. Source of Manpower. Assistance in World Economic Development Programs.* Problems Economic Growth Poses for Agriculture: *Impact on Demand and Cost of Production. Adjustments on Farms and in the Marketing System.*

APPENDIX

INDEX

PART I

Introduction

Chapter 1

INTRODUCTION

WHAT IS AGRICULTURAL ECONOMICS?

Economics centers around the use of resources to satisfy the needs and desires of a nation's citizens. The basic tenet of economics is that in any society at least some of the needed resources are limited in quantity—if resources were unlimited, no economic problem would exist. The economist, then, studies the economic system of the nation to determine how the resources of society might be most efficiently used to attain its goals. The economist may study resources, firms, industries, or an entire economy.

The agricultural economist applies the techniques and principles of economics to agricultural problems. He is interested in the efficient production and distribution of agricultural products. Further, he is interested in determining the types of agricultural products consumers want to buy. Some agricultural economists specialize in farm management, with the goal of increasing efficiency on individual farms. Others study the processes involved in marketing agricultural products. Still others study the consumption habits of users of agricultural products. In recent years, many economists have turned their attention to a study of government programs for agriculture.

Historically the agricultural economist has emphasized the study of farmers' problems. The problems of individual farmers are important; a significant portion of this text will be spent developing principles useful in managing farms and understanding farm problems. It has become increasingly evident, however, that the problems of agriculture are not independent of the rest of the economy. Moreover, the responsibility of agricultural research workers lies not only in bettering the economic position of the farm population but in increasing the efficiency of resource use in society as a whole and thereby benefiting all. For, as agricultural efficiency is increased, resources may be freed from production in agriculture and used to produce other goods. Thus, many agricultural economists now study the interrelationships between agriculture and the rest of the economy in an attempt to determine the causal forces behind many of the problems facing agriculture.

3

Procedures of the Agricultural Economist

When the soils specialist wishes to determine the effects of fertilizer on crop yields, he selects a plot of ground, lays out an experiment including varying rates of fertilizer, and measures the resulting yields. In a like manner, the chemist or the physicist may establish fundamental relationships through experimentation under carefully controlled laboratory conditions. The agricultural economist is not as fortunate—he must study a system of which he is a part and over which he has no control. When the economist would like to know the effects of a change in corn price upon the economy, he cannot change the prevailing market price of corn. How does he proceed? One way would be to guess—and this method is used all too often in our society, although, hopefully, not by professional economists. Another solution would be to write all possible alternatives on slips of paper and draw one at random from a hat. This method might not be superior to guessing. Rather than rely on such exotic procedures, the economist prefers to rely on a careful study of the economy around him.

Because he cannot artificially regulate the economy to determine the effects of a price change, the economist must rely on a complex system of logic.[1] He observes the economic system in an attempt to establish cause and effect relationships. These cause-effect relationships can then be used to deduce the effect of a given change. For instance, he might determine that a reduction in the price of steak would (1) cause present steak eaters to increase their consumption of steak and (2) stimulate people who presently eat hamburger to switch to steak. From this, the economist would deduce that an increased quantity of steak could be sold if the price of steak were reduced, i.e., the demand curve for steak slopes downward to the right.

The usefulness of economic principles depends upon their conformity with the actual situation; therefore, economists continually check and recheck their findings. If steak turns out to be the type of product people buy because it is high priced and if they purchase it only to demonstrate they can afford it, a reduction in the price may decrease sales unless the price reduction enables a less well-endowed but more numerous group of consumers to prove they too can afford it. In economics, as in any type of logical argument, the right conclusion can result from the wrong assumptions or vice versa. More often, however, the wrong assumptions lead to the wrong conclusion. Thus, the economist must continually check and recheck his assumptions and logic.

[1] Even if an economy could be regulated at the investigator's wish, there is little assurance that the results would be valid. Because of the importance of expectation in economics, the effect of an induced price change probably would not be the same as that of a real price change.

The logic of the economist, called economic theory, does not describe the real world in minute detail. It more truely represents models of the real world. Indeed, little advantage would be gained by developing a theoretical system as complicated as the real world, for the purpose of theory is to provide propositions of general usefulness that abstract from the infinite detail of the real world. The world is full of facts. Some facts are useful to a problem; some are not. The theory of the economist serves to identify useful facts and tie them together so that meaningful conclusions may be derived.

Economists present their principles in different ways. Some use geometry and graphs, some use mathematical symbols, and some prefer verbal discussions. Regardless of the method of presentation, they all seek the same thing: a set of principles useful in coordinating economic facts and making predictions and evaluations beneficial to society.

UNITED STATES AGRICULTURE—AN AGGREGATE VIEW

This text is concerned with both the progress and the problems of agriculture. But first, what is agriculture? In a society such as ours, the raw materials produced by farmers must be transported, processed, and distributed. There is, therefore, a tendency to use "agriculture" as an all-inclusive term referring to farmers and all others involved in producing farm inputs, processing food products, and placing the final product in the hands of the consumer. Viewed in this manner, about 20 percent of the 72 million people employed in the United States in 1965 were engaged in some phase of agriculture; 5.6 million were employed on farms and 8 or 9 million produced supplies and inputs used by farmers or were engaged in processing and distributing.

Agriculture is more often used to refer directly to farmers, that is, those directly involved in the production of raw food and fiber. When used in this way, agriculture is synonymous with the farm economy and agricultural products with farm products. When agriculture is so defined, only 5.6 million of the work force of 72 million were employed in agriculture. The appropriate definition of agriculture is perhaps somewhat arbitrary and depends upon the purpose of the user. For the discussion immediately following, "agriculture" is used to refer to the farm economy.

Farmers are in the business of feeding people, both at home and overseas, and the number of people in the world is increasing. Since 1910, the population of the United States has more than doubled, increasing from 92 million at that time to 194 million in 1965. At the same time the farm population dropped from 32 million to 12 million.

Personal income in the United States has also been increasing. In 1934, one of the Great Depression years, per capita personal income in the United States was $424; per capita income of farm people that year, $166, was approximately one third that of nonfarm people, $512. By 1965, even though population had tripled, per capita personal income increased to $2,748. And by this time, per capita farm income, $1,664, had increased to 57 percent of nonfarm income, $2,821. Even though these income estimates are not deflated, the increase is clearly substantial.

More people and more money would appear to make the future of the food business bright, and in many ways it is. But the picture is not simple—it never is. Although in 1910 people did not seem to have much money, they probably spent a lot of it on food. Estimates are not available for years prior to 1929, but by 1930, 24 percent of disposable personal income was spent on food, and by 1950, 22 percent. Since 1950, the percent of disposable income spent on food has decreased further to 17 percent.

Expenditures for food must be divided between marketing costs and farm value. Marketing costs represent all the costs of moving, processing, packaging, and placing the food on the grocer's shelf. Farm value represents the farmer's share. Between 1950 and 1965, farm value dropped from 8.7 to 5.4 percent of disposable income while the marketing bill dropped from 12.6 to 11.1 percent. Thus, as incomes have increased, the U.S. consumer has spent relatively less on food. The explanation for this is not complicated: as incomes increase, people who are not starving to begin with have little need for more food—better, perhaps, but not more. Therefore, increases in income are spent on houses, cars, clothes, travel, appliances, or other luxury items.

The first key point, then, is that consumers will prefer better but not necessarily more food. The marketing bill has in recent years remained at a rather stable 11 percent of disposable income; in many cases this means that part of the food preparation previously done at home is now done before the food product is sold. In other cases, new food products requiring more processing are being sold. Notice that this does not necessarily imply that the marketing sector of agriculture is receiving revenue which would otherwise go to the farmer, the raw material producer in agriculture. Rather, it often means that by improving its product the marketing firm is receiving a share of the increasing disposable income which might otherwise be spent outside of the food industry.

A second key point in the trend to better eating in the United States centers around the selection of food the housewife takes home. A general examination of the trends in eating habits from 1910 to the present shows that fruit and vegetable consumption per person increased until after World War II and has stayed steady since that time. Meat, fish, and poultry consumption has increased steadily since 1945 while consumption of dairy products and eggs has declined. Per capita consumption of potatoes and cereal products (wheat and other grains) has decreased almost steadily since 1910. As incomes increase, starchy foods are replaced by meats (protein) and fruits and vegetables. Of course, increased income is not the only influencing factor behind these trends. Technological changes, such as refrigeration and quick freezing of foods, influence eating habits. Another effect has been the increase in the urban population with its professional people, white-collar workers, and blue-collar workers in automated factories who neither want nor need the heavy foods once thought required for hard manual labor. As a result of mass advertising, women and men are more style and hence weight conscious. In recent years, findings of medical research have influenced food buying habits. All of these factors influence what the housewife carries home from the market and ultimately what farmers will grow.

FIGURE 1–1

REALIZED GROSS AND NET FARM INCOME, UNITED STATES, 1910–65

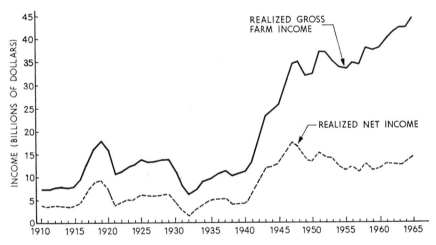

The percent of disposable income consumers spend on food is decreasing, but the amount of money spent for food is increasing. Thus, while agriculture is receiving less by relative measure, it is receiving more by absolute measure. Larger consumer incomes and increased numbers of consumers have more than offset the tendency of the consumer to spend less of each dollar on food. Realized gross farm income, defined as the sum of the cash value of livestock and crop marketings, government payments, rental value of buildings, and home consumption of farm products, is presented in Figure 1–1 for 1910 to 1965. In 1910, realized gross farm income was about $7 billion. Except for declines after the peaks attained in World War I and World War II and a drastic drop during the depression years, realized gross income increased steadily to a high of almost $46 billion in 1965. Realized net income, which is realized gross minus production expenses, is also shown in Figure 1–1. Realized net income roughly followed the same time path as realized gross (at a lower level) until 1947. Since 1947, realized gross, although subject to ups and downs, has surpassed the 1947 peak while net income has trended downward, never again to attain the 1947 peak, which occurred after World War II when our farmers fed a hungry Europe.

The difference between realized gross and realized net income is production expenses, set out more clearly in Figure 1–2. Except for a

FIGURE 1–2

FARM PRODUCTION EXPENSES, UNITED STATES, 1910–65

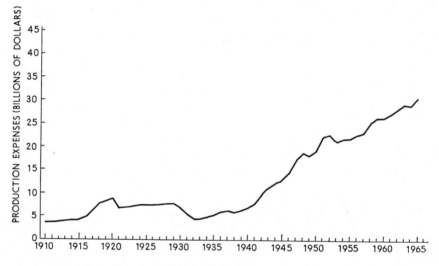

slight drop after each war and a more severe drop during the depression, production expenses have increased steadily. In 1910, production expenses were about $3.5 million or 50 percent of realized gross. By 1965, they had increased to $31 billion or 65 percent of realized gross.

The following picture has been established: Gross income to agriculture has been increasing—but so have production expenses. As a result, net income to agriculture has dropped from 1947 levels and has been fluctuating around $13 billion in recent years. But, as was mentioned before, per capita income in agriculture has been increasing. This increase has resulted from two factors: (1) a reduction in the number of farms and (2) an increase in nonfarm income accruing to farm people.

Off-farm employment is an increasingly important source of income for people living on farms. By 1965, approximately one third of the per capita income of farm people was earned off the farm. While off-farm work is obviously important, we are at this point more interested in establishing the productivity and profitability of resources used on farms. To do so, we turn to an examination of the number of farms and income per farm.

Figure 1–3 depicts trends in number of farms and total net income per farm (realized net plus inventory changes). Again using 1947 as a focal point, farm numbers have decreased steadily since that time while total net income per farm fluctuated below the 1947 level and only climbed above as late as 1960. The point to be made is that since 1949 an increase in income per farm has occurred. Farm size has increased as numbers decreased. Average farm size in 1967, 359 acres, was double that of 1900, but more significantly, average farm size has increased over 160 acres since 1945.

FIGURE 1–3

NUMBER OF FARMS AND TOTAL NET FARM INCOME PER FARM, 1929–65

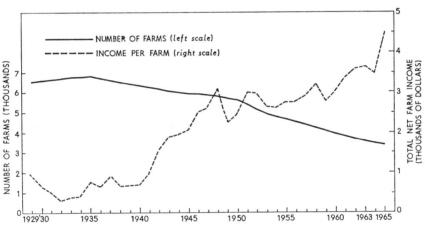

Obviously all farms do not share equally in the gross income of agriculture and all farmers do not earn one third of their disposable income off the farm. How is agricultural income divided? Some answer to this is supplied by data from the 1964 Census of Agriculture. Five percent of the farms, each selling over $40,000 worth of product, controlled 33 percent of the land and sold 42 percent of the total value of agricultural products. Farms with sales over $10,000, approximately 42 percent of all commercial farms, controlled 69 percent of the land, harvested 66 percent of the cropland, and sold 82 percent of the total value of product. These same farms, although only one third of the total number of farms, incurred almost 84 percent of the total expenditures for productive items listed by the Census. Thus, the distribution of earning in agriculture is skewed towards large (measured in volume of sales) farms. While farming does not appear to be a highly profitable occupation on the average, in actual fact many very profitable farms do exist in the United States today.

In summary, the total gross income to agriculture is increasing, despite the fact that each year the farmer gets a smaller share of the consumer's dollar. The total agricultural "pie," however, is not evenly divided—great differences exist in the earnings of agricultural firms. Reasons for this are many, and some will be touched on later. Farms are of different size, raise many varied products, and have managers of different temperament. Probably one of the most striking reasons, however, is the differences that can exist within the definition of a farm. In 1964, a place of 10 or more acres could be counted as a farm if sales from the place were $50. If less than 10 acres, sales had to amount to $250. Obviously the economic forces affecting these small farms differ from those facing the large California farm with over a million dollars in assets.

TABLE 1–1
(Billion Dollars)

	1945	1950	1955	1960	1965
ASSETS					
Physical Assets:					
Real estate	53.9	75.3	98.1	129.9	159.4
Nonreal estate:					
Livestock	9.0	12.9	11.2	15.6	14.4
Machinery and motor vehicles	6.3	11.3	16.2	22.3	25.7
Crops stored on and off farms	6.7	7.6	9.6	7.8	8.9
Household furnishings and equipment	5.6	8.6	10.0	9.6	8.7
Financial Assets:					
Deposits and currency	7.9	9.1	9.4	9.2	9.6
U.S. Savings bonds	3.4	4.7	5.0	4.7	4.2
Investments in cooperatives	1.2	2.1	3.1	4.8	7.2
Total Assets	94.0	131.6	162.6	203.9	238.1
CLAIMS					
Liabilities:					
Real estate debt	4.9	5.6	8.3	12.3	18.9
Nonreal estate debt to:					
Commodity Credit corporation	0.7	1.7	2.2	1.2	1.5
Other reporting institutions	1.6	2.8	4.0	6.7	10.0
Nonreporting creditors	1.1	2.4	3.3	4.9	7.1
Total Liabilities	8.3	12.5	17.8	24.9	37.5
Proprietor's equities	85.7	119.1	144.8	179.0	200.6
Total Claims	94.0	131.6	162.6	203.9	238.1

SOURCE: *Agricultural Statistics*, 1962, Table 639; *Agricultural Statistics*, 1966, Table 641.

As a final view of agriculture, and lest the reader think that agriculture is a declining industry financially as well as in the marketplace, a balance sheet for agriculture is presented in Table 1–1. Total assets in agriculture have increased from $94 billion in 1945 to $238.1 billion in 1965. Proprietor's equities, the part farmers own, increased $114.9 billion during the period, indicating that total liabilities (debts) increased only $29.2 billion. Thus, the value of assets increased and most of this value accrued directly to proprietors.

THE ECONOMICS OF PRODUCTION

The aggregate view of agriculture masks much of relevance to the agricultural economist. Although some farms are large relative to others, agriculture is composed of many farms that are small relative to the industry as a whole. How *do* individual firms react to the changing impact of the economic forces described above? How can the economist determine how they *should* react?

Changing consumer demands affect the prices offered for farm products as well as the prices charged for agricultural inputs. How is farm output affected by a change in output prices? Input prices? When will an input price change cause a resulting change in the method of production? Will the output of small farms and large farms react similarly to a price change?

Agriculture is typified by technological change. How do new inputs and new methods of production evidence their impact upon various segments of agriculture? How will production respond? What farms are most likely to be hurt (or helped) by a technological advance? When will specialization result?

Individual farmers must be prepared to cope with changes of the type just mentioned plus changes caused by the weather, credit availability, leases and rental arrangements, government programs, etc. The basic logic used by the agricultural economist to study problems of this nature is presented in Part II of this text, The Economics of Production. The principles set forth in that section might be called the "economics of farm management," although any such paraphrasing can never be satisfactory. Based on the premise of profit maximization, a deductive system is established to determine the "normative" reaction of the farm business to economic stimuli. The analysis is "normative" in the sense that it suggests a reaction based upon what the farm manager should do if he is to maximize profits—not what he actually does.

The principles of the economics of production are applicable to many types of businesses; they are not unique in any way to agriculture. In a sense, they represent a body of knowledge that economists must know before they can do economic analyses. Thus, just as a football player must know the rules of the game and the techniques of blocking, tackling, and other fundamentals of execution before he can play on a professional football team, so must the aspiring agricultural economist master the principles of Part II before he can undertake the job of an agricultural economist.

THE ECONOMICS OF AGRICULTURAL MARKETS

Competitive rivalry is one of the strongest forces affecting our economic system. In Chapters 11–17 we examine competition among farmers, among agricultural processors, among retailers, and among many other agribusiness firms. The understanding of many vital current issues depends upon an understanding of the interaction of economic forces within our markets.

Some issues and questions are as regular as the spring robins. Why are marketing margins so high? Why are farmers price takers while marketing firms are price makers? When x million hogs were sold one year for less total dollars than $x - 2$ million hogs were sold for the preceding year, why did farmers produce those extra hogs? Is it economically rational for a farmer to continue to feed 900-pound cattle after prices of cattle have fallen so low that the feeder is confident that he will lose $20 a head?

Farmers tend to believe that farm prices are made in Washington and in the corporate headquarters of retail food chains and food processors. Farmers are seldom satisfied with the levels of farm prices received. In the sixties the chain stores more than the meat-packers seem to be receiving criticisms of farmers. It is widely charged that the purchasing and/or the merchandising policies of chains hold down livestock prices. Sometimes these criticisms are inconsistent. Generally, high margins are criticized on the assumptions that retail price minus margin equals farm price, and the higher the margin the lower the farm price. Why does steak sell at retail for $1.29 when Choice cattle are only $0.25? A representative of the American National Cattlemen was expressing this concern about margins when he attacked a national packer for negotiating an "excessive" wage increase with its union. On the other hand, retailers are often criticized by farmers for consistently featuring low-price beef or hams or broilers. In this case, it is charged that a low price image is created which reduces the demand for the product at any normal price level. Thus the middleman is criticized for both too high and too low margins.

Promotion and merchandising are also issues which divide. On the one hand, the National Food Marketing Commission in its 1966 report was critical of the growing orientation of food marketing firms to merchandising and promotion. One of its principal criticisms of industry efficiency "is the cost devoted to selling efforts that yield little value to consumers."[2] On the other hand, many farm commodity groups have voluntary checkoffs or other programs for financing campaigns to promote and merchandise milk, meats, cotton, fruits, etc. Is it "better" for a farm group to advertise livestock products than for a meat-packer to advertise his brand of meat? When most nonfarm products are sold through effective advertising and merchandising, can farm products compete in any other way? Do the sales and incomes of hog producers largely depend upon how many new pork products are developed by processors and how effectively pork is merchandised by processors and retailers? Does federal grading of beef and lamb aid or hinder efficient and effective merchandising?

In the mid sixties there were "housewives rebellions" against high food prices and against certain retail practices such as stamps and giveaway contests which were alleged to increase consumer prices. There was a lively debate in the press as to whether trading stamps do increase prices. After the "rebellions," stamps and contests remained in many chains. Do retailer trading stamps raise food prices or lower farm prices or have no effect? Would such merchandising gimmicks continue to be used by retailers if their customers didn't "want" them?

You may recall seeing a cartoon of an elephant saying, "everyone for himself and free competition for all," as he pranced through a crowded broiler house. What does "free competition" mean when the sizes of the competing firms are sometimes as unequal as the elephant and the chickens? Some of the larger agribusiness firms have sales exceeding the combined sales of tens of thousands of the smaller farmers. Almost every farm sells to and buys from firms much larger than it. Is there any way that little firms can obtain market power equal to that of their larger rivals?

Several farm organizations have attempted to develop bargaining power. The organized holding actions of the National Farmers Organization in milk and livestock attracted nationwide attention. The American Agricultural Marketing Association of the American Farm Bureau began bargaining with processors of certain fruits and vegetables and of broilers in the mid sixties. Many farm organizations supported a bill in 1967 called the "Marketing Rights Bill" which would prohibit any processor from economic discrimination against farmers who engage in group bargaining. What are the economic limitations upon such bargaining activities by farmers? How are the economic consequences of group bargaining related to the type of competition existing among farmers? Is it to the advantage of farmers to try to obtain bargaining power equal to

[2] National Commission on Food Marketing, *Food from Farmer to Consumer* (Washington, D.C.: U.S. Government Printing Office, 1966), p. 101.

marketing firms? Should farmers rely solely upon government programs such as price supports? Should farmers recognize a "community of interest" with marketing firms and strive to cooperate with them in every way possible? More and more problems of farm policy are centering on farm markets and the exercise of economic power within them.

The markets in which many farmers sell are changing rapidly. The market for broiler chickens was virtually eliminated by vertical integration. An agricultural economist has predicted that one half of the nation's broiler chickens will be produced by 12 companies by 1970. Terminal markets for livestock in many areas handle only minor fractions of the sales. How is pricing information to be collected and disseminated when most sales are by private treaties made on individual farms and feedlots scattered over several states? So few eggs are sold through a terminal market that some substitute is being sought as a price indicator. Serious thought is being given to prices being set by a committee of buyer and seller representatives. Can a price equating supply and demand be determined by a committee? What kind of a free market is that? A USDA study indicates that weekly terminal market prices of cattle were depressed by a large packer buyer on that market via the slaughter of his own-fed cattle.[3] Does this study lend support to those farmers seeking legislation to prohibit the feeding of livestock by meat processors?

Our agricultural marketing system can only be described in superlatives. It is difficult to appreciate the immensity of the tasks of assembling, sorting, processing, storing, moving, distributing, and selling millions of tons of perishable foods. Likewise, it is difficult to comprehend the complexities of a system that distributes fresh eggs from thousands of producers scattered over the United States to more than 50 million consumer households. We take for granted equally complex systems which speed Grade A milk from sanitary farms to more than 200 million consumers—a system that always has sufficient milk available regardless of seasonal and other fluctuations in production and demand. Sometimes such a market channel includes hundreds of independent firms who somehow coordinate their actions with speed and efficiency. How do agricultural marketing firms compete? Are they really selling goods or services? How are prices determined at each level of the market—retail, processor, and farm? Why are some marketing firms giants while others are one-man pygmies? Does federal grading provide a market advantage to smaller firms? Are the special prices advertised by food retailers each weekend evidence of fierce price competition among retailers? What are the economic means by which affiliated independent retail firms have managed to keep pace with the chains?

[3] Arnold Aspelin and Gerald Engleman, *Packer Feeding of Cattle*, U.S. Department of Agriculture Marketing Research Report No. 776, November, 1966.

These questions are examples of those which relate to the economics of markets, i.e., to the interactions and relationships among competing firms. Almost every firm and every individual is a competitor. The nature of the competition varies rather greatly from one market situation to another. A study of the economics of markets in Chapters 11–17 will throw light on several basic market situations and on many current issues.

THE ECONOMICS OF POLICY

Neither farms nor marketing firms may ignore the presence and influence of government in the economy. Why? Would the results of decisions reached by farmers and the executives in marketing firms be unacceptable in the absence of governmental action? What are the conditions which give rise to pressure for rules, regulations, services, subsidies, and other activities of government which have an impact on firms operating in the agricultural economy?

Government involvement in the operation of the economy has obviously increased in recent decades. This is also true for the agricultural industry. Apparently a significant segment of society feels that the situation in the absence of public action would not be in line with the values and goals held with respect to agriculture. What kinds of values and goals are involved? As the economics of production and markets are examined, it would be a good idea to think about the extent to which the behavior of firms and the results of their actions coincide with the values and goals widely held in our society.

Economic conditions and the nature of government involvement in the agricultural economy have varied greatly over time. For example, how do public policy needs in periods such as the depression of the 1930's differ from those of wartime or the postwar era of near full employment and rapidly advancing agricultural technology?

With widely varying economic conditions and philosophical value systems, the degree of government involvement and the appropriate approaches to problems are controversial in nature. To what extent is overcommitment of resources in agriculture likely? Is agricultural output excessive? If so, how should supply be regulated or controlled? Would it be possible to expand the demand for agricultural products? To what extent can segments of the agricultural industry solve their own problems with a minimum of government assistance? The situations giving rise to such questions are constantly changing so the approaches must also change.

The policy questions being asked changed markedly during the decade of the 1960's. The emphasis shifted from problems of surplus stocks and excess productive capacity to means of increasing farmer bargaining power. How can farmer bargaining power be increased? Are withholding actions the answer? Are marketing orders the appropriate tool for more commodities? What role can cooperatives play? Are price supports and purchase programs no longer needed? Would surpluses or lower prices result if all government efforts to restrict production were eliminated?

World food needs continue to receive a great deal of attention. Farmers, leaders of farm organization, administrators of agricultural policies, and society in general must consider the effects of the changing situation throughout the world on the U.S. agricultural economy. Will there be a need for all the farm products our farmers can produce? Is the situation changing from one of excess capacity to a need for production incentives? Must exports be subsidized or will the developing countries be able to buy through the normal marketing channels? Is the "golden age" of agriculture just around the corner or will there continue to be a need for government price and income programs?

Since Utopia cannot be achieved with any single approach or combination of approaches to policy issues, it is necessary to search for general principles and insights which will have more general application. Economics will not provide all of these principles but will help. The concluding chapters of this book attempt to focus on some of the important policy issues, proposed solutions, and economic principles which are helpful in understanding government's role in the agricultural economy.

PART II

The Economics of Production

Chapter
2

A VIEW OF PRODUCTION
ON FARMS

The purpose of this chapter is to develop definitions basic to the study of production on farms as viewed by the agricultural economist. First, production is defined and an example of farm production is presented to illustrate the biological and technological environment in which the farmer must work. Second, based upon the example given, definitions and assumptions to be used in this section of the text are explained. Finally, the role of management in the production process is reviewed and the viewpoints of the economist and the manager are compared.

THE PRODUCTION PROCESS

Production is a process whereby certain goods and/or services are used to create goods and/or services of a different form. The goods and services used in the production process are called resources or inputs; and the resulting goods and services are called goods, outputs, products, or yields. The purpose of the production process is, of course, to produce a good that has more utility, and hence value, to society than the inputs used in the process.

This definition of production, common in textbooks of economic theory, is, to say the least, pure. It abstracts from all the complex milieu within which farm production by nature must take place. The farmer must cope with diverse and constantly changing economic, technical, and political influences. When studying the development of principles useful for economic analysis, it is important that the overall complexity of the agricultural production process not be forgotten. To illustrate this complexity, an example of the development of a particular type of farm in one area of the United States is presented next. As the description unfolds, the reader should observe the effects of government policies, technological developments resulting from industrial research far from the farm, weather, war and peace, prosperity and depression, and other economic factors, not to mention the complexity of the biological growth process of the crop and the problems involved in its management.

19

Farm Production, an Example

There are many agricultural production processes and probably no one typical process. However, one example should suffice to demonstrate the biological, institutional, and economic limitations within which the farmer must function. Thus a description of one type of farm production—winter wheat production in the northern Great Plains—will be presented to provide an overview of farm production. The Great Plains is a large area, extending from Texas to Canada, and the facts and figures presented are generally descriptive of cash-grain farming in Montana but not meant to be applicable to specific farms or areas.[1]

The climate in the northern Great Plains is semiarid (12 to 18 inches of annual rainfall) with cold winters and hot summers. The humidity is low; sunshine and strong winds often prevail. The area was among the last populated in the United States; land was still being homesteaded in the decade following 1910. Although farms in the area were initially small, limited in size by homestead laws, farm size has increased steadily until the present when farms of 2,000 acres or more predominate. This increase in farm size has been stimulated by increased technology, largely in mechanization, and by the occurrence of price-cost relationships that encouraged rapid adjustments.

Some history of agricultural development in this area is instructive in understanding how the farm production process is influenced by farmers' decisions, nature, and economic and political developments outside agriculture. Three types of farms predominate in this area: cash-grain, cattle and sheep, and river-valley irrigated farms. This discussion centers around cash-grain farms. These farms are in essence single-enterprise firms producing high-protein winter wheat for cash sale. Before mechanization, some feed grains were grown, and in recent years barley has been grown on cropland diverted from wheat production by government programs.

Homesteaders were allowed to claim up to 320 acres. Good weather and good prices prevailed from 1914 to 1920—Europe's war needs had to be met, and nature cooperated. In the 1920's a run of poor weather years commenced and prices declined, in no small measure as a result of declining export demands. Many farms were abandoned—farms in Montana decreased 19 percent between 1920 and 1925.

The fact was that the farms as established under the homestead laws were too small. Wheat farming in that area required large acreages of land relative to labor; that is, an adequate return to the farmer's management and labor was best earned by applying it to lots of land.

---

[1] Gordon E. Rodewald, Jr., Donald K. Larson, and D. C. Myrick, *Dryland Grain Farms in Montana,* Montana Agricultural Experiment Station Bulletin 579, July, 1963.

This was a change for the settlers, many of whom came from the Midwest or Europe, where farms were small and crops labor intensive. Thus, the crop technology of the time demanded larger farms.

On the other hand, farmers needed increased power to farm increased acreages. Horses, the primary source of power at that time, were not well suited to extensive agriculture. Most settlers didn't have the capital to obtain fine work animals (had they been available) and often didn't possess the husbandry experience to care for the animals they had. While crop technology demanded larger farms, farm power technology did not allow it, except to the exceptional manager. With falling prices and poor weather, many settlers pulled up stakes.

The first development permitting increased farm size was the 12-horse team of the early 1920's. These were rapidly supplanted by tractors as the decade passed. Tractors were adopted much more rapidly in dryland wheat areas than in the United States as a whole during this period because of the inadequacies of horsepower and because the first tractors, large and cumbersome, were best adapted to the wide open spaces. Expansion of farm size continued throughout this period, slowed during depression of the 1930's, and was again stimulated by wartime demands and good weather during the 1940's. Wheat prices in the early forties were high relative to debts incurred in the prewar years—thus, debts were easily paid and substantial amounts of farm income set aside for expansion. Technological advances in cropping and mechanization following the war, plus accumulated savings, stimulated further increases in farm size. The cost-price squeeze of the fifties affected these single-enterprise farms more severely than other areas of the United States and provided further incentive to increase farm size in the search for the benefits of large-scale production.

Land, free for the taking at the turn of the century, was valued at close to $100 an acre by 1960. Land quality and hence values vary greatly in the Great Plains. But in one study of the Montana Triangle farming area, cropland values were estimated to have ranged from $2 per acre in the 1920's to $115 per acre in the decade of the fifties. Government wheat control programs in effect during the 1950's and early 1960's allocated a permitted wheat acreage to each farm based on historical acreages and yields. Thus, the farmer interested in expansion had to buy "extra" land to obtain the wheat acreage he needed. The value of these allotments probably enhanced land values. Also, considerable price stability resulted from the program. This, along with increased yield stability due to technology, reduced the risk involved in large operations compared to 30 years past.

At present a large farm in this area would have perhaps 2,500 cropland acres. A fallow-cropping rotation would be used—each year half of the cropland lies fallow and is tilled both for weed control and moisture preservation. The other half would be planted to wheat and barley.

The cropping routine follows a typical pattern: Harvest occurs in late July or early August. The stubble lies untouched through the early fall. Due to the moisture requirements of the recent crop, the soil is usually quite dry during this period. If sufficient rainfall occurs in September, weeds, particularly grasses, may spring up in the stubble. If left until spring, these grasses may form a heavy sod and become difficult to kill, with the result that they will produce seed and use precious moisture from the soil. A common practice is to till the fall stubble (if weeds appear) with large offset discs or toolbars with spiked shovels mounted on large spring shanks. Such equipment, pulled by the large crawler or wheel tractors used in the area, enables one man to till up to 100 acres a day.

In the spring, late April or early May, the farmer will begin summer fallowing in earnest. The fallow fields will be tilled three to six times during the summer months using the large offset discs or toolbars. The purpose of this tilling is to prepare a smooth seedbed for fall planting, to work last year's stubble into the ground, and, most important, to kill weeds that sprout after rains which would deplete soil moisture if allowed to grow. Thus, part of the rainfall occurring during the fallow period is conserved in the subsoil for the next year's growing period.

Plows, either of the moldboard or disc variety, are no longer used in this area. Plows were used by the first settlers, and their use prevailed into the 1940's. However, plowing was slow, and thus expensive in both fuel and labor requirements, and plows were unable to adapt to the widely varying soil conditions often found on farms in these areas. Thus, in the fifties, farmers switched to the large toolbars using spikes or sweeps mounted on springs and to the large discs mentioned above.

In the fall, winter wheat is seeded in widely spaced rows using deep furrow drills. A common rule of thumb is to wait for rain before planting, but farmers have many opinions on the appropriate strategy. If moisture in the fallow is sufficient to stimulate fall growth, the farmer will usually decide to seed regardless of fall rains. If the soil is too dry to support plant growth, farmers will wait for rain. If, as sometimes happens, no rain occurs, then wheat and barley can be planted in the spring. The planting decision is crucial because winter wheat must come up in the fall and undergo cold winter temperatures as a necessary part of its biological life process. Also, fall growth stimulates the seedling to "stool"—grow additional stalks. If the seed fails to germinate or a poor stand is obtained, then the farmer must tear it out and reseed with spring crops.

Wheat seed can be grown on the farm, but before planting, seeds are treated chemically to prevent diseases which historically lowered

yields or caused crop failures. At one time, treating was done on the
farm, but now commercial firms clean and treat most seed wheat. This
gain is not without a cost—transferral of the seed to a commercial
elevator and back provides an opportunity for contamination. Rightly or
wrongly, farmers often attribute the presence of certain weeds in their
crops, such as rye, to contamination during commercial treating.

In the spring of the second year the farmer must seed a spring crop
on fallowed land not previously seeded to winter wheat. Also, he must
evaluate the condition of his winter wheat and decide whether to re-
plant. Usually replanting is not necessary. At the same time, of course, he
must begin summer fallowing for next year's crop. Spring planting is
begun as soon as weather conditions permit fieldwork. If labor is scarce,
seeding will take priority over fallowing.

As the summer progresses and the wheat grows, weeds also grow.
Before the advent of chemical sprays, weeds grew among the wheat
plants in abundance, competing with wheat for moisture and making
harvest difficult. Now weed sprays can be used to eradicate all broad-
leafed plants. Farmers can purchase spray equipment or hire commercial
spraying by airplanes—most farmers choose the latter. Weed sprays have
eliminated broadleaf plants as a hazard, but with their demise has come
increased competition from grasses and plants such as rye. Such plants
can be killed by appropriate sprays, but, unfortunately, the same sprays
also kill wheat plants.

Harvest begins in late July or early August—some 11 months after
seeding and perhaps 22 months after the first fall work on the fallow
land. The crop brought in represents the culmination of the effects of
almost two years of work, waiting, and weather. The farmer reaps not
only his crop but the deserved results of his management and the
undeserved hazards of the climate.

Wheat in the Great Plains is allowed to ripen in the field and is then
harvested by self-propelled combines. Although Mother Nature has no
more positive effects to contribute, she can make some negative contributions. Hail is a summer hazard that does not diminish in August. Hot and
dry southerly winds can cause the ripened grain to shatter to the ground.
At one time farmers harvested their crops themselves. Now they have the
alternative of hiring harvesting services. Harvesters, called "custom cutters," own combines and trucks and will harvest and haul wheat to
market or storage. These men start in Texas and follow the harvest north
to Canada. By following the same route each year, many custom cutters
have established a reliable farmer clientele.

The degree of dependence to place on custom harvesters is an
important decision facing the farmer. The hired cutter may not do a good
job, or if he is good, he may be unavailable when needed. The farmer
may purchase the needed equipment to do all harvesting himself, but

such equipment is expensive and labor (hired by the day) may not be available at harvest time. Most farmers have some harvesting equipment—at least one self-propelled combine and grain truck. Such units will harvest from 40 to 80 acres a day, depending upon yields, and they can be operated with family labor. Farmers typically have different solutions—some do all harvesting themselves and some rely solely upon hired cutters. Many maintain a flexible policy, doing part themselves, trading with neighbors when possible, and hiring custom cutters. Always, they must weigh harvesting costs and losses against hail and wind damage losses.

After harvest, the farmer faces marketing uncertainty. While much price uncertainty has been removed by government programs, the farmer still has considerable flexibility in planning his sales. Emphasis in this section of the text is placed on the biological and production processes on farms; marketing and government programs will be discussed in later chapters.

Agricultural production is thus seen to be the culmination of time streams of inputs and decisions over an entire production period. Although returns are often realized only at one point in the period, usually the end, costs are incurred over the longer period. Because of this sequencing of costs and decisions, the farmer, once committed to production, must move forward. He must always measure possible returns against present and future costs, ignoring costs previously incurred (sunk costs).

FARM INCOME AND COSTS

In this section some of the basic definitions involved in farm budgeting will be presented. A farm budget for a typical wheat farm is presented in Table 2–1[2]. The farm has 2,520 acres of cropland, half of which is farmed each year. Eight hundred acres are eligible for wheat production (the farm has an 800-acre wheat base under the government wheat allotment program in effect when the budget was published in 1962), and the remaining 460 acres are planted to barley. This farm has 2,180 acres of pasture which the farmer could either use or rent, and for purposes of this example, it is assumed he chooses not to raise livestock.

Total revenue is the value of the production of an enterprise or farm measured in dollars. It is computed by multiplying the units of output by the selling price per unit of output for each enterprise and adding over all farm enterprises. Wheat averages 20.2 bushels per acre, and a total 16,160 bushels would be grown on 800 acres. Assuming the

[2] Data source is Le Roy C. Rude, *Land Use Alternatives for Dryland Grain-Livestock Operators,* Montana Agricultural Experiment Station Bulletin 571 (Bozeman, Montana, October, 1962).

farmer produces his own seed (one bushel per acre), 15,360 bushels would be sold. Cash earnings from the wheat enterprise is thus 15,360 × $1.61 = $24,730, when the price for wheat is $1.61 per bushel. For barley, average yield is 25 bushels per acre and the price per bushel, $0.59, but 1.25 bushels per acre must be sowed for seed. Cash earnings from barley is thus 10,925 × $0.59 = $6,446. The pasture is rented for a dollar per animal-unit month for a five-month season; total revenue for pasture rental was computed to be $715. Approximately 15 acres of native pasture will carry one animal for five months. Summing for the three enterprises, cash earnings for the farm are $31,891. This figure, of

TABLE 2–1

BUDGET FOR A 5,080-ACRE GRAIN FARM

	Acres
Land use:	
Winter wheat....................................	800
Barley...	460
Summer fallow..................................	1,260
Pasture.......................................	2,180
Farmstead and waste...........................	380
Total.....................................	5,080

	Dollars
Cash receipts:	
Winter wheat..................................	$24,730
Barley..	6,446
Pasture rent..................................	715
Total.....................................	$31,891
Cash expenses.................................	8,317
Net cash income...............................	23,574
Depreciation..................................	3,734
Net farm income...............................	19,840
Interest on investment........................	13,106
Labor and management income...................	6,734

SOURCE: Le Roy C. Rude, *Land Use Alternatives for Dryland Grain-Livestock Operators*, Montana Agricultural Experiment Station Bulletin 571, October, 1962.

course, represents an average of what could be expected over a period of time—annual revenues will vary substantially about this expected amount.

Cash earnings are the total incoming cash flow for the year. Total revenue and cash earnings are identical for pasture rent but not for wheat and barley. Total revenue for the grains exceed cash earnings by the value of the seed. The farmer who sells 99 hogs and keeps one to eat has the same total revenue as the farmer who sells 100 hogs. The total cash receipts of the two farmers differ, however, by the value of one hog. The hog kept for home consumption represents a noncash portion of total revenue. Other noncash items, such as value of firewood and garden products, are often relevant when computing total revenue for a farm. Noncash returns are often difficult to estimate accurately, but they should be included if possible when computing the total revenue for a farm.

Costs, like revenue, can be either cash or noncash. Cash costs are incurred when resources are purchased and used immediately in the production process. For the most part, cash costs result from purchases of nondurable inputs such as gasoline, labor, or grease, which do not last more than one production period.

Cash expenses can be determined directly from the farmer's account books. For the grain farm they total $8,317 and include such expenses as fuel, oil, labor, repairs, grain storage, seed treatment, weed sprays, insurance, taxes, custom work, etc.

Net cash income from the production period is determined by subtracting cash expenses from total cash receipts. The Great Plains wheat farmer thus has a net cash income of $23,574. This is not "pure" profit, however, because noncash costs have yet to be considered.

Noncash costs consist of depreciation and payments to resources owned by the farmer. Depreciation represents an attempt to spread the investment cost or purchase price of durable inputs over their productive lifetime. A durable input, such as a tractor, can be used profitably for 15 years. But when purchased, the tractor must be purchased in one piece, not 15 pieces. To charge the total purchase price of the tractor as a cost during the year of its purchase would distort the cost structure of the farm for the first year and for the next 14 years. Profits would appear too low the first year and too high the next 14. To remedy this, an annual depreciation charge should be levied against the farm expenses each year of the tractor's productive lifetime. When the tractor is worn out, it should be completely "paid for" by depreciation, thus insuring that capital will be available to purchase another. When farmers are unable to make depreciation payments because of low farm earnings, they are said to be "living off their investment." They use the depreciation fund to pay annual living and farming expenses and are unable to replace durable equipment when it wears out.

Depreciation of durable resources used only on one enterprise can be charged directly to that enterprise; depreciation should be charged each time the production process is repeated. On a farm, durable assets such as tractors, trucks, and combines are commonly used in several enterprises; that is, they are involved in several production processes. In such cases allocation of depreciation among the enterprises is difficult and the depreciation is charged against the farm business as a whole.

The wheat farmer in the example has $30,470 invested in machinery, buildings, and other improvements. The estimated depreciation on these capital items is $3,734 per year. He must, in effect, save that much each year or reinvest it in durables or he will eventually find himself with worn-out equipment. His actual cash income is thus reduced by the amount of depreciation to determine net farm income, $19,840.

Net farm income is the source of payments to the farmer's labor, management, and capital. Before considering these payments, we must digress to explain one of the most important ideas in economics—opportunity costs. Every resource used in the productive process has but one true cost: its opportunity cost. The opportunity cost of a resource is the return the resource can earn when put to its best alternative use. Suppose a farmer has a ton of commercial fertilizer. Suppose further that spreading it on his wheat field will add $150 to the total revenue from wheat while spreading it on his barley field will add $100 to the total revenue from barley. If he fertilizes the barley, his opportunity cost is $150—he has foregone $150 to earn $100. If he fertilizes the wheat, his opportunity cost is $100—he has foregone $100 to earn $150. The most return from a unit of input is realized when the actual earned return is equal to or greater than the opportunity cost.

The best use of the fertilizer in the example just mentioned was to fertilize wheat. No mention was made of the cost of the fertilizer, and, indeed, none is needed. Once purchased, the cost of the fertilizer is irrelevant to the problem. It is a sunk cost. Whether the fertilizer cost $100 or $1,000, its best use is on wheat. Suppose now that the purchase price of the fertilizer is $110 per ton and the farmer has not yet purchased it. He may now keep the $110, buy and fertilize wheat, or buy and fertilize barley. If he fertilizes wheat, his opportunity cost is $110, for he could have had that much by not buying anything. If he fertilizes barley, his opportunity cost is $150.

Now consider payments to the farmer's owned resources. Farmers own many durable resources, such as machinery or land, used in the production process. Once purchased these resources are used over several production periods. Even though they do not have a purchase price each year, these resources do have an opportunity cost—the money they would earn from their best alternative use. The alternative uses of many of the items on a farm, such as plows, fences, or trucks, may be difficult to evaluate. Their opportunity costs could be evaluated directly, but a much easier convention is usually adopted. A dollar value is placed on all resources owned by the farmer; that is, the total amount of his investment in land, machinery, buildings, tools, etc., is figured. The opportunity cost of these items is then defined to be the amount the total capital investment could earn if invested in its best alternative use. This opportunity cost is called interest on investment.

The wheat farmer has land, buildings, and fences valued at $236,035. If he invested this money at 5 percent in a bank, it would earn

$11,802 per year. He also has $21,735 invested in equipment. This amount invested at 6 percent would earn $1,304 per year. (Short- and long-run investments are sometimes valued at different earning rates. Why?) Therefore, the wheat farm must return $13,106 to the farmer as a return on his investment. If it does not, he should consider alternative investments—the $13,106 is the opportunity cost of his capital.

Family labor represents another noncash cost. When budgeting, charges can be made for family labor used on the farm. These charges represent salaries the farm operator and his family could earn if employed off the farm. Just as with interest on investment, these off-farm salaries represent an opportunity cost. Farmers can also charge themselves the opportunity cost of their management services. If the opportunity cost of family labor and management is zero, then no cost for these items should be charged against the business. Rather than attempt to estimate the opportunity cost of the farmer's labor and management, the budgeter often simply labels the residual earnings "Labor and Management Income." The farmer can then decide for himself whether the return is satisfactory to him. In this example, if he could earn $15,000 in the city, he could better invest his capital at its opportunity cost, move to the city, and have a disposable income of $28,106 (neglecting taxes).

Profit is total revenue minus total cost. Care must be taken when interpreting accounts to determine the appropriate amount of profit. Because noncash items may be included in revenues or costs, profit is not the same as net cash receipts. Also, the income to labor and management listed in Table 2–1 is not profit to the farmer. To compute profit from this figure the farmer must subtract the value of labor he has contributed to the farm business as well as the value of his management. Suppose that the wheat farmer has contributed $2,400 of labor to the farming operation and he values his management abilities at $4,000. Then his profit amounts to $334. This profit is not the farmer's personal disposable income. His personal income is rather the return on all owned resources including interest on investment ($13,106), returns to labor ($2,400), and management ($4,000), plus pure profit ($334). When the farmer owns his land debt free, this $19,840 always represents a personal earning; if the land were mortgaged, a portion of these returns would be used to meet principal and interest payments on the land, thus reducing income to the farmer.

What is the pure profit ($334)? Total cost, you remember, included payments to all resources used in production. These payments were based on the opportunity costs of the resources and were therefore large enough to keep the resources committed to the farm business. Interest on investment, representing the opportunity cost of durable resources, along with the cash costs of nondurable resources, family labor, and management charges, are included in costs so that even if profit is zero the farmer is paid for the use of all of his resources and will have no desire to shift them to other uses. Profit, then, represents the surplus earnings remaining after all resources are "paid."

There are several views on the function and meaning of profit. Some believe profit is the reward of the entrepreneur for visualizing and organizing a production process—that it is due him because of his enterprise and ability to innovate.[3] Another view is that profit is a reward for risk taking. Profit is thus viewed as the entrepreneur's reward for the mental and physical wear and tear incurred by organizing and seeing through a production process. A third view is that profit is the reward for natural or contrived scarcity of resources. The farmer may earn a high profit because his soil is both highly productive and scarce relative to other agricultural soils. This type of scarcity is due to nature, and in a free enterprise economic system those people either lucky or smart enough to own scarce resources are allowed to retain the profit earned by those resources. Profits from contrived scarcities occur when production is deliberately limited, i.e., a productive resource is held out of production, a shortage of the product occurs, market values of products are thereby forced up, and profits increased.

ECONOMICS AND MANAGEMENT

A study of the production process must be an abstraction of the process itself. The production specialist studies agriculture to formulate basic production relationships—the accountant to obtain a balance sheet of assets, costs, and returns. The manager is interested in the efficient organization of the process and, as such, studies the technical relationships of the production specialist and the cost-return figures of the accountant. The manager is interested in more, however, in that the manager hopes to shape all facets of production into a cohesive whole.

The Manager

Management is the art of recognizing a problem, determining what to do about it, and doing it. The need for management arises because of uncertainty, that is, lack of knowledge about what the future will bring. Any given situation is called uncertain if the manager is not sure of the outcome at the time he must make the decision. Because of the nature of the world and man's inability to foresee the future, most important decisions are surrounded by some uncertainty. Management attempts to cope with this uncertainty.

---

[3] The entrepreneur is distinguished from a manager. The former is a pioneer, founding and developing industries. The latter is hired to manage an established business. Most farmers function in both capacities. A third category, the executive, carries out the orders of management.

The management of the farm business, perhaps because its owner is usually also its manager, is inextricably bound to the values and goals of the manager. Values are the manager's concept of "what ought to be." Goals are the ends towards which he strives. Values determine goals while goals, in turn, determine the types of decisions made by managers. Shift in values and goals will influence the decisions made. The source and types of values held by managers comprise an important area of study but will not be investigated further here. The important thing to remember is that values are the determinants of a manager's choices, and because all managers are people and therefore differ, managers' choices will differ depending on their values.

Values and goals provide the framework for managerial decisions. The management process itself, however, defies description. Much like a good cake recipe, it is difficult to determine which part of the management process contributes most to the success of the process as a whole. Nevertheless, a study of the managerial process can reveal several important actions that must be taken by managers. Five functions of management have been described as:

1. *Gathering facts in order to learn new methods and identify problems.* Managers are concerned with change. If the world were a stable place and no changes were possible, managers would not be needed. On the other hand, if changes are never made, even when needed, the manager is again not necessary. Progress comes through change, however, and the good manager is always interested in making changes.

One of the primary purposes of gathering facts is to identify problems and determine when a change is needed. Often, the difference between a good manager and a poor one is that the poor manager never realizes until too late that a change is in order. Thus, the good manager keeps abreast of the facts. He may keep a careful set of books which enables him to compute profits or losses from each enterprise on his farm. When one particular enterprise on the farm begins to lose money, the manager will be immediately aware of it. Another way to gather facts is to drive around the farm regularly to observe the fences, crops, cattle, etc. The good manager knows how to divide his time among these different pursuits. For example, the farmer who spends all his time studying his farm records may find the fence down and the cattle out while the one who views with pride but keeps no records may soon find himself at his own auction sale.

The observation process continues until the manager has all the information he needs or until he reaches the point where it is not economically feasible for him to obtain more information. This latter point occurs when the cost of obtaining additional information is greater than its value.

2. *Analyzing facts to formulate alternative production plans.* Gathering facts is not enough. Facts must be tied together in a meaningful fashion. Most farm boys are familiar with the farmer who goes to town everyday to gather facts but never puts together a workable plan. Every good manager must devise a method of organizing facts into a coherent plan of action. Clearly this step is not independent of step one. As soon as he obtains his first information on a new subject, the manager probably also begins to formulate a system of analysis. As more information is obtained, it is added to the system. When the manager feels he has adequate information and has considered the problem, he makes a decision.

3. *Deciding on one of the production plans.* The basic element of management is decision making. When faced with a new problem, the manager can make an immediate decision. More than likely, however, he will want to gather facts, analyze them, reflect on the problem for some period of time, and then make a decision. Occasionally, due to extenuating circumstances, he may have to make an immediate decision, without recourse to additional data or time for additional thought. This is called a forced action situation; in such cases, the manager must rely on information and principles developed in the past. More often, time is available to make a decision, and if the manager makes it immediately without gathering additional knowledge, he does so because he wants to.

An open mind is important for the good manager. The open mind, however, should not be interpreted as one which will never make a commitment to a position or a choice from alternatives. In this stage of the management process, the manager should keep an open mind until the needed facts are available. Then, he should weigh the facts carefully in light of the relevant situation and make the best decision possible. If new facts become available, he should be willing and able to reconsider the facts and adjust the decision if necessary.

4. *Putting the plan into action.* After the plan is formulated and decided upon, it must be activated. This is known as the executive function. Managers vary in their ability to execute. Some managers plan poorly but execute very well while others plan well and execute poorly.

Putting the plan into action involves organizing and supervising labor. On the one-man farm, the manager is also the laborer and therefore faces the relatively simple problem of making himself work. As the size of the farm business increases and more equipment and men are needed to accomplish any given task, the complexities of executing a plan increase.

5. *Accepting the responsibility for the consequences.* The decision maker must bear the responsibility for the outcome of his decisions. The fact that the manager is liable for his mistakes increases his desire to avoid error. When the person making decisions is not responsible for the

outcome, the chances of an incorrect decision would seem to increase. While no more will be said about this managerial function, it is of equal importance with the four other functions.

The five functions of management are not mutually exclusive steps in the managerial process. The manager is involved in all steps at all times. The management process does not cease but rather flows like a river. New facts are being gathered and studied, decisions are being made and revised, responsibility is being assumed for previous decisions, and new problems are continually being faced. Thus, the five functions of management can no more be separated individually from the overall management complex than can the individual ingredients be separated from the baked cake. As with the cake, however, all ingredients of management must be present if a successful result is to be attained.

The farmer is unique in our present-day society in that he must still perform all the managerial functions. As opposed to other businesses, farm businesses have not enlarged to the point where the managerial functions can be handled by specialists. In the typical modern-day corporation for example, one group of people are the owners, a second group provides the management, a third group provides the executive ability, a fourth group obtains market information, a fifth conducts research on production techniques, labor is provided by still another group, etc. Thus, all people do not have to be good at all things. This is not true of the farmer, however. The farmer must be able to carry out all the functions of management. If he is weak at any step, the entire management chain can break.

The demands upon the farm manager have increased as the complexity and size of the farm business have increased. Not only are farms larger in acres but they require more capital and more technical knowledge. The stakes are bigger, the margin of profit per unit of production is down, and financial losses can be large. All of this makes all five functions of management much more crucial. At one time the farmer who could do some of the functions but not all of them could survive. Now the survival of such an individual is much less certain. The stress on the chain of management is severe in modern-day agriculture.

A study of the managerial functions should make clear the distinction between management and labor. Management carries out all five of the above functions while labor is concerned with only part of number four. That is, a man can be a farm manager and never sit on a tractor seat or pick up a feed bag. Most farmers, along with their wives, perform all of the managerial functions and also supply a large part of the farm labor. Successful farmers know the amount of time to devote to each. In these days of scientific agriculture, a farmer whose income is falling cannot necessarily offset that decline by going to work earlier in the morning. In fact, his best bet might be to devote less time to labor functions and more to managerial functions. The answer is not always to do more but to do the right things.

The Economist

The economist studies the farm from two viewpoints. First, he is concerned with the efficient use of resources on farms. Efficient as used here means gaining the maximum output from a given amount of input or using a minimum of input to achieve a given output amount. The inputs used in agricultural production are scarce and hence of value to society. The economist seeks a set of principles to insure the most efficient resource use both for the individual owner and society. Second, the economist is concerned with the firm as an economic entity within the industry and the economy. The reaction of the firm to changes in price, technology, government programs, or other economic stimuli are evaluated. To do this, the economist seeks to establish a set of logical principles from which the behavior of the firm can be deduced.

Even the simplest of farm businesses embodies many complex facets of economic reality. All of these cannot be presented in detail in one introductory exposition. Three basic questions of economic significance to be considered in this section include:

1. *How long should the production period be?* In crop production this question is answered for the farm manager. One complete growing season is required to produce a crop. Thus, land, labor, and capital used to produce crops are committed to a biological production period. Livestock production is more flexible. Although animals require at least a minimum amount of time to grow to market weights, this length of time can be varied by changing rates of feeding and by marketing at different weights.

Given the specialized durable equipment he has purchased for livestock production, the manager must determine how many groups of animals to process each year to maximize profits. For example, specialized hog producing units require large investments in farrowing houses, feed mixing and distribution systems, etc. The farm manager would like to spread the high cost of this equipment by feeding out as many hogs as possible per year. In each case, however, he must weigh the increased feeding costs and the possible higher market weights against the gain obtained by spreading fixed costs among more hogs. The same problem occurs in beef, dairy, broiler, and turkey production. It is commonly called the replacement problem and is discussed in Chapter 7, along with a brief introduction to the complex problems of capital investment.

2. *How can the manager insure he will be in business at the end of a production period?* Survival of the fittest is one of the basic tenets of our economic system. The business that cannot compete will eventually be forced out of production. In the short run, the manager must contin-

ually strive towards survival of the firm. The Montana homesteaders unable to survive the low prices and drouths of the early twenties and thirties were unable to capitalize on the good prices and weather during World War II. Thus, given the length of time chosen for the production process, the manager's primary interest is to be in business when the next production period arrives.

The economist studying the production process from this standpoint must necessarily emphasize management. Stress is placed upon the manager's goals. The uncertainty of the production process is investigated, and possible actions of the manager under uncertainty are explored. The effectiveness of management "strategies" are determined. Even the elements of such problems are not simple; an introduction is presented in Chapter 8.

3. *How should production be organized within a production period?* The answer to this question comprises the main portion of the elementary theory, called the theory of the firm, to be studied in this text (Chapters 3 to 6). The economist studying this problem relegates to a secondary role the replacement and survival problems of the manager and concentrates upon the analysis of the relationships among inputs and outputs. The length of the production process is taken as given, for simplification only, and uncertainty arising through time is considered nonexistent. With these complications removed, the relationships among inputs and outputs, costs and revenues, and profits can be examined and general principles developed which, despite their development in such a pure state, have wide applicability to actual production processes.

The interests of the manager and the economist coincide in many respects. One wonders whether it would be more difficult to explain their similarities or differences. The manager is not primarily interested in the economists' view of the firm as an economic entity, reacting to outside stimuli, but it would not be fair to suggest that the manager is not interested in such reactions for they might well put him out of business. The economist is not primarily interested in how management achieves the job of production, only that they do, but again he is not disinterested because management policies or attitudes may affect reaction to economic stimuli. While the line between the two is difficult to draw, it does seem fair to say that economic theory does supply the manager with some of his tools. The economic principles of resource allocation developed in the following chapters are useful to the manager wishing to maximize profits. The manager needs more, however. The theory of production in economics proceeds from the assumption that the manager uses the best possible production techniques. The manager, on the other hand, must be concerned with all the problems in implementing such techniques. The economist attempts to abstract from many of the difficulties of management in order to study more fully the economic aspects of the production process.

Economics and Goals

Farmers have many and varied goals. Ideally, any analysis attempting to develop a set of principles for the farm manager to follow should consider all possible goals of all possible farmers. In practice, of course, this is impossible, for there are probably as many goals as there are farmers, and the result would mean a separate analysis for each farmer. Faced with this situation, the economist must find a reasonable alternative to establish as a goal towards which the principles of production economics are directed.

Two reasonable goals for the theory of the firm are (1) efficiency and (2) profit. From the standpoint of society, it seems reasonable to utilize all resources as efficiently as possible. Resources freed from the production of food and fiber can be used to manufacture other goods, cars, television sets, rockets, bombs, etc. Thus, efficient production enables society to receive more products from the total amount of resources. This is true regardless of who owns the resources or who consumes the added product.

At first sight profit does not seem like a fitting goal for an analysis, given the diversity of values found among people in any of the walks of life. Many farmers have not established money as their primary goals. In general, the objective of any farmer is to maximize satisfaction, where satisfaction means the sense of accomplishment accruing from the attainment of all goals, whether long run, intermediate, or short run. To attain this objective, principles of allocation could be developed to enable a farm family to accrue the most satisfaction for their time, money, and other resources. In fact, the principles of economics, properly interpreted and applied, will do just that. The problem is that a universally applicable method of measuring satisfaction cannot be found. While each person in our society apparently is able to measure his own level of satisfaction, comparing levels of satisfaction among different people has met with little success. Because of this, one person is unable to determine when another person's satisfaction is a maximum or sometimes even when it is increasing or decreasing.

To circumvent the problem of measuring satisfaction, the theory of the firm uses an alternative goal for the farm manager: the maximization of net farm income. Without worrying about goals and preferences that influence a man to select farming as a vocation, the basic assumption of this goal is that once he is a farmer he will want to use his time and resources as effectively as possible. There is no way of determining which of two farmers with equal resources is accruing the most satisfaction, but most people would probably agree that barring other differences, the one with the higher income is not worse off. Thus, the production economist is forced to take the position that whether profit is a short-run, intermediate, or long-run goal, it does not conflict with other goals sought by the farmer. This does not seem to be an unreasonable assumption.

The Economic Setting

This section will digress from the mainstream of thought to review the type of market in which farmers buy and sell. A more complete discussion of market structure can be found in Chapters 11 to 16.

To begin with, the analysis of a farm business can be broken into three parts: (1) the characteristics of the markets in which the firm purchases its resources; (2) the technical and economic characteristics of the production process within the firm, that is, the nature of costs, profits, etc.; and (3) the type of market in which the firm sells its products. These three facets of the firm's economic existence are not independent. Even though this part of our study is primarily concerned with production within the individual farm, the markets in which farmers buy and sell cannot be neglected, for they will influence his buying and selling policies.

Types of markets are classified according to the number and size of the firms which sell the product, the number of buyers who purchase the product and the amount they purchase, the similarity or lack of similarity among products sold by the firms, and the ease with which firms may enter into or cease production of the product. Consider the farmer as a seller. Farmers all over the nation produce and sell wheat, corn, beef, pork, etc. For any one product, corn, for example, so many sellers exist that the quantity sold by any one seller is infinitely small compared to the quantity sold by all the other sellers. The quantity of corn produced by one farmer is a drop in the bucket compared to the total amount of corn produced annually in the United States.

There are many sellers of agricultural products—but that is not all. Agriculture products of a given type are similar in appearance and quality. Thus farmers sell a homogeneous product. The corn or hogs raised by one farmer may be of higher quality than one of his neighbor's but may still be similar to the corn or hogs produced by a large number of other efficient farmers. The important thing, in any event, is that buyers of the agricultural products are either unaware of minor differences or regard them as unimportant. To the buyer, hard red winter wheat with a given protein content is the same regardless of who grew it and number two corn is number two corn regardless of where it originated. In general, buyers do not prefer the products of one farmer to the products of a second. The result is that individual farmers are unable to create a unique demand for their own particular products by special marketing methods such as advertising.

The two conditions, many sellers and homogeneous products, mean that an individual farmer cannot influence the market price of his product. If he holds his product off the market, prices will not increase due to reduced supply because his production is an insignificant portion of the total production. On the other hand, he does not need to offer to sell his product at less than market price because he can sell all he has at the market price. The farmer is often described as a price taker, meaning that he must take the market price as given.

Consider now the farmer as a buyer. In general, he is one of many buyers, all of whom need the same type of input. Thus, if an individual farmer decides not to buy a tractor or a bag of fertilizer, the market price of tractors or fertilizer is not affected because that farmer's purchases would represent an infinitesimal quantity relative to the total number of tractors or fertilizer bags sold. Therefore, the farmer must also regard the price of inputs as given.

There are exceptions to the general rule that farmers are price takers. Farmers who supply a particular type of product or purchase a given type of input may be able to influence the market prices of inputs or products if they are good merchandisers or hagglers. Local markets can sometimes be developed for products such as eggs. Farmers who buy labor from their teen-age sons may be able to determine both price and quantity, the latter being more doubtful than the former. Usually, however, these farmers are able only to influence market prices for themselves and not the general price level facing all farmers.

The type of market described above, with many buyers or sellers and a homogeneous product, is called a purely competitive market. Many of the markets in which farmers buy and sell approximate pure competition. The term "pure competition" could have been better chosen. There is nothing pure or impure about the type of market just described—the name "pure competition" simply describes a type of market. Further, there is no "competition" in an individual way among businesses which are pure competitors. The reverse is true. The amount of production by one farmer has no effect on either the amount another farmer may sell or the price he receives for it. The only competition among firms in pure competition is the indirect competition which occurs through increases in efficiency and reduction of costs. An alternative term, "atomistic competition," is often used interchangeably with "pure competition" to avoid the connotations of the word "pure."

Two more conditions must be mentioned before pure competition is completely defined. First, businesses must be free to enter into or cease production as they please. There must be no patents or other legal barriers placed before prospective producers. If the price of corn promises to be high relative to the price of soybeans, farmers who grew soybeans last year may decide to switch to corn this year. If they do decide to make the shift, there should be no restrictions in their path.

Second, for pure competition in the purest sense, there should be no artificial restrictions placed upon the supply of or demand for products. Thus, prices are free to vary and equilibrium levels will be reached in the marketplace. In this way, increased production by the industry results in a lower market price and an increase in the quantity demanded and vice versa.[4]

Pure competition, as described above, does not exist in the real world. It is considered worthy of study, nonetheless, for the following reasons. First, it comes closer to approximating market conditions in agricultural production than any other type of market. Second, one of the characteristics of an industry selling in a purely competitive market is that profits are the result of natural rather than contrived scarcity. Thus, ignoring farm programs for the moment, the profits earned by an Illinois corn farmer are due him because he owns a portion of corn land which is naturally scarce. Profits from contrived scarcity would result if a farmer were able to make corn supplies artificially scarce, perhaps by purchasing all corn land in the nation and removing all but a small portion of it from production, and thereby increase corn prices to excessive levels. In an industry selling in a purely competitive market, however, no individual producer owns enough of any productive resource to be able to create shortages.

REFERENCES

HEADY, EARL O. *Economics of Agricultural Production and Resource Use,* chap. i. Englewood Cliffs, N..J: Prentice-Hall, Inc., 1952.

JOHNSON, GLENN L., and HAVER, CECIL B. *Decision-Making Principles in Farm Management.* Kentucky Agricultural Experiment Station Bulletin 593, 1953.

————. *Managerial Concepts for Agriculturalists.* Kentucky Agricultural Experiment Station Bulletin 619, 1954.

LEFTWICH, RICHARD H. *The Price System and Resource Allocation,* chaps. i and ii. New York: Rinehart Co., Inc., 1955.

MALONE, CARL C., and MALONE, LUCILE H. *Decision Making and Management for Farm and Home,* chap. iii. Ames: The Iowa State College Press, 1958.

RODEWALD, GORDON E., JR.; DONALD K. LARSON; and D. C. MYRICK. *Dryland Grain Farms in Montana.* Montana Agricultural Experiment Station Bulletin 579, July, 1963.

RUDE, LE ROY C. *Land Use Alternatives for Dryland Grain-Livestock Operators.* Montana Agricultural Experiment Station Bulletin 571, October, 1962.

---

[4] By requiring also perfect mobility of labor and other resources and perfect knowledge by consumers and producers, pure competition could be improved to a state called "perfect competition."

Chapter 3

PRODUCTION AND COST FUNCTIONS

Farmers are concerned with both the change in output and the change in cost resulting from a change in resource use. An increase in output will not be profitable if the cost of the added input exceeds the value of the added output. The systematic application of this principle to the production process requires the development of basic fundamentals encompassing production response and costs. These fundamentals are contained in this chapter—applications will be made in subsequent chapters.

A simple production process involving one product and one variable input will be studied in this chapter. Not many production processes of this type will be found in agriculture—most production processes include many inputs, and some have more than one product. But, the simple production process provides an ideal place to start. The economic fundamentals derived from it can be directly applied to more complex situations.

First, the concept of a production function will be discussed. Next, a production function will be presented and its characteristics discussed; the nature of costs and their derivation from production functions will be discussed. Finally, different types of production functions will be presented.

THE CONCEPT OF A PRODUCTION FUNCTION

The production function is based on the idea that the amount of output of a production process depends upon the amount of input used in the process. Further, output depends upon input in such a way that there is one unique amount of output resulting from each possible amount of input. For any productive process, this unique relationship between output and input is referred to as the "production function" for the process.

In symbolic notation, a production function representing the output resulting from one variable input can be written

$$Y = f(X) ,$$

39

which is read "output, Y, is a function of the amount of variable input, X." Because there are fixed inputs in the production process, Y can be regarded as the output per unit of fixed factor, i.e., bushels of corn per acre or pounds of milk per cow. Also input can be regarded as the amount of input used per unit of fixed factor, i.e., pounds of fertilizer per acre or pounds of feed per cow. Other names for production functions are "yield curves" or "input-output relationships."

An Empirical Example

Perhaps the best way to picture the meaning of a production function is to examine one. Agricultural scientists are vitally concerned with production functions; much of the recent research in agriculture has attempted to find the relationships between the amount of feed a dairy cow consumes and her milk output, the amount and composition of hog feed and the rate of gain of the hog, the amount of fertilizer applied to a field and the resulting crop yield, etc.

An example of a production function for corn has been presented by Heady, Pesek, Brown, and Doll.[1] These scientists wished to determine the response of corn to applications of nitrogen and P_2O_5 fertilizer. To do this, a controlled experiment was conducted on Ida silt loam in western Iowa; nine rates of nitrogen and P_2O_5 ranging from zero to 320 pounds

TABLE 3–1

THE RESPONSE OF CORN TO FERTILIZER APPLICA-
TIONS, IDA SILT LOAM, IOWA

Units of Fertilizer Applied per Acre*	Bushels of Corn per Acre
0	0
1	44.9
2	83.6
3	110.1
4	127.3
5	136.9
6	139.9
7	137.1
8	129.2

* A unit of fertilizer is 40 pounds of nitrogen and 40 pounds of P_2O_5.

SOURCE: Earl O. Heady, John T. Pesek, William G. Brown, and John P. Doll, "Crop Response Surfaces and Economic Optima in Fertilizer Use," in Earl O. Heady and John L. Dillon (eds.), *Agricultural Production Functions* (Ames: Iowa State University Press, 1961), chap. xiv.

[1] Earl O. Heady, John T. Pesek, William G. Brown, and John P. Doll, "Crop Response Surfaces and Economic Optima in Fertilizer Use," in Earl O. Heady and John L. Dillon (eds.), *Agricultural Production Functions* (Ames: Iowa State University Press, 1961), chap. xiv.

per acre were applied to experimental plots. Plot yields were measured at the end of the growing season. The experimental data were then used to estimate the response of corn to applications of nitrogen and P_2O_5 fertilizer. The data in Table 3–1 show the response obtained from fertilizer where a unit of fertilizer is 40 pounds of nitrogen and 40 pounds of P_2O_5.

FIGURE 3–1

RESPONSE OF CORN YIELDS TO FERTILIZER APPLICA-
TIONS, IDA SILT LOAM, IOWA

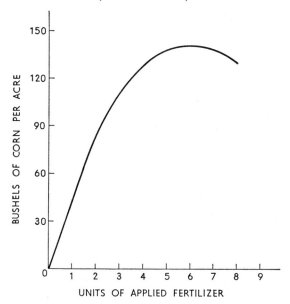

The data presented depict a production function relating the response of corn yields to applied fertilizer. The units of nitrogen and P_2O_5 represent the variable input while all the other inputs needed to produce corn, i.e., seed, labor, fuel, and land, are the fixed inputs. From examination of Table 3–1, it can be seen that large increases in corn yields result from the initial fertilizer applications, but the yield increase becomes very small at high levels of application. A maximum yield of 133.2 bushels occurred when 7 units of fertilizer, 280 pounds each of nitrogen and P_2O_5, were applied. Yields decrease when larger amounts were applied. The curve in Figure 3–1, drawn by plotting the points in Table 3–1 and drawing a smooth curve through them, shows graphically the same information.

One aspect of the production function in Table 3–1 is that no corn yield is forthcoming when fertilizer applications are zero. This is unusual and occurred in part because of a lack of fertility in the soil used for the experiment. In general, if a variable input is essential for plant growth and is not present in the soil, then corn yields would be zero. Most soils do contain some residual amounts of nitrogen and P_2O_5. If, however, the variable input had been seed or plant population, then yields would obviously have been zero when the variable input amount was zero, that is, when no seed were planted. Therefore, yield may or may not be zero when the amount of the variable input is zero, depending upon the particular production process being studied.

Production functions in agriculture may be determined experimentally, as in this case, or through the study of farm records and farm businesses. Many farmers probably have "mental pictures" of production functions for their farms, although they do not, of course, give them the name "production function." The farmer's knowledge of his production functions is the result of years of practical experience.

Production functions in agriculture are highly specialized. That is, the production function in Table 3–1 applies only to a certain soil type, soil fertility level, growing season, fixed inputs levels, etc. A change in any of these "givens" may cause a change in the production function. Thus, some Iowa farmers might find the production function in Table 3–1 quite well suited to conditions on their farm, at least for some years. On other Iowa farms, soil and growing conditions may differ considerably from those of the experimental site and the production function in Table 3–1 would be of little value. To be useful, the production function must be appropriate for the production process being studied.

Perfect Certainty ✔

Production economics is a study of principles to be used when making management decisions. The decisions made must guide future rather than past production. When determining the amount of fertilizer use for next year's corn crop, the farmer needs to know the production function for the coming season. The response of corn yields to fertilizer last year will be useful in next year's planning only if it represents next year's production function. Thus, to be useful in planning future actions, the production function must be looked upon as a future or "expected" relationship. It is a planning device.

For businesses employing automatic man-made machinery operating under carefully controlled environmental conditions, the production function for the last production period may provide an excellent estimate of the production function most appropriate for coming time periods. Thus, the manager of a wheat milling plant or a cotton gin may be reasonably sure of the performance of his machinery year in and year out. He has control of all the inputs and knows exactly how the machinery is built and how it operates. Agricultural production, however, involves many inputs which cannot be controlled, such as rainfall and other weather variables, and many processes which are not completely understood, such as animal and plant nutrition or photosynthesis. For agriculture, last year's production function may be a poor estimate of this year's production function. The Iowa farmer who bases his production decisions on the production function in Table 3–1 may be badly disappointed if the growing season for the coming year, for which he is planning, was not like that for 1952, the year when the production function was estimated. A management decision based on a production function can only be as accurate as the production function itself. This does not negate the production function as a useful concept; it does mean that care must be taken to select the appropriate production function for any given situation. Part of the manager's job is to select the appropriate production function or accept the consequences.

Problems arising because the future is unknown, called problems of "risk and uncertainty," will be introduced in Chapter 8. Study of such problems comprise an ever increasing portion of economic theory, but even an introduction to the subject is complex. To avoid these complexities, the following discussion will assume that the farmer knows at the beginning of the production period the eventual outcome of the production process. Under this assumption, the farmer knows the corn yields that will result from the use of varying amounts of fertilizer, he knows the number of pigs that will farrow and the number of hogs that will be marketed, and so on. Along with this, he knows the cost of fertilizer, the cost of feed, and the prices that corn and hogs will bring at the end of the production period. This assumption is known as the "perfect certainty" assumption. It simplifies our beginning analysis and permits a clear development of the basic principles of production economics.

Level of Technology

The production process itself implies a method or manner of production. Usually a product can be produced many different ways. In the general discussion of the production process, the common assumption is that the farm manager uses the most efficient process available to him, i.e., the one that results in the most product from a given amount of input. This assumption is not necessary, but it is convenient and reasonable. The method of production used is often called the "level of technology" or "the state of the arts."

Length of Time Period

The production function represents the amounts of output resulting from the production process during a given unit of time. Before discussing time periods in the production process, the general classification of resources used in production will be reviewed. A resource is called a "fixed resource" if its quantity is not varied during the production period. A resource is called a "variable resource" if its quantity is varied during the production period. All resources used are either fixed or variable. The group of all fixed resources at a particular time is often referred to as the "plant," an analogy drawn directly from manufacturing firms.

Resources may be fixed for several reasons. First, the manager may be using exactly the right amount of a resource, meaning that an increase or decrease in the quantity used would lower his profits. In this case, he would be foolish to change the amount of the resource he is using. Second, the time period involved in the production process may be so short that the farmer is unable to change the amount of resource he has. Land is a good example. A farmer may realize he needs more land but be unable to purchase it immediately because it is located too far away, because he cannot arrange for suitable financing, or because it is unavailable. Third, the farmer may not want to vary the amount of input. For example, a dairyman may change the rations fed to a milk cow in order to determine the effect of rations on the quantity of milk produced by the cow. For this evaluation, a cow is a fixed resource and the feed is a variable resource. He could change the size of his herd, but such a change is simply not relevant to the question he is investigating.

Fixed and variable resources are used to classify the length of the production period as follows:

Very short run—time period so short that all resources are fixed.
Short run—time period of such length that at least one resource is varied and at least one resource is fixed.
Long run—time period of such length that all resources are varied.

The above classification of time period is not completely satisfactory. The long-run situation would seem most likely to occur before any resources are purchased. Even in this situation, however, the management ability of the farmer could be limiting. Once resources are committed to a production process, the farmer must move expeditiously from one short-run situation to another, that is, he will usually always be faced with some fixed inputs. The line between short-run and long-run periods is often difficult to draw.

"Short-run" or "long-run" situations defined above serve to classify production situations and in some cases to simplify economic analyses. They should never be regarded as shackles placed on a manager. That is, the farmer doesn't say to himself, "Gee, I could sure make money by buying another tractor, but this is the short run and tractors are assumed fixed." Instead he sizes up his farm business, decides which inputs should be increased or decreased, and makes the appropriate changes. Even when he decides to purchase a tractor, however, some time is required to locate, purchase, and bring home a new tractor; during that short period, tractors available on the farm are fixed in number.

TOTAL PRODUCT, AVERAGE PHYSICAL PRODUCT, AND MARGINAL PHYSICAL PRODUCT

A production function for a specific production process, one involving corn production and fertilizer use on an Iowa soil, has been presented. To discuss all the production functions that now exist in agriculture would involve more space than in any one book and more time than possessed by any author. Agriculture researchers can never hope to measure and record all production functions in existence. The purpose of research on agricultural production functions is to provide general guides and indications useful to farm managers; each manager must ultimately determine the appropriate production functions for his farm.

Because all possible production functions cannot be discussed here, it becomes necessary to seek, in the manner of the agricultural research worker, some general principles that are applicable in all situations, regardless of the specific form of the production function. To begin with, certain measures derived from the production function, namely the average physical product and the marginal physical product, will be defined and computed. Next, costs of production, obviously of great importance to a manager making production decisions, will be defined and derived from a production function.

The production function to be studied in detail is presented in Figure 3–2 and Table 3–2. This production function will be used to demonstrate some general principles important in the economic analysis

FIGURE 3–2

THE CLASSIC PRODUCTION FUNCTION

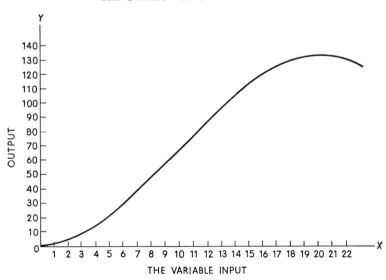

THE VARIABLE INPUT

TABLE 3–2

THE CLASSIC PRODUCTION FUNCTION

Input X	Output Y	Average Physical Product $Y/X = APP_x$	Marginal Physical Product $\Delta Y/\Delta X = MPP_x$
0	0	. . . .	
			3.7/2 = 1.9
2	3.7	3.7/2 = 1.9	
			10.2/2 = 5.1
4	13.9	13.9/4 = 3.5	
			14.9/2 = 7.5
6	28.8	28.8/6 = 4.8	
			18.1/2 = 9.1
8	46.9	46.9/8 = 5.9	
			19.8/2 = 9.9
10	66.7	66.7/10 = 6.7	
			19.7/2 = 9.9
12	86.4	86.4/12 = 7.2	
			18.1/2 = 9.1
14	104.5	104.5/14 = 7.5	
			15.0/2 = 7.5
16	119.5	119.5/16 = 7.5	
			10.1/2 = 5.1
18	129.6	129.6/18 = 7.2	
			3.7/2 = 1.9
20	133.3	133.3/20 = 6.7	
			−1/1 = −1.0
21	132.3	132.3/21 = 6.3	

Computation Note: ΔY is computed by subtracting the total output at the lower input level from the total output at the higher input amount. Between the input amounts of $X = 2$ and $X = 4$, $\Delta Y = 13.9 - 3.7 = 10.2$, etc. ΔX is computed in a similar manner.

of production. The reasons underlying the shape of this production function will be discussed later in this chapter. The form presented in Figure 3–2 is thought to be quite general; for that reason it is here termed the "classic" production function. It displays all of the characteristics necessary for a study of production functions. It is assumed to be a short-run production function.

The shape of the production function tells what happens to output, Y, as increasing amounts of variable input, X, are added to the fixed factor. In Figure 3–2, output is zero when input is zero. Output increases at an increasing rate as the first few units of input are added; it continues to increase but at a decreasing rate at higher input levels. In Figure 3–2, the maximum yield is 133.3 units of Y, resulting from application of 20 units of X. For higher input levels, output decreases.

Output, Y, is often called "total product" to distinguish it from the "average physical product" and "marginal physical product" defined below. In the following discussion, the terms "total product," "output," or the symbol "Y" may all be used to denote the output of the production process. Similarly, the terms "input," "resource," "factor," or the symbol "X" will be used to denote the resource used in the production process.

Average Physical Product (APP$_x$)

APP_x is the total amount of output, Y, divided by the total amount of variable input, X. From Table 3–2, when $X = 2$ and $Y = 3.7$, $APP_x = 3.7/2 = 1.9$; when $X = 10$ and $Y = 66.7$, $APP_x = 66.7/10 = 6.7$, and so on. The term "physical" means that average product is measured in physical units such as pounds, bales, tons, bushels, or number of eggs rather than in value units, dollars.

In Table 3–2 or Figure 3–3B, it can be seen that average physical product increases until $X = 15$ and $Y = 112.5$ and decreases for larger

FIGURE 3–3

THE CLASSIC PRODUCTION FUNCTION AND
THE THREE STAGES OF PRODUCTION

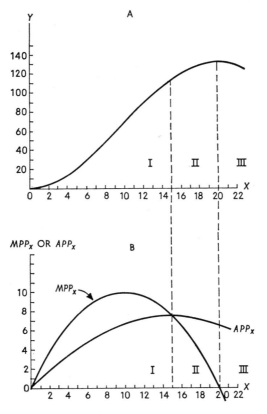

amounts of X. (Figure 3–3A contains the same production function as Figure 3–2; ignore the dashed lines for now.) The shape of the APP_x curve depends upon the shape of the production function. Thus, APP_x could have a different shape, depending on how output varies with input.

One of the concerns of agricultural economics is the efficient use of resources. Further, efficiency is measured as output divided by input. Therefore, APP_x measures the efficiency of the variable input used in the production process. Output, Y, is not the result of using the input, X, alone but rather is the result of using a combination of X with the fixed factors. For the production function in Figure 3–3, APP_x is zero when $X = 0$. Using no variable input with the fixed inputs is not an efficient situation. As more and more of the variable input is used with the fixed inputs, efficiency of the variable input increases and eventually decreases. When APP_x is a maximum, the return per unit of variable input or efficiency with which the variable input is used is a maximum.

Marginal Physical Product (MPP$_x$)

MPP_x is the change in output resulting from a unit increment in variable input. It measures the amount total output increases as input increases. Geometrically, MPP_x represents the slope of the production function. (For basic notions involved in determining slopes of curves and the MPP_x, see the Appendix on page 535.)

MPP_x is computed by dividing the change in output by the causal amount of input, that is, by the increment in input that caused the change in output. Algebraically, this can be expressed as

$$MPP_x = \frac{\Delta Y}{\Delta X},$$

where "ΔY" is read "change in the amount of output" and "ΔX" is read "change in the amount of input." In Table 3–2, MPP_x between the input amounts $X = 16$ and $X = 18$ is equal to

$$MPP_x = \frac{129.6 - 119.5}{18 - 16} = \frac{10.1}{2} = 5.1.$$

Between the input amounts of 16 and 18, an added unit of input increases total output by five units. MPP_x can be negative. Between the input amounts 20 and 21:

$$MPP_x = \frac{132.3 - 133.3}{21 - 20} = \frac{-1.0}{1} = -1.0.$$

Therefore, the addition of one additional unit of input when 20 units are already being used will cause total output to decrease one unit.

As mentioned, the marginal physical product represents the slope of the total output curve. To demonstrate this, the portion of the production function between $X = 16$ and $X = 18$ is shown greatly enlarged in Figure 3–4. MPP_x between $X = 16$ and $X = 18$ has been shown to be $\Delta Y/\Delta X = 10.1/2 = 5.1$. Examination of Figure 3–4 shows that 5.1 is also the slope of the straight line AB, drawn between the points $X = 16$, $Y = 119.5$ and $X = 18$, $Y = 129.6$. ΔY measures the vertical distance or the "rise" in the production, and ΔX measures the horizontal distance or the "run." The quantity "rise/run" is the slope.

The quantity 5.1 is not the marginal physical product at 16 units of input or at 18 units of input. Rather it is the marginal physical product

FIGURE 3–4

GRAPHIC MEANING OF THE MARGINAL PHYSICAL PRODUCT

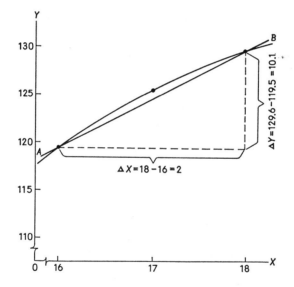

between these amounts; it means that each unit of input added will add an average of 5.1 units to total product, within the input limits of 16 and 18. For this reason, marginal physical products computed in this manner are placed halfway between the end points when graphed. For example, the marginal physical product of 5.1 is placed directly above $X = 17$ in Figure 3–3B. Actually the first unit of input added (to 16 units) will increase output more than 5.1 and the second less. When 17 units of X are used, output is 125.4 (Figure 3–3A). Thus, MPP_x between $X = 16$ and $X = 17$ is $(125.4 - 119.5)/(17 - 16) = 5.9$ and the MPP_x between $X = 17$ and $X = 18$ is $(129.6 - 125.4)/1 = 4.2$. The average of these two marginal physical products is 5.1. (See the Appendix on page 535 for further details.)

An examination of Table 3–2 and Figure 3–3B shows that MPP_x, like APP_x, is not constant for the classic production function but varies with the amount of input use. The shape of the MPP_x curve will depend upon the shape of the production function. For the production function under consideration here, MPP_x increases to a maximum at 10 units of input (when yield is 66.7) and decreases as input is increased further. MPP_x is equal to zero at 20 units of input where output is a maximum, 133.3, and is negative for larger input amounts. When MPP_x is increasing, total output is increasing at an increasing rate. When MPP_x is decreasing but positive, total output is increasing at a decreasing rate. When MPP_x is zero, the total output curve attains a maximum. When MPP_x is negative, total output decreases.[2]

THE LAW OF DIMINISHING RETURNS AND THE THREE STAGES OF PRODUCTION

The "law of diminishing returns" was developed by early economists and describes the relationship between output and a variable input when other inputs are constant in amount. It is believed by economists to have widespread application. The law can be stated as follows: *If increasing amounts of one input are added to a production process while all other inputs are held constant, the amount of output added per unit of variable input will eventually decrease.* When applied to a production process, the law means that there is some "right" amount of variable input to use in combination with the fixed input. The manager should neither use too much nor too little of the variable resource. The determination of the "right" amount of input from the economic point of view will be determined in the next chapter.

The law of diminishing returns requires that the method of production does not change as changes are made in the amount of variable input. It deals with the changing proportions in which the variable and fixed inputs are used and does not apply when all inputs are varied. The law of diminishing returns is often referred to as the "law of diminishing productivity" or the "law of variable proportions."

Application of the law of diminishing returns to the production function concept can result in a production function of the classic type (Figure 3–2). This production function displays first increasing marginal returns and then decreasing marginal returns. The law of diminishing

---

[2] The input and yield amount denoting the point on the total product curve at which MPP_x is a maximum (X equals 10 and Y equals 66.7 in Figure 3–3) is called the "point of inflection."

returns says nothing about increasing marginal returns when the variable input is used in small quantities, but it does specify that marginal returns eventually decrease. Thus, marginal returns could decrease beginning with the first applications of the variable input; the production function in Figure 3–1 illustrates this and satisfies the law of diminishing returns. In practice, the form of the production function is determined by biological and physical conditions of animal and plant growth on the farm. Here we seek general principles useful in all production situations. No generality is lost by assuming the classic function.

The Three Stages of Production

The "classic" production function can be divided into three parts or "stages," each important from the standpoint of efficient resource use. The three stages are shown in Figure 3–3.

Stage I occurs when MPP_x is greater than APP_x. APP_x increases throughout Stage I, indicating that the efficiency of the variable input is increasing throughout Stage I.

Stage II occurs when MPP_x is decreasing and less than APP_x. In Stage II, MPP_x is equal to or less than APP_x but equal to or greater than zero. In Figure 3–3, Stage II falls between and includes the input quantities of 15 and 20. The efficiency of the variable input reaches a peak at the beginning of Stage II, for an input amount of 15. The dashed line shows this boundary. On the other hand, the efficiency of the fixed input is greatest at the end of Stage II when the variable input equals 20.[3]

Stage III occurs where MPP_x is negative. Stage III occurs when excessive quantities of the variable input are used with the fixed input—so much, in fact, that total output begins to decrease. Another dashed line in Figure 3–3 shows the boundary between II and III. (The student should show that the production function in Figure 3–1 displays only Stages II and III and hence is a special case of the classic function.)

The Stages of Production and Economic Recommendations

In the next chapter, production functions will be used to determine the most profitable amount of variable input to use and the most profitable output amount to produce. Prices of the inputs and outputs must be known to make a complete economic analysis. However, when the technical relationship between input and output, i.e., the production function, is known, some recommendations about input use can be made even though prices are not specified.

[3] Because the number of units of the fixed inputs is constant, the output return per unit of fixed input must be the largest when total output from the production process is a maximum.

First, if the product has any value at all, input use, once begun, should be continued until Stage II is reached. That is because the efficiency of the variable resource, measured by APP_x, increases throughout Stage I; it is not reasonable to cease using an input when its efficiency in use is increasing. For the production function in Figure 3–3, at least 15 units of input should be used.

Second, even if the input is free, it will not be used in Stage III. The maximum total output occurs on the upper boundary of Stage II—further input increments decrease output. It is not reasonable to increase input use when total product is decreasing. Thus, in Figure 3–3, the largest amount of variable input that would be used is 20 units.

Stage II and its boundaries are the area of economic relevance. Variable input use must be somewhere in Stage II, but the exact amount of input can be determined only when input and output prices are known. If production is undertaken at all, then the most profit will be made somewhere in Stage II.

The Stages of Production and the Point of Diminishing Returns

A discussion of the law of diminishing returns and the classic production function inevitably leads into the determination of the "point" of diminishing returns, meaning the input and yield amount at which returns begin to diminish. But what is the point referred to? The law itself is ambiguous. Study of Figure 3–3 shows that marginal returns begin to decrease at an input level of 10, average returns begin to decrease at 15 units of input, and total returns begin to decrease at 20 units. Clearly, the point of diminishing returns depends on which of these three measures is being discussed.

To avoid this, some writers apply the law of diminishing returns directly to the marginal physical product. That is, they call it the law of diminishing marginal returns and specify in the definition that as successive units of the variable input are added, marginal returns eventually decrease. But if marginal returns decrease, eventually average returns and total returns will also decrease. Thus, it is certainly appropriate to define the law of diminishing returns in terms of the marginal physical product. Some ambiguity is caused, however, because the point of diminishing marginal returns, occurring at an input of 10 in Figure 3–4, differs from the boundary of Stage II, occurring where X is 15.

A solution has been suggested by Cassels.[4] First, the elasticity of production is defined to be

$$\epsilon_p = \frac{\text{Percent change in output}}{\text{Percent change in input}}.$$

[4] John M. Cassels, "On the Law of Variable Proportions," in American Economic Association, *Readings in the Theory of Income Distribution* (Philadelphia: The Blakiston Co., 1951), chap. v.

From this, the elasticity of production is determined to be

$$\epsilon_p = \frac{\Delta Y}{Y} \div \frac{\Delta X}{X} = \frac{X}{Y} \cdot \frac{\Delta Y}{\Delta X} = \frac{MPP_x}{APP_x}.$$

In Stage I, MPP_x is greater than APP_x. Therefore, ϵ_p is greater than one. In Stage II, MPP_x is less than APP_x and ϵ_p is less than one but greater than zero. In Stage III, MPP_x is negative and ϵ_p is negative.

The "point" of diminishing returns occurs where $MPP_x = APP_x$ and ϵ_p is one, the lower boundary of Stage II (input is 15 in Figure 3–3). This is also the minimum amount of input that would be used; it occurs where the efficiency of the variable input is a maximum. Using this definition of diminishing returns, it can be said that even without knowing the input and output prices, input use will always be extended to the point of diminishing returns. At the other boundary of Stage II where total output is a maximum and $MPP_x = 0$, ϵ_p is also zero.

COSTS OF PRODUCTION

Costs are the expenses incurred in organizing and carrying out the production process. Chapter 2 contained a general discussion of costs, beginning with opportunity costs and proceeding to cash and noncash costs. The cost concepts discussed below add to and refine further the general ideas discussed in Chapter 2.

Fixed and Variable Costs

A resource or input is called a "fixed resource" if its quantity is not varied during the production period. A resource is a "variable resource" if its quantity is varied during the production period. Most inputs have costs associated with them. In general, costs associated with fixed inputs are called fixed costs and costs associated with variable inputs are called variable costs.

Fixed costs do not change in magnitude as the amount of output of the production process changes and are incurred even when production is not undertaken. In farming, cash fixed costs include land taxes, principal and interest on land payments, insurance premiums, annual hired labor, etc. Noncash fixed costs include building depreciation and machinery and equipment depreciation caused by the passing of time, interest on capital investment, charges for family labor, and charges for management.

As stated above, fixed costs usually arise from fixed inputs because when the amount of a resource is fixed, the costs associated with it are also fixed. While this is generally true, it is not always true. A fixed cost requires only that the cost to the farmer be constant over the production period—not that the amount of input used be constant. For example, consider the farmer who subscribes to an electric power source and

TABLE 3-3

Cost Curves Derived from the Classic Production Function ($P_z = \$100$)

(1) Input X	(2) Output Y	(3) Total Fixed Costs TFC	(4) Total Variable Costs $TVC = P_z(X)$	(5) Total Costs TC	(6) Average Fixed Cost $AFC = \dfrac{TFC}{Y}$	(7) Average Variable Cost $AVC = \dfrac{TVC}{Y}$	(8) Average Total Cost $ATC = \dfrac{TC}{Y}$	(9) Marginal Cost $MC = \dfrac{\Delta TC}{\Delta Y}$
0	0.0	$1,000	0	$1,000	...	...	...	$54.1
2	3.7	1,000	$ 200	1,200	$270.3	$54.1	$324.4	19.6
4	13.9	1,000	400	1,400	71.9	28.8	100.7	13.4
6	28.8	1,000	600	1,600	34.7	20.8	55.5	11.0
8	46.9	1,000	800	1,800	21.3	17.1	38.4	10.0
10	66.7	1,000	1,000	2,000	15.0	15.0	30.0	10.1
12	86.4	1,000	1,200	2,200	11.6	13.9	25.5	11.0
14	104.5	1,000	1,400	2,400	9.6	13.4	23.0	13.3
16	119.5	1,000	1,600	2,600	8.4	13.3	21.7	19.8
18	129.6	1,000	1,800	2,800	7.7	13.9	21.6	54.1
20	133.3	1,000	2,000	3,000	7.5	15.0	22.5	54.1

agrees to pay a monthly charge regardless of the amount of electric power consumed. In this case, the cost of electricity is fixed but the amount used can be varied.

Table 3–3 includes the computation of costs for the classic production function presented in Figure 3–2 and Table 3–2. The production function is presented in columns 1 and 2 of Table 3–3. The cost per unit of variable input is assumed to be $100. Fixed costs are assumed to be $1,000. For simplicity, the $1,000 is assumed to represent exactly the costs associated with the fixed inputs used in the production process and the only variable cost is that incurred in purchasing the variable input.

Total fixed costs, *TFC*, are shown in the third column of Table 3–3. These costs are the same for all output levels. Thus, once computed from the farm or enterprise budget, *TFC* are known and unchanging. *TFC* are shown graphed in Figure 3–5A. *TFC* are $1,000 for all output levels. This

FIGURE 3–5

Cost Curves for the Classic Production Function

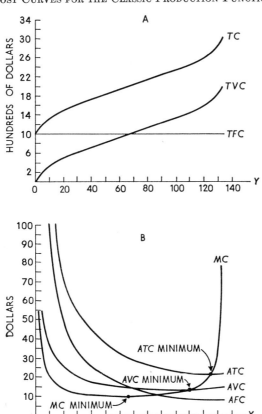

is represented by a straight line parallel to the horizontal or "Y-" axis and located 1,000 units up the vertical scale.

Total variable costs, TVC, are computed by multiplying the amount of variable input used by the price per unit of input. In symbolic notation, if X is the amount of variable input used and P_x is the price or cost per unit of input, then

$$TVC = P_x(X).$$

(A complete discussion of the use of this type of notation is presented in the Appendix on page 535.) From Table 3–3, when four units of input are used, $TVC = \$100(4) = \$400$. When 12 units of input are used, $TVC = \$100(12) = \$1,200$, etc. A graph of TVC, computed in column 4 of Table 3–3, is shown in Figure 3–5A. TVC is zero when output, and consequently the input, is zero. It increases as output increases. The shape of the TVC curve depends upon the shape of the production function; for the classic production function, TVC is always shaped as in Figure 3–5.

Total costs, TC, are the sum of total variable costs and total fixed costs. They are presented in column 5 of Table 3–3 and are obtained by adding TVC and TFC for any output level. For an output of 86.4 units, TC are \$1,000 plus \$1,200, or \$2,200. TC for other output levels are obtained similarly. When no variable input is used, $TC = TFC$. Total costs are graphed in Figure 3–5A. The TC curve is equal to the vertical addition of TFC and TVC. It is shaped exactly like the TVC curve but is always 1,000 units higher on the vertical axis. The shape of the TC curve, like that of the TVC curve, depends upon the production function. In symbolic notation, TC can be written

$$TC = TFC + TVC = TFC + P_x(X).$$

Average Fixed Cost, Average Variable Cost, Average Total Cost

Average fixed cost, AFC, is computed by dividing total fixed costs by the amount of output. AFC varies for each level of output—as output increases, AFC decreases. Thus, when economists refer to increasing output as a method of "spreading fixed costs," they mean increasing production to divide total fixed costs among more and more units of output, thereby reducing costs per unit. AFC is presented in column 6 of Table 3–3 and graphed in Figure 3–5B. AFC for output amounts of 13.9 and 104.5 are:

$$Y = 13.9: \quad AFC = \frac{TFC}{Y} = \frac{\$1,000}{13.9} = \$71.9$$

$$Y = 104.5: \quad AFC = \frac{TFC}{Y} = \frac{\$1,000}{104.5} = \$\,9.6.$$

When output is zero, AFC cannot be computed because division by zero is not permissible. AFC always has the same shape regardless of the production function. Its general location on the graph depends upon the magnitude of total fixed costs.

Average variable cost, AVC, is computed by dividing total variable costs by the amount of output. AVC varies depending on the amount of production; the shape of the AVC curve depends upon the shape of the production function. The height of the AVC curve depends upon the unit cost of the variable input. AVC as computed in column 7 of Table 3–3 are graphed in Figure 3–5B. AVC for two different output amounts are:

$$Y = 28.8: \quad AVC = \frac{TVC}{Y} = \frac{P_x(X)}{Y} = \frac{\$100(6)}{28.8} = \$20.8$$

$$Y = 133.3: \quad AVC = \frac{\$2,000}{133.3} = \$15.0 \,.$$

As AFC, AVC cannot be computed when output is zero.

Average variable cost is inversely related to average physical product. When APP_x is increasing, AVC is decreasing. When APP_x is at a maximum, AVC attains a minimum. When APP_x is decreasing, AVC is increasing. Compare the cost curves in Figure 3–5B to the production function in Figure 3–3, from which the cost curves were derived. APP_x attains a maximum at an input level of 15 when output is 112.5; in Figure 3–5B, AVC is a minimum at 112.5 units of output. For output amounts between 0 and 112.5, APP_x is increasing and AVC is decreasing. For output levels larger than 112.5, APP_x is decreasing and AVC is increasing. Thus, for a production function, APP_x measures the efficiency of the variable input; for cost curves, AVC provides the same measure. When AVC is decreasing, the efficiency of the variable input is increasing, it is at a maximum when AVC is a minimum, and it is decreasing when AVC is increasing. The relationship between APP_x and AVC can be shown algebraically as follows:

$$AVC = \frac{TVC}{Y} = \frac{P_x(X)}{Y} = P_x\frac{X}{Y} = \frac{P_x}{APP_x}$$

because $X/Y = 1/APP_x$.

Average total cost, ATC, can be computed two ways. Total costs can be divided by output or AFC and AVC can be added. ATC is presented in column 8 of Table 3–3 and in Figure 3–5B. The shape of the ATC curve depends upon the shape of the production function. In Figure 3–5B, ATC decreases as output increases from zero, attains a minimum, and increases thereafter. ATC is often referred to as the "unit cost" of production—the cost of producing one unit of output. The initial decrease in *ATC* is caused by the spreading of fixed costs among an increasing number of units of output and the increasing efficiency with which the variable input is used (as indicated by the decreasing *AVC* curve). As output increases further, *AVC* attains a minimum and begins to increase; when these increases in *AVC* can no longer be offset by decreases in *AFC*, *ATC* begins to rise. For the output amounts of 66.7 and 104.5, *ATC* are computed as follows:

$$Y = 66.7: \; ATC = \frac{TC}{Y} = \frac{\$2,000}{66.7} = \$30.0$$

or

$$ATC = AFC + AVC = \$15.0 + \$15.0 = \$30.0 \; .$$
$$Y = 104.5: \; ATC = \frac{\$2,400}{104.5} = \$23.0$$

or

$$ATC = \$9.6 + \$13.4 = \$23.0 \; .$$

Marginal Cost

Marginal cost, *MC*, is defined as the change in total cost per unit increase in output. It is the cost of producing an additional unit of output and is computed by dividing the change in total costs, ΔTC, by the corresponding change in output, ΔY. (The symbol "Δ" means "change in." See the appendix on page 535 for a more complete explanation.) Examples of marginal cost are presented in Table 3–3 and Figure 3–5B. Between the output amounts of 3.7 and 13.9, *MC* is computed as follows:

$$MC = \frac{\Delta TC}{\Delta Y} = \frac{\$1,400 - \$1,200}{13.9 - 3.7} = \frac{\$200}{10.2} = \$19.6 \; .$$

Between the output amount of 129.6 and 133.3, *MC* is

$$\frac{\$3,000 - \$2,800}{133.3 - 129.6} = \frac{\$200}{3.7} = \$54.1 \; .$$

By definition, the only change possible in total costs is the change in variable cost. That is, $\Delta TC = \Delta VC$. Therefore, *MC* could also be computed by dividing the change in variable cost by the change in output.

Geometrically, *MC* is the slope of the *TC* curve. This is shown in detail in Figure 3–6, a greatly enlarged portion of the *TC* curve in Figure 3–5A. *MC* between the output of 119.5 and 129.6 is

$$\frac{\Delta TC}{\Delta Y} = \frac{\$2,800 - \$2,600}{129.6 - 119.5} = \frac{\$200}{10.1} = \$19.8 \; .$$

But $19.8 is also the slope of the straight line *AB* in Figure 3–6 that passes through the points $Y = 119.5$, $TC = \$2,600$ and $Y = 129.6$,

$TC = \$2,800$. The slope of the line AB is the "average" slope of TC between these two points. Within these output limits, each unit of output added to total output will cost $19.8 to produce. MC between the outputs of 119.6 and 125.4 is equal to $(\$2,700 - \$2,600)/5.8$, or $\$17.2$.[5] Between

FIGURE 3–6

GRAPHIC MEANING OF MARGINAL COST

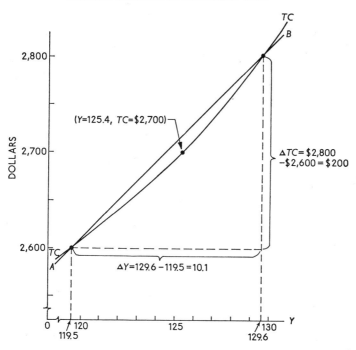

125.4 and 129.6, MC is $(\$2,800 - \$2,700)/4.2$, or $\$23.8$. Thus, when increasing output from 119.5 to 129.6, the marginal cost per unit of the first 5.8 units is less than that of the next 4.2. And, as with MPP_x, the marginal cost of $19.8 is not the marginal cost at 119.5 units of output or at 129.6 units of output but rather the marginal cost between these levels of output. Again, when graphing MC curves computed in this manner, MC must be located halfway between the outputs for which it is computed. (Compare this discussion of MC with the discussion of MPP_x on page 49.)

The slope of the MC curve is inverse to that of MPP_x. Compare the MC curve in Figure 3–5B to the MPP_x curve in Figure 3–3B. MPP_x is a maximum at 10 units of input; output at this point is 66.7. In Figure 3–5B, MC is a minimum at 66.7 units of output. For lower levels of output, MC

---

[5] When 17 units of X are used, output is 125.4.

is decreasing while MPP_x is increasing. For output levels above 66.7, MPP_x is decreasing while MC is increasing. Algebraically, the relationship between MPP_x and MC can be shown as

$$MC = \frac{\Delta TC}{\Delta Y} = \frac{\Delta VC}{\Delta Y} = \frac{P_x(\Delta X)}{\Delta Y} = P_x\left(\frac{\Delta X}{\Delta Y}\right) = \frac{P_x}{MPP_x},$$

where the change in variable costs between two output amounts, ΔVC, is equal to the change in the variable input used, ΔX, multiplied by the price of the input. The term $\Delta X/\Delta Y$ is, of course, equal to $1/MPP_x$.

MC and AVC are equal when 15 units of input are used and output is 112.5; this is the same point where MPP_x is equal to APP_x. For output amounts lower than 112.5, MC is less than AVC; for higher outputs, MC is greater than AVC. MC crosses ATC and is equal to ATC at the latter's minimum point.

Comments on Costs

Costs are usually computed as a function of output. That is, a manager is usually interested in the total cost of producing an output or in the unit cost at a level of output. Thus, the cost curves in Figure 3–5 are graphed with dollars on the vertical axis and units of output on the horizontal axis. Costs are graphed as a function of input (with units of input on the horizontal axis) only in special situations.

Costs are computed and cost curves graphed only for input and output amounts in Stages I and II of the production function; Stage III is an area in which no rational manager would produce. Stage II begins at the point where $MC = AVC$ and continues to the point where output is a maximum. In Figure 3–3, these limits are 112.5 and 133.3 units of output, inclusively. On the boundary between Stage II and III, MPP_x is zero. Therefore, on the same boundary, $MC = P_x/MPP_x = P_x/0$, which is an undefined quantity. Costs for Stage III will not be presented.

Marginal cost is a widely used concept in agricultural economics. Strictly speaking, it is the increase in total cost brought about by a one unit increase in output. Any other definition of marginal cost is not valid. That is, one could define a cost concept that measures the change in total cost caused by a one unit increase in input. Such a cost concept is valid and useful but is not marginal cost; when used, it is given a different name.

OTHER TYPES OF PRODUCTION FUNCTIONS

The classic production function has been discussed in great detail in this chapter. It is thought to have widespread applicability in agricultural production processes, but all production functions need not be shaped like the classic function. In fact, many probably are not. The production function, you remember, presents the output that results from using different amounts of variable input in combination with other inputs fixed in amount. It is a technical or engineering relationship. Many different production functions might be possible.

Elementary production functions can be classified by the type of marginal returns (increasing, constant, decreasing) they display. Exam-

TABLE 3–4

PRODUCTION FUNCTIONS SHOWING INCREASING, CONSTANT, AND DECREASING MARGINAL RETURNS

Increasing				Constant				Decreasing			
X	Y	APP_x	MPP_x	X	Y	APP_x	MPP_x	X	Y	APP_x	MPP_x
0	0	..		0	0	..		0	0	..	
			8				2				9
1	8	8		1	2	2		1	9	9	
			12				2				7
2	20	10		2	4	2		2	16	8	
			16				2				5
3	36	12		4	8	2		3	21	7	
			22				2				3
5	80	16		6	12	2		4	24	6	
			28				2				1
6	108	18		7	14	2		5	25	5	

TABLE 3–5

CHARACTERISTICS OF MPP_x AND APP_x FOR PRODUCTION FUNCTIONS POSSESSING ONE TYPE OF MARGINAL RETURNS
($Y = 0$ WHEN $X = 0$)

Increasing	*Constant*	*Decreasing*
MPP_x increasing	MPP_x constant	MPP_x decreasing
APP_x increasing	APP_x constant	APP_x decreasing
MPP_x greater than APP_x	MPP_x equal to APP_x	MPP_x less than APP_x

ples of these production functions and associated average physical product, marginal physical product, and cost curves are presented in Table 3–4 and Figure 3–7. Table 3–5 summarizes the characteristics of the marginal and average curves of each type of function.

It is important to remember that the production processes presented are ones in which one input is varied and all others are constant. Production functions presented represent output per unit (or units) of fixed inputs, and the quest of the manager is for the most appropriate ratio of variable inputs and fixed inputs. This is the "proportionality" problem. The terms "increasing," "constant," and "decreasing" describe the efficiency of the production process.

All agricultural production functions can be represented by one or more of the general types of marginal returns described here. That is,

FIGURE 3–7

MARGINAL PHYSICAL PRODUCT, AVERAGE PHYSICAL PRODUCT, AND COST CURVES
FOR DIFFERENT TYPES OF PRODUCTION FUNCTIONS

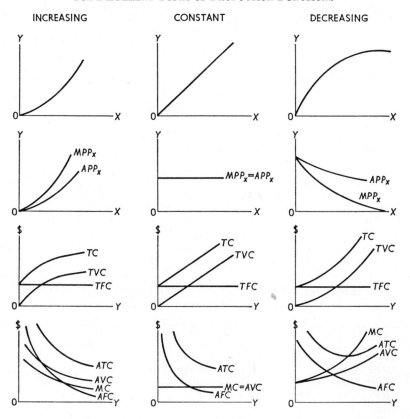

response of output to the variable input may first be typified by increasing marginal returns, then by constant marginal returns over a range, and finally by decreasing returns. Or, there may be no increasing returns; constant returns over a range may be followed by decreasing returns. Other combinations are possible. The classic function is now seen to be one where marginal returns are initially increasing but eventually decrease.

To the extent that the law of diminishing returns is applicable, production functions showing only increasing or constant marginal returns would not have widespread application in agriculture. When fixed inputs are present, diminishing returns generally prevail. Only the production function with decreasing marginal returns has the characteristics of Stage II of the classic function, the area of economic relevance. For production functions with only increasing or constant returns, input use should never stop—it would always pay to add an additional unit of input. For these situations, the manager's ability to dispose of the product would be the only limitation on input use.

APPENDIX TO CHAPTER 3

Symbols and notation are always a problem. The following have been introduced thus far in the text and are summarized here for your convenience:

X = A variable input or resource.

Y = An output or product.

APP_x = Average physical product of X, computed by dividing total output, Y, by the total amount of variable input, X.

$$APP_x = \frac{Y}{X}$$

MPP_x = Marginal physical product of a unit of X, computed by dividing the change in total output, ΔY, by the change in the amount of variable input, ΔX.

$$MPP_x = \frac{\Delta Y}{\Delta X}$$

ϵ_p = The elasticity of production, computed by dividing the marginal physical product by the average physical product.

P_x = Cost per unit of variable input, X.

TFC = Total fixed costs, do not vary with changes in output.

TVC = Total variable costs, vary with changes in output and computed by multiplying the total amount of variable input used, X, by the cost per unit of variable input, P_x.

$$TVC = P_x(X)$$

TC = Total costs, equals fixed costs plus variable costs.

$$TC = TFC + TVC = TFC + P_x(X)$$

AFC = Average fixed cost, computed by dividing total fixed costs by amount of output.

$$AFC = \frac{TFC}{Y}$$

AVC = Average variable cost, computed by dividing total variable costs by amount of output.

$$AVC = \frac{TVC}{Y} = (P_x)\frac{X}{Y}$$

ATC = Average total cost, computed by dividing total costs by amount of output *or* by adding average fixed and average variable cost.

$$ATC = \frac{TC}{X} = \frac{TVC + TFC}{Y} = \frac{TVC}{Y} + \frac{TFC}{Y} = AVC + AFC$$

MC = Marginal cost, change in total costs caused by a one unit increase in output.

$$MC = \frac{\Delta TC}{\Delta Y} = \frac{\Delta VC + \Delta FC}{\Delta Y} = \frac{\Delta VC}{\Delta Y}$$

because changes in fixed costs are zero by definition.

REFERENCES

ALLEN, C. L. *The Framework of Price Theory*, chaps. viii and xiii. Belmont, Calif.: Wadsworth Publishing Co., Inc., 1967.

CASSELS, JOHN M. "On the Law of Variable Proportions," *Readings in the Theory of Income Distribution*, chap. v. Philadelphia: The Blakiston Co., 1951.

FERGUSON, C. E. *Microeconomic Theory*, chaps. vi and viii. Homewood, Ill.: Richard D. Irwin, Inc., 1966.

HEADY, EARL O. *Economics of Agricultural Production and Resource Use*, chaps. ii and iii. New York: Prentice-Hall, Inc., 1952.

———; PESEK, JOHN T.; BROWN, WILLIAM G.; and DOLL, JOHN P. "Crop Response Surfaces and Economic Optima in Fertilizer Use," in *Agricultural Production Functions* (eds. EARL O. HEADY and JOHN L. DILLON), chap. xiv. Ames: Iowa State University Press, 1961.

Chapter 4

THE ALLOCATION OF ONE VARIABLE INPUT

Farmers typically have limited amounts of money to spend on variable inputs. Their problem is to use the total available amount of variable input so that farm profits are maximized. In his search for profits, the farm manager is faced with questions of the following type: How much input should be used in an enterprise? Should an enterprise be operated at peak technical efficiency or does economic analysis suggest a different solution? When more than one enterprise exists, how should the variable input be divided among them? Is maximum "returns per dollar" a valid criterion for input allocation among enterprises? Do maximum profits in one enterprise lead to maximum farm profits? Using the production function as a starting point, this chapter seeks the answers to these and related questions.

The concepts presented can be divided into two general problems. First, given that the farmer may obtain any amount of variable input that is needed, how much variable input should be used to maximize profits in an enterprise? In this case, attention is focused in one enterprise on the farm, and input use on that enterprise is considered independently of input use in any other enterprise. Profits per unit of fixed inputs are maximized. The second problem occurs when the farm manager is able to obtain only limited amounts of the variable input. He does not have enough variable input to operate all enterprises at the most profitable output. To expand one enterprise, he must take inputs away from another enterprise. In this situation, he must maximize profits from the limited or "fixed amount" of variable input.

Throughout this chapter, the assumption is made that farmers buy inputs and sell products in purely competitive markets. Prices and the production function are assumed to be known with certainty. Only production processes involving one variable input will be considered. Again, production processes involving but one variable input are not realistic in a study of agricultural production, but the principles developed in this chapter are general and will also be applied to more complex production processes.

PROFIT MAXIMIZATION FOR AN ENTERPRISE

The problem here is to determine the most profitable point of operation for an enterprise. This can be done by determining either the most profitable amount of input or the most profitable level of output. Either method results ultimately in the same answer. In economic terminology, the "most profitable" amount can also be called the "optimum" amount; both terms will be used here.

The optimum amount of a variable input is that amount that maximizes short-run profits from the production process. Once the optimum amount of input is being used, profits can be increased only by changes in technology or changes in the amounts of fixed inputs. And, as discussed later, managers are always willing to change technology or the amount of "fixed" inputs if by doing so profits are increased. At present, however, only production processes with one variable input will be considered.

Determining the Optimum Using Total Revenue and Total Costs

Total costs, TC, were defined in the last chapter. Another measure of importance in the production process, total revenue or TR, the total dollar value of the production of an enterprise, was defined in Chapter 2. In symbols, $TR = P_y(Y)$, where P_y is the price per unit of output and Y is the amount of output. For the production function in column 1 of Table 4–1, the same production function of the classic form discussed in Chapter 3, TR is shown computed for all output levels; the price of Y is $30 per unit. When the amount of input is 10, Y is 66.7 and TR is $30(66.7), or $2,001. When X is 18, Y is 129.6 and TR is $30(129.6), or $3,888. In pure competition, the farmer can sell all his product at the prevailing market price; thus P_y is $30 per unit for all levels of output. Because the farmer cannot sell enough product to influence the market price, he can regard the output price as given.

The production function is vital to the computation of profit. It relates total revenue to the amount of input and total costs to the amount of output. That is, total revenue is easily related to output—it is price times quantity. In the same way, total costs may be easily computed for various input amounts. Only the production function can tie together the relationship between input and revenue or output and cost.

Total revenue minus total costs gives profit, which also is often called net returns or net revenue. Using an input cost of $30 per unit and a fixed cost of $1,000, profit is presented in column 3 of Table 4–1. When input is zero, output is zero and profit is −$1,000, the amount of the fixed cost. As output increases, profits increase and reach a maximum, or $1,088 at 18 units of input and 129.6 units of output.

Maximum profits from an enterprise do not occur where output is a maximum. Output reaches a maximum of 133.3 at 20 units of input—profit at this point is $999. Therefore, the goal of maximum yield from a fixed input, such as bushels of corn per acre or pounds of milk per cow, is not compatible with the goal of maximum profit per unit of fixed input. The reason, of course, is that the efficiency of production decreases in

TABLE 4-1

DETERMINING THE OPTIMUM POINT OF PRODUCTION USING TOTAL COSTS
AND TOTAL REVENUE (P_y = $30, P_x = $100, AND TFC = $1,000)

(1)		(2)		(3)
Input X	*Output* Y	*Total Costs* $TC =$ $TFC +$ $P_x(X)$	*Total Revenue* $TR = P_y(Y)$	*Profit* $TR - TC$
0	0.0	$1,000	$30(0.0) = $ 0	−$1,000
2	3.7	1,200	30(3.7) = 111	− 1,089
4	13.9	1,400	30(13.9) = 417	− 983
6	28.8	1,600	30(28.8) = 864	− 736
8	46.9	1,800	30(46.9) = 1,407	− 393
10	66.7	2,000	30(66.7) = 2,001	1
12	86.4	2,200	30(86.4) = 2,592	392
14	104.5	2,400	30(104.5) = 3,135	735
16	119.5	2,600	30(119.5) = 3,585	985
18	129.6	2,800	30(129.6) = 3,888	1,088
20	133.3	3,000	30(133.3) = 3,999	999
21	132.3	3,100	30(132.3) = 3,969	869

Stage II of the production function, and beyond the maximum profit point, the added inputs cost more than they are able to earn. Thus, the quest for maximum yields, while perhaps an admirable goal, is not consistent with income maximization.

Determining the Optimum Amount of Input

The optimum amount of input is that amount which when used causes profit to be a maximum. Many input amounts result in a profit; in fact, Table 4-1 shows that any input amount between 10 and 21 earns a profit. The optimum amount, however, is that amount resulting in the largest profit.

All methods of determining the optimum amount of input can be derived from the study of total revenue and total costs. The optimum amount of input for the production function in Table 4-1, computed by

FIGURE 4-1

DETERMINING THE OPTIMUM AMOUNT OF INPUT USING
TOTAL CURVES, THE PROFIT CURVE, OR MARGINAL
CURVES

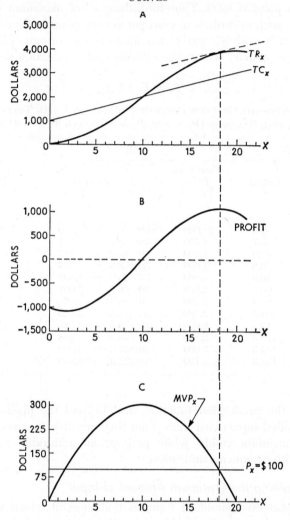

subtracting total costs from total revenue, is 18 units; the resulting maximum profit is $1,088. This same solution is presented in Figure 4–1A by graphing total revenue and total costs as functions of X.[1] Profits are a

---

[1] In Figure 4–1A, total revenue as a function of X is denoted TR_x; total costs as a function of X are denoted TC_x. A common name for total revenue as a function of X is the total value product, TVP. Total costs as a function of X are often called

maximum in the graph when total revenue exceeds total costs and the vertical distance between the two is a maximum. This occurs in Figure 4–1A at 18.2 units of input.

A second way to determine the optimum amount of input is to consider profit directly as a function of input. The optimum amount of input occurs where profit is a maximum. Profits, from column 3 of Table 4–1, are graphed in Figure 4–1B, and the maximum profit again occurs at 18.2 units of input.

The marginal criterion for determining the optimum amount of input is derived, as might be expected, from the slopes of the total revenue and total cost curves when those curves are plotted as functions of input, X. First, consider the slope of the total revenue function:

$$\frac{\Delta TR_x}{\Delta X} = \frac{\Delta(P_y Y)}{\Delta X} = P_y\left(\frac{\Delta Y}{\Delta X}\right) = P_y \cdot MPP_x .$$

Because P_y is constant, the change in TR_x is equal to change in output, ΔY, multiplied by the unit price, P_y. The ratio $\Delta Y / \Delta X$ is of course the marginal physical product of X, the number of units of output added by a unit of input. The slope of TR_x is thus $P_y(MPP_x)$, the value of the yield increment resulting from the use of an additional unit of input. This quantity, $P_y(MPP_x)$, is often called the marginal value product, MVP_x.[2]

The slope of TC_x is given by

$$\frac{\Delta TC}{\Delta X} = \frac{\Delta VC}{\Delta X} = \frac{\Delta(P_x X)}{\Delta X} = P_x\left(\frac{\Delta X}{\Delta X}\right) = P_x$$

because, by definition, the change in variable cost and total costs are identical and P_x is a constant in pure competition. The slope of TC_x is

---

total factor costs, TFC. Unfortunately, the symbols "TFC" are also used to denote total fixed costs. To avoid confusion, the symbols TR_x and TC_x are used. The subscripts will be omitted when total revenue and total costs are expressed as functions of output, Y.

[2] Terminology is a problem at this point. There are two measures of interest here: MVP_x and VMP_x. In general, VMP_x, the value of the marginal physical product is defined as the unit price of output multiplied by the marginal physical product. MVP_x, the marginal value product, is marginal revenue multiplied by the marginal physical product, marginal revenue being the addition to total revenue forthcoming from the sale of an additional unit of output. In pure competition the firm need never reduce price to sell an additional unit of output, marginal revenue equals the output price, and MVP_x equals VMP_x. Therefore, either term can be used for a firm selling in a purely competitive market. MVP_x is adopted here because it is widely used in agricultural economics. For example, see Earl O. Heady, *Economics of Agricultural Production and Resource Use* (Englewood Cliffs, N.J.: Prentice-Hall, Inc., 1952), chap. iv; L. A. Bradford and G. L. Johnson, *Farm Management Analysis* (New York: John Wiley & Sons, Inc., 1953), chap. viii. MVP_x is also often called marginal revenue product, MRP. When additional inputs change the quality of the output, then MVP_x and VMP_x would also differ. For example, feeding a hog to a heavier weight could cause quality and price per pound to change. Quality differentials are not considered in the present discussion.

thus seen to be P_x—the increment to total cost caused by using an additional unit of input is equal to the cost of the unit of input. In general the slope of TC_x is called the marginal factor cost, MFC. When the firm buys in a purely competitive market, $MFC = P_x$. But when the price of the input increases as the firm buys increasing amounts of the input, then MFC will exceed P_x.

TABLE 4–2

DETERMINING THE MOST PROFITABLE AMOUNT OF VARIABLE INPUT
USING THE PRODUCTION FUNCTION ($P_y = 30 AND $P_x = 100)

(1)			(2)		(3)	
X	Y	MPP_x	$MVP_x =$ $P_y(MPP_x)$	P_x	$P_x(\Delta X)$	$P_y(\Delta Y)$
0	0.0					
		1.9	$ 57	$100	$200	$111
2	3.7					
		5.1	153	100	200	306
4	13.9					
		7.5	225	100	200	447
6	28.8					
		9.1	273	100	200	543
8	46.9					
		10.1	300	100	200	594
10	66.7					
		9.8	297	100	200	591
12	86.4					
		9.1	273	100	200	543
14	104.5					
		7.5	225	100	200	450
16	119.5					
		5.1	153	100	200	303
18	129.6					
		1.9	57	100	200	111
20	133.3					
		−1.0	−30	100	100	−30
21	132.3					

When profits are maximized, MVP_x must equal P_x, i.e., the slopes of TR_x and TC_x are equal. The manager will keep adding variable inputs to the production process as long as the addition to revenue exceeds the addition to cost. At the point where added returns equal added costs, the optimum is reached.

MVP_x is computed in column 2 of Table 4–2. By reading down the column and comparing MVP_x with P_x, 18 units of input are determined to be the most profitable. Between 18 and 20 units of input, MVP_x is $57 per unit, less than the $100 cost. Therefore, additional units will not be used. A note of caution must be inserted here. The MVP_x of $57 represents the "average" MVP_x of the input units between 18 and 20. As explained in the last chapter when discussing MPP_x, the 19th unit of input would have a MVP_x larger than $57 and the 20th unit a MVP_x smaller than $57. There is not sufficient data in Table 4–2, however, to compute this additional information. In general, it is not necessary anyway. Farmers are fortunate, indeed, if they have as much information as presented in Table 4–2.

The MVP_x is presented in Figure 4–1C. The computed values in column 2 of Table 4–2 are graphed halfway between input values in a manner similar to MPP_x. The price of the input, $100, is represented by a straight line parallel to the horizontal axis and $100 up the vertical scale. This line says that the first unit of input costs $100, the second costs $100, the third costs $100, etc. This is because the farmer buys his inputs in a purely competitive market; if he did not, and there may be some cases in agriculture where this is true, the marginal factor cost and the price of the input would differ and the "price line" would not be parallel to the horizontal axis.

The price line intersects MVP_x at 18.2 units of input. This is 0.2 more than the amount determined from the table. This difference occurs, of course, because the graph contains more information about the shapes of the curves and enables the optimum to be determined exactly. For all practical purposes the difference is negligible. The price line and MVP_x also intersect at 1.8 units of input. This intersection is outside Stage II, the area of economic relevance, which was determined in the last chapter to fall between 15 and 20 units of input.

From a study of Figure 4–1, it is not obvious that input use can fall only in Stage II. The validity of this requirement can be demonstrated using information from Table 4–2. The MVP_x curve in Figure 4–1 was computed for an output price of $30. Suppose that input prices rose to $225 per unit with P_y still constant at $30. When P_x is $225, it can be determined from Figure 4–1C that the optimum amount of input is 15. At this point, output is equal to 112.5, $TR = P_y(Y) = \$30(112.5) = \$3,375$, $TVC = P_x(X) = \$225(15) = \$3,375$, and profit is $-\$1,000$. Total revenue from the enterprise exactly covers variable costs, and the manager loses his fixed costs. In the short run, fixed costs must be paid even when no product is forthcoming; therefore, producers will operate in the short run as long as they can cover variable cost. If the price of the input rises above $225, the marginal criterion would dictate the use of less than 15 units of input, but at this lesser input rate variable cost could not be covered, and it is therefore rational for the profit maximizing manager to use no input, i.e., cease production. For example, compute total revenue and total cost for an input price of $250 per unit, assuming the "optimum" to be 14 units of input. Therefore, the marginal criterion for determining the optimum amount of input is that $MVP_x = P_x$, given that total revenue is equal to or greater than total variable cost. The point where $X = 1.8$ actually maximizes losses. MVP_x in Stage II represents the farmer's demand curve for the input.

Determining the Optimum Amount of Output

The optimum input and output is by definition the combination that results in maximum profit. Using the data in Table 4–1, the optimum combination was determined to be 18 units of input and the resulting 129.6 units of output. Using Figure 4–1, the optimum amount of input was found to be 18.2, the 0.2 difference being caused by the increased accuracy of the graph. By referring back to a graph of the production function, for example Figure 3–2 of Chapter 3, the output resulting from an input of 18.2 is found to be 130.

The optimum output can also be determined by comparing total revenue and total cost at each output amount. TR and TC computed in Table 4–1 are graphed in Figure 4–2A. Because the farmer sells in a purely competitive market, TR is a straight line when plotted against output. Each additional unit sold adds exactly the same amount, P_y, to total revenue. Regardless of the amount sold, P_y is constant and determined in the marketplace rather than by the farmer. The shape of the TC curve is determined by the production function. A profit occurs whenever TR is greater than TC; a "break-even" point occurs at an output of 66.6 (compare to Figure 4–1A where profit is zero at an input of 9.9; an output 66.6 would result from an input of 9.9). Profit is the greatest where the vertical distance between TR and TC is the largest ($TR - TC = $ a maximum). This point occurs at an output of 129.6 in Table 4–1 and is determined more exactly to be 130 in Figure 4–2A.

Profit can also be considered directly as a function of output. Profits, from column 3 of Table 4–1, are graphed in Figure 4–2B; again the maximum occurs at an output of 130. This solution is analogous to that presented above for inputs.

The marginal conditions used to determine the optimum amount of output are derived from the slopes of the total revenue and total cost curves when those curves are plotted as functions of output. The slope of the total revenue curve is given by

$$\frac{\Delta TR}{\Delta Y} = \frac{\Delta(P_y Y)}{\Delta Y} = \frac{P_y(\Delta Y)}{\Delta Y} = P_y$$

because, as before, the price of output does not change as output changes. In general, regardless of the type of market in which the output is sold, the addition to total revenue caused by a unit change in output is called marginal revenue, MR, and is computed $\Delta TR/\Delta Y$. In pure competition, $MR = P_y$. The slope of the total cost function is marginal cost, MC (see Chapter 3, page 54).

FIGURE 4–2

C<small>OST AND</small> R<small>EVENUE</small> C<small>URVES FOR THE</small> C<small>LASSIC</small> P<small>RODUC-</small>
<small>TION</small> F<small>UNCTION</small>

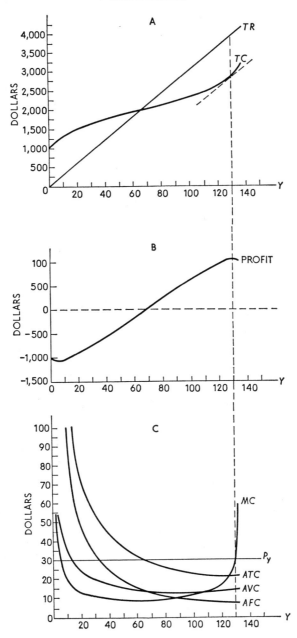

Marginal costs and P_y are graphed in Figure 4–2C. The price of output, P_y, is represented by a straight line parallel to the horizontal axis and 30 units up the vertical ($) scale. Because the farmer sells in a purely competitive market, the output price is constant. MC and P_y intersect at an output of 130; the vertical dashed line shows that optimum output is the same for both the total and the marginal curves.

The farmer will use inputs as long as the price of the output intersects marginal cost on or above average variable cost. When the price line, P_y, falls below AVC, the manager is losing his fixed costs and part of his variable costs. As explained above, in the short run he will produce as long as he is able to cover variable costs—on Figure 4–2C, this means that P_y must always be equal to or above AVC. The optimum output always occurs on the MC curve and on or above the AVC curve. This is the portion of MC that is in Stage II; it is the output supply curve.

The cost curves in Figure 4–2 are relevant only for specified fixed costs and unit cost of the input. For the example presented, $FC = \$1,000$ and $P_x = \$100$. For these costs, the lowest output price at which the farmer would produce is $13.3, the magnitude of MC where it equals AVC. Under no circumstances would more than 133.3 units of output, the maximum, be produced.

The producer who sells in a purely competitive market must equate P_y to MC to determine the most profitable output. In general, regardless of the type of market the manager sells in, the optimum input occurs where marginal cost equals marginal revenue, provided that marginal cost is equal to or greater than average variable costs. Managers who sell in markets other than pure competition, such as monopolists, have control over price or quantity, and for these firms, MR is no longer necessarily equal to P_y. For the farmer, who is a pure competitor, MR does equal P_y, and the criterion of equating MR and MC can be simplified to the equality of P_y and MC.

Marginal revenue is the slope of the total revenue curve just as marginal cost is the slope of the total cost curve. By equating marginal cost to marginal revenue, the criterion determines the point where the slopes of TR and TC are equal, i.e., where the two are increasing at exactly the same rate. In Figure 4–2A, a dashed line is drawn tangent to TC and parallel with TR. This is equivalent to equating MR, which is P_y, and MC. The distance between TR and TC, representing profit, is a maximum where the slopes are equal (Figure 4–2B).

Comparison of the Methods of Determining the Optimum

All methods of determining the most profitable level of output or input lead to comparable answers. Notice that the input criterion, $MVP_x = P_x$, can be written

$$P_y \cdot MPP_x = P_x$$

$$P_y \cdot \frac{\Delta Y}{\Delta X} = P_x$$

or $\qquad\qquad P_y \cdot \Delta Y \quad = P_x \cdot \Delta X$

The expression $P_y \cdot \Delta Y$ measures returns added by an increase in output while $P_x \cdot \Delta X$ measures the cost added by the increase in input. Thus, added costs must equal added returns at the point of maximum profit (see column 3, Table 4–2). But from the output criterion, $P_y = MC$, the same added-cost–added-return expression can be derived:

$$P_y = MC = \frac{P_x}{MPP_x} = P_x \frac{\Delta X}{\Delta Y}$$

or $\qquad\qquad P_y \cdot \Delta Y = P_x \cdot \Delta X \,.$

Thus, the two methods of determining the optimum are comparable. Care must be taken in using terminology, however.

Marginal value product and marginal factor cost (P_x) refer to added inputs. A unit of input increases total revenue by the amount of the MVP_x; it increases total costs by the amount of the MFC.

Marginal revenue and marginal cost refer to units of output. An added unit of output increases TR by the amount of MR; it increases TC by the amount of MC. MR and MC should never be used when referring to added returns or costs of inputs. In a like manner, MVP and MFC are never used when referring to added units of output. This is convention, but it is very useful when keeping concepts in place.

Another point to remember is that cost and total revenue curves are conventionally plotted with output on the horizontal axis. Again, this is done because managers are usually interested in costs per unit of output.

Short-Run Equilibrium

The firm operating where marginal costs equals marginal revenue is said to be in equilibrium. When fixed factors are present and the firm is operating in a short-run situation, this equilibrium is called a short-run equilibrium. Over a long period of time, when the firm is able to make changes in the "fixed factors" as well as the variable inputs, it is said to be in a long-run situation and attempting to attain a long-run equilibrium. All that is required in the short run is that variable inputs be used such that $MR = MC$; in the long run all inputs must be used according to that criterion.

When pure competition exists in the markets, P_y and P_x are determined by the interplay of supply and demand in the market. No individual farmer, either as a buyer of inputs or a seller of products, is able to influence the market prices. Once the price is determined by the market, the only hope of the manager is to organize his productive resources in such a way that satisfactory profits can be made. If he is unable to do this, he will eventually go out of business. In this way the free enterprise system promotes productive efficiency.

In the short run, the manager's primary concern is staying in business. Thus, short-run equilibrium is determined by the output where $P_y = MC$, as long as MC is equal to or greater than AVC. In the short run the manager will operate even if he cannot cover fixed costs because these costs must be paid regardless of the amount of production. In the long run, a business that does not repay all costs cannot be operated— therefore all costs must be covered in the long run.

In the short run, the firm may sometimes operate where $P_y = MC$, but P_y is greater than ATC. When the manager operates where $P_y = MC = ATC$, all costs including opportunity costs are being paid and the manager's return is exactly that needed to keep him in business in the long run. When the P_y is greater than ATC, the manager is making a profit in excess of that needed to keep him in business. This excess profit, sometimes called rent, accrues only in the short run. In the long run, additional producers begin supplying the product, existing producers expand output, and the product is thus in more plentiful supply and its price falls. As a result, market prices facing the pure competitor are forced down to the point where $P_y = MC = ATC$; total costs are covered, the manager is earning exactly that amount needed to induce him to stay in business, and because there is no excess profit, new producers are not tempted to enter into production.

APPLICATION TO AN ACTUAL FARM ENTERPRISE

Since the production function depicting corn yield response to fertilizer applications on an Iowa soil was presented in Chapter 3, the discussion has centered around theoretical concepts and hypothetical examples, apparently far removed from agriculture. On the contrary, however, these concepts represent the types of relationships inherent in agriculture, and as developed later in this book, they provide the basis for both the problems and the prosperity of agriculture. The production function for corn presented in Table 3–1 of Chapter 3 will be used to demonstrate the application of the principles developed thus far to an agricultural enterprise.

Table 4–3 contains a listing of costs incurred in growing an acre of corn. These costs are hypothetical—they are not from an actual farm record book. In practice, the cost of growing corn will vary among farmers because of differences in the value and efficiency of machinery and labor, inherent fertility and productivity of land, value placed on land, etc. When any attempt is made to budget expenses for examples applied to more than one farm, costs are always approximate. When planning for their own purposes, individual farmers can better estimate their costs.

The costs in Table 4–3 represent the fixed costs in this example. Actually, as corn yield increases, some increases in labor requirements and harvesting charges will occur. These charges are small and will be regarded as fixed for the sake of simplicity. Fixed costs total $62 per acre, the unit of fixed input.

The marginal value product of fertilizer is presented in Table 4–4; corn is valued at $1.10 per bushel. A unit of fertilizer, 40 pounds each of nitrogen and P_2O_5, costs $8.40. Fertilizer will thus be applied until its MVP is $8.40. Application of the fifth unit of fertilizer returns $10.56; the

TABLE 4–3

COST OF GROWING AND HARVESTING CORN PER ACRE
HYPOTHETICAL EXAMPLE

Tractor: fuel and oil, repairs, depreciation.................$ 6
Machinery: repairs and depreciation..................... 11
Seed..   1
Sprays, insecticides, etc.................................   1
Lime and phosphate...................................... 16
Labor... 10
Land charges—taxes and interest on investment........... 15
Interest on machinery and tractor investment............   2
　　　Total..$62

sixth unit adds only $3.30. Therefore, as determined from the data in Table 4–4, the optimum amount of fertilizer is five units. The marginal value product curve for fertilizer is presented in Figure 4–3. The price line, a straight line parallel to the horizontal axis and measured vertically up the dollar axis 8.4 units, intersects the MVP curve at 4.7 units of fertilizer. Thus, the estimate of five units from Table 4–3 is refined somewhat by the added information in Figure 4–3. Reference back to the production function, Figure 3–1 of Chapter 3, shows that the yield resulting from the use of 4.7 units of fertilizer is 135 bushels of corn.

Cost computations for the corn enterprise are presented in Table 4–5 and Figure 4–4. Variable cost and total costs increase at an increasing rate. In this case, fixed costs comprise a greater portion of total costs than do variable costs. MC increases as yield increases and is always larger than AVC; MC intersects ATC at the latter's minimum point. MC and the price of corn, $1.10, intersect at a yield level of 135, the optimum yield. Also, $TR - TC$ or profit is the largest at this point. Thus, use of the input criterion of $MVP_x = P_x$ results in the same answer as the use of the output criterion $MC = P_y$.

TABLE 4–4

DETERMINING THE OPTIMUM AMOUNT OF FERTILIZER TO USE IN
CORN PRODUCTION ON IDA SILT LOAM; PRICE OF A UNIT OF FER-
TILIZER IS $8.40; PRICE OF CORN IS $1.10 PER BUSHEL

Units Applied per Acre*	Bushels of Corn per Acre	Average Product of Fertilizer per Unit	Marginal Product of Fertilizer per Unit	Marginal Value Product of Fertilizer
0	0	...	....	....
			44.9	$49.39
1	44.9	44.9		
			38.7	42.57
2	83.6	41.8		
			26.5	29.15
3	110.1	36.7		
			17.2	18.92
4	127.3	31.8		
			9.6	10.56
5	136.9	27.4		
			3.0	3.30
6	139.9	23.3		
			−2.8	−3.08
7	137.1	19.6		
			−7.9	−8.69
8	129.2	16.2		

* A unit of fertilizer is 40 pounds of nitrogen and 40 pounds of P_2O_5.

For a yield of 135 bushels and a variable input of 4.7 units of
fertilizer, profit is $47 per acre. The optimum yield of corn occurs in the
area of economic relevance. *MC* is increasing and greater than *AVC*;
MPP_x is decreasing and less than APP_x.

FIGURE 4–3

DETERMINING THE OPTIMUM AMOUNT OF FERTILIZER
TO USE IN CORN PRODUCTION ON IDA SILT LOAM

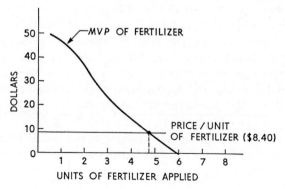

FIGURE 4–4

Determining the Optimum Corn Yield from the Use of
Fertilizer on Ida Silt Loam

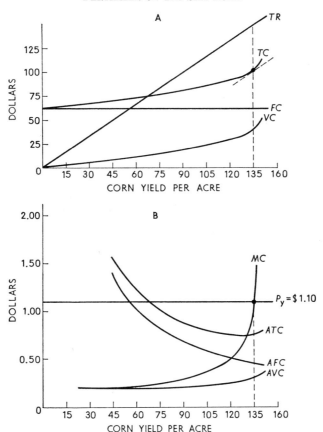

The growing season was very favorable for fertilizer use at the experimental site in Iowa during 1952, the year of the experiment. The residual fertility of the soil was low, causing initial fertilizer applications to produce large increments in corn yields. The first unit of fertilizer increased yield 45 bushels.

The magnitude of fixed costs in this example has been mentioned. This situation is typical of farming today. Due to increased size of farm, increased investment in machinery, increased value of land, etc., most commercial farmers today are faced with high fixed costs. One of the important effects of fertilizer is to increase yield substantially and thereby cause AFC to decrease rapidly (Figure 4–4B). While fixed costs per acre are high, $62, AFC at the optimum is $0.46 per bushel. Also, the

TABLE 4-5

DETERMINING THE OPTIMUM CORN YIELD FROM THE USE OF FERTILIZER ON IDA SILT LOAM; PRICE PER UNIT OF FERTILIZER IS $8.40; FIXED COSTS ARE $62

Units of Fertilizer per Acre	Bushels of Corn per Acre	Fixed Costs	Variable Costs	Total Costs	Average Fixed Costs	Average Variable Costs	Average Total Cost	Marginal Cost
0	0	$62	$ 0	$ 62.00	...	...	...	$0.19
1	44.9	62	8.40	70.40	$1.38	$0.19	$1.57	0.22
2	83.6	62	16.80	78.80	0.74	0.21	0.94	0.32
3	110.1	62	25.20	87.20	0.56	0.23	0.79	0.49
4	127.3	62	33.60	95.60	0.49	0.26	0.75	0.88
5	136.9	62	42.00	104.00	0.45	0.31	0.76	2.80
6	139.9	62	50.40	112.40	0.44	0.36	0.80	

high fixed costs cause the "break-even" yield to be high, 69 bushels per acre. Thus, while fertilizer would not be used if it were not profitable to do so, one of the important effects of using it is to spread high fixed costs among additional units of output.

ALLOCATING ONE VARIABLE INPUT AMONG SEVERAL FARM ENTERPRISES

Earlier in this chapter, two basic problems of resource use were mentioned. The first problem was the determination of the optimum amount of variable resource to use per unit of fixed resource. In this case, it is assumed that no limit was placed on the amount of variable input available to the farm manager. Profits were maximized per unit of fixed input by using the input criterion of $MVP_x = P_x$ or the output criterion of $P_y = MC$.

The assumption of an unlimited amount of variable resource is not realistic in agriculture. It means that the farm manager has enough capital to purchase all the feed needed for his livestock enterprises, all the fertilizer needed for his crop enterprises, plus all the labor, fuel, machinery, etc., needed on his farm, depending, of course, on just what inputs are regarded fixed for a particular management decision.

Few, if any, farmers have unlimited capital with which to purchase variable resources. When this is true, the second basic problem in the allocation of variable resources comes to the fore. Namely, given that a farmer has a limited amount of a variable resource, where "limited" means that he does not have enough resource to produce at the optimum in all of the enterprises on his farm, how should this limited amount of resource be allocated among the different enterprises on the farm? In this case, the problem is to determine the maximum profit that can be earned with the limited quantity of variable input—returns to the variable input are maximized. For example, suppose labor is the variable input and the farmer uses labor on many different farm enterprises. But if the amount of labor available to him is restricted to the amount he can do himself, he can only increase labor use on one enterprise, say hogs, by reducing labor use on some other enterprise, such as corn production. Assuming all other inputs fixed and, as shown in the next chapter, this need not be the case, the farmer's problem is to use labor most advantageously, i.e., maximize the profit from his given amount of labor.

Most allocation problems dealt with in farm management courses and faced by farmers are of the limited resource type. If resource quantities are such that the optimum amount of input can be used in each enterprise, the allocation problem is a fairly simple one. Each enterprise can be considered independently of all other enterprises. The use of more resource on one enterprise does not result in others using less. Likewise, one enterprise and a limited amount of resource cause little difficulty—just use all available resource on the one enterprise. When resources are limited, however, the enterprises are interrelated.

The Criterion

To allocate a limited amount of a variable input among several enterprises, the production function and relevant prices must be known for each enterprise. Next, the MVP_x schedule must be computed for each enterprise. Finally, using the opportunity cost principle developed earlier, units of the input are allocated to each enterprise in such a way that the profit earned by the input is a maximum.

Decisions regarding resource use are made using MVP_x as a guide. Profits from a limited amount of variable resource are maximized when the resource is allocated among the enterprises in such a way that the marginal earnings of the input are equal in all enterprises. In symbolic notation, this can be stated

$$MVP_{xa} = MVP_{xb} = MVP_{xc} = \ldots = MVP_{xn}$$

where MVP_{xa} is the marginal value product of X used in product A, MVP_{xb} is the marginal value product of X used on product B, and so on. n is the number of enterprises under consideration.

The opportunity cost principle works in this way: Suppose an input is used on two enterprises, corn and soybeans. If the MVP of the input is $10 for corn and $6 for soybeans, removal of one unit from soybean production and adding it to corn production would reduce returns on beans by $6 and increase returns from corn by $10—a net gain of $4. If after the unit had been transferred, the MVP of the input were $9 on corn and $7 on beans, transfer of another unit from beans to corn would increase returns by $2. If after this second transfer, the MVP of the input were equal at $8 in each enterprise, further transfer of the input would not increase returns from the limited stock of input.

It is important to remember that the economics now being studied, called the theory of the firm and dealing with costs, returns, and resource use on individual farms, is essentially a planning framework. We are like a field general who is trying to determine beforehand all of the possible strategies he could use to win a big battle. In the case of the farmer, the battle is for profits so that he might stay in business and he is armed with production functions, input and output prices, and opportunity cost principles. Economics is not a study of what has been but rather is a study of how to proceed in the future. The logic being presented pertains to the planning period.

Two important conditions are placed on the criterion requiring the equality of the marginal value product of an input in all its uses. First, and as always, the manager's goal is assumed to be the maximization of profit from his limited amount of input. Second, input use on all enterprises must be within the area of economic relevance, Stage II of the production function. If the quantity of the input is not sufficient to extend input use to the point where APP_x is a maximum in all enterprises, the input will be used to the point of maximum APP_x in some enterprises, the ones that are the most profitable, and no input will be used on the rest of the enterprises. Thus, when sufficient quantities of the variable input are not available to extend input use into Stage II for all enterprises, it will pay the manager to leave some fixed resources idle.

This principle can be illustrated using the classic production function presented in Table 4–2 of this chapter. APP_x attained a maximum at an input amount of 15 units; output at this level was 112.5. Suppose for this production process that the farmer owns 15 units of the fixed factor; in actual practice, these might be 15 dairy cows, 15 acres of land, etc. If the farmer has 30 units of X, he could allocate two units of X to each fixed factor and produce a total 55.5 units of product, because output is 3.7 when input is two. However, by using 15 units of X on each of two fixed factors, the output could be boosted to 225. By leaving 13 units of the fixed factor idle, the farmer can increase production by 169.5 units. The same principle holds true when dealing with enterprises with different production functions, that is, with different marginal earnings. The principles of allocating a limited amount of input among several competing enterprises, that is, labor among cattle, hog, and crop enterprises, or land between corn and soybean enterprises, are the same principles used to allocate a limited amount of input among units of fixed factors for the same enterprise, for example, fertilizer amounts among acres of corn land, feed among dairy cows, etc. (A more complete analysis of this problem is contained in Chapter 10, page 243.)

Example of an Allocation Problem

Production functions for three enterprises, A, B, and C, are presented in Table 4–6. The enterprises are labeled A, B, and C because the data are hypothetical; they could represent any three enterprises on a farm that use or "compete for" an input. Machinery must be used for several different enterprises; fertilizer may be spread on several fields and different crops; labor may be allocated to various crop and livestock enterprises. Much of farm management is composed of decisions relating the use of a limited amount of input on several enterprises.

The MVP_x values in Table 4–6 were determined by first computing MPP_x and then multiplying MPP_x by the appropriate product price. The MVP of X used on enterprise A is denoted MVP_{xa}, the MVP of X used on enterprise B is denoted MVP_{xb}, etc. For simplicity, assume input use to be in Stage II for all enterprises.

It is important to again note that the manager is in a planning situation; he is faced with the production functions in Table 4–6 and has to decide on his future actions. Suppose he has five units of X and can allocate them one unit at a time to any of the three enterprises. According to the opportunity cost principle, he will allocate each successive unit of input to the use where its marginal return, MVP_x, is the largest. The first unit of X earns \$20 in A, \$18 in B, and \$14 in C; using it on A insures that the opportunity cost, \$18 or \$14, is less than the actual earnings, \$20. Thus, the first of the five units is applied to enterprise A. Having applied the first unit to A, the second unit can earn \$16 in A, \$18 in B, and \$14 in C;

TABLE 4–6

ALLOCATING AN AMOUNT OF VARIABLE INPUT AMONG
THREE ENTERPRISES ($P_{ya} = \$2$, $P_{yb} = \$1$, $P_{yc} = \$2$)

Enterprise A			Enterprise B			Enterprise C		
X	Y	MVP_{xa}	X	Y	MVP_{xb}	X	Y	MVP_{xc}
0	0		0	0		0	0	
		\$20			\$18			\$14
1	10		1	18		1	7	
		16			13			12
2	18		2	31		2	13	
		12			11			10
3	24		3	42		3	18	
		10			9			8
4	29		4	51		4	22	
		8			7			6
5	33		5	58		5	25	
		6			6			4
6	36		6	64		6	27	

the second unit is applied to B. After applying the first and second unit, the third unit will earn \$16 in A, \$13 in B, and \$14 in C; the third will go on A. Continuing in this manner, the best use of five units of X is:

Units of X	Enterprise Used on—	MVP_x
First....................	A	\$20
Second.................	B	18
Third..................	A	16
Fourth.................	C	14
Fifth...................	B	13

Two units of input go on A, two on B, and one on C. Used in this manner the five units of input will earn \$81. No other use of the five units on the three enterprises will earn as much. After the fifth unit of input is applied, MVP_x is \$12 in A, \$13 in B, and \$12 in C. The marginal earnings of X are not quite equal in each enterprise. This is due to the discontinuities or "lumpiness" of the data in Table 4–6. More refined data, such as provided by graphs, would be necessary to equate the marginal earnings exactly. The principles used would be the same, however.

As yet, the cost of the five units of input has not been discussed. The cost of the inputs raises several interesting problems—let us review the opportunity cost principles discussed earlier. Suppose the inputs cost \$6.50 per unit and the manager has \$32.50 of capital, enough to purchase five units. He could then make \$48.50 (before paying fixed expenses) by buying the five units and using them as described. Before doing so, however, he would want to be sure he could not earn more than \$48.50 profit by using the \$32.50 of capital in some off-farm enterprise, for example, the stock market or a business in the next town. The first point, then, is that the capital will be used to purchase inputs for enterprises A, B, and C only if it won't earn more elsewhere.

Next, suppose that the manager already owns the inputs, having bought them in the past. The cost of the inputs may be \$1 or \$1,000, but in either case it has already been paid. Will the manager now use the inputs on enterprises A, B, and C? Not necessarily. If he can sell the inputs (say) to his neighbor for more than \$81, he will do so. Only if he cannot dispose of the inputs for more than they will earn on his farm will he use them. To summarize, if the manager has capital to purchase the inputs, the opportunity cost is determined by the earnings of that capital in alternative uses. If he already owns the inputs, the opportunity cost is represented by the disposal value of the inputs, regardless of their original cost. Thus, when discussing input use for one or more enterprises, the manager must have considered and rejected all alternative uses for his capital or inputs.

What is the maximum amount of input needed for enterprises A, B, and C? To find out, the manager must determine the most profitable amount of input for each enterprise. When inputs cost \$6.50 per unit, these amounts are 5 for A, 5 for B, and 4 for C. Profit is \$77. Thus, the manager would never use more than a total of 14 units of inputs on A, B, and C, no matter how many units he could afford to buy. This defines what is meant by "limited" and "unlimited" capital situations. In this case, if the manager has sufficient capital to purchase 14 or more units of input, capital is termed "unlimited." It actually isn't unlimited. The manager doesn't have a personal fortune; he does have enough capital to use the optimum amount of input in each enterprise. If the manager does not have enough money to purchase 14 units of input, then capital is "limited." Input use on one enterprise can be increased only by decreasing input use on some other enterprise. The enterprises are said to "compete" for the input or, more generally, the capital used to purchase inputs.

Returns per Dollar Spent

A common phrase in farm management is "returns per dollar spent." Applied farm management men often state that the farmer desires to maximize returns per dollar spent. This is either true or not true, depending upon the situation to which it is applied.

When applying a variable input to fixed inputs, returns per dollar spent on the variable input will be maximized when APP_x is a maximum. When capital is unlimited, the optimum amount of input to use is where $MVP_x = P_x$; at this point profits are a maximum, but APP_x is less than a maximum. Therefore, the criterion calling for the maximization of returns per dollar spent is incorrect for these circumstances.[3]

Returns per dollar spent is an appropriate criterion for limited capital situations, but it must be subject to strict interpretation. If a farm manager has a given quantity of capital available to purchase variable inputs, then his goal is to maximize the amount earned by this quantity of capital; i.e., he wants to maximize the total earnings of the limited amount of capital. But for a given stock of capital, maximizing the total earnings is the same as maximizing the average earnings.

For example, in Table 4–6 five units of input were allocated, two each to A and B and one to C. When so allocated, their total earnings were $81. Any other manner of allocation would have earned less. The cost of five units of input, at $6.50 per unit, was $32.50, and returns per dollar spent were $81/$32.50, or $2.49. Returns per dollar spent are a maximum for the five units of input. Any other use of the five units of input would have lowered returns per dollar spent. Thus, given a limited amount of capital, the farmer's goal is to maximize returns per dollar spent, and this goal is attained by equating the marginal earnings of the input in each enterprise.

Maximizing returns per dollar spent without specifically stating that capital is limited is to be studiously avoided. As long as input use is in Stage II, returns per dollar spent are increased by reducing input use— this, of course, is due to the law of diminishing returns. For example, referring to Table 4–6, returns per dollar spent are $38/$13 = $2.92 when two units of inputs are purchased and one unit each applied to enterprises A and B. For five units of input, returns per dollar were $2.49. Thus, returns per dollar were increased by using fewer inputs; profits, however, were reduced from $48.50 to $25. If returns per dollar were to

---

[3] The assumption here is that short-run equilibrium will not occur where $MPP_x = APP_x$. If it did, maximizing returns per dollar would also maximize profits. The theory of pure competition specifies that the long-run equilibrium does occur where $MPP_x = APP_x$. Thus, the two goals would be consistent for the long-run situation.

be maximized, one unit of input would be purchased and used on A and profit would only be $13.50. On the other hand, at the point of maximum profit, $77, returns per dollar are $1.85 = $168/$91. Thus, independent of the amount of capital available, returns per dollar is not a goal to be attained in and of itself. However, for any specified sum of money, maximizing returns per dollar is the same as maximizing total return or profit from that sum.

PROFIT MAXIMIZATION FOR THE FARM
AND FOR THE ENTERPRISE

The farmer must manage all enterprises on a farm simultaneously. He must decide whether to expand an enterprise by committing additional resources to it or whether to withdraw resources from the enterprise. When resources are limited, and they usually are in the short run, expansion can come about only by decreasing resource use in one or more other enterprises. Ability to make decisions of this type distinguish the good manager from the poor one.

When variable resources are "unlimited," the farm manager need not worry about the allocation of variable inputs. He needs only to use the optimum amount of all enterprises. His problem, which may be considerable, is the selection of the most profitable enterprises. Resource use in one enterprise is independent of resource use in other enterprises—one enterprise can be expanded without forcing a reduction in other enterprises. The problem is to determine the optimum in each case. Because the optimum is used, $MVP_x = P_x$ in all enterprises and the MVP are therefore equal. Thus, producing the optimum in an enterprise is consistent with maximizing farm profits.

When capital is limited, however, marginal earnings of the input are equated—but less than the optimum—for all enterprises. In this case farm profits would be reduced by extending resource use to the optimum in one enterprise. Farm profits could be increased by removing inputs from the enterprises extended to the optimum and applying those inputs where their marginal earnings are higher. Thus when inputs are limited, a paradox appears—total profits from the farm can be maximized only if profits in individual farm enterprises are not maximized. In this case, profits to the limited amount of variable inputs are maximized; when resources are unlimited, profits to the fixed inputs are maximized.

REFERENCES

HEADY, EARL O. *Economics of Agricultural Production and Resource Use,* chaps. ii and iii. Englewood Cliffs, N.J.: Prentice-Hall, Inc., 1952.

VINCENT, WARREN H. (ed.). *Economics and Management in Agriculture,* chap. iii. Englewood Cliffs, N.J.: Prentice-Hall, Inc., 1962.

Chapter 5 | PRODUCTION WITH TWO OR MORE VARIABLE INPUTS

The production processes studied in previous chapters dealt only with one output and one variable input; all other inputs were considered fixed in quantity. This type of production process does not have wide application in practice; its advantage lies in its simplicity. Many basic concepts were developed in Chapters 3 and 4 while the complexities of multiple input problems were sidestepped. The next step towards the attainment of an economic description of a production process is to increase the number of variable inputs used in the production process.

In this chapter the fundamental relationships among two or more variable inputs will be developed. The principles presented will not negate but rather will build upon those developed earlier. As before, the assumption is made that the farm manager buys inputs and sells products in purely competitive markets. Thus, unit prices of inputs and outputs are determined by economic forces beyond the control of the manager and can be regarded by him as given. Second, the assumption is made that at least one productive input is fixed in quantity so that all production processes discussed in this chapter are short-run situations to which the law of diminishing returns is applicable. If all inputs are variable, the law of diminishing returns no longer holds, the short run is replaced by the long run, and the economic interpretation of the relationship among inputs and outputs differs somewhat from that presented in this chapter. A further development of the long run is presented in Chapter 7.

To simplify the analysis in the beginning, the special case of one output resulting from two variable inputs will be discussed. First, the production function will be discussed conceptually and presented geometrically. Second, the basic problem facing the manager when more than one variable input is used, that of finding the "right" combination of inputs, will be analyzed. Third, the optimum or most profitable combination of inputs will be determined. Finally, the analyses developed in detail for two inputs will be generalized to include any number of variable inputs. An empirical example will be presented.

AN EXAMPLE FROM AGRICULTURE

Chapter 3 began with an example of a production function depicting corn yield response to fertilizer. To begin the study of yield response to two variable inputs, an empirical example will again be presented.

Table 5–1 contains the response of corn yields to variations in

TABLE 5–1

RESPONSE OF CORN YIELD IN BUSHELS PER ACRE TO TWO
INPUTS, POUNDS OF APPLIED NITROGEN AND NUMBER OF
PLANTS PER ACRE, NORTH MISSOURI RESEARCH CENTER,
1962

Pounds of Nitrogen Applied per Acre	Number of Plants per Acre				
	9,000	*12,000*	*15,000*	*18,000*	*21,000*
0	50.6	54.2	53.5	48.5	39.2
50	78.7	85.9	88.8	87.5	81.9
100	94.4	105.3	111.9	114.2	112.2
150	97.8	112.4	122.6	128.6	130.3
200	88.9	107.1	121.0	130.6	135.9

SOURCE: John Ambrosius, "The Effects of Experimental Size upon Optimum Rates of Nitrogen and Stand for Corn in Missouri," unpublished manuscript, 1964.

pounds of nitrogen applied per acre and number of plants per acre. These data were the result of a controlled experiment conducted in North Missouri, 1962. Seven rates of nitrogen and four rates of plant population were applied to experimental plots located on Seymour silt loam near Spickard, Missouri. The resulting yields were measured and used to estimate the "smooth" production function contained in Table 5–1.[1]

The production function in Table 5–1 can be regarded as series of individual or "subproduction" functions. For example, the first row of the table depicts corn yield response to increasing numbers of plants when nitrogen is held fixed at zero. Other rows in the table represent yield response to plant populations for higher levels of applied nitrogen. In a

[1] The corn yield values presented in Table 5–1, predicted using regression procedures, were taken from John Ambrosius, "The Effects of Experimental Size upon Optimum Rates of Nitrogen and Stand for Corn in Missouri," unpublished manuscript, 1964. The treatment means for the experiment are contained in Table 3 of Earl M. Kroth and John P. Doll, *Response of Corn Yields to Nitrogen Fertilization and Plant Population in Missouri, 1962*, Progress Report No. 2, Missouri Agricultural Experiment Station Special Report 27, March, 1963.

like manner, each column represents corn yield response to nitrogen given a fixed number of plants. In total, 10 subproduction functions are contained in Table 5–1. All yields, of course, represent the corn yields that would result from the use of one acre of land, the combinations of nitrogen and plant population shown, along with a host of fixed inputs, including weather, not described here.

The yields resulting from two variable inputs are not as readily depicted graphically as those resulting from one variable input. In general, a three-dimensional drawing is needed. One way to picture this type of production situation is to consider only the input levels contained in Table 5–1 and draw a picture as in Figure 5–1A. For each level of nitrogen and plant population a block is drawn to represent corn yield. The height of the block is determined by the amount of the corn yield. By placing these blocks in tiers, the corn yield response to both inputs can be simulated. In total, 25 blocks would be needed to trace out response to the 25 input combinations. To avoid clutter, only a few of these are presented in Figure 5–1A.

Figure 5–1A represents yields resulting from 0, 50, 100, 150, and 200 pounds of nitrogen and 9,000, 12,000, 15,000, 18,000, and 21,000 plants per acre. In general, these inputs can be used at any rate—they are perfectly divisible. The farmer may apply 47, 175, 20, 199, or any other rate of nitrogen. The same is true of plant population. Thus, the method of picturing yield response shown in Figure 5–1A is not only cumbersome but does not depict yields resulting from all possible input combinations. In reality the yields in Table 5–1 represent but 25 points through which a smooth curve can be drawn. Such a "surface" is depicted in Figure 5–1B.

The base of Figure 5–1B measures the units of plants and nitrogen—these units mark off a grid similar to a checkerboard. The intersections of the lines on the base represent an input combination. The point immediately above each intersection represents the corn yield resulting from the input combination. For example, to find the corn yield resulting from 100 pounds of nitrogen and 15,000 plants per acre, locate in the base grid the intersection of the lines marked 100 and 15,000 respectively, and then place a perpendicular line segment (such as a flagpole) on the intersection so that it (the perpendicular line segment) exactly touches the surface above. The height of this perpendicular line segment represents the resulting corn yield, in this case, 111.9 bushels. In Figure 5–1B, this point is seen to occur exactly at the point where the two subproduction functions, one resulting from varying stand while nitrogen is fixed at 100 pounds per acre and the other from varying nitrogen while stand is fixed at 15,000 plants per acre, intersect in space. By imagining that a perpendicular is raised from each point of intersection in the base grid and that a smooth sheet of (say) plastic is stretched over the tops of the perpendiculars (flagpoles), the resulting production surface can be de-

FIGURE 5–1

CORN YIELD RESPONSE TO NITROGEN AND PLANT POPULATION, NORTH MISSOURI
RESEARCH CENTER, 1962

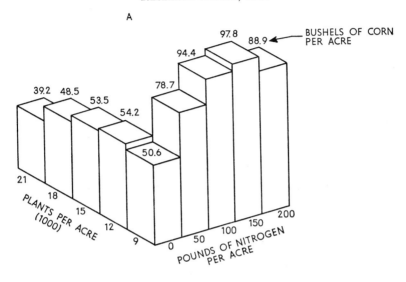

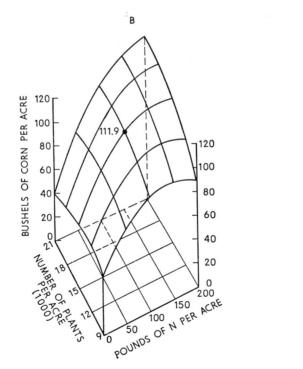

veloped. In Figure 5–1B, 10 curves, each representing a subproduction function from Table 5–1, are interlaced to depict the general shape of the surface—points in between are not depicted but are imagined to exist. The surface thus depicts the corn yields resulting from *any* combination of nitrogen and plant population from 0–200 and 9,000–21,000, respectively.

The surface shown in Figure 5–1B demonstrates the new problems faced when more than one variable input is included in the production function. First, what is the most profitable corn yield? Clearly, of the many yields possible, one is the most profitable. Second, what combination of nitrogen and plant population should be used to produce the most profitable yield? The second question arises because the possibility now exists that a given corn yield can be produced using many different combinations of nitrogen and plant population. For example, from Table 5–1 it appears that 100 bushels of corn can be produced using 15,000 plants and slightly more than 50 pounds of nitrogen, 12,000 plants and slightly less than 100 pounds of nitrogen, 150 pounds of nitrogen and some planting rate between 9,000 and 12,000 plants per acre, etc. In other words, a perpendicular line segment representing 100 bushels would fit snugly between the surface and the grid in many places in Figure 5–1B. The manager who decided to produce 100 bushels must decide which of these many combinations to use. The next section of this chapter is directed mainly at these two questions: (1) what output amount should be produced, and (2) what input combination should be used to produce it.

THE PRODUCTION FUNCTION
FOR TWO VARIABLE INPUTS

The production function for two variable inputs will now be introduced in more general terms. Conceptually, this production function does not differ from that for one variable input. Each combination of the two inputs produces a unique amount of output. If the amounts of either or both inputs are changed, the resulting amount of product is also changed. In symbolic notation, the production function for two variable inputs is often written

$$Y = f(X_1, X_2) ,$$

where Y is the amount of product and X_1 and X_2 are amounts of the two variable inputs. This expression says that the amount of output, Y, depends in a unique way upon the amounts of the two inputs, X_1 and X_2, used in the production process along with the other fixed inputs. Strictly speaking, this type of notation is not needed in this text; however, notations of this type are often commonly used and are presented here for completeness.

The Production Surface

A hypothetical production function for two variable inputs is presented in Table 5–2. Amounts of the two inputs, called X_1 and X_2 for

TABLE 5–2

OUTPUT RESULTING FROM VARIOUS COMBINATIONS OF TWO INPUTS

	10	80	93	104	113	120	125	128	129	128	125	120
	9	81	94	105	114	121	126	129	130	129	126	121
	8	80	93	104	113	120	125	128	129	128	125	120
	7	77	90	101	110	117	122	125	126	125	122	117
Input	6	72	85	96	105	112	117	120	121	120	117	112
One	5	65	78	89	98	105	110	113	114	113	110	105
(X_1)	4	56	69	80	89	96	101	104	105	104	101	96
	3	45	58	69	78	85	90	93	94	93	90	85
	2	32	45	56	65	72	77	80	81	80	77	72
	1	17	30	41	50	57	62	65	66	65	62	57
	0	0	13	24	33	40	45	48	49	48	45	40
		0	1	2	3	4	5	6	7	8	9	10
						Input Two (X_2)						

convenience, are listed along the left side and bottom of the table. The body of the table presents, in appropriate units of bushels, tons, bales, etc., the amount of output resulting from each combination of inputs. Thus, zero output results when no inputs are used, 30 units result from one unit each of X_1 and X_2, 56 units of output from two units of each input, and so on. The maximum possible output, 130, results from the use of 9 units of X_1 and 7 units of X_2.

The data in Table 5–2 are regarded as continuous, and the input-output combinations presented represent only a few of all possible combinations. Thus, for two units of X_1 and 2.5 units of X_2, some amount of output, between 56 and 65, will be produced. The same is true for any other input combinations that are not whole numbers. All of these combinations are not presented in Table 5–2 because the table, already large, would thereby expand without limit. All points can be represented geometrically using a smooth surface, however.[2]

The production function in Table 5–2 represents an expected relationship that is useful for planning purposes. It tells the amount of product forthcoming if a particular combination of inputs is used. It is subject to all the restrictive interpretations placed upon the production function for one variable input. Changes in the amount of fixed factors or in the technology used will, in turn, affect the production function.

Isoquants

The first new problem of economic concern can be found in Table 5–2. With the exception of the minimum output, zero, and the maximum output, 130, all output levels can be produced using several different input combinations. For example, 105 units of output can be produced using the following input combinations (Table 5–2):

X_1	X_2
9	2
6	3
5	4
4	7
5	10

As pointed out above, the input-output combinations in Table 5–2 represent only a few of all possible combinations, the rest of which were not presented because of space limitations. Therefore, there must exist many other input combinations that also produce 105 units of output. For example, when X_2 is 5, some amount of X_1 greater than 4 but less than 5 would produce 105 units of product. Similarly, when used with 6 units of X_2, slightly more than 4 units of X_1 would also produce 105 units.

The curve representing all combinations of X_1 and X_2 that produce a given level of output is called an "isoquant" ("iso" meaning equal and "quant" meaning quantity). The meaning of the isoquant for 105 units of output is shown in the three-dimensional drawing of Figure 5–2A. The isoquant traces out all input combinations that produce 105 units of output. If a perpendicular line is dropped from any point on the surface exactly 105 units above the input base, it will always touch the base grid at a point on the isoquant for 105 units of output.

The isoquant is more conventionally drawn in two dimensions. If the production surface in Figure 5–2A were viewed directly from above,

[2] The production function in Table 5–1 was computed using the mathematical equation $Y = 18X_1 - X_1^2 + 14X_2 - X_2^2$. Using this equation the output from any combination of inputs can be computed.

FIGURE 5–2

RELATIONSHIP OF ISOQUANTS TO THE PRODUCTION SURFACE

A

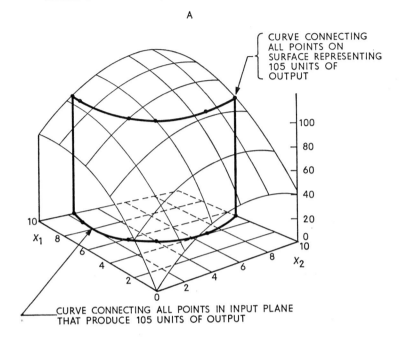

CURVE CONNECTING ALL POINTS ON SURFACE REPRESENTING 105 UNITS OF OUTPUT

CURVE CONNECTING ALL POINTS IN INPUT PLANE THAT PRODUCE 105 UNITS OF OUTPUT

B

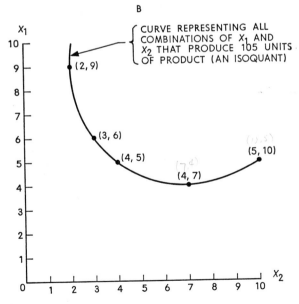

CURVE REPRESENTING ALL COMBINATIONS OF X_1 AND X_2 THAT PRODUCE 105 UNITS OF PRODUCT (AN ISOQUANT)

(2, 9)

(3, 6)

(4, 5)

(4, 7)

(5, 10)

it would appear as in Figure 5–2B. This diagram contains all the information in Figure 5–2A and has the additional advantage of simplicity. In fact, the isoquant for 105 units of output can be determined directly from Table 5–2 without recourse to the production surface. The input combinations from Table 5–2 can be located on the graph (denoted by the heavy dots in Figure 5–2) and connected by a smooth curve. The result will be the same isoquant depicted in Figure 5–2A. All points falling on the curve are those which will produce 105 units of product. For example, in addition to the points already mentioned, $X_1 = 7$ and

FIGURE 5–3

OUTPUT ISOQUANTS FOR A HYPOTHETICAL PRODUC-
TION FUNCTION

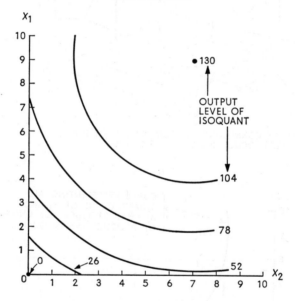

$X_2 = 4.4$, $X_1 = 4.4$ and $X_2 = 5$, $X_1 = 4.1$ and $X_2 = 6$ will all produce 105 units of product.[3]

Isoquants can be determined for any particular output level, or, conversely, every output level has an isoquant. For the example under discussion, there is an isoquant for every output between and including 0 and 130. Several isoquants for this example are shown in Figure 5–3. This

---

[3] The accuracy of the curve depends upon the number of points available for plotting. If a mathematical expression can be derived for the production function, then the equation of the isoquant can be determined. In this example, the production function has the equation $Y = 18X_1 - X_1^2 + 14X_2 - X_2^2$ and the isoquant, expressing the relationship $X_1 = g(X_2, Y)$, has the equation $X_1 = 9 \pm (81 + 14X_2 - Y)^{\frac{1}{2}}$. When equations are not available, the points in the table are the only guides.

isoquant map was drawn using points from Table 5–2 (extra points needed were derived using the isoquant equation in footnote 3). The isoquants presented are for 26-unit increments in output, 0, 26, 52, 78, 104, and 130. The 105-unit isoquant is not included only to demonstrate that isoquants can be derived for any output levels of interest to the manager.

The isoquant map has the same interpretation as a contour map used to demonstrate the topography of a countryside. On a contour map, the contour lines represent the altitude above sea level; by following the contours, the lay of the land can be determined. The isoquant map in Figure 5–3 indicates the shape of the production surface which, in turn, indicates the nature of the output response to the inputs. In Figure 5–3, each isoquant measures the output above zero; the shape of the isoquants indicate that output increases smoothly to the maximum point, 130.

The Marginal Rate of Input Substitution

The marginal rate of input substitution is represented by the slope of the isoquant. The 105-unit isoquant is presented in Figure 5–4. When $X_2 = 2$, $X_1 = 9$, but when $X_2 = 3$, $X_1 = 6$. Thus, if output is to be held constant at 105 units when X_2 is increased from 2 to 3 units, X_1 must be decreased from 9 units to 6 units. This type of problem is analogous to the mountain climber who two miles above sea level on the southwest

FIGURE 5–4

MEASURING THE MARGINAL RATE OF SUBSTITUTION BE-
TWEEN TWO POINTS ON AN ISOQUANT

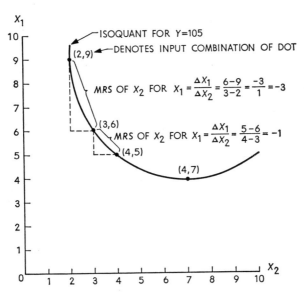

slope of a mountain asks himself the question, "If I walk south one mile, how far east must I go to remain two miles above sea level?" In this case the marginal rate of substitution of X_2 for X_1 is defined as the amount by which X_1 must be decreased to maintain output at a constant amount when X_2 is increased by one unit. Between the points $X_2 = 2$, $X_1 = 9$ and $X_2 = 3$, $X_1 = 6$, the marginal rate of substitution of X_2 for X_1, abbreviated MRS of X_2 for X_1, is

$$MRS \text{ of } X_2 \text{ for } X_1 = \frac{\Delta X_1}{\Delta X_2} = \frac{6 - 9}{3 - 2} = \frac{-3}{1} = -3,$$

where ΔX_1 is the change in X_1 and ΔX_2 is the change in X_2. The MRS is negative because the isoquant slopes downward and to the right.

MRS of X_2 for X_1 varies depending upon the points on the isoquant considered. Between the points $X_2 = 3$, $X_1 = 6$ and $X_2 = 4$, $X_1 = 5$,

$$MRS \text{ of } X_2 \text{ for } X_1 = \frac{\Delta X_1}{\Delta X_2} = \frac{5 - 6}{4 - 3} = \frac{-1}{1} = -1.$$

The addition of one unit of X_2 will require a simultaneous reduction of X_1 by one unit if output is to be held constant at 105.

TABLE 5–3

COMPUTATION OF THE MARGINAL RATE OF SUBSTITUTION OF
X_2 FOR X_1 FOR AN OUTPUT OF 105

Units of X_2	Units of X_1	ΔX_2	ΔX_1	MRS of X_2 for X_1
2	9.0			
		1	−3.0	−3.0
3	6.0			
		1	−1.0	−1.0
4	5.0			
		1	−0.6	−0.6
5	4.4			
		1	−0.3	−0.3
6	4.1			
		1	−0.1	−0.1
7	4.0			
		1	0.1	0.1
8	4.1			

Marginal rates of substitution of X_2 for X_1 are computed in Table 5–3 for the 105-unit isoquant. Because the isoquant is curved, the slope changes continuously, and as the amount of X_2 increases, the MRS of X_2 for X_1 decreases absolutely (ignoring the negative sign). This type of substitution is known as a "decreasing rate of substitution." As the amount of X_2 increases, its ability to increase output decreases and one unit of X_2 successively replaces smaller and smaller amounts of X_1. (This

same concept is sometimes called "*increasing* rate of substitution" because as X_1 increases, successively *increasing* amounts of X_1 are needed
to replace one unit of X_2. The two names imply the same concept and
arise because of the "convex" shape of the isoquant. In general, a curve is
convex between two points if a straight line connecting the two points
lies on or above the curve.)

   If a straight line were drawn between the bracketed points in
Figure 5–4, the slope of that line would represent the MRS computed
between the points. As with the marginal physical product (see the
Appendix on page 535 and Chapter 4), the MRS between two points

FIGURE 5–5

MEASURING THE EXACT MARGINAL RATE OF SUB-
STITUTION AT A POINT

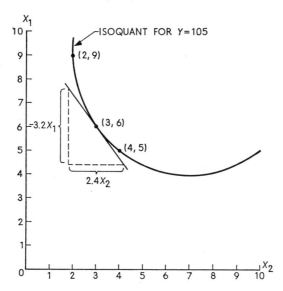

represents only approximately the slope of the isoquant. This approximation can be improved by moving the two points together until in a
limiting sense the slope of the tangent at any point on an isoquant
represents the exact MRS at that point. This is illustrated in Figure 5–5,
where a straight line is drawn tangent to the isoquant at the point
$X_2 = 3$, $X_1 = 6$. The slope of this straight line is equal to the MRS of X_2
for X_1 at the point $(3, 6)$, and from measurement on the graph, it is equal
to $-3.2/2.4 = -4/3$. This MRS is different from the MRS between the
points $(2, 9)$ and $(3, 6)$ or $(3, 6)$ and $(4, 5)$.

   The production function is a relationship between input and output that can be used when planning business activity. Isoquants are derived from production functions and have the same interpretation. Movement along an isoquant can be interpreted in a planning sense only; *if* a certain combination of inputs were to be used, *then* the MRS would take a specific value. In practice, once a combination of inputs has been selected and used, that combination cannot be immediately altered. In general, isoquants and marginal rates of substitution are physical (technical) relationships that result from and describe the characteristics of the production function.

FIGURE 5–6

TOTAL OUTLAY SURFACES

A

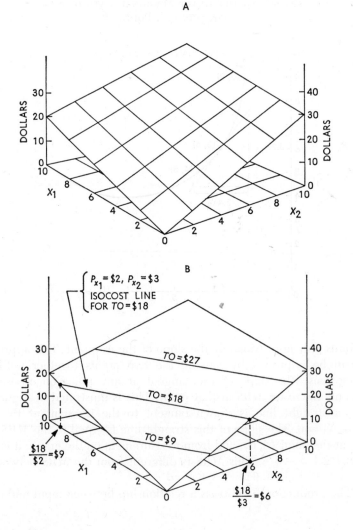

Isocost Lines

Each combination of inputs has a cost associated with it. Denoting the cost per unit of X_1 as P_{x_1} and the cost per unit of X_2 as P_{x_2}, then the total outlay, TO, is given by

$$TO = P_{x_1}X_1 + P_{x_2}X_2 \, .$$

The input prices are assumed known, and as a result TO can be computed for each input combination. If $P_{x_1} = \$2$ and $P_{x_2} = \$3$, then the cost of 5 units of X_1 and 2 units of X_2 is $\$2\cdot5 + \$3\cdot2 = \$16$. Thus, TO is a function of the amount of X_1 and X_2 and can be graphed in a manner similar to a production surface. A total outlay surface is shown in Figure 5–6A. The TO surface touches zero at $X_1 = X_2 = 0$ because no variable costs are incurred at that point. The slope of TO on a line parallel to the X_2 axis (X_1 held constant) is equal to P_{x_2}, and vice versa. The surface is linear because input prices are constant in pure competition.

Just as production surfaces are characterized by isoquants, total outlay surfaces can be described using isocost lines—"iso" again meaning equal. An isocost line traces a set of points on the cost surface which are an equal distance above the input base or "grid." For example, suppose $TO = \$18$, that is, the farmer has $18 to spend on variable inputs. He may then purchase $TO/P_{x_1} = \$18/\$2 = 9$ units of X_1 or $TO/P_{x_2} = \$18/\$3 = 6$ units of X_2. The appropriate isocost line for $18 can then be located using the TO surface (Figure 5–6B). For perspective, the isocost lines for total outlays of $9, $18, and $27 are also shown in Figure 5–6B.

Isocost lines determine all combinations of the two inputs that cost the same amount. In the example, this amount was $18, but in general it could be any amount equal to or greater than zero. The isocost line can be placed on a two-dimensional graph. If the TO surface in Figure 5–6B were viewed directly from above, an isocost map would be the result. Such a map is shown in Figure 5–7A. (To avoid clutter, only isocost

FIGURE 5–7

THE CONSTRUCTION OF ISOCOST CURVES

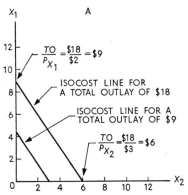
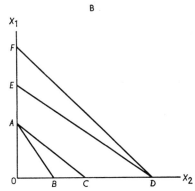

lines for $TO = \$9$ and $TO = \$18$ are included in Figure 5–7A.) The isocost lines in Figure 5–7A can be derived directly by locating the end points $X_2 = 6$ and $X_1 = 9$ for $TO = \$18$ and connecting them with a straight line. The TO surface is needed only to more fully explain the meaning of the isocost line.

The equation of the isocost line is found by solving

$$TO = P_{x_1}X_1 + P_{x_2}X_2$$

for X_1 as an explicit function of X_2. For example,

$$P_{x_1}X_1 = TO - P_{x_2}X_2$$

and

$$X_1 = \frac{TO}{P_{x_1}} - \frac{P_{x_2}}{P_{x_1}} X_2 .$$

From this expression it can be seen that the slope of the isocost line is $-P_{x_2}/P_{x_1}$ while the intercept on the X_1 axis is given by TO/P_{x_1}. For the prices given, the isocost line for $TO = \$18$ in Figure 5–7A is

$$X_1 = 9 - \frac{3}{2} X_2 .$$

The total outlay surface is linear and may be imagined as a ply-wood board touching the floor (input base) only at the origin. As a result isocost lines are linear—they are completely determined by their end points. The reason for this is that the inputs are purchased in a purely competitive market; the price of the input does not change with the quantity purchased.

The two important aspects of the isocost line are (1) its distance from the origin and (2) its slope. When prices do not change, each possible total outlay has a different isocost line. As total outlay increases, the ratio TO/P_{x_1} increases and the isocost line moves to higher points on the outlay surface, located further from the origin. An isocost line for \$9 is drawn in Figure 5–7A; it lies halfway between the origin and the \$18 outlay line. Both lines have the same slope, however, because input prices are the same in both cases.

Changes in the input price change the slope of the isocost line. A decrease in the input price means that more can be purchased with the same total outlay; an increase means that less can be purchased. In Figure 5–7B, if AB were the original isocost line and the price of X_2 dropped, then AC would represent the new isocost line. If AC were the original isocost curve and the unit price of X_2 increased, then AB would represent the new isocost curve. The lines DE and DF represent similar changes for the price of X_1, given that the price of X_2 is constant.

The Least-Cost Criterion

The concepts now available can be used to determine the combination of inputs that will produce a given output at a minimum of cost. As seen, a given level of output can be produced using many different combinations of the two variable inputs. Usually, no two of these input combinations will have the same cost (a special case where they do will be discussed later); therefore one combination must necessarily be cheaper than all others. The problem of cost minimization is to determine that combination.

One possible way to determine the least-cost combination is to compute the cost of all possible combinations and then select the one with minimum cost. This method is satisfactory when only a few combinations produce a given output. Table 5–4 contains seven combinations of inputs that produce 105 units of output (these points were read from Figure 5–4). If the price of X_1, denoted P_{x_1}, is $2 per unit and the price

TABLE 5–4

Computation of the Minimum-Cost Combination of Inputs for an Output of 105, $P_{x_1} = \$2$, $P_{x_2} = \$3$

Units of X_2	Units of X_1	Cost of X_2	Cost of X_1	Total Outlay
2	9.0	$ 6	$18.0	$24.0
3	6.0	9	12.0	21.0
4	5.0	12	10.0	22.0
5	4.4	15	8.8	23.8
6	4.1	18	8.2	26.2
7	4.0	21	8.0	29.0
8	4.1	24	8.2	32.2

of X_2, denoted P_{x_2}, is $3 per unit, the cost of each combination can be determined by multiplication. For example, the cost of 2 units of X_2 and 9 units of X_1 is equal to $(\$3 \cdot 2) + (\$2 \cdot 9) = \$24$. This cost is similar to total variable costs and is here called "total outlay," because the term "total variable costs" is reserved for cost analyses under the assumption that the minimum-cost combination of inputs is used.

Of the seven combinations in Table 5–4, 3 units of X_2 and 6 units of X_1 represent the least-cost combination of inputs, $21. For many purposes, this may be as accurate an estimate of the least-cost combination as is needed. However, Figure 5–4 demonstrates that in addition to the seven combinations of X_1 and X_2 in Table 5–4, many other combinations of the two inputs will produce 105 units of output. Some combination of inputs on the isoquant to the right or to the left of the point $X_2 = 3$,

$X_1 = 6$ may be cheaper than the combination $(3, 6)$. The exact location of the least-cost combination of inputs can be determined geometrically, but to do so, concepts associated with the marginal rate of input substitution and the isocost line must be utilized.

Seven input combinations are presented in Table 5–4; the cost of each combination was computed and the one with the least cost was easily found. However, the isoquant in Figure 5–2B has an infinite number of points—computation of the cost of each combination would be impossible. A new criterion, preferably one which could be easily applied geometrically, is needed. The criterion which will work, called the least-cost criterion, is

$$MRS \text{ of } X_2 \text{ for } X_1 = -\frac{P_{x_2}}{P_{x_1}}$$

or because of the definition of MRS

$$\frac{\Delta X_1}{\Delta X_2} = -\frac{P_{x_2}}{P_{x_1}} \, .$$

This criterion can also be written

$$-P_{x_1}(\Delta X_1) = P_{x_2}(\Delta X_2)$$

because ΔX_1 is always negative in the economically relevant range. If at any point on the isoquant,

$$-P_{x_1}(\Delta X_1) > P_{x_2}(\Delta X_2) \, ,$$

then the cost of producing the given output amount could be reduced by increasing X_2 and decreasing X_1 because the cost of an added unit of X_2 is less than the cost of the units of X_1 it replaces. On the other hand, if at any point on the isoquant,

$$-P_{x_1}(\Delta X_1) < P_{x_2}(\Delta X_2) \, ,$$

then the cost of producing the specified quantity of output can be reduced by using less X_2 and adding X_1. The equality of the least-cost criterion signifies that a change in the input combination would increase the cost of producing the output. To insure that the least-cost criterion determines a minimum, the isoquant must be convex.

Isoquants and isocost lines can be drawn on the same graph. Every possible output level can be represented by an isoquant, and every possible total outlay can be represented by an isocost line. This is a very flexible arrangement—an isoquant can be determined for any given total outlay, or an isocost line can be drawn for any particular isoquant. The least-cost criterion is

$$\frac{\Delta X_1}{\Delta X_2} = -\frac{P_{x_2}}{P_{x_1}} \, .$$

The left side of this expression is represented by the slope of an isoquant; the right side by the slope of the isocost line. Thus, the least-cost combination of inputs occurs at the point where the isocost line is tangent to the isoquant, given that the isoquant is convex.

Figure 5–8 depicts the least-cost solution for the 105-unit isoquant. In this case the minimum total outlay needed to produce 105 units of product is unknown; in fact, it is the solution being sought. This solution can be found, however, by finding the point where a straight line with a

FIGURE 5–8

DETERMINING THE COMBINATION OF INPUTS THAT
WILL PRODUCE 105 UNITS OF OUTPUT AT A MINIMUM
COST ($P_{x_1} = \$2$ AND $P_{x_2} = \$3$)

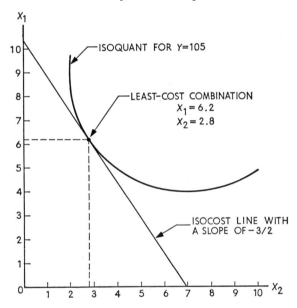

slope of $-3/2$ is tangent to the isoquant, i.e., finding the point where the isoquant has a slope of $-3/2$. Once located, this straight line *is* the isocost line and can be extended to the input axes. As shown in Figure 5–8, the point of tangency occurs at $X_1 = 6.2$ and $X_2 = 2.8$. The total outlay for this combination is $(6.2 \times \$2) + (2.8 \times \$3) = \$20.80$, slightly less than the cheapest combination in Table 5–4 when only discrete (whole) units of inputs were considered.

The nature of the solution obtained by the least-cost criterion can be illustrated using a three-dimensional drawing. The isocost line defines the set of inputs that can be purchased with the given total outlay—$20.80 in the example. The manager can buy zero amounts of the inputs or any amounts up to and including all combinations that cost $20.80. For each of these "feasible" input combinations, there exists an associated output. These are depicted in Figure 5–9. The production surface is vertically sliced above the isocost line—these outputs and all outputs resulting from less expensive input combinations make up the segment of the production surface shown in Figure 5–9. The curve *AB* represents all outputs that could result from an expenditure of $20.80—the maximum of the outputs on the line *AB* is 105, resulting from 2.8 units of X_2 and 6.2 units of X_1. No other combination of inputs in the

FIGURE 5–9

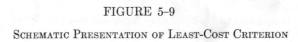

SCHEMATIC PRESENTATION OF LEAST-COST CRITERION

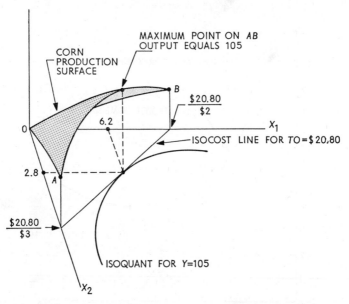

feasible set will produce more output; also, no other point on the 105-unit output isoquant is contained in the feasible set. In general, each possible isocost line defines a corresponding "feasible" set of inputs and a corresponding maximum output. The analysis in Figure 5–9 shows that the least-cost solution for the production of 105 units of output corresponds exactly to the solution of the problem of maximizing output from spending exactly $20.80 total outlay.

The Meaning of Input Substitution and MRS

Input substitution in production processes refers to the addition of one input while simultaneously decreasing the amount of the second input, thereby holding output constant. For this to be possible, the inputs must both increase output. The amount by which the second input must be decreased to maintain a constant output when the first input is increased one unit is, of course, the marginal rate of substitution, and the two inputs are termed "substitutes" because they have the same effect on output.

In farming, land can be substituted for labor, machinery can be substituted for labor, fertilizer can be substituted for land, etc. This is possible because many different combinations of land, labor, and capital can be used to produce a certain amount of farm output. The fact that the inputs are substitutes does not mean they perform the same technical or physiological function in the production process but only that their function, whatever it is, is output increasing.

For example, isoquants can be derived for plant population (number of corn plants per acre) and nitrogen in corn production. This means only that a given corn yield can be obtained using many different combinations of nitrogen and plant population. It does not mean that nitrogen and plant population increase corn yield biologically in the same manner. In fact, they are known to affect yield differently. Nitrogen is a chemical that stimulates growth within the plants while an increase in plant population increases the number of plants growing per acre of soil. Despite their completely different biological effects, however, these inputs are substitutes in an economic sense because they have an increasing effect on corn yield.

Thus far, little has been said about the marginal products of the inputs. This may seem unusual—marginal analysis was singularly emphasized in preceding chapters. Actually, the MRS is a convenient way to examine two marginal products simultaneously.

A small portion of the 105-unit isoquant is reproduced in Figure 5–10. The MRS of X_2 for X_1 on the isoquant between B and C equals $(6 - 9)/(3 - 2) = -3$. This is equivalent to finding the slope of a straight line connecting B and C where the "rise" is equal to the distance AB and the "run" equal to the distance AC. But the output at point A, where $X_1 = 6$ and $X_2 = 2$, is 96 units (Table 5–2). Thus, between A and B,

$$MPP_{x_1} = \frac{105 - 96}{9 - 6} = \frac{9}{3} = 3\,,$$

while between A and C

$$MPP_{x_2} = \frac{105 - 96}{3 - 2} = \frac{9}{1} = 9\,.$$

Thus, it is apparent that

$$-\frac{MPP_{x_2}}{MPP_{x_1}} = -\frac{9}{3} = -3 = MRS \text{ of } X_2 \text{ for } X_1 \text{ between } B \text{ and } C\,.$$

FIGURE 5–10

COMPUTING THE MARGINAL RATE OF SUBSTITU-
TION ALONG AN ISOQUANT

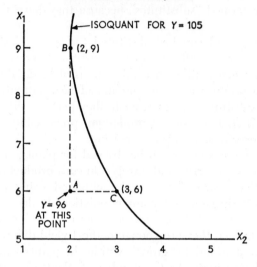

The negative sign must be added because the isoquant slopes downward to the right. The *MRS* therefore represents the ratio of the marginal products. The least-cost criterion can now be written

$$-\frac{MPP_{x_2}}{MPP_{x_1}} = -\frac{P_{x_2}}{P_{x_1}}.$$

Because in this example X_2 costs 1.5 times more than X_1, it must at the margin produce 1.5 times as much. If MPP_{x_1} is 2 then MPP_{x_2} must be 3 at the least-cost position. If MPP_{x_1} is 20, MPP_{x_2} must be 30, etc.

Isoclines and Profit Maximization

Isoclines Defined. Isoquants can be derived for each possible output level, and for a given price ratio, one combination of inputs on each isoquant is the least-cost combination. Thus, a least-cost combination of inputs exists for every possible output level. A line (or curve) connecting the least-cost combination of inputs for all output levels is called an isocline—"iso" meaning equal and "cline" representing inclination. Thus, the isocline passes through all isoquants at points where the latter have a similar slope.

Isoclines can be constructed from an isoquant map.[4] In Figure

---

[4] Also, isocline equations can be derived mathematically by substituting into the least-cost criterion $MPP_{x_2}/MPP_{x_1} = P_{x_2}/P_{x_1}$. For the example used here, the isocline equation is $X_1 = [P_{x_1}/P_{x_2}(7-X_2)] + 9$ or $X_1 = 13/3 + 2/3X_2$ when the price ratio is 1.5.

5–11, an isocost line with a slope of $-3/2$, representing $P_{x_2} = \$3$ and $P_{x_1} = \$2$, is drawn tangent to each isoquant. Then a line, the isocline, is drawn connecting the points of tangency. At all points on this isocline

$$MRS \text{ of } X_2 \text{ for } X_1 = -\frac{3}{2}.$$

The isocline for the price ratio $-3/2$ intersects the X_1 axis at $X_1 = 4.3$, where output is 59. Outputs below this amount would be most cheaply produced using only X_1; outputs above this amount can be produced at least cost using some combination of the two inputs. For 52

FIGURE 5–11

IsoQUANT MAP WITH ISOCLINES FOR THREE DIFFERENT
INPUT PRICE RATIOS

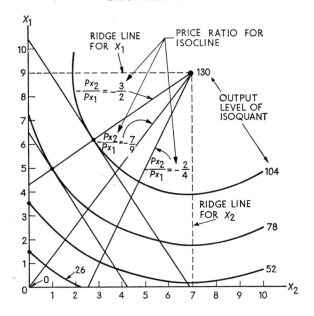

units of output, the least-cost combination is $X_1 = 3.6$ and $X_2 = 0$; for 78 units, $X_1 = 5$ and $X_2 = 1$; for 130 units, the least-cost and only possible combination is 9 of X_1 and 7 of X_2.

Just as there is an isoquant for each output level, there is an isocline for each price ratio. Two additional isoclines are included in Figure 5–11; the corresponding isocost lines are omitted for clarity. Note that as the cost of X_2 drops relative to the cost of X_1, increasing amounts of X_2 are included in the least-cost combination for any given output. For 78 units of output, the least-cost combination is $X_1 = 5$ and $X_2 = 1$ when the price ratio is $-3/2$, but it is 3.3 and 2.6 when the price ratio is $-7/9$ and 2.6

and 3.8 when the price ratio is $-2/4$. All isoclines converge at the point of maximum output.

The dashed lines in Figure 5–11 represent a special type of isocline called ridge lines. Ridge lines represent the limits of economic relevance; the boundaries beyond which the isocline and isoquant maps cease to have economic meaning. The horizontal ridge line represents the points where MPP_{x_1} is zero; the vertical line, the points where MPP_{x_2} is zero.

The slope of the isoquant was shown to be

$$MRS \text{ of } X_2 \text{ for } X_1 = -\frac{MPP_{x_2}}{MPP_{x_1}}.$$

On the ridge line for X_1, MPP_{x_1} is zero, the tangent to the isoquant is vertical and has no defined slope. On the ridge line for X_2, MPP_{x_2} is zero and the isoquant has a zero slope. Ridge lines are so named because they trace the high points up the side of the production surface, much like mountain ridges that rise to the peak of the mountain.

Ridge lines represent the points of maximum output from each input, given a fixed amount of the other input. When $X_1 = 1$, output can be increased by adding X_2 up to the amount denoted by the ridge line (seven units). At that point, output from X_2 is a maximum given one unit of X_1 and MPP_{x_2} is zero. Past $X_2 = 7$, MPP_{x_2} is negative while MPP_{x_1} is positive; the inputs have an opposite effect on output and are no longer substitutes. Thus, the ridge lines denote the limits of substitution. Inside the ridge lines, the isoquants have a negative slope and the inputs are substitutes. Outside the ridge lines the inputs do not substitute in an economically meaningful way. Output is a maximum, 130, where the ridge lines, and all other isoclines, converge.

Isoclines can be determined for all possible combinations of input prices. However, when planning a business operation at any particular time, only one set of input prices will be relevant and that is the set the manager believes to be most appropriate for the coming production period. The isocline for these relevant prices is the one the manager should use for planning purposes and is called the "expansion path" to distinguish it from all other possible isoclines. At any particular time, only one expansion path is possible. If X_1 is free, the horizontal or X_1 ridge line is the expansion path; if X_2 is free, the vertical or X_2 ridge line is the expansion path. When the inputs are purchased in purely competitive markets, the expansion path always coincides with one of the isoclines.

Profit Maximization. The isocline traces out the least-cost combination of inputs for every possible output level. This question now arises: which output level is the most profitable? Conceptually, this question is answered by proceeding out the expansion path, i.e., increasing output, until the value of the product added by increasing the two inputs along the expansion path is equal to the combined cost of the added amounts of the two inputs. Viewed from the input side, this is the same as saying that the *MVP* of an input must equal the unit price of the input; viewed from the output side, it is the same as saying marginal cost must equal marginal revenue. Thus, while all points on an isocline represent least-cost combinations, only one point represents the maximum profit output.

There is no convenient way of determining the most profitable input and output amounts on an isocline map such as Figure 5–11. Graphically, two methods are available.

First, the input and output amounts traced by the isocline can be regarded as a separate production function, sometimes called a subproduction function because it is only a small portion of the larger production surface. This production function could be graphed with output on the vertical axis and the two inputs in least-cost combination graphed along the horizontal scale such that for each amount of one input the corresponding least-cost amount of the second input is listed. The marginal value product of the two inputs can then be derived and equated to the added cost of the two inputs to determine the optimum amounts of input.

A simpler way to graphically determine the optimum output is to develop the appropriate cost curves. Inputs often are measured in different physical units and have different prices; any difficulties caused by differences in physical measures can be avoided by converting to dollar measures and computing costs. Once the appropriate curves are derived, the optimum output can be found by equating *MC* to P_y. This method is illustrated in Table 5–5 and Figure 5–12.

TABLE 5–5

COMPUTATION OF COSTS FOR LEAST-COST COMBINATION OF INPUTS; $P_{x_1} = \$9$ AND $P_{x_2} = \$7$; LEAST-COST COMBINATIONS READ FROM FIGURE 5–11

Least-Cost Combinations of X_1 and X_2 for the Indicated Outputs:			Minimum Total Outlay for Output	Average Variable Cost	Marginal Cost
X_1	X_2	Y	TVC	AVC	MC
0.00	0.00	0	0	. . .	
					$0.53
0.96	0.75	26	$ 13.89	$0.53	
					0.58
2.00	1.55	52	28.85	0.56	
					0.72
3.30	2.55	78	47.55	0.61	
					0.95
5.00	3.90	104	72.30	0.70	
					2.22
9.00	7.00	130	130.00	1.00	

The left side of Table 5–5 contains points from the subproduction function determined by the isocline (expansion path) for the input prices $P_{x_1} = \$9$ and $P_{x_2} = \$7$. These points were determined from Figure 5–11 by determining where the isocline intersects each isoquant. *TVC*, *AVC*, and *MC* were then computed for each output level. Fixed costs are omitted in this example for brevity. *TVC* is the combined cost of X_1 and X_2; for example, in line 2, Table 5–5, $\$13.89 = \$9(0.96) + \$7(0.75)$. *AVC* and *MC* are computed as always.

FIGURE 5–12

DETERMINING THE OPTIMUM OUTPUT FOR A PRODUCTION PRO-
CESS UTILIZING TWO VARIABLE INPUTS

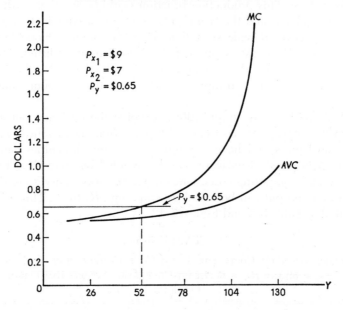

AVC and *MC* are graphed in Figure 5–12. If the price per unit of output is $0.65, represented by the horizontal line 0.65 units up the dollar axis, then the optimum output is 53 units of output, determined by dropping a perpendicular from the intersection of *MC* and P_y. Reference to Figure 5–11 shows that 53 units of output would result from the use of a combination of inputs on the isocline slightly past the 52-bushel isoquant. (When computed mathematically using the equation in footnote 3, page 92, the combination turns out to be 2.1 units of X_1 and 1.6 units of X_2. These latter points can be found on the isocline.) Profits can be computed in the usual manner.

The criterion for the optimum amount of one variable input was

$MVP_x = P_x$. In the case of two variable inputs, this same criterion is expanded to the following system of equations:

$$MVP_{x_1} = P_{x_1}$$
$$MVP_{x_2} = P_{x_2}.$$

Thus, the marginal earnings of each input must be equal to its cost; this must be true for both inputs simultaneously. Profit will be a maximum at this point if for each input, $MP < AP$ and both are decreasing, i.e., input use is in Stage II. This criterion has no simple geometric interpretation, but it must be fulfilled at the point of maximum profit; it is the familiar requirement of diminishing returns. Also, total revenue must equal or exceed the cost of the variable inputs.

The optimum criterion for two variable inputs is often expressed in different algebraic forms. By dividing each equation by the appropriate input price, i.e., the top equation by P_{x_1} and the bottom equation by P_{x_2}, the set of equations can be rewritten

$$\frac{MVP_{x_1}}{P_{x_1}} = 1$$
$$\frac{MVP_{x_2}}{P_{x_2}} = 1.$$

And because both expressions are equal to one, they are equal to each other. Thus, another common expression of the profit maximizing criterion is

$$\frac{MVP_{x_1}}{P_{x_1}} = \frac{MVP_{x_2}}{P_{x_2}} = 1.$$

Relationships between Inputs

Inputs have been defined as substitutes if they have the same effect on output. When an increment of either of two inputs decreases output, they are strictly speaking substitutes. In general, however, the situation has economic importance only when the inputs are output increasing. The important relationships between inputs that are output increasing will be discussed in this section.

Decreasing Rates of Substitution. Decreasing rates of substitution occur when the input being increased substitutes for smaller and smaller amounts of the input being replaced. Thus, if the MRS of X_2 for X_1 decreases numerically (ignoring the negative sign) as X_2 is increased along an isoquant, then a decreasing rate of substitution is exhibited.

Decreasing rates of substitution are caused by the law of diminishing returns. The MRS of X_2 for X_1 is defined as MPP_{x_2}/MPP_{x_1}. When diminishing returns are present, MPP_{x_2} decreases as X_2 increases and MPP_{x_1} increases as X_1 decreases. Thus, the ratio decreases numerically. Decreasing rates of substitution are quite common among most inputs.

The production function in Table 5–2 is characterized by decreasing rates of substitution. Therefore, further illustrative tables will not be presented here. Figure 5–13A contains some hypothetical isoquant maps illustrating decreasing rates of substitution. In the left-hand diagram, the isoquant intersects each input axes; thus, the output represented by the isoquant can be produced using only X_1, only X_2, or some combination of

FIGURE 5–13

ISOQUANTS REPRESENTING DIFFERENT TYPES OF SUBSTITUTION BETWEEN INPUTS

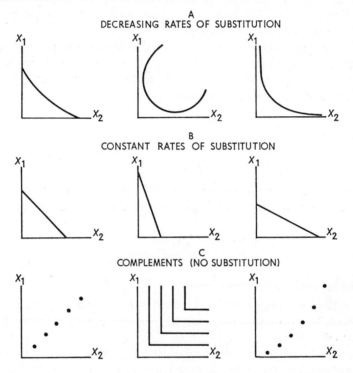

A
DECREASING RATES OF SUBSTITUTION

B
CONSTANT RATES OF SUBSTITUTION

C
COMPLEMENTS (NO SUBSTITUTION)

X_1 and X_2, depending upon the input price ratio. In the center figure, the isoquant does not intersect either axis, signifying that the output cannot be produced unless a minimum amount of both inputs are present. Also, the isoquants attain a positive slope, signifying that if too much of one input is used, increasing amounts of the other must be applied to maintain output. The zone of economic relevance is, of course, that portion which has negative slope. The isoquant in the right-hand diagram becomes parallel to each input axis as the amount of either input is increased indefinitely; in this case the inputs substitute within limits, but after one input decreases to a certain low, the second can be added in any amount without changing either output or the amount of the first input.

Constant Rates of Substitution. Constant rates of substitution occur when the amount of one input replaced by the other input does not change as the added input increases in magnitude. Thus, the MRS of X_2 for X_1 is a constant and the isoquant is a straight line.

Examples of production functions with inputs that substitute at constant rates are presented in Table 5–6. In Table 5–6A, one unit of X_2 substitutes for one unit of X_1 at each output level (except 20). In this case, the production function displays constant marginal returns to the inputs, but, in general, this is not a requirement. When one unit of an input replaces exactly one unit of another input, the inputs are the same

TABLE 5–6

EXAMPLES OF PRODUCTION FUNCTIONS WITH INPUTS THAT SUBSTITUTE AT CON-
STANT RATES

		A								B					
	5	10	12	14	16	18	20		5	5	7	9	11	13	15
	4	8	10	12	14	16	18		4	4	6	8	10	12	14
X_1	3	6	8	10	12	14	16	X_1	3	3	5	7	9	11	13
	2	4	6	8	10	12	14		2	2	4	6	8	10	12
	1	2	4	6	8	10	12		1	1	3	5	7	9	11
	0	0	2	4	6	8	10		0	0	2	4	6	8	10
		0	1	2	3	4	5			0	1	2	3	4	5
				X_2								X_2			

from an economic point of view. The isoquant forms 45-degree interior angles with the input axes (see the figure on the left, Figure 5–13B).

Table 5–6B illustrates a production function with the property that one unit of X_2 replaces two units of X_1 at each output level. In this case the isoquant no longer forms a 45-degree interior angle with the axes. Two general cases are possible: (1) A unit of X_2 replaces more than one unit of X_1. This is the case in Table 5–6B and the center diagram in Figure 5–13B. (2) A unit of X_2 replaces less than one unit of X_1. This situation is illustrated in the right-hand diagram, Figure 5–13B.

Isoquants representing constant rates of substitution are easily confused with isocost lines. Both are straight lines; when placed on the same graph they must be clearly labeled. The lines in Figure 5–13B are all isoquants. If isocost lines were placed on these graphs, three possibilities would result. If the isocost line had less slope (ignoring sign) than the isoquant, cost would be minimized by using only X_1. If the isocost line had a greater slope than the isoquant, cost would be minimized by using only X_2. If the isocost line had the same slope as the isoquant, then all combinations of X_1 and X_2 would have identical costs and any combination could be used. Actually, probably one or the other would be used out of convenience.

Inputs that substitute at a constant rate often involve quality differentials, for example, two grades of tractor fuel, two soil types, or two laborers. Constant rates of substitution are not widespread in agriculture, principally because of the law of diminishing returns. Constant rates of substitution require that for the given level of output, increments of one input and decrements of the second are such that the ratio of the marginal products is unchanged. For a given production surface, it is not necessary that the isoquants be parallel or equidistant. In some economic literature, inputs that substitute at constant rates are termed "perfect" substitutes.

TABLE 5–7

EXAMPLES OF PRODUCTION FUNCTIONS WITH INPUTS THAT ARE COMPLEMENTS

		A								B					
X_1	5	0	0	0	0	0	15	X_1	5	0	2	4	6	8	10
	4	0	0	0	0	14	0		4	0	2	4	6	8	8
	3	0	0	0	12	0	0		3	0	2	4	6	6	6
	2	0	0	9	0	0	0		2	0	2	4	4	4	4
	1	0	5	0	0	0	0		1	0	2	2	2	2	2
	0	0	0	0	0	0	0		0	0	0	0	0	0	0
		0	1	2	3	4	5			0	1	2	3	4	5
				X_2								X_2			

Complementary Inputs. Inputs that increase output only when combined in fixed proportions are called complements. Complements represent the exact reverse of substitutes. "Substitutes" imply that a range of input combinations will produce a given output amount; "complements" imply that only one exact combination of inputs will produce the specified output.

Two examples of production functions showing complementary relationships between inputs are presented in Table 5–7. These examples are illustrative—many other possibilities exist. In Table 5–7A, the inputs must be combined in a 1:1 ratio; any deviation from this ratio causes output to drop to zero. If one unit of X_2 is used, one unit of X_1 must also be used. Any other amount of X_1 results in no output. In Table 5–7B, if one unit of X_2 is used, then at least one unit of X_1 must also be used to attain an output of two. If more than one unit of X_1 is used, output is not diminished but neither is it increased.

Figure 5–13C illustrates some possible complementary relationships. The diagram on the left is comparable to Table 5–7A. Isoquants degenerate to single points. The center diagram (Figure 5–13C) portrays the production function in Table 5–7B. In this case the isoquants appear as right angles set within the input axis. The diagram on the right suggests a situation where a fixed ratio is needed for each output but the ratio varies among output levels.

When the isoquant degenerates to a dot, only one possible combination of inputs may be used regardless of cost. In this case, the isocost line has no significance and the inputs can be considered in combination as one input. Either it pays to use both in combination or none is used. When the isoquant appears as a right angle (center, Figure 5–13C), the input combination at the vertex is used—any other combination on the isoquant would produce no more but would cost more.

Complementary inputs are common in agriculture. A trivial example would be all the parts that make up a machine—tractor tires and other components of tractors, etc. Other common examples are tractors and tractor drivers, fuel and grease, fence wire and posts. Chemical compounds used in agriculture are also examples—water is composed of two parts hydrogen and one part oxygen, etc.

Often complements are regarded as single inputs, such as a horse and a man versus a tractor and a man. In each case, the man and the power source are complements; however, each combination may be regarded as a single input that substitutes for the other combination. Thus, the same amount of work may be accomplished using many different combinations of tractors and men as compared to horses and men.

Lumpy Inputs. The discussion presented up to this time, along with the graphs drawn, have assumed that each of the variable inputs is completely divisible. If both of the inputs are not completely divisible but come only in discrete units, then the isoquants appear as a series of dots rather than a continuous curve. The economic principles of cost minimizations do not change, however. A further discussion of this problem is contained in Chapter 10.

Alternative Isocline Forms

Discussion of different types of substitution between inputs is actually a discussion of the shape or form of the production surface; the two are different ways of looking at the same thing. Also, the type of substitution (or the shape of the production surface) determines the shape of the isoclines. All of these are interrelated and in practice are determined by the technical relationship among the inputs and the output.

Alternative forms of isoclines are shown in Figure 5–14. These do not represent all possible types of isoclines, but they do represent common types. Each type should be studied to determine the corresponding isoquant map and the shape of the production surface.

FIGURE 5–14

ALTERNATIVE FORMS OF ISOCLINE MAPS

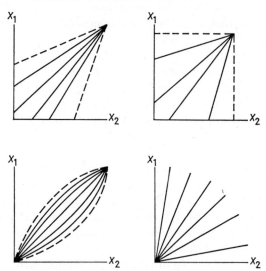

None of the isoclines presented in Figure 5–14 are applicable to the case of constant *MRS*. When constant rates of substitution exist and isoquants are parallel, then the isocline either is coincident with one of the axes or consists of the entire input plane. In the latter case, the isocost line would be parallel to the isoquant and the manager would be indifferent about the combination of inputs used.

GENERAL CRITERIA FOR TWO OR MORE INPUTS

Thus far production processes with one and two variable inputs have been discussed. These simple production processes do not represent situations that occur frequently in agriculture, but they are useful for the presentation of fundamental relationships. Most production processes involve many inputs. Some of these inputs are readily available and free, such as sunlight and the gases in the air. These are not of economic concern. Other inputs that are scarce and therefore have a cost are of economic importance.

The physical production function for many inputs is often written

$$Y = f(X_1, X_2, X_3, \ldots, X_n),$$

where n signifies the number of variable inputs and can be any number, four, five, six, etc. As usual, although it does not affect the criteria presented below in any way, the assumption is made that there is at least one fixed input. Thus, a short-run production period is specified.

Minimizing Cost

To produce any output at a minimum of cost the following criterion must be fulfilled:

$$\frac{MPP_{x_1}}{P_{x_1}} = \frac{MPP_{x_2}}{P_{x_2}} = \frac{MPP_{x_3}}{P_{x_3}} = \cdots = \frac{MPP_{x_n}}{P_{x_n}}.$$

The ratio of the price to the marginal physical product must be equal for all inputs. Thus, if one input costs twice as much as the other inputs, it must produce twice as much on the "margin." For two inputs, the minimum-cost criterion is

$$\frac{MPP_{x_1}}{P_{x_1}} = \frac{MPP_{x_2}}{P_{x_2}}$$

which after some algebraic rearrangement is the requirement that the MRS of X_2 for X_1 equals the negative of the inverse price ratio $-P_{x_2}/P_{x_1}$.

The ratios of the marginal physical product to the unit input costs need not be equal to any particular value but should be positive and equal each other. For example, if X_1, X_2, and X_3 cost \$1, \$2, and \$3, respectively, then a least-cost combination would exist if the marginal physical products of the inputs were 1, 2, and 3, in the same order. However, a least-cost combination would also exist if the marginal physical products of X_1, X_2, and X_3 were 2, 4, and 6, 0.3, 0.6, and 0.9, or even 0, 0, and 0. The latter combination would exist at the maximum output.

When n variable inputs are used, a geometrical interpretation no longer exists for the expansion path. However, for a given set of input prices, there will exist for each output one combination of inputs that minimizes cost. For this combination of inputs, total variable cost, TVC, is computed as

$$TVC = P_{x_1}X_1 + P_{x_2}X_2 + P_{x_3}X_3 + \cdots + P_{x_n}X_n.$$

Other cost curves are computed as always to derive a complete set of costs for each output amount.

Profit Maximization

Profits from the production process are maximized when marginal value product of each input equals the unit cost of that input. In symbolic notation

$$MVP_{x_1} = P_{x_1}$$
$$MVP_{x_2} = P_{x_2}$$
$$MVP_{x_3} = P_{x_3}$$

$$\cdot$$
$$\cdot$$
$$\cdot$$

$$MVP_{x_n} = P_{x_n}.$$

To attain the optimum, all of these equalities must be satisfied simultaneously. Thus, the marginal earnings of each input must be equal to its cost. Again, if an input costs twice as much as another input, its marginal earnings must be twice as much. In order to have an optimum, decreasing marginal and average products are required for all inputs and total revenue must equal or exceed total variable cost.

By dividing each equality in the above statement by the input price on the right and rearranging, the optimum criterion can also be expressed

$$\frac{MVP_{x_1}}{P_{x_1}} = \frac{MVP_{x_2}}{P_{x_2}} = \frac{MVP_{x_3}}{P_{x_3}} = \cdots = \frac{MVP_{x_n}}{P_{x_n}} = 1.$$

Because the ratios are all equal to one at the optimum, they also equal each other. The ratios in the expression above are equated to one. They would never be equated to a number less than one because to do so would require input use above the optimum. When capital available to buy inputs is limited, the ratios may equal some value larger than one. For example, when the ratios equal two, each dollar used to purchase variable inputs is earning a marginal return of two dollars. In this case the combination being used is a least-cost combination but not an optimum combination. Thus, an alternative way of expressing the least-cost criteria is to equate the optimum criteria to values greater than one.

The profit maximizing combination of inputs is always a least-cost combination of inputs. The converse is not necessarily true, of course.

AN EMPIRICAL EXAMPLE

Milk production represents an important agricultural example of a production process involving two variable inputs. Regarding a dairy cow as the fixed input, many different combinations of hay and grain can be used to produce milk. The economic problem of feeding a dairy cow can be divided into the two basic problems of input combination: (1) what combination of hay and grain should be used to produce a given amount of milk at a minimum of cost and (2) what combination of hay and grain should be used to produce the profit maximizing amount of milk, that is, maximize profits per cow? To simplify discussion of this example, possible limitations on capital available to purchase feed and alternative earnings of inputs in other enterprises will not be considered. That is, the example presented will be a simplified enterprise analysis, not an entire farm budgeting plan.

Research workers at Iowa State University investigated the hay-grain relationships in dairy cow feeding.[5] An experiment using 36 Holstein cows was conducted over a 17-month period. After calving, the cows were placed under experimental conditions and fed the same ration during an adjustment period. For the experiment, four hay-to-concentrate ratios were selected, ranging from a ration in which 75 percent of the energy came from hay and 25 percent from concentrates to one in which 15 percent of the energy came from hay and 85 percent from concentrates. The four hay-to-concentrate ratios used were 75:25, 55:45, 35:65, and 15:85. For convenience and to more closely follow the presentation by the researchers at Iowa, the concentrate mix will hereafter be called "grain." Pastures were not used in the experiment.

Milk production per cow was measured and used to estimate a production function for milk. In the symbols used earlier in this chapter, milk represents the output, Y, for a four-week period while pounds of hay and pounds of grain consumed for the four-week period represent the variable inputs, X_1 and X_2. The dairy cow represents the fixed input, along with other inputs such as management, buildings, labor, etc.

The estimated milk production is presented in Figure 5–15A. Pounds of hay fed per cow during the four-week period and pounds of grain fed per cow during the four-week period are measured along the input axis; pounds of milk produced during the four-week period are measured along the vertical axis. The surface sits back from the input origin to represent the minimum amount of feed needed to insure animal maintenance. Examination of the surface shows that increasing amounts of hay and grain increase total milk production but at a decreasing rate. Thus, the marginal products of hay and grain are positive but decreasing. Because of this, the milk production isoquants, representing the various combinations of hay and grain that produce a given amount of milk during the production period, are curved and lie farther apart at high output levels.

The production surface is useful; however, a more detailed picture of the relationships between milk production and feed input can be

---

[5] The example presented is from Earl O. Heady, J. A. Schnittker, N. L. Jacobson, and Solomon Bloom, *Milk Production Functions, Hay/Grain Substitution Rates and Economic Optima in Dairy Cow Rations,* Iowa State Agricultural Experiment Station Research Bulletin 444, October, 1956. The discussion included here is quite general; the bulletin should be examined for details.

FIGURE 5–15

MILK PRODUCTION SURFACE, ISOQUANTS, AND ISOCLINES

A

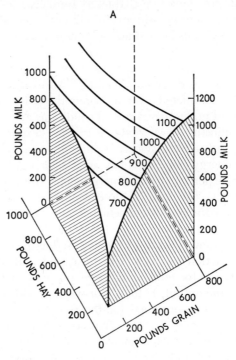

B

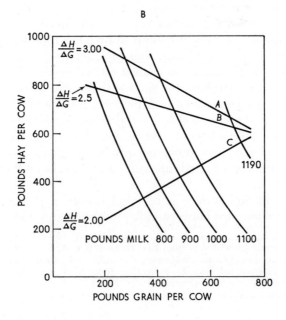

gained by examining the isoclines and isoquants. The isocline-isoquant map for the milk production surface is presented in Figure 5–15B, and selected points from the 800-, 1,000-, and 1,190-pound milk isoquants are contained in Table 5–8.

Table 5–8 has this interpretation. When 250 pounds of grain are used, 577 pounds of hay must be used to attain a production of 800 pounds of milk during the four-week period. At this point on the 800-pound isoquant (grain = 250, hay = 577), the marginal rate of substitution of grain for hay, $\Delta H/\Delta G$, is -2.24. If one pound of grain is added, hay can be reduced 2.24 pounds and output over the four-week period will remain at 800 pounds of milk. If 1,032 pounds are fed along with 250 pounds of grain, 1,000 pounds of milk will be produced during the

TABLE 5–8

Combinations of Hay and Grain Needed to Produce Specified Amounts of Milk for a Four-Week Period

Pounds of Grain	Pounds of Hay Required to Maintain Milk Output at—			Pounds of Hay Replaced by One Added Pound of Grain on Isoquant		
	800	1,000	1,190	800	1,000	1,190
150	815	...	...	−2.54	...	...
250	577	1,032	...	−2.24	−3.41	...
350	365	744	...	−2.02	−2.53	...
450	172	513	...	−1.85	−2.13	...
550	...	314	...	...	−1.87	...
650	...	138	...	...	−1.66	...
750	...	...	575	...	...	−2.09

Source: Earl O. Heady, J. A. Schnittker, N. L. Jacobson, and Solomon Bloom, *Milk Production Functions, Hay/Grain Substitution Rates and Economic Optima in Dairy Cow Rations*, Iowa State Agricultural Experiment Station Research Bulletin 444, October, 1956.

four-week period and the marginal rate of substitution at that point on the 1,000-pound milk isoquant is -3.41. Addition of a pound of grain will replace 3.41 pounds of hay and still maintain production at 1,000 pounds.

The milk isoquants in Figure 5–15B exhibit a slight curvature; thus, hay and grain substitute at decreasing rates as suggested above. The milk isoclines are linear and converge towards the point of maximum output per cow. As discussed earlier in this chapter, the marginal products of the feeds are constant relative to each other along the isocline. Thus, one pound of grain substitutes for three pounds of hay for all combinations traced out by isocline A. For a grain/hay price ratio of three, isocline A traces out least-cost feed combinations for all levels of milk production. In a like manner, isoclines B and C trace out least-cost combinations for possible grain/hay price ratios of 2.5 and 2.0 respectively.

The isoclines are linear but do not pass through the origin. Thus, as milk production is increased, the ratio of grain to hay must change if least-cost combinations of feed are to be used. Feeding a constant ratio and increasing production by increasing amounts fed would not be the most economical way of producing milk; only if the isocline were a straight line passing through the origin would such a recommendation be valid. Because of the slight curvature of the isoquants, a relatively small shift in the grain/hay price ratio can cause a large change in the least-cost feed ratio for a given milk production level. Compare for example, the input combination needed to produce 800 pounds of milk on isocline *B* to that of isocline *C*.

TABLE 5–9

ESTIMATED OPTIMUM FEED QUANTITIES AND MILK PRODUCTION FOR
SELECTED PRICE RATIOS; MILK PRODUCTION FOR A FOUR-WEEK
PERIOD

Milk per Cwt.	Grain per Cwt.	Hay per Ton	Pounds of Grain	Pounds of Hay	Pounds of Milk
$4	$2	$15	560	710	1,143
4	3	25	476	662	1,080
4	4	35	390	618	988
5	2	15	612	686	1,163
5	3	25	544	649	1,121
5	4	35	476	613	1,064

SOURCE: Earl O. Heady, J. A. Schnittker, N. L. Jacobson, and Solomon Bloom, *Milk Production Functions, Hay/Grain Substitution Rates and Economic Optima in Dairy Cow Rations*, Iowa State Agricultural Experiment Station Research Bulletin 444, October, 1956.

Optimum amounts of hay and grain and the resulting milk production for a four-week period are presented in Table 5–9. For purposes of illustration, several different price combinations are presented. These optima are derived using the theoretical conditions for maximum profit; the marginal value product for each input must be equated to the input cost. The relationships

$$MVP_G = P_G$$
$$MVP_H = P_H$$

were used, where P_G is the cost per pound of grain and P_H is the cost per pound of hay. The marginal value products are also expressed in pounds. The techniques used to derive these estimates from the production function are mathematical in nature and will not be discussed here.

Examination of Table 5–9 reveals some important economic consideration involved in feeding problems. First, none of the production rates represent the maximum possible production per cow, which was over 1,190 pounds for the four-week period. Secondly, as the price of feed rises relative to the price of milk, the optimum feed quantities and milk production decrease. Third, the ratio of grain to hay in the optimum feed combination varies with the price ratio. For a milk price of $5 per hundredweight, 612 pounds of grain and 686 pounds of hay, almost a one-to-one ratio, represent the optimum combination when grain is $2 per hundredweight and hay is $15 per ton. However, when grain increases to $4 per hundredweight and hay to $35 per ton while milk remains at $5 per hundredweight, the optimum ration is 476 pounds of grain and 613 pounds of hay, approximately a 2:3 ratio. Also, when grain and hay are $2 and $15, respectively, the ratio of the optimum feed changes when milk increases from $4 to $5 per hundredweight.

Feeding dairy cows is more complex than represented in this example. Production varies during the lactation period. Inherent differences exist in the productive ability of cows. Nutrient requirements and stomach capacities must be considered. The experimental data presented in this section are not meant to be used for recommendations but rather are illustrative of the principles developed in this chapter.

REFERENCES

ALLEN, CLARK LEE. *The Framework of Price Theory,* chap. iv. Belmont, Calif.: Wadsworth Publishing Co., Inc., 1967.

DOLL, JOHN P. "The Allocation of Limited Quantities of Variable Resources among Competing Farm Enterprises," *Journal of Farm Economics,* Vol. XL, November, 1959, pp. 781–89.

FERGUSON, C. E. *Microeconomic Theory,* chap. vii. Homewood, Ill.: Richard D. Irwin, Inc., 1966.

HEADY, EARL O. *Economics of Agricultural Production and Resource Use,* chaps. v and vi. Englewood Cliffs, N.J.: Prentice-Hall, Inc., 1952.

————; SCHNITTKER, J. A.; JACOBSON, M. L.; and BLOOM, SOLOMON. *Milk Production Functions, Hay/Grain Substitution Rates and Economic Optima in Dairy Cow Rations.* Iowa State Agricultural Experiment Station Research Bulletin 444, October, 1956.

KROTH, EARL M., and DOLL, JOHN P. *Response of Corn Yields to Nitrogen Fertilization and Plant Population in Missouri, 1962.* Progress Report No. 2, Missouri Agricultural Experiment Station Special Report 27, March, 1963.

MUNSON, R. D., and DOLL, JOHN P. "The Economics of Fertilizer Use in Crop Production," *Advances in Agronomy* (ed. A. G. NORMAN), pp. 133–67. New York: Academic Press, Inc., 1959.

Chapter 6

PRODUCTION OF TWO OR MORE PRODUCTS

Up to this point the economic view of the production process has been largely from the input side. Chapter 3 dealt with production functions describing the relationships that can exist between input and output. Chapter 4 presented a discussion of the allocation of one variable input, and Chapter 5 dealt with the combination of two or more variable inputs in the production of one output.

This chapter presents a different view of the production process. Rather than emphasize the allocation of variable inputs within an enterprise or among enterprises, this chapter discusses enterprise combination, often called product-product relationships. The question asked is not "How should these inputs be allocated among enterprises?" but rather "What combination of enterprises should be produced?" The two questions arrive ultimately at the same answer. Only the vantage point differs.

The logic presented in this chapter represents a formalization of procedures used in budgeting or planning the farm business. The assumptions of this chapter remain unchanged from previous chapters, i.e., perfect certainty, pure competition in the farmer's buying and selling markets, input use limited to Stage II of the production function, etc.

THE PRODUCTION POSSIBILITY CURVE

The production possibility curve is a convenient device for depicting two production functions on one graph. To begin with, suppose that one variable input, X, can be used to produce two products, Y_1 and Y_2, and that all other inputs used to produce Y_1 or Y_2 are fixed or highly specialized so that their use cannot be diverted. Thus, the farm manager must determine how much of input X to use on each product. The relevant question here is "How much input is available?" The two possible situations are termed (1) unlimited and (2) limited.

Unlimited: When the amount of available input is unlimited, resource allocation is determined by equating the price of an input to the MVP of the input. No new problem arises. The manager can use the optimum amount in both enterprises. Increasing input use on one production process will not reduce the amount available for use in the other.

Thus, other than the fact that the enterprises are on the same farm and are under the direction of the same manager, they are not related to each other.

The term "unlimited" means that the manager has a sufficient quantity of the input to use the optimum amount in all enterprises. It does not actually imply that an unlimited supply of the input is available; if that were true, the input would be a free good. Often the term "unlimited capital" is used instead of "unlimited input." The two terms have the same meaning, the assumption being that the variable input may be readily purchased if not already owned.

Limited: When the amount of input is limited, the optimum amount cannot be used in each enterprise. Thus, by definition, "limited" means that the total amount of input available is less than that amount needed to apply the optimum to each enterprise. The primary purpose of the production possibility curve is to determine the most profitable combination of enterprises for a limited amount of input.

Limited input situations are also referred to as "limited capital" situations. Again, the implication is that the variable input can be purchased if it is not already owned and that the amount purchased will be limited by the amount of capital available. Limited capital therefore means that the capital available is not sufficient to allow the manager to use the optimum amount of input in each enterprise.

When inputs are limited in quantity, enterprises on the farm become uniquely related. No longer can they be considered independently. If output in one enterprise is to be expanded, resources must be diverted to that enterprise, and output of other enterprises must be reduced. The job of management is to determine the most profitable combination of enterprises, given the resource limitation.

Deriving Production Possibility Curves from Production Functions

Production possibility curves have yet to be defined. The purpose of this section is to do so by deriving production possibility curves from production functions.

Two production functions, one for Y_1 and one for Y_2, are presented in Table 6–1A. These production functions use the same variable input, X. All other inputs are assumed fixed. MPP_{xy_1} denotes the marginal physical product of X used on Y_1, etc.

Suppose that four units of input were available. Production functions represent planning curves, and before any input is actually used, the manager has the opportunity of considering all possible ways the input can be used. By using all four units of input on Y_1, he can produce 22 units of Y_1, or if all four are used on Y_2, 36 units of Y_2 can be produced. Many other combinations are possible within these two extremes. One unit applied to Y_1 and three to Y_2 will produce 7 and 30, re-

TABLE 6–1

DERIVATION OF PRODUCTION POSSIBILITY CURVES FROM PRODUCTION FUNCTIONS

A

X	Y_1	MPP_{xy_1}	X	Y_2	MPP_{xy_2}
0	0		0	0	
		7			12
1	7		1	12	
		6			10
2	13		2	22	
		5			8
3	18		3	30	
		4			6
4	22		4	36	
		3			4
5	25		5	40	
		2			2
6	27		6	42	
		1			1
7	28		7	43	
		−1			−1
8	27		8	42	
		−2			−4
9	25		9	40	

B	
Production Possibilities for X = 4:	
Y_2	Y_1
36	0
30	7
22	13
12	18
0	22

C	
Production Possibilities for X = 7:	
Y_2	Y_1
43	0
42	7
40	13
36	18
30	22
22	25
12	27
0	28

spectively, of these two products. Dividing the four inputs evenly between the two outputs will produce 13 units of Y_1 and 22 units of Y_2. Three units of input to Y_1 and one unit to Y_2 will produce 18 units of Y_1 and 12 of Y_2. These combinations represent some of the production possibilities for four units of input; they are presented as a group in Table 6–1B. Each combination in Table 6–1B has one common feature—four units of input are required in total to produce each combination.

Graphs of the production functions and the production possibility curve are presented in Figure 6–1. The production possibility curve for four units of input is the counterpart of the production possibilities presented in Table 6–1B. The output combinations in Table 6–1B were graphed, and a smooth curve was drawn through the points. Thus, the graph presents additional output combinations not included in Table 6–1B.

The production possibility curve in Figure 6–1B presents all possible combinations of the two products that can be produced using four units of input. It must be regarded as a planning curve because obviously one and only one combination of outputs can be produced with four units of input. Thus, while all combinations should be considered when planning production, only one combination will eventually be produced. The production possibility curve is affected by all the same factors that affect the production function. A change in technology or in the intensity

FIGURE 6–1

PRODUCTION FUNCTIONS AND PRODUCTION POSSIBILITY CURVES

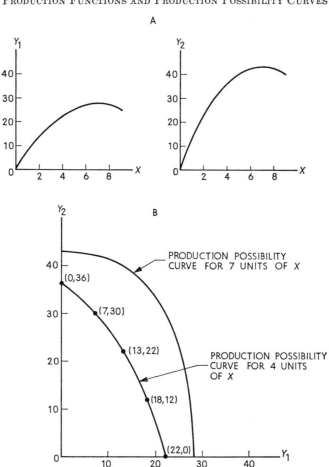

FIGURE 6–1—*Continued*

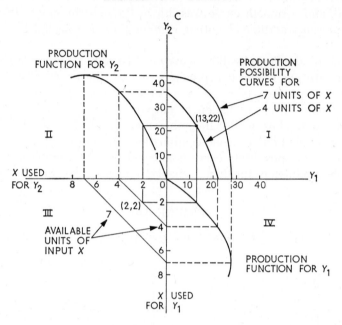

of fixed inputs will cause a shift in the production functions and also a shift in the production possibility curve.

The production possibility curve is a convenient method of comparing two production functions simultaneously, but only within the limits determined by the available input. That is, the production possibility curve for four units of input (Figure 6–1B) compares the production functions for Y_1 and Y_2 only within the limits allowed for four units of input. If more or less than four units of input are available, a different production possibility curve is produced. Suppose seven units of input were available. Then combinations of Y_1 and Y_2 ranging from 43 of Y_2 and zero of Y_1 to zero of Y_2 and 28 of Y_1 are possible; production possibilities for $Y = 7$ are presented in Table 6–1C. The corresponding production possibility curve is presented in Figure 6–1B (to avoid clutter, the output combinations are not labeled on this curve).

The production possibility curve for seven units of input represents a higher level of production of both products and is located farther from the origin than the production possibility curve for four units of input. Also, it has a somewhat different shape than the production possibility curve for four units of input. If a production possibility curve were drawn for less than four units of input, say three, this production possibility curve would be located closer to the origin than the one for four units.

Figure 6–1C presents an alternative method of viewing the production possibility curve graphically. All axes of the graph are assumed to measure positive quantities. The straight line in the third quadrant depicts the limited amount of input. When $X = 4$, all may be used to produce Y_2, all may be used to produce Y_1 or some combination can be used to produce the two outputs. Any possible combination chosen must be on the straight line labeled $X = 4$ in the third quadrant. The production functions in quadrants two and four are used to determine the outputs resulting from the combination of X selected. The resulting outputs can then be plotted in the first quadrant to determine the production possibility curve. For example, when two units of input are used on each product, a vertical movement from the point $(2, 2)$ in the third quadrant to the production function for Y_2 in the second quadrant shows that 22 units of Y_2 will result. A horizontal movement from point $(2, 2)$ into quadrant four shows that 13 units of Y_1 will result. Plotting the point $(13, 22)$ in quadrant one determines a point in the production possibility curve for $X = 4$. Similarly, all points on the production possibility curve for $X = 4$ result from some combination of X falling on the straight line in the third quadrant. The production possibility curve for $X = 7$ is derived in similar fashion.

Production possibility curves are sometimes called isocost curves, opportunity curves, or isoresource curves. "Isocost" refers to the fact that each product combination on any given curve has the same total cost; the term "isocost" is avoided here because of its use for a different purpose in Chapter 5. "Opportunity curve" is used because the curve presents all possible production opportunities. Finally, "isoresource" refers to the fact that each output combination on a given curve has the same resource requirement.

The Marginal Rate of Product Substitution

The marginal rate of product substitution, MRPS, is the amount by which one output changes in quantity when the other output is increased by one unit, given that the amount of input used remains constant. The marginal rate of product substitution (MRPS) of Y_1 for Y_2 is

$$\frac{\Delta Y_2}{\Delta Y_1}.$$

Marginal rates of product substitution for output combinations possible from seven units of input are presented in Table 6–2. Computation is similar to marginal products and marginal rates of input substitution and is not repeated here. In Table 6–2, as the amount of Y_1 produced increases, the amount of Y_2 sacrificed steadily increases. This is due to the decreasing marginal returns displayed by the production functions.

The MRPS represents the slope of the production possibility curve.

TABLE 6–2

Computation of the Marginal Rate of Product Substitution

Production Possibilities for $X = 7$:		ΔY_2	ΔY_1	Marginal Rate of Product Substitution of Y_1 for $Y_2 = \Delta Y_2/\Delta Y_1$
Y_2	Y_1			
43	0			
		-1	7	$-\frac{1}{7}$
42	7			
		-2	6	$-\frac{1}{3}$
40	13			
		-4	5	$-\frac{4}{5}$
36	18			
		-6	4	$-\frac{3}{2}$
30	22			
		-8	3	$-\frac{8}{3}$
22	25			
		-10	2	-5
12	27			
		-12	1	-12
0	28			

FIGURE 6–2

Approximate and Exact Measures of the Marginal Rate of Product Substitution

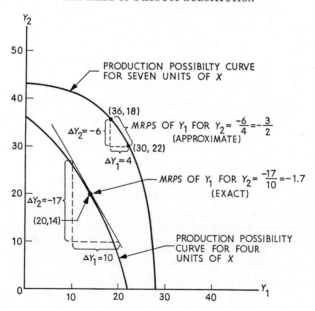

As with the marginal product and marginal rate of substitution, there are two measures of the *MRPS*: the approximate measure and the exact measure. The approximate measure is computed from a table or between points on a graph. Consider the output combinations $Y_2 = 36$, $Y_1 = 18$ and $Y_2 = 30$, $Y_1 = 22$ on the production possibility curve for seven units of input. The *MRPS* of Y_1 for Y_2 between these combinations is

$$\frac{\Delta Y_2}{\Delta Y_1} = \frac{30 - 36}{22 - 18} = \frac{-6}{4} = -\frac{3}{2}.$$

This computation is presented in Table 6–2 and in Figure 6–2. From Figure 6–2, it can be seen that the *MRPS* of $-3/2$ represents the approximate slope between the two output combinations.

The exact *MRPS* is the slope at any point on the production possibility curve and can be determined by drawing a tangent at the point in question and then measuring the slope of the tangent. This is illustrated in Figure 6–2 on the production possibility curve for four units of input. At the point $Y_2 = 20$ and $Y_1 = 14$, a tangent has been drawn. The slope of this tangent is -1.7, and therefore the exact *MRPS* at the point is -1.7. An increase in Y_1 by "one unit" could only be possible if Y_2 is decreased by "1.7 units."

The Isorevenue Line

Total revenue is the value of the output produced. For example, if 36 units of Y_2 and 18 units of Y_1 were produced and if price per unit of these products were $1 and $2, respectively, then

$$\text{Total revenue} = \$1(36) + \$2(18) = \$72 ,$$

or in symbolic notation,

$$\text{Total revenue} = P_{y_1}(Y_1) + P_{y_2}(Y_2) ,$$

where Y_1 and Y_2 represent symbolically the total amount of the two products.

A line representing any given total revenue can be drawn on a graph. For example, consider a total revenue of $80. When $P_{y_2} = \$1$ and $P_{y_1} = \$2$, the $80 revenue could be earned by selling 80 units ($80 divided by $1) of Y_2 and no Y_1 or 40 units ($80 divided by $2) of Y_1 and no Y_2. Other combinations of product will also earn $80. For example, 20 units of Y_1 and 40 units of Y_2, 30 units of Y_1 and 20 units of Y_2, and 10 units of Y_1 and 60 units of Y_2 would all earn $80 in revenue. These points when graphed lie on a straight line (Figure 6–3A) called an isorevenue line.

The isorevenue line in Figure 6–3A passes through all combinations of Y_1 and Y_2 that earn a revenue of $80. The line is straight because the output prices do not change regardless of the amount of output sold. Thus, the location of an isorevenue line for any total revenue can easily be deter-

FIGURE 6–3

ISOREVENUE LINES

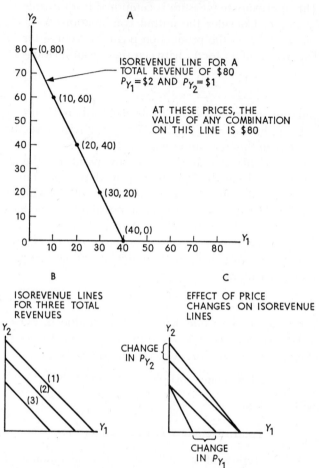

A

ISOREVENUE LINE FOR A
TOTAL REVENUE OF $80
$P_{Y_1} = \$2$ AND $P_{Y_2} = \$1$

AT THESE PRICES, THE
VALUE OF ANY COMBINATION
ON THIS LINE IS $80

B

ISOREVENUE LINES
FOR THREE TOTAL
REVENUES

C

EFFECT OF PRICE
CHANGES ON ISOREVENUE
LINES

CHANGE
IN P_{Y_2}

CHANGE
IN P_{Y_1}

mined by computing the points on the axes and connecting these points with a straight line. The point on the Y_2 axis is always equal to TR/P_{y_2} while the point on the Y_1 axis equals TR/P_{y_1}. These points determine the amount of either Y_2 or Y_1 needed to earn the total revenue (TR) when the other product is not produced.

The distance of the isorevenue line from the origin is determined by the magnitude of the total revenue. As total revenue increases, the isorevenue line moves away from the origin. Thus, in Figure 6–3B, the isorevenue line labeled (1) represents a higher total revenue than (2) and (3) while (2) represents a higher total revenue than (3). The isorevenue lines in Figure 6–3B are parallel because output prices have not changed.

The slope of the isorevenue line is determined by the output prices. The slope of a straight line may be measured between any two distinct points. For convenience, the slope can be measured between the points where the isorevenue line intersects the output axes. The Y_2 axis is intersected at the point $Y_1 = 0$ and $Y_2 = TR/P_{y_2}$; the Y_1 axis is intersected at the point $Y_1 = TR/P_{y_1}$ and $Y_2 = 0$. The slope of the isorevenue line is

$$\frac{\text{Rise}}{\text{Run}} = \frac{0 - \dfrac{TR}{P_{y_2}}}{\dfrac{TR}{P_{y_1}} - 0} = -\frac{\dfrac{TR}{P_{y_2}}}{\dfrac{TR}{P_{y_1}}} = -\frac{P_{y_1}}{P_{y_2}}.$$

Thus the output price ratio is the slope of the line. The negative sign, of course, means that the isorevenue line slopes downward to the right. The slope of the isorevenue line in Figure 6–3A is $-P_{y_1}/P_{y_2} = -2/1 = -2$. When the output prices remain constant, the isorevenue lines representing different total revenues are parallel. But a change in either price will change the slope. These effects are illustrated in Figure 6–3C. An increase in the price of Y_1 shifts the intersection of the isorevenue line with the Y_1 axis closer to the origin; fewer units of Y_1 are required to earn a given total revenue. A decrease in the price of Y_1 shifts the intersection of the isorevenue line further from the origin on the Y_1 axis. Similar changes are evidenced on the Y_2 axis by a change in the price of Y_2.

Isorevenue lines in this chapter and the isocost lines in Chapter 5 appear the same on a graph. The slopes of both are determined by the relevant price ratios. The two should not be confused, however. They are used for different purposes.[1]

The Maximum Revenue Combination of Outputs

The production possibility curve presents all possible combinations of two products that could be produced using a given amount of variable input. Only one combination of output will be produced in practice. The two relevant questions are: (1) what combination should be produced and (2) how can that combination be determined?

Total costs are constant for all output combinations on a production possibility curve. Profits from the limited amount of variable resource will be the greatest or losses the smallest if the output combination returning the maximum total revenue is selected. To avoid confusion with the most profitable combination of outputs, which may be on a different production possibility curve, the revenue maximizing combination of output on a given production possibility curve will be called the "maximum revenue" combination. When the production possibilities are presented in

---

[1] It should be noted that isorevenue lines represent "level" lines of a total revenue surface defined above the base grid of the outputs Y_1 and Y_2. This development would be analogous to the development of isocost lines in Chapter 5.

a table, the total revenue can be computed for each output combination and the maximum revenue combination selected. This has been done in Table 6–3, using the production possibilities presented first in Table 6–1C and the prices $P_{y_1} = \$2$ and $P_{y_2} = \$1$. The maximum revenue combination of products is 30 units of Y_2 and 22 units of Y_1. The total revenue earned is $74. Every other combination of outputs in Table 6–3 returns less.

Calculating the total revenue from each output combination and selecting the maximum revenue combination is only feasible for a small number of combinations. An infinite number of output combinations exist along the production possibility curve; computation of the total revenue

TABLE 6–3

COMPUTATION OF THE MAXIMUM REVENUE COMBINATION OF
PRODUCTS GIVEN SEVEN UNITS OF INPUT
$(P_{y_1} = \$2, P_{y_2} = \$1)$

Production Possibilities for X = 7:		Revenue from Y_2 $P_{y_2} = \$1$	Revenue from Y_1 $P_{y_1} = \$2$	Total Revenue
Y_2	Y_1			
43	0	$43	$ 0	$43
42	7	42	14	56
40	13	40	26	66
36	18	36	36	72
30	22	30	44	74
22	25	22	50	72
12	27	12	54	66
0	28	0	56	56

resulting from all combinations would be impossible. The maximum revenue combination of outputs on a production possibility curve can be determined using the criterion

$$MRPS \text{ of } Y_1 \text{ for } Y_2 = -\frac{P_{y_1}}{P_{y_2}},$$

or using the expression for the MRPS,

$$\frac{\Delta Y_2}{\Delta Y_1} = -\frac{P_{y_1}}{P_{y_2}}.$$

The left side of the criterion represents the slope of the production possibility curve and the right side the slope of the isorevenue line. Graphically, the maximum revenue point is that point where the isorevenue line is tangent to the production possibility curve. For the production possibility curve resulting from seven units of input, the maximum revenue combination is determined in Figure 6–4A. An isorevenue line with a slope of −2 (because $-P_{y_1}/P_{y_2} = -\$2/\$1$) is drawn tangent to

FIGURE 6–4

SELECTION OF THE MAXIMUM REVENUE COMBINATION OF
PRODUCTS ON A PRODUCTION POSSIBILITY CURVE

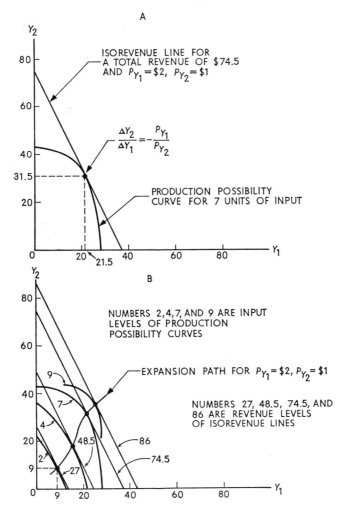

the production possibility curve. The point of tangency occurs at $Y_2 = 31.5$ and $Y_1 = 21.5$; the total revenue at this point is $1(31.5) + $2(21.5)$, or $74.50. When the isorevenue line is drawn, the total revenue is not known—all that is known is that it will be the maximum for the output combinations on the production possibility curve. In general, the farther the isorevenue line is located from the origin, the higher will be the total revenue. In Figure 6–4A, any other isorevenue line drawn farther from the origin would not touch the production possibility curve and therefore would represent a total revenue unattainable with seven units of input. Any isorevenue line drawn closer to the origin would represent a lower total revenue.

The revenue earned by seven units of input was $74.50 in Figure 6–4A; the maximum revenue combination in Table 6–3 was $74. The same data were used in both cases. The answer on the graph is more accurate because more output combinations can be considered.

Further consideration of the criterion for determining the maximum revenue combination of outputs will yield some insight into its meaning. Suppose that the criterion

$$\frac{\Delta Y_2}{\Delta Y_1} = -\frac{P_{y_1}}{P_{y_2}}$$

were rewritten as follows:

$$P_{y_2}(\Delta Y_2) = -P_{y_1}(\Delta Y_1).$$

(The negative sign is necessary because ΔY_2 is negative and the two negatives cancel each other.) The criterion as rewritten states that at the maximum revenue point the increase in revenue due to adding a minute quantity of Y_1 is exactly equal to the decrease in revenue caused by the reduction in Y_2. Thus, there is no incentive to change the output combination. When $-P_{y_2}(\Delta Y_2) > P_{y_1}(\Delta Y_1)$, the amount of Y_1 should be decreased in favor of Y_2. When $-P_{y_2}(\Delta Y_2) < P_{y_1}(\Delta Y_1)$, then Y_1 should be increased at the expense of Y_2.

TABLE 6–4

COMPUTATION OF THE MAXIMUM REVENUE COMBINATION OF PRODUCTS USING THE MAXIMUM REVENUE CRITERION
$(P_{y_1} = \$2, P_{y_2} = \$1)$

Production Possibilities for X = 7		ΔY_2	ΔY_1	MRPS of Y_1 for Y_2
Y_2	Y_1			
43	0			
		−1	7	−1⁄7
42	7			
		−2	6	−2⁄6
40	13			
		−4	5	−4⁄5
36	18			
		−6	4	−6⁄4
30	22			
		−8	3	−8⁄3
22	25			
		−10	2	−10⁄2
12	27			
		−12	1	−12⁄1
0	28			

The maximum revenue criterion can be used when production possibilities are presented in a table. Table 6–4 shows this procedure for the example being considered. The price ratio of -2 lies between the $MRPS$ of $-6/4$ and $-8/3$; therefore the most profitable combination of outputs is 30 of Y_2 and 22 of Y_1. Computationally, this method does not seem to offer any advantages over computing the total revenue for each output combination. However, it does serve to explain more fully the theory of enterprise combination.

Ordinarily the production possibility curve is used when the amount of variable input is constant at a particular value; thus only one production possibility curve would be relevant. However, by assuming varying amounts of the variable input to be available, an expansion path for outputs can be derived. Essentially, such an expansion path would have the same interpretation as an expansion path for inputs.

Figure 6–4B contains production possibility curves for two, four, seven, and nine units of input (derived from the data in Table 6–1). The production possibility curve for nine units of input does not extend to the axis because of the assumption that input use will never be extended into Stage III; thus, the most input used on either product is seven and the least is two. An isorevenue line with a slope of -2 is drawn tangent to each production possibility curve. The line connecting these maximum revenue points is called an output expansion path. For each level of input the maximum revenue combination of outputs will fall on the expansion path. However, only one combination of outputs is the optimum or high profit combination, resulting from the use of the optimum amount of input (where marginal cost equals marginal revenue). All other points are the maximum revenue points, given the limited amount of input. The optimum combination cannot be located geometrically on Figure 6–4B, but it will be some point on the expansion path.

The Production Possibility Curve and the Marginal Criterion for Resource Allocation

Apparently two criteria have been presented for the allocation of a limited amount of variable resource. (1) The resource, X, should be allocated between the two (or more) enterprises in such a way that the MVP_x is the same in each enterprise (Chapter 4). (2) The resource should be allocated so that revenue from the two (or more) products is the maximum possible. These two criteria are essentially the same. The first views the production process from the input side; the second from the output side.

The two criteria are compared in Table 6–5, where the production functions from Table 6–1 are repeated. For two units of input, one unit would be applied to Y_1 where it would earn \$14 and the second to Y_2 for

TABLE 6–5

COMPARISON OF MARGINAL CRITERION FOR RESOURCE ALLOCATION AND THE PRODUCTION POSSIBILITY CURVES ($P_{y_1} = \$2$, $P_{y_2} = \$1$)

X	Y_1	MPP_{xy_1}	MVP_{xy_1}	X	Y_2	MPP_{xy_2}	MVP_{xy_2}
0	0			0	0		
		7	$14			12	$12
1	7			1	12		
		6	12			10	10
2	13			2	22		
		5	10			8	8
3	18			3	30		
		4	8			6	6
4	22			4	36		
		3	6			4	4
5	25			5	40		
		2	4			2	2
6	27			6	42		
		1	2			1	1
7	28			7	43		

Units of Input Available	Solution Equating MVP			Solution Using Production Possibility Curves (Figure 6–4B)		
	Y_1	Y_2	TR	Y_1	Y_2	TR
2	7	12	$26	9	9	$27.0
4	13	22	48	15.5	17.5	48.5
7	22	30	74	21.5	31.5	74.5
9	25	36	86	25.5	35.0	86.0

an earning of $12. The total revenue would be $26. (The second unit could also go to Y_1, and earnings would be unchanged.) From the production possibility curve for two units of input in Figure 6–4B, the maximum revenue combination of outputs is nine each of Y_1 and Y_2. Reference to the production functions in Figure 6–1A shows that 0.7 units of X used on Y_1 and 1.3 units of X used on Y_2 will produce nine units of each. Nine units of each output produces a total revenue of $27, slightly more than the allocation using marginal criteria. Thus, the geometric approach is slightly more accurate, but for any practical situation the difference is negligible. Solutions from other input amounts are similarly close.

The two criterions can be shown to be identical algebraically. For the two outputs and one input, the marginal criterion is

$$P_{y_1} MPP_{xy_1} = P_{y_2} MPP_{xy_2} ,$$

or, substituting in the symbols for the marginal product,

$$P_{y_1}\left(\frac{\Delta Y_1}{\Delta X}\right) = P_{y_2}\left(\frac{\Delta Y_2}{\Delta X}\right).$$

But ΔX is a constant because the exact amount of input added to Y_1 must be removed from Y_2. In practice, ΔX will be a number such as 1, 2, 3, etc. Thus, multiplying both sides of the above expression by ΔX results in $P_y(\Delta Y_1) = P_y(\Delta Y_2)$ which was shown earlier to be the same (adding signs) as

$$\frac{\Delta Y_1}{\Delta Y_2} = -\frac{P_{y_2}}{P_{y_1}}.$$

Production Possibility Curves for Two or More Variable Inputs

Thus far production possibility curves have been discussed assuming only one variable input. At first glance this seems unrealistic. However, if the variable input is capital and the assumption is made that all other inputs can be purchased, the situation is quite plausible.

When each of the two products is produced using two or more variable inputs, the least-cost combination of inputs must always be used in each production process. Thus, any output of Y_1 on the production possibility curve results from a minimum-cost combination of inputs, and similarly for Y_2. Assuming the two inputs are always used in the appropriate combinations, the production possibility curve can be formulated as usual and the maximum revenue combination of outputs selected. This is analogous to advancing out the input expansion paths for the outputs until the ratio of the marginal earnings to unit costs are equal for all inputs. This concept will be developed more fully later in this chapter.

RELATIONSHIPS AMONG PRODUCTS

The mechanics of the production possibility curves have been stressed up to this point. However, while essential for facile handling of the graphic analysis, the geometric mechanics and details should not be permitted to mask the important economic concepts. The logic of enterprise combination is one of the most important concepts facing the farm manager.

In preceding chapters, empirical examples were presented to illustrate concepts. The logic of enterprise combination is all-encompassing, however, and the best example would be a complete discussion of how to budget farms illustrated with a plan for an actual farm. Obviously, material of this extent cannot be presented here. Instead, the types of relationships existing among enterprises on a farm will be presented and possible explanations explored.

Competitive Products

Products are termed competitive when an increase in one product can come about only by reducing the output of the other product. The production possibility curves discussed earlier in this chapter were for competitive products. Outputs are competitive because they require the same inputs at the same time. Often when planning the farm business,

FIGURE 6–5

PRODUCTION POSSIBILITY CURVES SHOWING POSSIBLE
RELATIONSHIPS AMONG ENTERPRISES

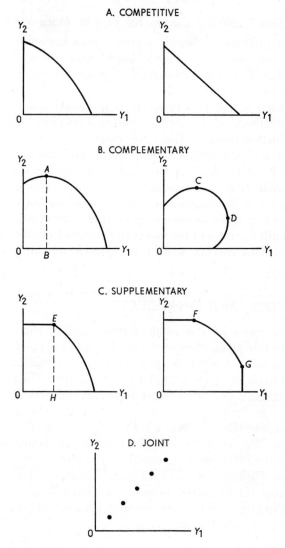

the manager can expand production of one output only by diverting inputs, i.e., labor, capital, management, from one enterprise to the other.

When the production possibility curve has a negative slope, the products concerned are competitive. Two examples are presented in Figure 6–5A. The curved production possibility curve results when the production functions for the product show decreasing returns. As increasing amounts of input are applied to one product, the marginal product of the input in that use becomes increasingly smaller while the marginal product of the input in the other use becomes increasingly larger. Thus, each one unit increment of one product requires a successively larger sacrifice of the competing product.

Curved production possibility curves might exist when allocating labor among enterprises such as hogs and cattle. If all labor were used on cattle, no hogs could be grown. However, the last few hours spent on cattle would not be very productive, i.e., would have a small marginal product relative to the alternative marginal earnings on hogs. This would occur because more could be earned by fulfilling the basic labor requirements of the hog enterprise, thus allowing hogs to be produced, than could be earned by accomplishing the last few details on the cattle enterprise.

Also, when decreasing returns to fertilizer exist, production possibilities for applying commercial fertilizer on two crops would assume a curved shape. Many other examples can be found in animal feeding, etc.

A straight line or linear production possibility curve for competitive products is also shown in Figure 6–5A. In this case, the *MRPS* is constant. Diminishing returns do not exist for either production function. This type of production possibility curve would be appropriate when a reasonably homogeneous field of soil is being diverted to either of two crops. For example, suppose a field of soil will produce 80 bushels of corn or 25 bushels of soybeans per acre. Each acre diverted from corn to soybeans will reduce corn production 80 bushels and increase soybean production by 25 bushels. This is true for the first acre diverted from corn, and it also is true for all successive acres. Thus, the production possibility curve is linear. In practice, given a linear production possibility curve, the isorevenue line will usually intersect the production possibility curve on one axis or the other, i.e., it will be most profitable to produce all corn or all soybeans. Fields are usually not divided between crops because of the profit motive.

Complementary Products

Two products are complementary if an increase in one product causes an increase in the second product when the total amount of inputs used on the two are held constant. Production possibility curves for complementary products are shown in Figure 6–5B. In the left-hand figure, Y_1 is complementary with Y_2 until the point A is reached. To the right of A, the two products are competitive. Thus, if the farmer wishes to produce the maximum possible amount of Y_2, he should grow at least $0B$ amount of Y_1. When larger quantities of Y_1 are produced, the two products become competitive and the manager will select the combination that maximizes revenue. This will be some point between A and the Y_1 axis, depending upon the prices of the outputs. When the price of Y_1 is zero, then the isorevenue line is horizontal and the most profitable combination is at A. The *MRPS* is positive for complements.

The production possibility curve on the right in Figure 6–5B shows a situation where each output is complementary to the other output over a certain range. Thus, Y_1 is complementary to Y_2 up to C and Y_2 is complementary to Y_1 up to D. Between C and D, the two products are competitive.

Complementarity usually occurs when one of the products produces an input used by the other product. An example of this is the use of a legume in a rotation with cash crops. The legume may add nitrogen and improve soil structure or tilth and improve weed and insect control. These factors, in turn, serve as "inputs" for the cash crops thus causing an increase in the production of cash crops over the period of time required by the rotation. For example, in a four-year rotation with three years of corn and one of alfalfa, the "inputs" supplied by alfalfa may increase corn yields to such an extent that more corn is produced in three years' production than could otherwise be produced in four.

Complementarity often occurs over time. Alfalfa and corn are competitive in a single year, giving rise to a linear production possibility curve. Over a period of years, however, the legume contributes to the production of corn. Some products, such as nurse crops, may give rise to complementarity in a single year.

The complementary products eventually must become competitive. That is, when a large amount of the resource in question is devoted to one product, production of the other product must decrease. The maximum revenue combination of products (for the given input amount) must then be determined in the usual manner.

For example, while one year of alfalfa in a four-year rotation may be complementary, two, three, or four years of alfalfa could be produced only by successive reductions in the cash crops. The quantities of cash crops and alfalfa would then be determined according to their relative profitability. A change in technology may also change the complementary relationship among products. For example, commercial fertilizer may cause the complementary relationship between corn and alfalfa to change into a competitive relationship. If the products never become competitive, then they are not termed complementary but are called joint products (discussed below).

Supplementary Products

Two products are called supplementary if the amount of one can be increased without increasing or decreasing the amount of the second. Production possibility curves for supplementary enterprises are shown in Figure 6–5C. For the diagram on the left, Y_1 is supplementary to Y_2. Y_1 can be increased from zero to $0H$ amount without effecting the amount of Y_2 produced. Past E on the production possibility curve, the two inputs become competitive and the revenue-maximizing combination is selected in the usual way. For the diagram on the right, Figure 6–5C, each enterprise is supplementary to the other and competitive between FG.

Supplementary enterprises arise through time or when surplus resources are available at a given point in time. Once purchased, a tractor is available for use throughout the year. Its use in one month does not preclude its use in another month. Thus, a tractor purchased to plow and plant may be put to a lesser use during the off season. Or, a combine may be used to harvest wheat in June and soybeans in the fall; clearly the hours of use in June have no bearing on the hours of use in the fall. If the two crops were harvested at the same time, however, the relationship would be competitive—use on one could come about only by reducing the amount of use on the other.

Another common supplementary enterprise is hogs following beef animals fed on corn. In this case, at the same point in time, the hogs forage in the droppings and utilize corn that would otherwise be wasted. If no hogs are produced, cattle production is unaffected. Hog production can be increased until the corn available in the droppings is fully utilized. Beyond that point, more hogs can be grown only by diverting corn fed to the cattle to the hog enterprise.

Small flocks of chickens, family gardens, and milk cows may all represent supplementary enterprises on some farms. In each case labor or some other input is available for use on a small scale, and rather than let it go idle, a small enterprise is undertaken.

Joint Products

Products which result from the same production process are termed joint products. As a rule, the two are combined and production of one without the other is impossible. Production possibility curves for joint products are presented in Figure 6–5D; each level of resource gives rise to a production possibility curve that is a point. No substitution is possible.

Agricultural examples of joint products include wool and mutton, cows and cowhides, and, in general, any of the integral parts of an animal or plant. Production is varied by increasing or decreasing both products in proportion rather than substituting one product for the other. Thus, joint products can be handled conceptually in the same manner as single output production situations.

Production Relationships and Farm Management

The art of farm management centers around a knowledge of the competitive, complementary, and supplementary relationships among farm enterprises. The farm manager tries to combine enterprises to take maximum advantage of supplementary and complementary relationships. This becomes complicated because the relationship between enterprises differs depending upon the input considered. Thus, wheat and soybeans may be supplementary enterprises with respect to combine use because one is harvested in June and the other in September. With respect to land, assuming single cropping, they are competitive because if an acre of land is used to grow wheat, it cannot be used to grow soybeans the same season. Two crops may be competitive with respect to labor use during the spring planting time, but due to different harvest times, they may be supplementary with respect to labor use during the harvesting periods.

Livestock enterprises usually compete with crop enterprises for capital, at least within a given production period. And inasmuch as pastureland can be used for crops, livestock and crops also compete for land. However, livestock enterprises can usually be planned to be supplementary to crops with respect to labor use. For example, farrowing can be timed so that hog labor requirements are small during harvest and the high labor requirements for hogs occur when crop needs are small. Livestock enterprises are often planned to require substantial labor loads during winter months.

Livestock enterprises differ from crop enterprises in that major portions of the inputs in livestock enterprises may consist of crops grown on the farm. Products grown on the farm and used as inputs for other farm products are called intermediate products. Forage and hay are intermediate products for livestock enterprises. Corn fed to hogs is an intermediate product; corn sold is a final product.

The most appropriate combination of intermediate products can only be selected by considering the consuming livestock enterprises. Thus, suppose that for a given farm the available supply of land, capital, labor, etc., will permit the production of grain and forage as shown in Figure 6–6A. Suppose further that the livestock enterprise selected by the farmer has an isoquant map as represented in Figure 6–6B. This isoquant map would be derived, as explained in Chapter 5, from a production function depicting meat production as a function of the amount of grain and forage fed. Isoquants can be derived for any amounts of meat

FIGURE 6–6

DETERMINING THE MAXIMUM REVENUE COMBINATION OF
INTERMEDIATE PRODUCTS

A

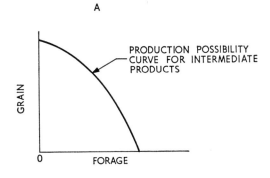

B

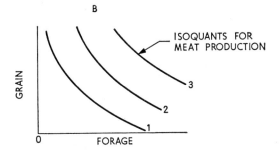

C

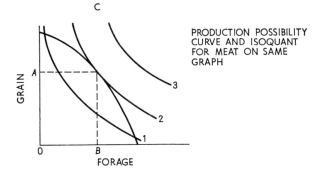

production; for convenience, however, the isoquants in Figure 6–6B are
labeled 1, 2, and 3 to denote increasing amounts of production.

The problem is to coordinate grain and forage production in such a
way that the maximum amount of meat is produced. The outputs represented by the production possibility curve are the same as the inputs for

the isoquants. Therefore, the two can be imposed upon one graph (Figure 6–6C). Because isoquants can be derived for any possible level of meat production, there will be one isoquant tangent to the production possibility curve. This tangency determines the highest possible level of meat production. 0B amount of forage and 0A amount of grain will be grown. (This solution assumes that the isorevenue line for grain and forage, which in this case is also the "isocost" line, is tangent to the production possibility curve at the same point the isoquant is tangent to the production possibility curve. How would the solution be changed if this were not true?)

The graphs on Figure 6–6 depict one of the basic problems in farm management. Used in this manner, the isoquants and production possibility curves provide a very simplified view of the theory of budgeting. The problem is oversimplified as stated, of course. Usually, more than two intermediate products and more than one final product is produced on a farm. The principle involved is sound, however. The *MRPS* of forage for grain (the intermediate products) must be equal to the *MRS* of forage for grain in the production of meat (the final product).

GENERAL EQUIMARGINAL PRINCIPLES

The economic view of the production process has increased in complexity. The remaining chapters in this section of the text will present somewhat different aspects of production theory—therefore a summary of some of the principles presented, along with some logical extensions, seems useful at this time. The most general view of the production process is obtained by studying the input side—the allocation of variable inputs among competing uses. As shown above, this approach, based on production functions, leads to the same results as the production possibility curves discussed earlier in this chapter. As always in this section, pure competition is assumed in both the input and output markets.

The input view of the production process is based on the marginal increment or marginal products—the marginal product being defined as the change in total product caused by a one-unit increase in the variable input. The marginal product is measured in physical units, bushels, tons, pounds, etc. The economist and farm manager, however, are interested in the revenue earned by the enterprise, and so the marginal product is multiplied by the product price to obtain the marginal value product. Thus, if one pound of fertilizer increases wheat yield by one half a bushel and wheat sells for $1.50 per bushel, the marginal value product of fertilizer is $0.75.

Suppose that two different enterprises on the farm use two different variable inputs, each of which may be readily purchased in the marketplace. The question the farm manager must answer when he does not have unlimited capital to purchase inputs is: How much of each input should be purchased for use in each enterprise? If some input is being used in each enterprise, the manager may decide to compare the marginal value product of each input. If so, he may find that X_1 (used on Y_1) has a marginal earnings or marginal value product of $4 and X_2 (used on Y_2) has a marginal value product of $16. Should he decide to purchase more X_2 to use on Y_2 because one unit of X_2 will return four times as much as X_1? Not necessarily. In fact, he can't make a wise economic choice until he knows the cost of X_2 relative to the cost of X_1. Suppose X_1 costs $1 and X_2 cost $8. Then a dollar's worth of X_1 will return $4 while a dollar's worth of X_2 will only return $2. X_1 is a better buy because it earns more relative to its cost (on the margin). It will continue to be a better buy until as it is purchased and applied its marginal product and thus marginal earnings drops to the same level as X_2.

The marginal criterion used is

$$\frac{MVP_{x_1y_1}}{P_{x_1}} = \frac{MVP_{x_2y_2}}{P_{x_2}}$$

where $MVP_{x_1y_1}$ denotes the marginal value product of X_1 used on Y_1, etc. For the example in the last paragraph, the ratios are

$$\frac{\$4}{\$1} \text{ which is larger than } \frac{\$16}{\$8}.$$

Marginal returns from the two inputs will be balanced when X_1 is purchased and used to the point where its marginal earnings are $2 so that

$$\frac{\$2}{\$1} = \frac{\$16}{\$8}.$$

Notice that the ratio of the marginal value product divided by the unit price is not "average return per dollar spent" but rather is "marginal returns per added dollar spent." When the ratio is equal to one, an added dollar spent earns exactly one dollar and the optimum amount of input is being used. The optimum amount of input cannot be used in one enterprise unless it is used in all enterprises—otherwise the marginal earnings of the inputs would be out of balance.

The general equimarginal criterion states that the ratio of the marginal value product of an input to the unit price of the input (MVP_x/P_x) be equal for all inputs in all enterprises. This presumes, of course, that input use in all enterprises is in the zone of economic relevance. When the criterion is fulfilled, a dollar spent on any enterprise will have the same marginal earning, i.e., will add a similar amount to total revenue. In order to fulfill the equimarginal principle, all complementary and supplementary relationships among products must be expanded until competitive relationships exist. Total revenue must equal or exceed total variable costs at the point of equilibrium.

Two Inputs—One Product

One of the simplest cases of input allocation occurs when two inputs, X_1 and X_2, are used to produce one product, Y. Then the equimarginal principles dictates the following equality:

$$\frac{MVP_{x_1 y}}{P_{x_1}} = \frac{MVP_{x_2 y}}{P_{x_2}}.$$

Thus the marginal earnings of each input must be the same per unit of cost. When both ratios equal one, the optimum has been reached. Remembering that $MVP_{xy} = P_y MPP_{xy}$, both sides of the above equality can be divided by P_y to obtain

$$\frac{MPP_{x_1 y}}{P_{x_1}} = \frac{MPP_{x_2 y}}{P_{x_2}}.$$

This equality specifies the minimum-cost combination of inputs for the production of any given level of output, the level of production depending upon the amount of capital available to purchase inputs. Thus, the general equimarginal criterion automatically specifies the minimum-cost combination of inputs within each enterprise considered. The results presented above are identical to those in Chapter 5.

Two Products—One Input

Another simple case exists when two products, Y_1 and Y_2, are produced with one input, X. Then this equimarginal criterion is

$$\frac{MVP_{xy_1}}{P_x} = \frac{MVP_{xy_2}}{P_x},$$

where MVP_{xy_1} represents the marginal value product of X used on Y_1, etc. When the ratios both equal one, the optimum amount of input is used in both enterprises. Because P_x is a constant, both sides of the ratio can be multiplied by P_x and the criterion then becomes

$$MVP_{xy_1} = MVP_{xy_2}.$$

The marginal earnings of the input must be the same in both uses. This is easily generalized to more products and is identical to the solution in Chapter 4.

Three Inputs—Three Products

Suppose that three inputs, X_1, X_2, X_3, are used to produce three products, Y_1, Y_2, Y_3, in such a way that

$$Y_1 = f(X_1)$$
$$Y_2 = f(X_1, X_2)$$
$$Y_3 = f(X_3)$$

then the equimarginal criterion specifies that input use should be such that the following ratios hold true:

$$\frac{MVP_{x_1y_1}}{P_{x_1}} = \frac{MVP_{x_1y_2}}{P_{x_1}} = \frac{MVP_{x_2y_2}}{P_{x_2}} = \frac{MVP_{x_3y_3}}{P_{x_3}},$$

where $MVP_{x_1y_1}$ signifies the MVP of X_1 used on Y_1. Again, when all ratios equal one, the optimum amount of input is used in each enterprise. When the ratios are equal but greater than one, the marginal earnings per dollar of cost are equal for all inputs in all enterprises. Note that whether at the optimum or below it, a least-cost combination of inputs is always used in Y_2.

Further examples of the equimarginal principles will not be presented. The reader should develop examples for other combinations of inputs and outputs.

Allocation of Owned Resources

The equimarginal principles discussed above tacitly assumes that all inputs are purchased. This is true for the beginning farmer or for the businessman who completely depletes his inputs each production period. Usually, however, production is carried on with some combination of purchased and owned resources. Purchased resources can be allocated according to the equimarginal principle until all available capital is utilized. The problem is somewhat different with owned resources. Usually these resources are durables, i.e., inputs that last several production periods. Further, they usually fall in two groups. The highly specialized inputs, sugar beet harvesters, cotton pickers, corn pickers, fence post hole diggers, and so on, can only be used for specific jobs and present no allocation problems. The sugar beet harvester has no use at all if sugar beets are not grown; under no circumstances can it be used for any other purpose.

The other types of durable inputs represented by tractors, plows, combines, trucks, land, buildings, etc., can be utilized in many different enterprises. A given quantity of these inputs, or more exactly the services of these inputs, are available to the farm manager to allocate among competing enterprises. The inputs are already owned so there is no unit purchase cost; operating costs are zero or constant in all uses. The criterion for allocating such inputs is to use them in such a manner that the marginal earnings of their services are equal in all uses (and exceed operating costs, if any). In this way the value of the input services is maximized. Any other use of the inputs will result in less total earnings.

The Equimarginal Principles—General Discussion

When several enterprises exist on one farm, the equimarginal principles specify that the optimum amounts of inputs will not be used in one enterprise unless they are used in all enterprises. Only when inputs are unlimited, i.e., available in quantities such that the optimum can be used in each enterprise, will the optimum amount of inputs be used in all enterprises. Therein lies the difference between maximizing farm profits and maximizing profits from an individual enterprise. When inputs (capital) are limited, farm profits are the maximum possible given the resource restrictions when marginal returns per added dollar cost are equalized. On the other hand, profits from any one enterprise are at a maximum at the optimum, where $MVP_x = P_x$, or alternately, the ratio MVP_x/P_x equals one. Thus, use of the optimum amount of input in one enterprise is consistent with earning the maximum farm profits only when inputs are unlimited. In this latter case, of course, farm management problems are greatly simplified.

The equimarginal principles, along with other concepts presenting the economic view of the production process, have now been developed in great detail. This development does not mean to imply that exact usage of the principles are possible in actual situations. In practice, of course, the manager has imperfect knowledge about production functions, prices, and future events and thus is unable to deal with the refinements as presented here. This should not negate, however, either the economist's desire to present these principles clearly and precisely or the manager's desire to apply them to the extent of his knowledge and ability. The student of economics needs a vigorous statement of the fundamentals of economic analysis. The manager needs to understand clearly the principles of profit maximization so that he may apply them in practice, albeit crudely.

REFERENCES

BRADFORD, L. A., and JOHNSON, G. L. *Farm Management Analysis,* chap. xi. New York: John Wiley & Sons, Inc., 1953.
COHEN, K. J., and CYERT, R. M. *Theory of the Firm—Resource Allocation in*

the Market Economy, chap. vii. Englewood Cliffs, N.J.: Prentice-Hall, Inc., 1965.

HEADY, EARL O. *Economics of Agricultural Production and Resource Use,* chaps. vii, viii, and ix. Englewood Cliffs, N.J.: Prentice-Hall, Inc., 1952.

VINCENT, WARREN H. (ed.). *Economics and Management in Agriculture,* chap. v. Englewood Cliffs, N.J.: Prentice-Hall, Inc., 1962.

THE PRODUCTION PROCESS
THROUGH TIME

In the study of a subject, the most basic and fundamental concepts must be introduced first. These concepts then serve as a skeleton around which firmer fabric can be draped. The most fundamental concept in the economic theory of the firm is the production function. In the last four chapters, the characteristics of the production function and the marginal concepts of resource allocation based on the production function were discussed in great detail—always under the assumptions of perfect certainty and timelessness. Future prices, yields, and other events relevant to the production process were assumed to be known, and problems unique to the passage of time were not considered. In this chapter, the economic picture of the production process will be broadened by a consideration of the effects of time upon the production process. Background material and analytical techniques will be developed to make time analyses amenable to the marginal principles previously developed.

The type of theory presented in previous chapters is often called "static" because it ignores the fact that production can only occur with the passage of time. Static analyses regard production as a network at a point in time rather than a flow through time. Consideration of time as such, however, does not mean that the analysis of the present chapter is "dynamic," particularly in view of the fact that perfect certainty is assumed.

A GENERAL PICTURE

An analysis of the effects of time on production must include time considerations within a production period as well as consideration of a sequence of production periods. In the latter case, two new considerations are immediately brought to the fore: durable inputs and profit as a stream or flow through time.

The manager purchases inputs to obtain the productive services they provide. In previous chapters, the distinction between input quantities and services were not emphasized, the reason being that the production services of the so-called "variable" inputs were assumed to be completely utilized in one production period. Quantities and services were thus synonymous. Durable resources, however, are defined to be those resources which give off productive services for more than one production period. In large part, the fixed costs discussed in previous chapters were costs associated with durable inputs. While these fixed costs were acknowledged, their exact nature was ignored.[1] The introduction of time into the analysis permits a more complete discussion of these costs.

In the purest sense, a farmer or other businessman can be pictured as a manager with a sum of capital. At any point in time, he is interested in diverting this capital to its highest use, that is, to that use which will earn the most profit per unit of time. He undertakes a particular type of production because his capital earns more in that use than any other. In this state the manager is perfectly flexible; he can and will divert his capital to its best use. He is the ultimate maximizer.

Once a particular type of production, such as farming, is selected, the next purest form is constructed by assuming the manager has all of his capital in liquid form at the beginning of the production period and receives all his capital and profit in liquid form at the completion of the production process, where "liquid" means currency or some other perfectly negotiable form. In this type of production process, fixed costs arise from the purchase of input quantities at the beginning of the production period which are completely utilized by the end of the period but which cannot be varied during the period. At the end of the period no services remain in the input, and production decisions relevant to the next production period can be made independently of past decisions. Labor hired on an annual basis or land rented on a yearly contract are examples of this type of fixed cost. The manager incurs these types of fixed costs only when he decides to produce. In essence, this describes the type of fixed cost assumed present in previous chapters.

When the manager receives all his capital and profit in liquid form at the end of the production process, he again is free to invest his capital in its highest earning use. Once he decides to produce he is committed for the production period, but if at the end he realizes his capital earned less in farming than it would in, say, a savings and loan account, he is able to place all his capital in the savings and loan firm.

A more realistic production process arises when the manager must invest in some durable resources if he is to undertake production. These durable inputs embody a "lump" of services too large to be used in one

---

[1] The makeup of fixed costs were not omitted through any weakness in the analysis but rather because of a search for simplicity. The principles of production functions, cost curves, and marginal allocation were introduced without all the clutter of time and durable inputs. Because the analysis was assumed to be timeless, the length of the production period could be selected to be that period of time in which all services of all inputs are completely utilized.

production period. At the end of the production period, the manager has some profit, some liquid capital, and some durable inputs possessing unused services.[2] A decision to produce or not to produce during the next production process cannot be made without consideration of these unused services. Present decisions are thus influenced by past decisions. And a manager with a stock of durable inputs may rationally react quite differently to output or input price changes than the manager with liquid capital.

The abstract picture of a business, then, is that of a manager subtly guiding his capital through time in search of maximum profit. Profit in this sense is not a once-over lump at a point in time but rather a stream of receipts into the future—in actuality, a rate of capital growth. The production process can be visualized as a capital "pool" with input costs flowing in at various dates and output revenues flowing out at other dates. Usually, part of the capital invested in the process is in the form of durable services.

COMPOUNDING COSTS AND DISCOUNTING REVENUES

Compounding Present Costs

Suppose that you are a farmer who has the opportunity to buy a tract of forest land for $100. For simplicity, suppose that this tract has no annual upkeep and you can sign a contract now to sell the tract for $150 at the end of five years. Should you buy the tract of land?

First, assuming that you want to invest the $100 in some type of production process rather than spend it on a consumption item, you should evaluate alternative production possibilities. Suppose the best alternative investment is a savings and loan firm in your town which pays 5 percent per year on savings accounts. If you were to invest your money in the savings and loan, you would earn money as follows: At the end of the first year you would receive 5 percent of your investment, or $5. Thus, if you invest P (for present) dollars at i interest rate per year, you would own at the end of one year exactly $P + Pi$ dollars. In the example, this would be $100 + ($100)(0.05)$, or $105. This is not a mathematical derivation—it is what you and the savings and loan agree upon. Notice the $P + Pi$ could be written $P(1 + i)$. Thus $105 = $100(1.05)$.

If you reinvest your money, at the end of the second year you will receive as interest 5 percent of the reinvested amount or $($105)(0.05) = 5.25 and you will have in total $105 + $5.25 = 110.25. In symbolic terms, you now have the amount earned at the end of the

---

[2] One of these durables with unused services is management skill acquired from previous production. Thus, as a manager ages, his commitment in "durable" management services adaptable only to his business increases.

first year, $P + Pi$, plus the interest that amount earned during the second year, $(P + Pi)i$, or $(P + Pi) + (P + Pi)i$ which can also be written

$$P(1 + i) + Pi(1 + i)$$

which after factoring $(1 + i)$ results in

$$(P + Pi)(1 + i) .$$

Factoring a P from the left term gives

$$P(1 + i)(1 + i) = P(1 + i)^2 .$$

Thus, $110.25 = 100(1.05)^2$. One hundred dollars invested at 5 percent compounded annually, meaning that the interest earned in the first year earns interest in the second year, is worth $110.25 at the end of two years.

If you invest your $110.25 at 5 percent for a year, it will earn $5.51 and you will have $115.76. Thus, $115.76 = 100(0.105)^3$. The $115.76 earns $5.79 the fourth year, and you have a total of $121.55, or $100(1.05)^4$. For the fifth and final year, the $121.55 earns $6.08, and your total amount of money is $127.63, or $100(1.05)^5$.

The easy way to determine the value of $100 compounded annually at 5 percent is to apply the compounding factor directly. The compounded value is equal to $100(1.05)^5$, which becomes $100(1.2763) = 127.63$ because $(1.05)^5 = 1.2763$. In general, the compounded value, F (for future value), of a present sum P invested at an annual interest rate i for n years is

$$F = P(1 + i)^n .$$

This procedure is called compounding, and in economic applications the amount being compounded is often an outlay or expenditure. Hence the term "compounding costs." For convenient study, the quantities derived above in the text are summarized in Table 7–1.[3]

Investing the $100 in the savings and loan, assumed here to be the next best investment opportunity, results in an earning of $27.63 and a total amount of $127.63. Your basic dilemma was comparing $100 now with $150 at the end of five years. You now find that $100 invested now is the same as $127.63 five years from now. Your cost and return figures

---

[3] The compounding expression for one year, $F = P(1 + i)$, and for two years, $F = P(1 + i)^2$, were derived in the text. To save space, the expression was not derived for three, four, or five years. The student should try it. If that's too easy, prove the general expression is true.

are now dated at the same period in time (five years hence) and are comparable. Anyone rational would spend $127.63 at one point in time to receive $150 at the same point in time. Thus, you should buy the forest tract. The $50 you make by so doing is divided into two parts: $27.63 which represents what you could have earned anyway (opportunity cost) and $22.37 profit from the forest tract.

Earlier the businessman was described as a profit maximizer who undertakes a unique production process (such as purchasing forest tracts) only if it will earn more than the usual types of investments, such as savings and loan firms or other conventional capital investments. The rate of capital growth within the business is called the internal rate of return (or interest). The interest rate paid by common investments such as accounts in banks and other financial agencies is called the market or external rate of return (interest). Production is undertaken when the internal rate of return is greater than the external rate of return.

TABLE 7–1

THE PROCEDURE FOR COMPOUNDING COSTS; THE ORIGINAL AMOUNT, P, IS $100; ANNUAL INTEREST RATE IS 5 PERCENT

Year	Beginning Amount	Interest Earned by End of Year	Ending Amount = Beginning Amount + Interest	Compounding Formula
1........	$100.00	$100.00(0.05) = $5.00	$105.00	$105.00 = $100(1.05)^1$
2........	105.00	105.00(0.05) = 5.25	110.25	$110.25 = 100(1.05)^2$
3........	110.25	110.25(0.05) = 5.51	115.76	$115.76 = 100(1.05)^3$
4........	115.76	115.76(0.05) = 5.79	121.55	$121.55 = 100(1.05)^4$
5........	121.55	121.55(0.05) = 6.08	127.63	$127.63 = 100(1.05)^5$

The internal rate of return can be found using the compounding formula. For the forest tract, the internal rate of return is that value for i such that $150 = $100(1 + i)^5$. Solving this equation yields a value for i of 8.5 percent.[4]

Although policy implications are discussed elsewhere in this text, a hypothetical example here will suffice to demonstrate the uses of the concepts discussed above. Suppose the government decided for some reason that investment in forestry tracts was proceeding too rapidly and that market interest rates should be increased. The reasoning behind this

---

[4] To solve let $(1 + i) = x$. Then, $150 = $100x^5$, or $1.5 = x^5$. Converting to logarithms gives:

$$\log 1.5 = 5 \log x$$
$$\log x = \frac{\log 1.5}{5} = \frac{0.17609}{5} = .03522 .$$

Therefore $x = 1.085$ and $i = .085$, the internal rate of interest.

would be that as market interest rates increased businessmen would divert funds from forest tracts to other investments. The effectiveness of this action would depend upon the relative magnitudes of the internal and external rates of interest. If the internal rate of interest in the forest tract "industry" is equal to or only slightly above the external rate, a slight increase in the external rate would cause businessmen to disinvest (withdraw capital) from forest lands with all due haste. However, if as in the example, the internal rate is much higher than the external rate, a slight increase in market rates would have no effect on capital use.

If the capital to purchase forest land is borrowed at the market rate of interest, the same principles still hold true, except that interest rates now represent a real rather than an opportunity cost. In this case, if the internal rate is much higher than the external, the only effect of a small interest rate increase is to divert profits from the businessman to the owners of the capital.

Discounting Future Revenues

Costs incurred at one point in time cannot validly be compared with revenues forthcoming at a later date. The solution presented above enables costs to be compounded to the date the revenues are forthcoming. The appropriate equation, where P is the sum at the present time, F its future value, i the interest rate, and n the number of years, was shown to be

$$F = P(1 + i)^n .$$

By dividing both sides of this equation by $(1 + i)^n$, the following equation is obtained

$$P = \frac{F}{(1 + i)^n} .$$

Thus, if a payoff, F, is due n years in the future, its present value, P, can be determined using the above expression where i is the interest rate. This procedure is known as discounting future returns.

What is the present value of $127.63 received at the end of five years if the appropriate discount rate is 5 percent? In this case, the discounting expression is

$$P = \frac{\$127.63}{(1.05)^5} = \frac{\$127.63}{1.2763} = \$100 .$$

But, as seen in the compounding example above, the future value of $100 compounded five years at 5 percent is $127.63. Discounting, then, is seen to be the opposite of compounding.

Suppose that in the forestry example presented above, rather than compounding the costs forward, you decided to discount the $150 received at the end of five years back to the present at a 5 percent interest rate. Then

$$P = \frac{\$150}{(1.05)^5} = \frac{\$150}{1.2763} = \$117.53 .$$

Thus, $150 received at the end of five years has the same value to you as $117.53 received now. By investing $100 today, you receive the equivalent of $117.53 today. Therefore, you buy the tract of land and make a profit of $17.53. But $17.53 compounded five years at 5 percent is equal to $22.37. The profit earned is the same whether you decide to discount or compound.

Discounting can be used to determine the present value of the future income stream earned by a durable input. Suppose a farmer has a chance to buy a small, secondhand tractor for $850. For simplicity, assume that the tractor has a remaining serviceable life of four years and will be sold for $150. Should he invest in this durable input?

The farmer must first evaluate the worth of the tractor to him. Suppose he determines that after paying all costs of nondurable inputs used within each annual production period, the tractor will add to his yearly revenues the amounts of $300, $250, $200, and $50 at the end of years one through four, respectively. Assuming the appropriate discount rate is 6 percent, the discounting calculations are shown in Table 7–2.

TABLE 7–2

DISCOUNTING FUTURE EARNINGS OF A DURABLE INPUT

Year	Added Revenue at Year's End	Added Revenue Discounted at 6 Percent
1	$300	$300/1.06 = $283.02
2	250	$250/(1.06)^2$ = 222.50
3	200	$200/(1.06)^3$ = 167.92
4	200*	$200/(1.06)^4$ = 158.42
Total	$950	$831.86

* $50 earnings plus $150 salvage value.

The total added revenues attributed to the tractor over the period are $800; this added to the salvage value gives a total of $950 the farmer can realize from purchasing the tractor.[5] This $950 is not a lump sum

[5] Durable inputs provide the added problem of depreciation. Depreciation is considered in detail below. For this example, added revenue due to the durable input must include payments for depreciation as well as profits per se.

accruing at any point in time—rather it is the sum of an income "stream" occurring over a four-year span. This stream must be discounted back to the present and compared to the present cost. When this is done as in Table 7–2, the total discounted present value of the tractor's future earnings is $831.86. The farmer would thus lose $18.14 by purchasing the tractor. He could invest $831.86 at 6 percent per year and withdraw $300, $250, $200, and $200 in that order at the end of each year; in other words, he could have the same amounts of money at the same times by investing $18.14 less. Therefore, the present cost of the tractor is greater than the discounted value of its future earnings and the farmer should not buy. In general, investment in a durable input is profitable only if the sum of the discounted future revenues is greater than the cost of the input.

All costs do not have to be incurred at one time. Annual costs incurred for investments in durables (but not for nondurables expended in one production period—these are paid out of annual revenues) can be compounded or discounted in a similar manner.

What Is the Interest Rate?

The methods of compounding and discounting presented above are standard types of mathematical computations used in computing interest. The only unique aspect of these formulas is the interest rate, i. The meaning of this interest rate is of primary importance in economic theory of the firm.

The basic consideration in compounding and discounting is that money received at different points in time has different values. A dollar received now does not necessarily have the same value to a person as a dollar received a year from now. An individual's preference for money through time is called his time preference.

When the manager is pictured as an individual with a bundle of capital at a certain point in time, investment in a business is not his only opportunity. He may choose to spend it all immediately or to put it in a checking account (earning no interest) to spend for consumption goods over some future period. What he will do depends upon the satisfaction, or utility if you like, he will derive from spending the money now versus spending it in the future. Viewed in this context, there is no reason to assume the existence of a general rule stating that a dollar now is worth either more or less than a dollar in the future. For consumption, each person's time preference can be different. In some cases, such as retirement or education of children, a dollar in the future might be worth more than a dollar now. Those who hold large amounts of cash during inflationary periods apparently are willing to sacrifice future buying power for the security gained from certain possession of the cash.

Just why the individual decides to invest a portion of his money in a productive process is an issue much broader than can be discussed adequately here. Presumably, the opportunity to forego consumption of a lump of capital now to create a future flow of income could be based upon a combination of goals including a steady future income, a chance to increase present income or a chance for wealth of great magnitude, personal satisfaction, creation of an estate, or power. But once the individual decides to invest rather than spend, to become an entrepreneur rather than a consumer, he should never as a profit maximizer accept less than the usual market rate of interest. As a businessman, to accept less would be irrational.

The interest rate used to discount or compound sums of money should at least be as large as the current or usual market rate of interest. How much higher it might be depends upon the manager's opportunity costs. Ideally, in a perfect sense, the manager should be aware of all production possibilities open to him and select the most profitable of these. If the oil business is more profitable than the grocery business, the grocer will make the switch. Once he has selected the most profitable business, the appropriate rate of interest to use in compounding or discounting is the (internal) rate of interest earned in the next most profitable business. In fact, because of fixed investments in management inputs (abilities), managers usually are not able to skip from business to business. Grocers do not know how to run oil businesses. Because of this and other institutional limitations, the external or market rate of interest is commonly used in budgeting, discounting, and compounding. The interest rate, then, represents an opportunity cost. But from here on for simplicity the discount rate will be referred to as the market or external rate of interest. The reader should remember that one of the "markets" could be an alternative production investment.

Usual farm budgeting procedures include a charge for capital owned by the farmer. Owned capital must earn a return comparable to usual market interest rates. Profits earned by the farm are defined to be over and above what the capital, labor, and management abilities of the farmer could earn elsewhere. When budgeting for discounting, however, an opportunity cost in the form of interest must not be charged for the durable item being evaluated, for example the tractor in the example above, because the discounting procedure accounts for the opportunity cost of the capital investment in the durable.

PROFIT MAXIMIZATION FOR PRODUCTION PERIODS OF VARIABLE LENGTH[6]

When time is introduced into the economic analysis, the goal of the manager will, in some instances, need to be revised. While other time

---

[6] The cases considered here are the most elementary. The reader is referred to the bibliography for more complete and complex analyses.

periods may sometimes be relevant, the usual accounting period for most firms is a year. The manager wishes to maximize profits for each accounting period, however long it might be. He is no longer interested in maximizing profits from one production process in and of itself but rather seeks to maximize profits per unit of time and will organize his business to attain that end. The time period itself is not important because of the fixed relationship among units of time. A year has 365 days. Therefore, profit per day is maximized simultaneously with profit per year.

If the production process is such that the period of production lasts exactly one year, assumed here to be the relevant time period, then equating marginal revenue with marginal cost maximizes profits to the production process and for the year. Maximization of profits for the production process is consistent with maximizing annual profits for the firm.

Only in exceptional cases will the period of production correspond to the calendar year. When the two are different, two important situations exist: (1) the length of the production period is fixed and (2) the length of the production period is variable.

The production period is fixed in length for many important agricultural production processes. Crops are notable examples. Corn must be planted in the spring and harvested in the fall. Winter wheat must be fall planted and harvested the next summer. The time required to bring crops to fruition is determined by nature—not by the farm manager. Some latitude exists as to timeliness of operations, but production cycles cannot be changed to the extent that more than one cycle can be squeezed into one year. Hence, maximization of profits to the production process is the same as maximization of profits for the year, and the criterion equating marginal revenue to marginal cost for the production process remains valid.

Variable Length Production Process—No Discounting

When the production process is variable in length, the criterion requiring maximization of profit for an enterprise does not give the same solution as the criterion requiring maximum profits per unit of time. In this case, the appropriate criterion is maximum profit per unit of time. An example will suffice to demonstrate this.

Livestock feeding operations are probably the most typical examples of an agricultural production process which can be varied in time. Among the important time decisions facing the livestock feeder are: (1) What type of ration and feeding system should be used? The choice of diet will affect the rate of gain and time when the animal is marketed. (2) When should the animals be marketed to obtain the best possible price? (3) Given the ration and market price, how long should the production process be to maximize profits per unit of time? An example will be given to answer the third question. The first two, although important, are beyond the scope of this chapter.

The production process to be considered is a drylot cattle feeding operation.[7] A 600-pound animal is to be purchased and fed a specified ration for an unspecified length of time. Upon sale of the animal, another will be purchased and the production process repeated. Costs to be considered are the purchase price of the animal and feed costs. For simplicity, other costs of production are assumed to be constant. The animal can be bought and sold for $0.20 a pound. Differences in quality due to length of feeding period are ignored. Costs and returns for this example are presented in Table 7–3; as demonstrated in previous chap-

TABLE 7–3

COSTS AND RETURNS OF A FEEDER CATTLE ENTERPRISE
THROUGH TIME

Units of Time (10 Days)	Total Costs	Total Revenue	Profit	Marginal Profit	Average Profit
0	$120.00	$120.00	0		....
				−$0.91	
2	124.05	122.24	−$ 1.81		−$0.91
				0.85	
4	128.43	128.32	−0.11		−0.03
				1.97	
6	133.45	137.28	3.83		0.64
				2.45	
8	139.43	148.16	8.73		1.09
				2.29	
10	147.70	160.00	13.30		1.33
				1.48	
12	155.58	171.84	16.26		1.36
				0.04	
14	166.39	182.72	16.33		1.17
				−2.04	
16	179.44	191.68	12.24		0.76

SOURCE: Simplified from example presented by J. Edwin Faris, "Analytical Techniques Used in Determining the Optimum Replacement Pattern," *Journal of Farm Economies*, November, 1960, pp. 755–66.

ters, these are derived from a production function (not presented here) relating output, weight of the feeder, to the input, time. A graph of the data in Table 7–3 is presented in Figure 7–1.

From examination of Table 7–3, profit from the feeder animal is at a maximum at 14 units of time. The marginal profit column indicates that the marginal profit of time is very small between 12 and 14 units. Therefore, the exact profit maximizing amount probably falls somewhere

[7] This example was simplified from data developed by J. Edwin Faris, "Analytical Techniques Used in Determining the Optimum Replacement Pattern," *Journal of Farm Economics*, November, 1960, pp. 755–66.

between these limits. Reference to Figure 7–1 shows that the maximum
profit point—the units of time at which the profit curve is horizontal—is
13.1 units. At this point, of course, the marginal profit is zero and the
marginal profit curve intersects the time input axis. (Note that all curves

FIGURE 7–1

TOTAL, MARGINAL, AND AVERAGE PROFIT OF TIME RESULTING FROM FEEDER
CATTLE ENTERPRISE

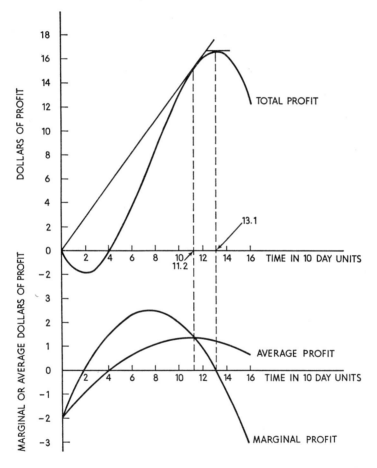

are profit curves rather than physical input-output curves. When the
input has a positive price, the marginal *physical* product is not zero when
profit is a maximum. In this case the marginal curve is a profit curve, not
a physical curve, and thus is zero when profit is a maximum.) Using the
marginal criterion presented in earlier chapters, profit from a single

animal or any multiple thereof fed simultaneously is a maximum at 13.1 units or 131 days.

However, the cattle feeder's interest is in maximizing yearly income; thus, he wants to earn the maximum profit per unit of time rather than per animal. The data in Table 7–3 suggests that average profit is a maximum near 12 units of time. Figure 7–1 shows that maximum average profit occurs at 11.2 units, where marginal and average profit are equal. To maximize annual income from cattle feeding in this example, the feeder should sell each lot after 112 days of feeding.

The average profit per unit of time for 11.2 units is approximately $1.40; for 13.2 units, it is about $1.25 (read from Figure 7–1). Thus, the feeder makes about $0.15 more per unit of time by replacing after 11.2 units of time. A year contains 36.5 units of time—thus he makes $5.48 more per unit of animal capacity per year. In a real feeding situation this may not be judged important, but it suffices here to demonstrate the principle.

As an explanation of the solutions, the solution of 13.2 units assumes feed to be the variable input, the animal the fixed input, and time to be available in infinite quantities. The solution of 11.2 is determined assuming feed and animals to be variable and the amount of time to be limited. In this solution, the feeder is "applying" feed and animals to a fixed amount of time. If the feeder does not intend to repeat the feeding operation, that is, if he feeds just one lot a year, then he should maximize returns to the animal rather than to time.

Variable Length Production Process—Discounting

The cattle feeding process used as an example in the preceding section was carried out within the span of a year. For that reason, discounting and compounding were not needed. The increase in cost during each period was due only to the cost of feed needed for the animal; no interest was charged for the money invested. Many production processes last longer than a year. In such cases, compounding and discounting procedures must be used. An example will now be presented which assembles all the basic considerations of compounding and discounting presented above.

Consider a production process which requires an initial outlay of $100. The product of this process, like that of the feeder cattle operation, comes only at one time—the time of sale. For simplicity, assume that the sale can be made only at the year's end and annual costs are negligible. At the end of each year the manager is able to determine the sale value (total revenue) of his product.

Table 7–4 summarizes the essential revenue data for this example. At the beginning, the product can be sold for $100, which is the purchase price. At the end of the first year, the product could be sold for $120, etc.

(These amounts are not annual earnings but represent the sale value of the product at the end of each year provided the product is not sold earlier.) As usual, these total revenues would have to be based on a production function and a product price, but these details, developed in earlier chapters, are omitted here. No annual costs are present. Therefore, a simple method of determining the most profitable length of time to "grow" the product is to discount future revenues. Assuming an interest rate of 8 percent, the appropriate discount factors and the discounted total revenue are shown in Table 7–4.

Discounted total revenue is at a maximum and equal to $153.48 at the ends of years 4 and 5. Usually, a maximum will be attained only in one year. This particular feature was built in the data to illustrate a later point. To determine a specific optima, assume the manager will produce

TABLE 7–4

DISCOUNTING TOTAL REVENUE FOR A PRODUCTION PROCESS

Year	Total Revenue	Discount Factor*	Discounted Total Revenue
0........	$100.00	. . . .	. . . . . .
1........	120.00	$(1.08)^1 = 1.0800$	$111.11
2........	150.00	$(1.08)^2 = 1.1664$	128.60
3........	180.00	$(1.08)^3 = 1.2597$	142.89
4........	208.80	$(1.08)^4 = 1.3604$	153.48
5........	225.50	$(1.08)^5 = 1.4693$	153.48
6........	239.03	$(1.08)^6 = 1.5869$	150.63
7........	250.98	$(1.08)^7 = 1.7138$	146.45

* Using a discount rate of 8 percent, $120 ÷ 1.0800 = $111.11, etc.

as long as his business earns at a rate at least equivalent to the discount rate. Once he invests, he won't disinvest as long as he is doing as well as the market. Year 5 is then the year he should sell, and his discounted profit would be $53.48. By investing in the process now, he will receive at the end of five years an amount of profit equivalent in value to $53.48 now.

The above method is simple to apply and yields a valid solution under a certain assumption—that the production process is not repeatable. A more detailed approach to the problem will reveal the nature of this solution and suggest an alternative criterion when the process is repeatable. A more complete analysis of the example is presented in Table 7–5.

Column 1 in Table 7–5, Total Revenue, is taken from Table 7–4. Column 2, Total Costs, is the original $100 investment compounded at 8 percent and represents the cost incurred to the end of any particular

TABLE 7–5

HYPOTHETICAL EXAMPLE OF A PRODUCTION PROCESS OVER SEVERAL YEARS

Year	Total Revenue (1)	Total Costs (2)	Profit* (3)	Annual Addition to—		Annual Percent Change†		Discounted Profit‡ (8)	Internal Rate of Return§ (9)
				Revenue (4)	Costs (5)	Revenue (6)	Costs (7)		
0	$100.00	$100.00	$ 0.00					...	...
1	120.00	108.00	12.00	$20.00	$ 8.00	20	8	$11.11	20.0%
2	150.00	116.64	33.36	30.00	8.64	25	8	28.60	22.5
3	180.00	125.97	54.03	30.00	9.33	20	8	42.89	21.6
4	208.80	136.04	72.76	28.80	10.07	16	8	53.48	20.2
5	225.50	146.93	78.57	16.70	10.89	8	8	53.48	17.6
6	239.03	158.69	80.34	13.53	11.76	6	8	50.63	15.6
7	250.98	171.38	79.60	11.95	12.69	5	8	46.45	14.1

* For each year, the column 1 entry minus the column 2 entry.
† Computed by dividing the addition to total revenue (total costs) by the amount of total revenue (total costs) at the beginning of the year. For year 1, the percentage increase in total revenue is (20/100) = 0.20, or 20 percent.
‡ For each year, the entry in column 3 discounted by the appropriate discount factor from Table 7–4. For year 6, discounted profit is $80.34/1.5869 = $50.63.
§ Computed by substituting the original cost, $100, in the compounding formula and solving for the interest rate which would yield a compounded amount equal to total revenue for the year in question. For year 4, the equation to be solved is $208.80 = 100(1 + i)^4$ and $(1 + i) = 1.202$.

year. In this example, total costs are the $100 investment plus the interest it could have earned elsewhere. For example, the cost at the end of year 2 is $116.64, or $100 original investment plus $8 interest the first year plus $8.64 interest the second.[8]

Column 3 is profit determined by subtracting total costs from total revenue for each year. This undiscounted profit attains a maximum in year 6, suggesting an optimum time of six years rather than five as previously derived. Further examination will show why five is appropriate.

Columns 4 and 5 show annual additions to total revenue and total costs. When divided by the appropriate total revenue and total cost figures, as shown in the table footnotes, the percentage change in total revenue (Column 6) and total costs (Column 7) is determined. Percentage change in total revenue increases and then decreases. Percentage change in total costs, 8 percent, is constant; this need not be true when annual costs are incurred.

The percentage increase in revenue exceeds 8 percent in years 1 through 4. In year 5, the earnings of the production process are 8 percent, exactly equal to the interest rate used. (This explains why years 4 and 5 have identical discounted total revenues; the firm is earning the same interest rate as the market.) In year 6, the revenue increases only 6 percent. The manager could sell at the end of year 5, invest the money received at 8 percent and realize more revenue than by producing another year. Thus, five years, rather than six, is the optimum time span. The computation of discounted profit (Column 8) verifies this. Profit from the enterprise is not increased in year 5 over year 4, thus the firm is not earning at a higher rate than the market in year 5. But discounted profit from year 6 decreases—suggesting that the market earns more than the firm in year 6.

The general criterion for the optimum solution, then, is that the percentage increase in total revenue must equal the percentage increase in total costs. When this is true, discounted profits are at a maximum. In the simple case in which the only cost incurred is at the start of the period, the solution can be obtained by discounting total revenue for each year and selecting the maximum (Table 7–4). When costs are incurred each year, the general criterion can be invoked and the method presented in Table 7–5 used.

The above optimum solution, five years, assumes that time is not limited or that the process is not repeatable within the time horizon of the manager. This may be true for some types of slow-growing crops

---

[8] An annual cost would be compounded in the same manner. Thus, if $20 annual cost were incurred in year 1, 8 percent interest would be paid on it thereafter. At the end of year 1, interest would be due on $128. Annual costs remain invested in the process until time of sale and therefore must be compounded.

such as forests, vineyards, orchards, or other production processes that require the major part of a man's lifetime. If the production process is immediately repeatable, however, a different profit maximizing criterion applies. Time becomes valuable, and the manager should maximize the profit per unit of time, commonly called the internal rate of return.

The internal rate of return is presented in Column 9 of Table 7–5. These rates were computed by solving the compounding formula for the interest rate. The internal rate of return is a maximum 22.5 percent at the end of the second year. Thus, because the process is repeatable, the manager will stop the process and reinvest the $150 in a similar production process. If he does, at the end of two more years or four years in all, the $150 would grow to $225.[9] (But if he left the $150 invested in the original production process, it would only grow to a value of $208.80, undiscounted, after four years). The $225 could then be reinvested for a period of two years at an interest rate of 22.5 percent, etc.

If the manager wished to maximize his income stream rather than investment in the business, he would withdraw all earnings above $100 each time he repeated the production process. An investment (production) period of two years would still be the optimum for he could withdraw $50 for the good life every two years and still have $100 invested. No other period of investment would yield as large an income stream over time.

ECONOMIC ASPECTS OF DURABLE INPUTS

Depreciation

Production is the transformation of certain goods and/or services into goods and/or services of a different form. In agricultural production, tractor fuel, labor, seed, and other inputs are essentially transformed into bushels of corn, pounds of pork, beef, or whatever the end product may be. If all inputs were nondurable, that is, completely transformed to product in one production period, the earnings of the production process could easily be assessed. Profit would be the cash remaining at the end of the period after actual and imputed costs are paid.

Services embodied in durable inputs are forthcoming over several production periods. Thus, at the end of any particular production period, the manager possesses some cash and the unused services of his durable inputs. It is in this context that depreciation becomes important. Assuming no changes in market prices or technology (obsolescence), depreciation is the value of the services of a durable input that are transferred into product during a production period. Each production period a portion of the value of the durable is transformed into product, and this

[9] $150(1.225)^2 = $225.

reduction in value is equal to the depreciation. This type of depreciation is often called "use" depreciation.

The cash receipts from a production period must be of sufficient magnitude to cover costs of nondurable inputs, actual labor costs, imputed family labor and management costs, depreciation of durables and interest on capital invested in production, including the capital invested in durables at the beginning of the period. Profit is any surplus left after paying these costs and, of course, may be positive, negative, or zero.

If the amount attributed to depreciation is set aside at the end of each production period into what is often termed a sinking fund, then when the services of the durable input are depleted, the sinking fund should contain enough capital to purchase another durable input. The unprofitable business will not be able to maintain a sinking fund large enough to replace durable inputs and thus will not survive in the long run. Businesses which survive until their durable inputs are worn out are said to be living off of depreciation.

Depreciation is a cost because it is a payment for services rendered during a particular production period. The investment in a durable input (value of the unused services) is not a cost as such, but the interest imputed to that investment is a cost. The present production process should yield cash receipts sufficient to pay the interest on these "stored-up" future services, but the cost of the services is incurred only when the services are used.

Obsolescence and Market Effects

The concept of depreciation in and of itself is reasonably simple. But computation of depreciation is compounded by obsolescence and other market effects.

Obsolescence is in essence a rating of the efficiency of an input in operation. A machine is technically obsolete when another machine can do the job more efficiently. Usually this efficiency means doing the same job at lower cost, but other management considerations, such as reduction of time required to do the job or reduction of physical effort, may also make one machine more desirable than another. For example, a grain auger is more expensive than a scoop shovel, but many farmers buy the auger to save labor during busy times and to ease their workday. Power steering on tractors saves no time but reduces the physical effort required to drive tractors.

Increases or decreases in market value also confound the apparent effects of true depreciation. When prices in the nation are generally on the rise, farmers often find they can sell durable inputs for more than the original cost or at least for more than they expected to gain from sale at the time of purchase. This phenomena has been particularly true for farm land, but it is also true to a lesser extent of other durables. In times of rising prices, trade-in allowances for old tractors can equal or exceed the original cost, particularly if traded on a larger unit.

Obsolescence and effects of market values on depreciation are sometimes called "time" depreciation. Time and use depreciation are often both included in the meaning of the general term "depreciation." When buying durable inputs, the manager must weigh the possible effects of obsolescence and market prices, neither of which he can know beforehand, as well as the machine's productive value on the farm. Thus, he becomes, whether he likes it or not, something of a market speculator as well as the manager of a business.

Methods of Computing Depreciation

In practice, the actual depreciation of a durable input is not known. Between the times a durable input is bought and sold, its value is largely unknown. If the input is of the type that is commonly bought and sold, a market price might be available. But many times such market prices are not available or do not indicate the true value to the firm. The firm must, of course, determine a value for depreciation which is as accurate as possible. If the input is "depreciated out" too fast, profits computed for the period are artificially depressed at the expense of profits for a later period. If depreciation is too slow, profits for early periods appear too large. A sinking fund must be established to replace the input when its services are depleted.[10]

Suppose that a machine costs $1,200 and sells for $200 at the end of its useful life, five years. The $200 salvage value is affected by the use depreciation of the machine, its obsolescence, and changing market values. (Whether the latter two are "costs" will depend on the situation. The machine may or may not be obsolete, and market values may increase or decrease.) The $1,000 depreciation must be allocated in some manner among the five years of use.

One method of estimating depreciation is called the "straight line" or "linear" method. To use this method, the amount of depreciation, $1,000, is divided by years of use, five, to given an annual depreciation of

---

[10] The durable input may be purchased either with borrowed funds or owned funds. When borrowed funds are used, the depreciation payment is used to make an annual payment on the loan. Interest on capital invested becomes actual on that part of the loan outstanding and imputed on owned capital. As the loan is repaid, more and more of the "total" interest becomes imputed. When the input is depreciated out and the loan is repaid, the firm is unencumbered and may incur another loan. Setting aside a sinking fund from profits is known as "internal" financing as compared to credit or "external" financing. One of the reasons for the tremendous expansion in farm production in recent decades has been due to a shift from internal to external financing on farms. From an economic point of view, the same costs are incurred either way. In fact, internal financing may be less risky. It is interesting to note that some industries which do not face much risk (relative to farming), such as the steel industry, adhere to internal financing.

$200. The machine is worth $1,200 at the beginning of the first year, $1,000 beginning the second, $800 the third, $600 the fourth, $400 the fifth, and $200 at the end.

A second method of estimating depreciation is called the "declining balance" method. This method makes use of the assumption that depreciation is a proportion, k, of the actual value of the durable input. If P is the purchase price, the value of input at the end of the first production period is kP, the value at the end of the second period is $k(kP)$, or k^2P, etc. For the example given above, $k = 0.7$.[11] Using this method, the machine is worth $1,200 beginning the first period, $1,200(0.7) = $840 at the beginning of the second, $840(0.7) = $588 beginning the third, $588(0.7) = $411.6 the fourth, $411.6(0.7) = $288.12 beginning the fifth, and $288.12(0.7) = $201.68 at the end of the fifth.

The "straight line" and "declining balance" methods of depreciation are two common methods of depreciation estimation. Other methods are also possible. Besides the establishment of a sinking fund, depreciation estimation is necessary in the estimation of profits. Many a farmer has thought he was making a sound profit until the services of his durable inputs were depleted. Equally as important, accurate estimates of profit will indicate when further investments in durables are justified. The next section will be devoted to the theory of investment in durable inputs.

THE THEORY OF INVESTMENT IN DURABLE RESOURCES

A durable input will be purchased if the sum of the discounted revenues from its use is greater than the sum of the discounted costs incurred in its purchase. The revenues from its use are actually marginal in the sense that all other durables are held constant and revenue considered results only from additions of the durable input. These revenues must be net of all actual and imputed costs except investment costs associated with the durable input being considered. Nondurable inputs costs associated with the durable, such as gasoline and grease required by a tractor, are paid out of annual revenues and are not treated as an investment cost. Similarly, interest on investment in the durable is included in the discount rate and thus should not be subtracted from added revenue.

When durable inputs can be varied, a production function can be visualized. A production function for tractors, expressed in value terms, is presented in Table 7–6. The data in Table 7–6 represent profits added by additional tractors. For simplicity, the underlying technical production

---

[11] Let S = salvage value, P = purchase price, k = the proportion, and t = time, then $S = k^tP$. This can be solved for k using the method of footnote 4.

TABLE 7–6

HYPOTHETICAL DATA ILLUSTRATING A PRODUCTION FUNCTION FOR TRACTORS

Year	Added Number of Tractors					Discount Factor
	1	2	3	4	5	
1........	$1,500	$2,500	$3,000	$3,250	$3,375	$(1.10)^1 = 1.1$
2........	1,300	2,200	2,650	2,875	2,990	$(1.10)^2 = 1.21$
3........	1,100	1,900	2,300	2,500	2,600	$(1.10)^3 = 1.331$
4........	900	1,500	1,800	1,950	2,025	$(1.10)^4 = 1.464$
Four-Year Total...	$4,800	$8,100	$9,750	$10,575	$10,990	
MVP of trac-tors....	$4,800	$3,300	$1,650	$ 825	$ 415	

function is omitted. The first tractor earns $1,500 the first year, $1,300 the second year, $1,100 the third year, and $900 the fourth year. The fourth year's earnings also include the tractor's salvage value. (Four years are used to keep the problem small.) Two tractors earn $2,500, $2,200, $1,900, and $1,500 in the first through fourth years, consecutively. Three tractors earn $3,000 the first year, $2,650 the next, etc.

Over the four-year period, the marginal value product of the first tractor is $4,800, the second $3,300, the third $1,650, the fourth $825, and the fifth $415. But these marginal earnings do not accrue at one point in time but represent a stream over the four years. Hence they must be discounted. Assuming a discount rate of 10 percent, the discounted earnings of the tractor are presented in Table 7–7. A graph of the discounted *MVP*'s is presented in Figure 7–2.

The discounted *MVP*'s represent what the tractors will earn on the farm and are therefore called the "use" value. But all durables have three

TABLE 7–7

DATA FROM TABLE 7–6 DISCOUNTED AT A RATE OF 10 PERCENT

Year	Added Number of Tractors				
	1	2	3	4	5
1..................	$1,363.63	$2,272.72	$2,727.27	$2,954.54	$3,068.18
2..................	1,074.38	1,818.18	2,190.08	2,376.03	2,471.07
3..................	826.45	1,427.50	1,728.02	1,878.29	1,953.42
4..................	614.75	1,024.59	1,229.51	1,331.97	1,383.20
Discounted Total.....	$3,879.21	$6,542.99	$7,874.88	$8,540.83	$8,875.87
Discounted *MVP*....	$3,879.21	$2,663.78	$1,331.89	$ 665.95	$ 335.04

prices or values: the purchase price, the use value, and the salvage value.[12] Any decision regarding the optimum amount of durables must consider all three. The following rules are important: (1) If the use value exceeds the purchase price, more of the durable will be purchased. If the farmer has one tractor and new tractors cost $2,500, he will buy a second because the use value of the second, $2,663.78 (see Table 7–7), exceeds the purchase price. (2) If the use value of the durable is less than the salvage value, some of the durables will be sold. In Figure 7–2, if the farmer owns three tractors and the salvage value for tractors is $1,500, then one tractor will be sold because its sale value exceeds the present value of its future earnings. (3) If the use value of the durable exceeds the salvage value and is smaller than the purchase price, then the optimum amount of durable resource is being used and the resource should not be purchased or sold. As illustrated in Figure 7–2, if tractors

FIGURE 7–2

DISCOUNTED MARGINAL VALUE PRODUCT OF TRACTORS; TAKEN FROM TABLE 7–7

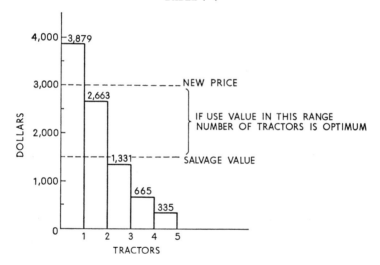

cost $3,000 new (rather than the $2,500 suggested above), have a salvage value of $1,500 and the farmer owns two, he will neither buy nor sell. He has the optimum amount. Tractors are fixed in quantity because profits cannot be increased by varying them.

The importance of the distinction between purchase costs and salvage values for durable inputs can be illustrated using short-run cost curves. In this case suppose the only "fixed" input is a machine with

[12] For nondurables, the purchase price and salvage value is identical.

salvage value lower than the purchase price. Assuming that variable costs do not change with the value of the machine, average total cost, *ATC*, will depend only upon fixed costs which in turn depend on the value placed on the machine. Fixed costs, and thus *ATC*, will be the highest when the machine is valued at the purchase price. As the machine depreciates, fixed costs and *ATC* will fall to a lower level determined by the salvage value. Therefore, in Figure 7–3, the appropriate *ATC* curve for a farmer with a newly purchased machine is marked *ATC—PURCHASE* while a farmer with a machine depreciated out to

FIGURE 7–3

EFFECTS OF VALUATION AT PURCHASE PRICE AND
SALVAGE VALUE UPON ENTERPRISE PROFIT

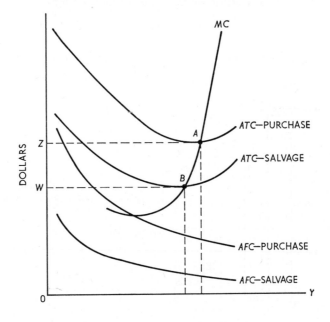

salvage value would have the total costs denoted by *ATC—SALVAGE*. *ATC* curves for other values of the machine would fall between these extremes.

As illustrated in Figure 7–3, if the product price is above *OZ*, the farmer without a machine could afford to purchase a new machine because it will earn above normal profits. If the price falls below *OW*, the farmer who owns a machine will lose money even when his machine is valued only at the salvage price, and he will sell the machine if that price persists. When the price is between *OW* and *OZ*, the farmer will neither buy nor sell the machine because he is covering costs when the machine is valued at salvage value but is not earning enough to justify purchase of another machine. From a beforehand view, when the price is less than OZ, he also is not earning enough to purchase a machine. The effects of durable inputs upon the supply of agricultural commodities will be discussed in another section. However, the effects of the above analyses on the supply of agricultural products can be seen in Figure 7–3. Once the input is purchased, the segment AB is added to the supply curve.

SIZE OF FARM IN LONG RUN

Over time the durable inputs owned by the firm wear out and can be replaced by new, usually more efficient, inputs. The manager is therefore able to vary the size of his firm and will seek the most efficient size. The collection of all durables owned by the firm is often called the "plant," and that term will be used here to signify the land, machinery, buildings, and other durables found on farms (or other businesses). An increase in any one of the durables will increase the size of the plant.

FIGURE 7–4

DERIVATION OF THE LONG-RUN AVERAGE COST

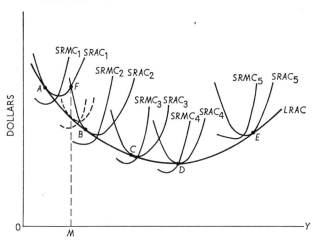

For each possible output of the firm a corresponding optimum plant size exists. This is the familiar idea that a minimum-cost combination of inputs exists for any output level. Also, a set of cost curves can be developed for each plant size. By putting these two ideas together, a long-run average cost curve, *LRAC*, can be derived.

In Figure 7–4, derivation of a long-run average cost curve is shown; $SRAC_1$ and $SRMC_1$ are the average and marginal costs for plant size 1.

(All average costs are average total costs.) $SRMC_2$ and $SRAC_2$ are the marginal and average costs for a larger plant size, plant size 2. Each plant size represents a set of durable inputs fixed at a certain level. Many plant sizes exist between 1 and 2, but to avoid clutter their cost curves are not shown. Plant size 2 produces all outputs above (to the right of) amounts $0M$ more efficiently than does plant size 1. As output increases further, plant size 3 becomes more efficient than 2, and 4 becomes more efficient than 3. For plant sizes larger than 4, added output is obtained only at increased cost per unit.

The *LRAC* is represented by a smooth curve drawn tangent to each of the *SRAC* curves. Such a curve (the *LRAC*) is called an "envelope" curve. To the left of *D* (Figure 7–4) the *LRAC* curve is tangent to short-run curves to the left of the latter's minimum. At *D*, both long-run and short-run costs attain a minimum. To the right of *D*, *LRAC* is tangent to the short-run curves to the right of the latter's minimum.

The *LRAC* depicts the minimum average cost for each output level and by so doing determines the optimum plant size. Plant size 1 is most efficient in the production of the output corresponding to *A*, plant size 2 for *B*, plant size 3 for *C*, etc. While plant size 2 is more efficient than size 1 for all amounts of output to the right of the line *FM*, there are plants which will produce the amounts between *A* and *B* more efficiently than either 1 or 2. At point *F*, a plant could be built which has a *SRAC* depicted by the dashed line. This plant would produce amount $0M$ at less cost per unit than either plant size 1 or plant size 2.

Why does *LRAC* decrease to point *D* and increase thereafter? Decreasing costs associated with size are usually attributed to technical efficiencies. Some efficient types of machines, such as self-propelled combines, cotton pickers, or sugar beet harvesters, can only be utilized on large acreages. Up to a point, rewards to management effort increase with size. A farmer with 100 cows has more incentive to learn proper management techniques than the one-cow farmer. Mastery of a given husbandry technique also has a larger payoff for the large farm. As the size of business increases, the manager may also be able to purchase inputs at a discount, thereby gaining market economies. *LRAC* are believed to increase (past *D*) because of managerial inefficiencies. Past *D* the business becomes so large that management red tape outweigh further technical or market efficiencies. Also, some technical efficiencies may turn into technical inefficiencies at extremely large sizes.

The shape of the *LRAC* curve in Figure 7–4 is by no means thought to be general. Other combinations of increasing, constant, or decreasing costs are possible; some examples are presented in Figure 7–5. Figure 7–5A depicts a constant cost situation—minimum *SRAC* is always constant and equal to *LRAC*. Plant size has no effect on efficiency. Figure 7–5B depicts an increasing cost situation. Increased output is attained

FIGURE 7–5

<small>DIFFERENT TYPES OF LONG-RUN AVERAGE COST CURVES</small>

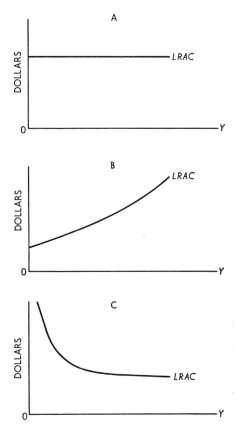

only by an increase in unit costs. The smallest sized plant is also the most efficient. The *LRAC* in Figure 7–5C represents a situation which might be typical in many businesses. *LRAC* falls rapidly as output is increased, remains constant over a wide range of output, and begins to increase at extremely high outputs, if at all. Indeed, while classic economic theory usually accepted the *LRAC* depicted in Figure 7–4 as typical—in fact, inevitable, the *LRAC* of Figure 7–5C may be more realistic for many businesses.

It is important to remember that the *LRAC* is a long-run or planning curve. Once a plant is built and production is undertaken, the firm is operating on one of the short-run curves.

Expansion Pressure When LRAC Decrease

When economies of size exist, the firm will tend to expand. In Figure 7–6, the firm operating on $SRAC_1$ will produce output $0A$ when the output price is P_1. But $0A$ can be produced at less cost by expanding the plant and operating on $SRAC_2$. Once the plant is expanded, $0C$ becomes the optimum output and further efficiencies can be gained by expanding plant size to $SRAC_3$ and so on. This process will continue until $LRAC$ and a $SRAC$ are tangent at the optimum output level. At output price P_1, this tangency can only occur if $LRAC$ eventually increases. Otherwise expansion will continue until one or perhaps a few firms supply the entire industry output.

If a firm is operating on $SRAC_2$ (which is irrational from the long-run profit maximizing viewpoint) and output price falls to P_2, perhaps because of expansion of other firms in the industry, then the firm must expand (say to $SRAC_2$) if it is to survive. Once on $SRAC_2$, the firm's

FIGURE 7–6

PRESSURE TO EXPAND WHEN DECREASING $LRAC$ EXISTS

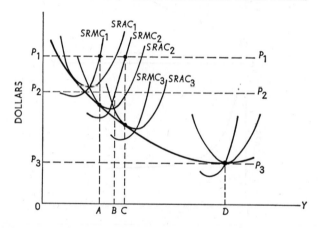

output will be $0B$, and if it wishes to maximize profits, it will again have the pressure to expand described above.

Long-run equilibrium will occur at output price P_3 when the firm's output is $0D$. At this output, profits are zero (imputed costs are paid, of course) and the firm is producing at its most efficient level. The firm has no reason to expand or contract, and new firms will not enter the industry because profits are zero.

REFERENCES

BOULDING, K. E. *Economic Analysis*, chaps. xxxv and xxxvi. Rev. ed. New York: Harper & Bros., 1948.

CARLSON, SUNE. *A Study on the Pure Theory of Production*, chap. iv. New York: Kelley and Millman, Inc., 1965.

Faris, J. E. "Analytical Techniques Used in Determining the Optimum Replacement Pattern." *Journal of Farm Economics,* November, 1960, pp. 755–66.

Heady, Earl O. *Economics of Agricultural Production and Resource Use,* chap. xiii. Englewood Cliffs, N.J.: Prentice-Hall, Inc., 1952.

Johnson, G. L. "The State of Agricultural Supply Analysis," *Journal of Farm Economics,* May, 1960, pp. 435–52.

———, and Hardin, L. S. *Economics of Forage Evaluation.* Purdue Agricultural Experiment Station Bulletin 623, April, 1955, pp. 6–12.

Vincent, Warren H. (ed.). *Economics and Management in Agriculture,* chap. vi. Englewood Cliffs, N.J.: Prentice-Hall, Inc., 1962.

Chapter 8

DECISION MAKING IN RISK AND UNCERTAINTY

Chapters 3 through 6 present an economic picture of the production process under the assumptions of perfect certainty and time-lessness. The concepts presented in these early chapters form the foundation needed for a basic understanding of the theory of the firm; however, it is clear that these basic concepts do not embody all or even most of the important characteristics of a dynamic, growing business. But, just as algebra must be mastered before higher mathematics can be attacked, so must the basic ideas of economic logic be mastered for later use.

Chapter 7 included a discussion of the problems encountered when time is introduced into the basic timeless analysis. Now, an introduction to the theory of decision making under conditions of risk and uncertainty will be presented. Again, many of the concepts developed in earlier chapters will be applied directly, but as was seen in Chapter 7, the relaxing of a key assumption usually requires some generalizations not previously called forth.

A GENERAL PICTURE

Perfect certainty, the ability to predict exactly the future outcome of present actions, does not usually exist for the manager, at least in situations of important consequence. When a farmer buys a red tractor, he knows it will stay red for some time to come. But that is at best trivial knowledge. He is far more interested in its power, its fuel consumption, and its dependability. Some of these unknown factors may be determined to a more or less certain degree, depending upon the conditions of purchase. If the tractor is new, the farmer will expect a high degree of dependability, and he will be able to determine estimates of fuel consumption and drawbar power from demonstrations, experience of neighbors, or published information. If the tractor is second hand, the farmer may have some estimate of these factors, based upon the reputation of the previous owner or seller, but will face a larger degree of uncertainty than if he had purchased a new machine.

Of the many uncertainties facing the farmer, uncertainties regarding the quality of machinery are probably relatively minor. Indeed, the dependability and efficiency of modern farm machinery is one of the reasons accounting for the rapid mechanization of farms in the last two decades. Price and yield fluctuations of major farm commodities comprise a far more important source of uncertainty.

When the dryland farmer of the Great Plains plants his winter wheat each fall, he can only speculate on the yield at the next summer's harvest. As the season passes, the degree of uncertainty surrounding the expected yield diminishes until immediately before harvest, when the farmer will be able to closely determine his expected yield. He still cannot be sure of the crop, however, because a hail storm may blow up on a moment's notice. Thus, perfect certainty of yield realization exists only after the crop is safe in storage.

Price variation creates uncertainty for hog farmers of the Corn Belt. Uncertainties arising from disease, quality of feed, hereditary characteristics of the animals, and death losses (from causes other than disease) can be controlled by the competent husbandryman, but the aggregate supply and demand factors determining the price of hogs are beyond his control. Prices may be high at the beginning of the production period and fall steadily until marketing time or they may do the reverse. Again, as the time of sale approaches, uncertainty surrounding the price to be received diminishes.

Many other examples of uncertainty may be found in agriculture. The vineyard owner in Washington faces the hazard of early frost. An asparagus crop in the same area may go unharvested or grow too large because of labor scarcity. The problem common to all of these situations is that inputs must be allocated at one point in time while returns accrue at a later date. Because the future cannot be foretold, the inputs must be allocated without perfect assurance of a particular return.

The above discussion reveals that knowledge about the future exists in different degrees. That the color of the tractor would be red was quite likely but quite unimportant. That there will be a price for hogs or a yield of wheat (even if it is zero) is certain, but the exact magnitude of that price or yield is uncertain. Thus, some classification of outcomes is apparent even for situations involving less than perfect certainty. Having dashed aside the assumption of perfect certainty, we must now replace it. As a prelude to understanding the logic developed for and applied to uncertain situations, the next section will include a short introduction to the theory of probability.

PROBABILITY

The study of probability is one of the most recently developed of the sciences and, along with economics, one of the most intriguing. The first studies of probability appeared after 1650, when the calculus of probability was applied to games of chance. Possible scientific applications were largely ignored. But as the understanding of the research process grew, scientists came to realize that perfect prediction is impossible; and as a result, probability concepts were introduced into all areas of science. Today probability has become an area of science of such importance that no scientist can afford to be without a knowledge of its fundamental concepts. Thus, while the following introduction is for later use in this chapter, the reader should recognize that probability theory has a great cultural and scientific value and can well be studied for its own sake.

The probability of an event is the relative frequency with which the event occurs over a very long sequence (large number) of observations. Suppose a poultry farmer has a 2 percent death loss annually. Then the relative frequency of death among this man's chickens is 2 from every

TABLE 8–1

Year	Chickens Purchased	Death Losses	Percent Loss	
			Annual	Total over Years
1	5,000	200	4.0	4.0
2	5,000	50	1.0	2.5
3	5,000	100	2.0	2.3
4	5,000	50	1.0	2.0
5	5,000	100	2.0	2.0

100. Therefore, at the time the chicks are purchased or hatched, the probability that a chick will die during the year is 2/100.

The death loss among chickens will vary from year to year. Some years the farmer may lose more than 2 percent, and other years less. To be interpreted as a probability, the 2 percent must be interpreted as the relative frequency over a long time period or over a large number of observations. How "long" is the time period or how "large" is the number of observations? The answer is that the number of observations must be large enough that the value of the relative frequency approaches a limit. This limiting value is then the probability of the event.

For example, suppose a poultry man raises 5,000 chickens a year for 5 years and his losses are as listed in Table 8–1. Over the 5-year period, 25,000 chickens were purchased and 500, or 2 percent, died. As the years passed, the total percentage loss approached and eventually equaled 2 percent. Suppose that the death loss in year 6 equaled that of year 1, 200 chickens, then the average death loss over the six-year period would be 2.3 percent as compared to 4 percent for year 1. An increase in the time period (the number of observations) diminishes the effect of a deviation of given magnitude upon the long-time average loss. As the number of observations increases to very large numbers, the annual deviations in the cumulate loss percentage become so small that for all practical purposes it becomes stabilized at 2 percent. In this sense, 2 percent becomes the limiting value of the relative frequencies and is called a probability.

Note that the number of observations and not the length of time is relevant for the determination of a probability. A farmer may raise a sufficient number of chickens in one production period to establish a stable death loss value. When the number of observations in each time period are too small to establish the stable or limiting value, observations over time must be considered.

Observations must be taken under identical conditions. A change in management technique could effect the death loss and the limiting value of the relative frequency. Consequently the probability of an event can only be determined experimentally, and in each case the conditions under which the experiment is to be conducted must be suitably defined. Consider flipping a coin which on one side is labeled heads and the other side tails. The coin is flipped a suitable height in the air, rotating on its axis at an adequate speed, and lands on a suitable surface such that it cannot be lost. Counts could be taken of the number of times the head faces up, the tail faces up, or the coin stands on edge. Theoretically, the experiment could be repeated (coin flipped) until the three probabilities were estimated as accurately as desired. In practice, the coin would eventually begin to wear and thus change the conditions of the experiment. Other experiments with the same coin could be considered by changing the manner of flipping or the surface on which the coin falls. A change in these factors could change the probability of the events.

Some Properties of Probability

The following properties of probabilities are important:

1. A probability must always be between zero and one, inclusive.
2. The sum of the probabilities of all possible outcomes of an experiment must be one.
3. If $P[A]$ is the probability an event will occur, the probability it will not occur is $1 - P[A]$ ·
4. When two events, A and B, are mutually exclusive, the probability that one *or* the other will occur is given by $P[A \text{ or } B] = P[A] + P[B]$ ·
5. When two events, A and B, are independent, the probability that A *and* B will occur is given by $P[A \text{ and } B] = P[A]P[B]$ ·

Probability Distributions. Using the rules of probability outlined above, the probability of various combinations of events can be determined. These probabilities can, in turn, eventually be used as an aid in decision making. As mentioned earlier, this type of analysis was first applied to games of chance. Because such games are familiar to most students, they will be used here to introduce the concept of a probability distribution.

In games of chance, such as flipping coins, rolling dice, or drawing cards, equal probabilities are commonly assigned to all simple events. When flipping a coin, two events are possible. Assuming these to be equally likely results in a probability of one half being assigned to each possible occurrence—heads and tails. When rolling a die—a cube with sides labeled 1 to 6—the assumption of equally likely outcomes results in the probability of each number being equal to 1/6, i.e., $P[1] = P[2] = P[3] = P[4] = P[5] = P[6] = 1/6$. In similar fashion, if equal probabilities are associated with drawing cards from a deck of 52 cards, then the probability of any one card on a single draw is 1/52. In general when n mutually exclusive events are assumed to be equally likely, then the probability of occurrence of any one event is $1/n$.

Once the frequency of occurrence of all possible events (outcomes) is determined, a probability distribution can be defined. Consider a coin-tossing experiment involving a fair coin flipped in such a way that only heads or tails are possible. When the coin is flipped, the probability is 1 that something will happen. This "total" probability has to be divided among the expected outcomes. When the coin is fair, the two outcomes are equally likely and equal to one half. The probability distribution for this simple experiment is:

Outcome	Probability of Occurrence
Heads...............	$\frac{1}{2}$
Tails...............	$\frac{1}{2}$

Thus a probability distribution assigns a probability to each possible outcome of the experiment. The probability distribution can be presented in tabular form, on a graph, or as a mathematical equation.

By regarding the outcome variable of the experiment as the number of heads occurring, the probability distribution for the coin experiment can be graphed. Thus, $P[\text{tail}] = P[0 \text{ heads}]$, $P[\text{head}] = P[1 \text{ head}]$, and the outcomes can be placed on a numerical scale (Figure 8–1A).[1]

---

[1] The graph of a probability distribution to be used here is the common bar graph or histogram. The usual procedure for graphing a probability distribution is to make each bar one unit wide with height equal to the value of the probability. Thus, the area of the bar also represents the probability of occurrence. For zero heads, the bar is centered over zero and is one half a unit high; for one head, the bar is centered on one and is again one half a unit high. The same scale need not be used on both axes.

FIGURE 8–1

GRAPH OF PROBABILITY DISTRIBUTIONS FOR FAIR COINS

A. PROBABILITY DISTRIBUTION FOR ONE
   FAIR COIN

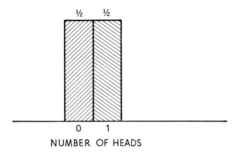

NUMBER OF HEADS

B. PROBABILITY DISTRIBUTION FOR TWO
   FAIR COINS

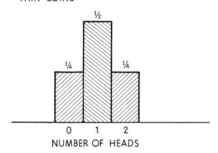

NUMBER OF HEADS

A more interesting probability distribution is derived by considering the number of heads occurring in two flips of a balanced coin. Now,
zero, one, or two heads can occur. The following cases will be studied in
detail to illustrate the use of the rules of probability presented above: T_1
indicates a tail on the first flip and T_2 a tail on the second flip; H_1 and H_2
are defined similarly for heads. The three following cases arise:

> *Zero Heads*—The probability of no heads is the same as the probability
> of two tails. Because the trials are independent, $P[T_1$ and $T_2] =
> P[T_1]P[T_2]$. Thus $P[0$ heads$] = P[T_1]P[T_2] = ½ · ½ = ¼$. From this
> it can be determined that the probability of *at least* one head must
> be ¾.
>
> *One Head*—To obtain exactly one head in two independent trials, the
> head must occur on the first or the second trial but not on both. Be-
> cause the trials are independent, the two possibilities are $P[H_1$ and
> $T_2] = P[H_1]P[T_2] = ½ · ½ = ¼$, $P[T_1$ and $H_2] = P[T_1]P[H_2] = ½ ·
> ½ = ¼$. But these two possibilities are mutually exclusive, if one oc-

curs the other cannot. Therefore $P[1 \text{ head}] = P[H_1 \text{ and } T_2] + P[T_1 \text{ and } H_2] = \frac{1}{4} + \frac{1}{4} = \frac{1}{2}$.

Two Heads—The probability of two heads on two independent trials is $P[H_1 \text{ and } H_2] = P[H_1]P[H_2] = \frac{1}{4}$.

The probability distribution for the experiment consisting of flipping a balanced coin twice is given by:

Outcome	Probability
Zero heads............	$\frac{1}{4}$
One head............	$\frac{1}{2}$
Two heads............	$\frac{1}{4}$

The distribution is graphed in Figure 8–1B.

As a final example of a probability distribution resulting from games of chance, the simultaneous rolling of a pair of fair dice will be considered. (The probability distribution of each die should be clear; it will consist of six bars each $\frac{1}{6}$ of a unit high, one unit wide, and centered over the numbers 1, 2, 3, 4, 5, 6.) The outcomes to be considered are the sum of the digits on the surfaces facing upward after the dice come to rest. The probability distribution for this experiment is:

Sum of Dice	Probability
2............	$\frac{1}{36}$
3............	$\frac{2}{36}$
4............	$\frac{3}{36}$
5............	$\frac{4}{36}$
6............	$\frac{5}{36}$
7............	$\frac{6}{36}$
8............	$\frac{5}{36}$
9............	$\frac{4}{36}$
10............	$\frac{3}{36}$
11............	$\frac{2}{36}$
12............	$\frac{1}{36}$

A graph of this distribution is presented in Figure 8–2. Examples of the method of computing the probabilities of each sum are:

Sum $= 2$—This can happen only if a 1 occurs on each die. Because the dice are independent,

$$P[2] = P[1 \text{ and } 1] = P[1]P[1] = \frac{1}{6} \cdot \frac{1}{6} = \frac{1}{36} .$$

Sum $= 3$—This can happen by getting either a 2 with the first die (2_1) and a 1 with the second die (1_2), or vice versa. Because the outcome of one die is independent of the outcome of the other,

$$P[2_1 \text{ and } 1_2] = \frac{1}{6} \cdot \frac{1}{6} = \frac{1}{36}$$

and

$$P[1_1 \text{ and } 2_2] = \frac{1}{6} \cdot \frac{1}{6} = \frac{1}{36} .$$

But because the sum of 3 can occur either of the two mutually exclusive ways,

$$P[3] = P[1_1 \text{ and } 2_2] = P[2_1 \text{ and } 1_2] = \tfrac{1}{6} \cdot \tfrac{1}{6} + \tfrac{1}{6} \cdot \tfrac{1}{6} = \tfrac{2}{36} \cdot$$

FIGURE 8–2

GRAPH OF A PROBABILITY DISTRIBUTION FOR TWO BALANCED DICE

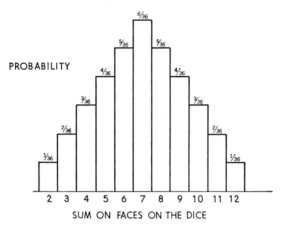

Random Variables Defined. A random variable is a phenomenon which when observed repeatedly under similar circumstances does not always take the same value but rather assumes any of a number of values, each with a definite probability. The number of heads (tails) occurring when a coin is flipped is a random variable. The sum of two dice represents a random variable.

Other more important phenomena are also random variables. Some climatological factors, such as rainfall, may be regarded as random variables. Crop yields closely associated with rainfall are also random variables. Death losses or egg breakage can be viewed as random variables. Indeed, many of the everyday phenomena can be regarded as random variables.

Continuous Probability Distribution. Random variables can be classified as discrete or continuous. The analogy is identical to that of discrete or continuous inputs (see the Appendix, page 535). A random variable is called discrete if it can assume only a countable number of values, that is, a particular number of values that are separated from one another. The number of heads occurring when coins are flipped or the sum of numbers on the upward faces of dice are discrete random variables. Discrete random variables often assume the integer values, i.e., 0, 1, 2, 3, 4, ..., etc. They are often associated with counts, such as the number of chicks hatched or the number of calves born.

Continuous random variables can assume all values of a continuous scale. Continuous random variables are usually associated with measurements, such as weight, time, length, yield, etc. A corn yield can be 80.0 bushels per acre or 80.1 bushels per acre. A temperature reading might be 65.1 degrees or 87.7 degrees or any value on the scale. The accuracy of measurement (number of decimals) of the continuous variable depends upon the preciseness of the measuring instrument. Crop yields or animal weights could be determined to 10 decimal places if desired.

Just as bar graphs, or histograms, can be used to depict graphically the probability distribution of a discrete random variable, a smooth curve can be used to depict the probability distribution of a continuous random variable. The histogram is drawn so that each bar is one unit wide and with a height equal to the probability. The area of each bar is therefore equal to the probability that the discrete random variable will take that value. The sum of the areas of all bars is one.

In a like manner, the area under the continuous probability distribution is equal to one and the probability that the random variable will take on a value between any two numbers is equal to the area under the curve between the two numbers.

Figure 8–3 presents graphs of probability functions for a discrete and a continuous random variable. The discrete random variable can take only the values 0, 1, 2, 3, 4, 5, or 6 while the continuous variable can assume any of the infinite number of values between −2 and 11.

Expected Values. As important as probabilities are, they are used to derive an equally important concept—that of the long-run expected average or, more simply, the expected value. If a random variable may take on the mutually exclusive values $X_1, X_2, X_3, \ldots, X_n$ with probabilities $P_1, P_2, P_3, \ldots, P_n$, respectively, then the expected value of the random variable, $E(X)$, is

$$E(X) = X_1 P_1 + X_2 P_2 + X_3 P_3 + \ldots + X_n P_n$$

Suppose a balanced coin is flipped and you win a dollar if a head occurs and lose a $0.50 if a tail occurs. Then the random variable is the amount you win or lose and

$$X_1 = \$1.00 \qquad P_1 = \tfrac{1}{2}$$
$$X_2 = -\$0.50 \qquad P_2 = \tfrac{1}{2}$$

so that $E(X) = \$1.00(1/2) + (-\$0.50)1/2 = \$0.25$.

This means that you would expect to win in the long run $0.25 each time you played the "game." The interpretation of the expected value is important. Each time you will either win one dollar or lose 50 cents— there is no possible way you can win 25 cents from a single game. But the expected values says that if you play the "game" a large number of times then when you divide total winnings by the number of games played,

FIGURE 8-3

GRAPHS OF PROBABILITY DISTRIBUTIONS

A. PROBABILITY DISTRIBUTION FOR A DISCRETE
   RANDOM VARIABLE

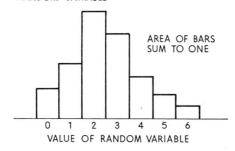

B. APPROXIMATION OF A DISCRETE DISTRIBUTION
   BY A CONTINUOUS DISTRIBUTION

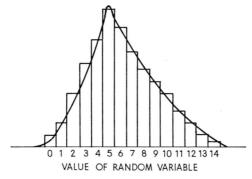

C. PROBABILITY DISTRIBUTION FOR A CONTINUOUS
   RANDOM VARIABLE

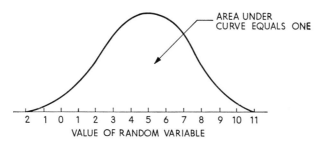

you will expect to find that you have won an average of 25 cents per
"game." A "game" is called "fair" if each participant's expected winnings
are zero.

The second thing to remember about the expected value is that
regardless of what you expect to win, each time you play the game a

finite number of times, say n times, you can win as much as n dollars or lose as much as $n/2$ dollars. If you played the above game 10 times in a row, you could win $10 or lose $5. Because heads and tails are equally likely and independent, the probability of these two extreme values is identical and equal to $(1/2)^{10} = 1/1024$.

A second example of the expected value of a game of chance can be illustrated by the following game. Suppose a fair die is rolled and you pay your opponent the face value of the die (in dollars) if the outcome is even while he pays you the face value of an odd outcome. Then your expected winnings are

$$E(X) = \$1(\tfrac{1}{6}) - \$2(\tfrac{1}{6}) + \$3(\tfrac{1}{6}) - \$4(\tfrac{1}{6}) + \$5(\tfrac{1}{6}) - \$6(\tfrac{1}{6}) = -\$0.50.$$

Expected values have more important uses. Suppose an insurance company annually insures against loss by fire 10,000 barns valued at $5,000 each. If the probability that a barn will burn is 1/100, then the company can expect $10,000 (1/100) = 100$ barns to burn each year, and can expect to pay $500,000 in claims each year. This is an average of $50 for each of the 10,000 farmers. If the overhead costs of insuring a barn are $20, then the company can charge $70 to insure each barn for $5,000 damages. In essence, the insurance company is "playing" the following "game" with each farmer: You give me $70 and I will give you $5,000 if your barn burns this year. The company's expected earning from this contract is $E(X) = \$70 \ (99/100) - \$4,930 \ (1/100) = \$20$. The company, of course, plays the game 10,000 times while each farmer plays but once.

Because the incidence of fires may be greater some years than others, insurance companies are required to maintain reserves. In general, however, the companies try to stabilize earnings at or near expected earnings by increasing in size, i.e., increasing the number of customers until the probability of barns burning among their customers becomes very stable from year to year. The success of this procedure is attested to by the large number of prosperous insurance companies existing in the United States today.

RISK

Risk and Uncertainty Defined

The lack or absence of perfect certainty can be broken down into two subclasses: risk and uncertainty. These were defined in the classic work of Frank H. Knight, listed in the bibliography of this chapter.

A manager is faced with a risk situation when he knows the possible future outcomes that could occur in a management situation and the probability associated with each outcome. When an input, output, or price is a random variable, the manager is faced with a risk situation.

Uncertainty exists when the probability of a future outcome is unknown. Two subclasses are possible here. First, the possible outcomes of a situation may be known but the relative frequency of these outcomes unknown. Or, even the possible outcomes are unknown—thus ruling out any possibility that relative frequencies could be determined.[2]

Random Variables in Agriculture

The most striking examples of random variables in agriculture are those associated with the weather. Many agricultural production processes involve some random weather inputs. In these cases, yields resulting from random weather inputs are also random variables. And because income depends upon yield, income becomes a random variable. For example, in the wheat-growing areas of the Great Plains, rainfall, the limiting input, is a random variable, and wheat yields and net farm income, which are largely dependent upon rainfall, are also random variables. Thus, the Great Plains wheat farmer certainly faces a risk situation. In general, any farm operation depending in part or wholly upon rainfall for crop growth is a risk situation. But the variability of rainfall affects the degree of risk in different areas of a country.

Other meteorological inputs are random variables. Hail and wind occurring during critical harvesting periods represent random variables. The number of workdays available for routine tasks such as plowing, planting, and cultivating are random variables. These random "inputs" can be associated not only with rainfall but humidity, sunshine, wind, or temperature.

Many risk situations also exist in livestock production. Death losses were used earlier in the chapter to illustrate probability; in most cases of livestock and poultry production, normal death losses can be classified as risk situations. Egg breakage represents another risk. The large producer knows that a percentage of his eggs will be broken each day and adds this breakage to costs (or discounts it from revenue).

When is an event to be regarded as a risk rather than uncertainty? The definitions of risk and uncertainty should resolve that question, but consideration of some borderline cases is useful.

1. The flooding of a river-bottom farm: If the river floods fre-

---

[2] Recent writers in the area of uncertainty have reworked the definitions of risk and uncertainty given here, arguing that decisions *must* be made in uncertain situations even if the decision maker has only subjective information about outcomes and related probability distributions. Thus, the distinction between conceptual models used to analyze rational decision making under risk and uncertainty is not as abrupt as suggested by Knight's analysis. For example, see the book by Fellner, listed in the bibliography, chap. ii. The modern approach rests heavily on the existence of a utility function, as originally derived by von Neumann and Morgenstern (see Chernoff and Moses, chap. iv, also listed in the bibliography). While these more recent advances cannot be neglected by professional economists, the classification of Knight is sufficient for the introductory material presented here.

quently and if the farmer is aware of the relative frequency of these floods, such as once in every five years, then flooding represents a risk. The farmer can discount expected earnings in accordance with the expected flood frequency. If after such discounting, expected profit is negative, the farmer shouldn't buy it. On the other hand, if flooding is unheard of in a particular region, then the occurrence of a flood represents an uncertainty.

In the latter case, one might argue that flooding is a risk because the valley floods perhaps once every 2,000 years. The only answer is that the farmer and other qualified observers have no knowledge of such a probability and therefore cannot prepare for it.

2. The death of a prize bull: If the farmer has but one prize bull and takes extra precautions with him, his death would represent an uncertainty. While over a hundred-year span, he might well expect to lose one or two prize bulls, man's planning horizon is not that long—and for good reason. In the same way, death losses due to unknown or unpreventable diseases constitute an uncertainty. An epidemic could not be anticipated by the good husbandryman, so that certainly an annual repetition would not be expected.

Production Processes with Random Inputs

Agricultural production processes involve inputs controlled by the manager as well as inputs that are beyond the control of the manager. The "uncontrollable" inputs may be random variables, such as those "controlled" by nature, or they may be inputs controlled by government agencies or economic forces beyond the farm.

Uncontrollable inputs which are not random variables are prevalent and important in agriculture. Indeed, the last two major portions of this text, dealing with marketing and farm policy, consider in detail some "inputs" of this nature. Government regulations on the use of antibiotics in cattle feeding, sprays for insect and weed control, etc., are typical examples. Other factors, such as the type, quality and size of farm machinery, are determined by aggregate forces beyond the farmer's control. The farmer who prefers to bind, shock, and thresh his oats will find that the economic system has passed him by. Prices of inputs and outputs are determined by supply and demand factors far from the farm. Farm labor shortages can be created by industrial development, war, or immigration laws regulating the entry of aliens into the United States. As mentioned, these important subjects will be discussed in later chapters. Attention now is turned toward another type of important uncontrollable input—inputs that are random variables.

Assume for purposes of the following discussion that the production process being considered has two inputs, one controlled and one a random variable. The principles presented can easily be generalized to more variables. The time period considered is such that both inputs are variable. Two important cases must be distinguished.

First, the controlled and random variables may interact in the production process. "Interaction" means that the production response to one input depends upon amount of the second input used in the production process. For example, in most areas of the United States, rainfall and nitrogen fertilizer interact in corn production. The yield response to nitrogen increases as rainfall amounts increase. In livestock feeding, feed additives can interact with basic rations to increase weight response— neither of these are random inputs, indicating that interaction is possible among either of the two types of inputs.

Figure 8–4A represents a hypothetical production response resulting from interaction between the random and controlled inputs. The

FIGURE 8–4

INTERACTION OF CONTROLLED AND RANDOM INPUTS; R_1, R_2, AND R_3
REPRESENT THREE LEVELS OF THE RANDOM INPUT

A. INTERACTION PRESENT

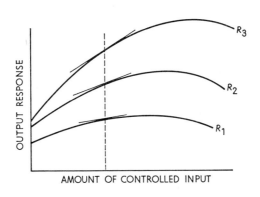

B. NO INTERACTION

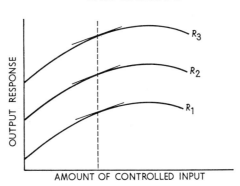

three production functions illustrate response to the controlled input at three levels of the random input. In the presence of interaction, a change in the random input changes not only the amount of yield resulting from a given amount of the controlled input but also the marginal product or slope of the production function.

When the random and controlled inputs do not interact, production *response* to the controlled input is the same regardless of the amount of the random input—total product of the controlled input will vary but marginal product will not. Figure 8–4B depicts production response when the inputs do not interact. In this case the total production increases as the random input increases but the slope of the production function, measuring the marginal product of the controlled input, does not change.

Random and Controlled Inputs Do Not Interact. In the absence of interaction the controlled input can be set at its optimum amount and output becomes dependent upon the random input (assuming, as above, that only two inputs are involved). Because the marginal product of the controlled input is invariant to changes in the random input, the optimum amount of the controlled input is also invariant. The manager would be irrational not to use the usual profit maximizing criterion.

The random input may affect profit by changing revenues, costs, or both. Favorable rainfall for wheat production would increase yields and revenues but also harvesting, storage, and marketing costs. Hail would decrease revenue, leave production costs unchanged, and reduce storage and marketing costs. When increasing amounts of the random input create a need for preventive measures, such as increasing the height of a levee during a flood or maintaining smudge pots during a freeze, costs may increase while revenues stay constant.

Cost and revenue functions for the random input are combined in Figure 8–5A; the functions could assume other shapes. In Figure 8–5A, L and U represent the limits of the random input within which a profit is realized. Outside of these break-even points, profit is negative.

If a controlled input were being discussed, the information depicted in Figure 8–5A would be sufficient—the manager would apply that amount of input which maximizes profit. But the input is random, therefore the information in Figure 8–5A cannot stand alone—the probability distribution of the random input must be known. The graphs in Figure 8–5B and 8–5C represent two possible probability distributions. In Figure 8–5B, almost 100 percent of the area under the probability distribution falls outside the break-even points, L and U; when combined with the cost and revenue functions in Figure 8–5A, this distribution suggests that the manager can expect to lose money most of the time. If the random inputs were distributed as in Figure 8–5C, then the manager could expect a profit almost 100 percent of the time.

FIGURE 8–5

COST AND REVENUE FUNCTIONS AND PROBABILITY DISTRIBUTIONS FOR A RANDOM
INPUT (OPTIMUM AMOUNT OF CONTROLLED INPUT USED—NO INTERACTION)

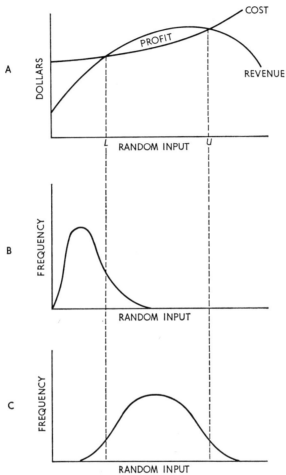

When costs, revenues, and the probability distribution are known, expected profits, $E(P)$, from the farm enterprise can be computed using methods analogous to those described above in the section on probability. When $E(P) \geq 0$, then the enterprise is profitable over time. When $E(P) < 0$, it is unprofitable.

The revenue and cost functions in Figure 8–5A result from the use of specified technologies in the production process—in corn production, the variety used represents such a technological choice. When several technologies result in an $E(P) \geq 0$, the manager will select the technology which yields the maximum $E(P)$. Thus, the corn grower selects the hybrid that performs best on his farm.

When $E(P) < 0$, the enterprise is unprofitable over time. The manager must either make a change in technology or abandon the enterprise. A change in technology could (1) spread the break-even points L and U (Figure 8–5A) and thereby increase profits, the probability of a profit, and $E(P)$; and (2) increase the magnitude of profits when they do occur in such a way that $E(P)$ increases even when the probability of a profit stays the same or even is reduced. Another technological change may change the timing of the operation so that it is no longer dependent upon the random input in question. Farmers in Alberta, Canada, mow and windrow wheat because standing wheat usually does not ripen adequately during the cool Alberta summers. Finally, an enterprise may be made completely independent of the random input. Irrigation relieves the farmer's dependence upon rainfall in many areas of the United States.

In summary, the following procedure is followed when the random and controlled inputs do not interact for a given enterprise:

1. Use the optimum amount of the controlled input as determined by usual marginal criteria.
2. Identify the random input and determine cost and revenue functions resulting from its occurrence.
3. Determine the probability distribution of the random input.
4. Select and use that combination of technologies which results in a maximum $E(P)$ for the enterprise.
5. If $E(P) < 0$ for the best possible combination of technologies, abandon the enterprise.

When several enterprises yield an $E(P) > 0$, the manager will select that enterprise with the largest $E(P)$.

Random and Controlled Inputs Interact. In this case, the marginal product of the controlled input depends upon the magnitude of the random input; thus, the optimum amount of the controlled input also becomes a random variable. The manager faces the classic dilemma of using too little of the controlled input and foregoing a profit some years or of using too much of the controlled input and incurring a loss other years.

For example, consider the production functions and marginal value product curves in Figure 8–6. If the manager uses $0A$ amount of input and a wet year occurs, his yield, $0D$, is about half of what it would have been, $0F$, had he used $0C$ amount of input. This is a loss in the real sense of the word—even though the extra income was never physically possessed, it was possessed in the sense that it was attainable with appropriate managerial judgment. On the other hand, if the manager uses $0C$ of

FIGURE 8–6

A MANAGERIAL DILEMMA CAUSED BY DRY, NORMAL, AND WET YEARS

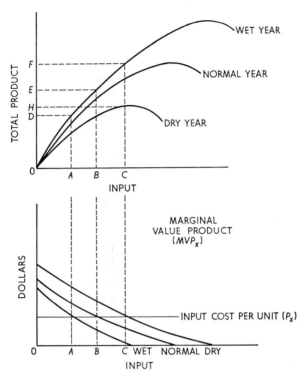

the input and a dry year occurs, $0H$ amount of output results and he suffers a loss by exceeding the optimum, $0A$ amount of input. This loss is an actual out-of-pocket loss (compare the area under the cost line, P_x, to the area under the MVP_x for the dry season).

This problem can be solved by determining the break-even points and $E(P)$ for each possible amount of the controlled input.[3] Assuming that the best level of technology is chosen for each amount of controlled input, the manager then picks the level of the controlled input which maximizes $E(P)$. An example of such a solution is presented in Figure 8–7.

In Figure 8–7A, the controlled input is utilized at the first "unit" and a loss is incurred regardless of the occurrence of the random input. Figure 8–7B and 8–7C are drawn to represent situations where the

[3] Assuming the controlled input takes on or is assigned only a finite number of values. This assumption, probably adequate for most empirical applications, would not be needed if the principles of calculus could be used.

FIGURE 8-7

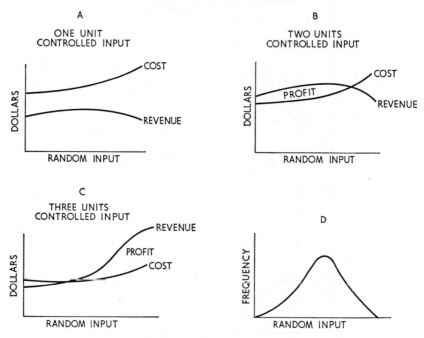

probability of a profit is maximized when two units of the controlled input are used and $E(P)$ is maximized when three units are used (given a probability distribution for the random-input as shown in Figure 8-7D). Thus, if the manager can afford but one unit of the controlled input, perhaps due to capital limitation, he should not undertake production. If, as discussed in the next section, he wants to maximize the probability of a profit, he should use two units. In the long run, profits will be maximized by using three units of controlled input. Of course, results could differ from this example and will, in actual applications, depend on the production function and the probability distribution.

In summary, when the random and controlled input interact for a given enterprise:

1. Identify the random input and determine its probability distribution.
2. Using that level of technology which maximizes $E(P)$ for each amount of controlled input, determine, for each level of the controlled input, costs and revenues resulting from the random input.
3. Select the amount of the controlled input that maximizes $E(P)$.
4. If the maximum $E(P)$ selected in 3 is less than zero, abandon the enterprise.

When several enterprises yield an $E(P) > 0$, the manager will select the enterprise with the largest $E(P)$.

Why Managers Do Not Maximize $E(P)$. Do business managers in general, or farmers in particular, maximize expected profits? The answer to this question is not known, at least to the authors. It is probably true, however, that many farmers do not, and for at least two good reasons.

First, managers may not be aware of the relevant probability distributions, even for common random inputs. In agriculture, very little research has been devoted to determining the frequency of occurrence of important random inputs. In the past, such determinations have been left to applied farm management specialists who have developed rules of thumb or ignored the problem by relying on "long-time" average prices, yields, labor requirements, etc. Without knowledge of the relevant probability distributions, the manager is placed in the situation defined as uncertainty. In many instances, farmers are left to learn by experience, and much of what is classified as management "experience" in farming is in part a result of being a farmer long enough to evaluate subjectively the probability distributions associated with important random inputs.

That farmers do this there is little doubt. Oranges are not a common crop in Minnesota; coffee beans are not produced in Montana. Less dramatic examples also exist, such as the gradual shift from corn to milo to winter and spring wheat as one travels west out of the Corn Belt. Much of the uncertainty faced by farmers could undoubtedly be changed to risk by appropriate investigations of the important random inputs found on farms. Until this is done, only farmers with unusual managerial insights coupled with long experience will be able to maximize $E(P)$; other farmers will continue to operate in a state of increased uncertainty and decreased efficiency.

Limited capital is the second reason why many farmers do not maximize $E(P)$. An unlimited amount of money would be needed to realize the expected earnings in a game of chance; no matter how large a player's stock of money might be, there always exists theoretically a long enough losing streak to wipe him out. The same thing is true for the farm manager. While he will never have or need an unlimited amount of capital because he will at most play the "game" a finite number of times, he must have enough to survive a possible run of bad luck. When the manager does not have sufficient capital to survive the most probable turn of events, he may choose to adjust his production procedure to maximize some criterion other than $E(P)$.

The basic problem, then, is that even though the manager knows a production plan will maximize profits in the long run, he may hesitate to follow this plan in the short run because he fears his business may not survive to realize the promised long-run profits. In the short run, the manager may act to maximize the probability of firm survival. Suppose a manager has the following two possible production alternatives:

I		II	
Profit	*Probability*	*Profit*	*Probability*
$ 0	¼	−$1,200	⅓
1,000	½	− 300	⅓
2,000	¼	9,000	⅓

Expected profits are:

Alternative I: $E(P) = \$0(¼) + \$1,000(½) + \$2,000(¼) = \$1,000$
Alternative II: $E(P) = -\$1,200(⅓) - \$300(⅓) + \$9,000(⅓) = \$2,500$

If the manager needs $1,000 to survive, he may choose I. If he is not concerned with short-run survival, II will result in the most profit over time. Choosing either of these alternatives could be rational depending on the manager's capital reserve and goals. How large a reserve would a manager need to forsake I for II? That depends on the manager and his willingness to take a chance.

Notice that in the short run when the manager does not know the outcome of the production process, he still is faced with an inherently different situation than in uncertainty. In uncertainty, the manager has no idea of the probability of the possible outcomes. In the short run, when the probability distribution is known, the manager knows the probability with which each outcome will occur although he doesn't know which will occur.

This discussion may be summarized by saying that the manager evidently holds something more dear than money. In certain situations, such as when sufficient capital is available, the manager will maximize $E(P)$ because by so doing he also maximizes this something else, whatever it is, or because by maximizing $E(P)$ he at least doesn't prevent the maximization of this something else. What is this underlying something else? A short discussion of goals was included in Chapter 2; a more complete presentation is beyond the scope of this book—the bibliography at the end of this chapter will provide a starting point for interested readers.

An Application to Agriculture—a Risk Situation

Commercial fertilizers have become an increasingly important input in American agriculture. Chapter 4 contained an application demonstrating how optimum rates of fertilization should be determined when the production function is known with perfect certainty. In practice, of course, production response to fertilizer is not known with certainty. An application will now be presented to demonstrate the use of production functions and probability distributions to determine the expected earnings from the use of commercial fertilizer.[4]

Two experiments were set up in Tennessee to determine the response of pearl millet to nitrogen under irrigated conditions. For one experiment, five rates of nitrogen applications ranged from 0 to 240 pounds per acre. Four "levels" of irrigation were used, i.e., irrigation water was applied in the appropriate amounts and at the proper times to maintain soil-moisture levels in each set of plots at four predetermined saturation levels. The second experiment was similar but used four rates of nitrogen and three levels of irrigation.

The unit used to measure the effects of weather on plant growth during the growing season was called a "drouth day." Computation of a drouth day is explained in detail in the reference cited; it is sufficient here to define a drouth day as a day during the growing season when the plant is unable to obtain moisture from the soil. The use of the drouth day as a measure of moisture enables the researcher to consider the water-holding capacity of the soil, the contribution of rainfall and irrigation to soil moisture, the drying effects of sunlight, temperature, and other climatic factors affecting plant growth. The number of drouth days increases with the severity of drouth during the growing season.

The results of the experiments were used to determine the response of pearl millet yields to nitrogen and drouth days. The researchers were able to obtain an estimate of a production function with two variable inputs, similar in nature to those described in Chapter 5.[5] Using this production function, they derived yield isoquants for millet (Figure 8–8). Notice that as the number of drouth days increase, the isoquants become more steeply sloped, particularly at high nitrogen levels. Thus, for any given level of nitrogen (on any horizontal line), the marginal product of nitrogen decreases as the number of drouth days increase.

One objective of the research was to determine the most profitable amount of nitrogen to use on pearl millet, given that the production function could not be predicted with perfect certainty. This problem could be approached by conducting the experiment with variable nitrogen applications at the same location for many years. The data from these experiments could then be analyzed to determine the nitrogen rate most profitable in the long run. However, by using irrigation, the re-

---

[4] The research results presented below are taken from J. L. Knetsch and W. L. Parks, *Interpreting Results of Irrigation Experiments—A Progress Report*, TVA Report No. T-59-1 AE, Knoxville, Tennessee, August, 1958.

[5] The production function presented by Knetsch and Parks is given by $Y = 3.07 + 0.1506N + 0.0010D - 0.0023N^2 - 0.0007D^2 - 0.0005ND$, where Y is the estimated yield of forage in tons, N is 10-pound units of nitrogen, and D is the number of drouth days in the June–September growing period. The production function is not presented in graphs or tables here due to space limitations. From a theoretical standpoint, it is similar to those presented in Chapter 5.

FIGURE 8–8

YIELD ISOQUANTS SHOWING COMBINATIONS OF NITROGEN AND DROUTH DAYS
NEEDED TO PRODUCE SPECIFIED YIELDS OF PEARL MILLET

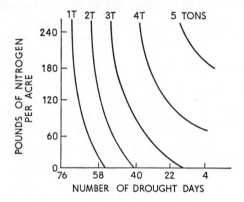

searchers were able in only one year to simulate yield response under many different moisture conditions. The data from the experiment were used to determine yield response to a wide range of nitrogen rates and drouth days while rainfall and other meteorological data collected by the United States Weather Bureau were used to estimate the number of drouth days per season for as many years back in time as the researchers deemed relevant. Thus, all the data needed to determine the expected profit from nitrogen fertilizer were available: (1) a probability distribution of drouth days, based on historical climatological data, and (2) a production function relating millet yield to nitrogen—the controlled input—and drouth days—the random weather input. The results of their analysis are presented in Table 8–2.

For purposes of the analysis, the drouth days occurring at the experimental location (Ashwood, Tennessee) for the period 1927–56 were classified under six headings: 19, 29, 38, 47, 56, and 73 drouth days. This classification provided enough different growing seasons to be meaningful yet simplified the analysis. The drouth classifications were further selected so that they occurred with equal probability, ⅙.

From Table 8–2, it can be seen that none of the nitrogen applications return a profit at the high drouth level, 73 days, but as much as $20 per acre additional profit can be returned by nitrogen application at the low drouth level, 19 days. The probability of a profit is the same for all nitrogen amounts, but the probability of a loss is ⅙ when nitrogen is used and zero when nitrogen is not used.

The expected profits from each amount of nitrogen, computed as explained earlier in this chapter, are presented in the right-hand column of Table 8–2. The nitrogen rates 150 and 180 pounds per acre yield the

TABLE 8–2

ESTIMATED RETURNS PER ACRE ABOVE FERTILIZER COSTS FOR NITROGEN APPLIED
TO MILLET AT ASHWOOD, TENNESSEE*

Nitrogen Lbs./A.	Number of Drouth Days†						Expected Profit
	73	56	47	38	29	19	
0	$ 0	$23.34	$39.34	$52.50	$62.83	$70.98	$41.50
30	−5.96	26.06	42.40	55.90	66.56	75.09	43.34
60	−9.48	29.74	46.42	60.26	71.26	80.16	46.39
90	−7.46	32.39	49.40	63.58	74.92	84.19	49.50
120	−6.44	34.00	51.35	65.86	77.54	87.19	51.58
150	−6.56	34.58	52.27	67.12	79.13	89.16	52.62
180	−7.65	34.12	52.15	67.34	79.69	90.09	52.62
210	−9.78	32.63	50.99	66.52	79.21	89.98	51.59
240	−12.95	30.10	48.80	64.66	77.69	88.84	49.52

* Assumed prices are forage $25 per ton, nitrogen $0.132 per pound, and an application rate of $2 per acre was charged.
† The drouth days were classified so that each occurs with equal probability, ⅙.
SOURCE: J. L. Knetsch and W. L. Parks, *Interpreting Results of Irrigation Experiments—A Progress Report*, TVA Report No. T-59-1 AE, Knoxville, Tennessee, August, 1958.

same expected profit, about $12 per acre more than would result if no nitrogen were used. The farmer wishing to maximize $E(P)$ would use 150 pounds of nitrogen per acre and would expect to suffer a loss one year in six. The more conservative farmer, or one limited in capital, might note that the long-run expected gain from increasing nitrogen use from 90 to 150 pounds is only $3 per acre, $3 gained from the use of $8 of additional fertilizer.

UNCERTAINTY

A manager is said to face an uncertain situation when he does not know the probabilities with which various outcomes may occur. More than this, the unknown variable need not be random but may be determined by a set of known or unknown forces. Price changes may be caused by the interaction of demand and supply in an urban market far from the farm, government regulations may be imposed in Washington, or the renter may be faced with a one-year lease.

A number of widespread and quite well-known courses of action have been recommended to farmers since the beginnings of scientific agriculture. These actions, discussed briefly below, are sometimes applied to both risk and uncertainty situations and are often recommended without regard to the manager's goals or without careful examination of the short-run and long-run profits. Although they have been successfully used in the past and will continue to be successfully used in the future, they should not be applied as wholesale recommendations appropriate for all conditions.

Diversification

Diversification means growing two or more products in an attempt to avoid the yield and price uncertainty of a single product. By growing more than one crop of livestock enterprises, the farmer reduces his reliance upon the physical, economic, and social forces that may send the price or yield of a single product skidding to the depths. The hope is that when the earnings of one crop are low, the earnings of the others will be high or at least sufficient to provide a minimum income.

The ultimate in diversification would be to select two products with prices (yields) that are inversely related (negatively correlated). That is, when one price is at its peak, the other price would be at its minimum, with the same type of relationship existing between yields. If the price (yield) variability for both crops is large, the manager will find that in many years only one product is profitable. Each year a portion of his productive resources will be committed to a product that is unprofitable. Diversification under these circumstances may sacrifice long-run expected earnings for the maintenance of a minimum income level. On the other hand, when yield and crop variations are small, diversification accomplishes little.

In actual fact the prices and yields of most agricultural products are positively correlated, i.e., rise and fall together.[6] Therefore, opportunities for reduction of uncertainty are substantially reduced from the ideal condition of negative correlation. Even when prices or yields have zero correlation, the farmer could be subjected to a large degree of uncertainty, for the prices or yields of both products could drop simultaneously.

Diversification would be of most value when the products selected are subject to entirely different physical and economic forces. In this respect, crop and livestock diversification is common in many parts of the United States. Output and price factors for these two types of products are enough different, at least in the short run, that some stability can be attained, hopefully without large sacrifices in long-run income. Another diversification scheme might entail producing an extremely stable product with a more variable one.

Insurance

Farmers may take out hail, fire, crop, or other insurance against unknown hazards. The reasoning is that the farmer is unable to evaluate the probability of an adverse occurrence while the insurance company, which presumably operates over a large area and has a large number of

---

[6] Heady, cited in the bibliography, presents correlations for common agricultural products, pp. 519–20.

clients, can determine with reasonable accuracy the number of clients who will suffer losses each year. As was pointed out above, the insurance company in essence "gambles" with its clients, but because the company has a good estimate of the relevant probabilities, it can set premiums at levels needed to return a positive profit. The farmer, on the other hand, considers the premium as a cost which he must pay to be relieved of the possibility that a big loss could put him out of business.

The feasibility of insurance depends upon the farmer's ability to withstand a loss and upon his willingness to take a chance. For example, a farmer may not take out fire insurance on a barn because (1) he believes he could get along without a barn, (2) he has money enough to build another, (3) he could build another from native lumber, (4) he believes that proper precautionary measures will prevent fire. Another farmer may choose to insure a large modern dairy barn built with the help of a loan.

Contracts

The farmer may remove all or part of the future uncertainty cloaking an enterprise by signing a contract with an outside party. For example, a landlord may rent his farm for a cash sum rather than take a livestock and crop-sharing agreement. In this way all uncertainty surrounding the amount of annual rent is removed. Farmers also sometimes contract the sale of a crop, that is, agree at some time before harvest upon a sale price for the crop when delivered, and this action transfers price uncertainty to the other party of the contract. More recently, contracts in the poultry industry have become more involved. Farmers provide housing, labor, and some management while the outside party, usually a feed company, supplies chicks, feed, and aids with certain management decisions, such as marketing.

Flexibility

Flexibility means the ability to shift production plans to take advantage of or avoid severe losses from previously unforeseen yield or price changes. Generally, a flexible farm plan would be one which could be changed more quickly and at a lower cost than an inflexible plan. Annual crops are more flexible than perennial crops. Livestock enterprises with quick turnover, such as hogs or poultry, provide more flexibility than fattening cattle. To attain flexibility, the farmer can purchase equipment to be used to produce a wide variety of crops. He may use barn and pasture arrangements adaptable to different types of livestock. He may maintain a large bank account to permit him to take advantage of particularly favorable input purchases.

Another type of flexibility is provided not by the way the farmer invests but by the way he doesn't invest. That is, the hog farmer can avoid the highly specialized feeding operation using expensive farrowing and fattening facilities in favor of a converted stock barn or farrowing huts and pasture facilities. Because he hasn't made investments in large specialized equipment, he is free to vary his hog enterprise if need be.

Farmers often "overinvest" in machinery, meaning they apparently purchase more than their needs as determined by long-time farm plans. This overcapacity may provide flexibility in case of adverse weather or other contingencies. In recent years the practice of hiring custom work has provided additional labor and machinery flexibility. The farmer can hire a complete crew with machinery during peak seasons.[7]

The Manager as a Production Process

The manager, as he faces uncertain situations, is similar in many respects to any production process. Inputs, in the form of experience, gathered information, inherent knowledge, intuition, etc., flow in and management decisions flow out. Costs as well as returns are associated with the decision process. The manager eventually reaches the point where the (expected) added cost of delaying a decision exceeds the (expected) returns added by the delay. Several reasons exist for this.

First, any immediate decision is suboptimum in time. The last chapter discussed some of the reasons for this. Another reason is the uncertainty of the future. We do not go to extremes to select an optimum now because unforeseen future events might negate our best efforts anyway. The manager has many decisions to make. He cannot ignore all others while lingering over one.

Second, the number of possible actions are usually so numerous that the individual cannot consider all with care. As pointed out above, the costs would eventually exceed the returns. Many alternatives are ignored. Most farmers, for example, do not even consider the possibility of moving to Australia when faced with a farm program they abhor. Herbert Simon has suggested that decision makers do not attempt to maximize but rather select from a set of alternatives they consider satisfactory.[8]

Finally, in most important decision situations, many of the determining factors cannot be controlled by the manager. This has been discussed earlier in detail. Nonetheless, when faced with such occurrences as war, peace, accidents, disease, depression, and overkill, as well as many other unknowns, the decision maker attempting to carefully weigh all factors would probably find himself with an insoluble dilemma.

It is probably true that people do not have an irrational passion for

---

[7] The reader should study Heady, chaps. ix and xv–xviii for a more prolonged view of the issues raised here.

[8] See the reference listed at the end of this chapter.

dispassionate rationality.[9] On the other hand, decisions must be made and, as evidenced by the world around us, can be made successfully. Managers may not be ultimate maximizers, but they do attempt to act rationally in the attainment of their goals.

REFERENCES

Bross, I. D. J. *Design for Decision.* New York: The Macmillan Co., 1959.

Chernoff, H., and Moses, L. E. *Elementary Decision Theory.* New York: John Wiley & Sons, Inc., 1959.

Fellner, William. *Probability and Profit.* Homewood, Ill.: Richard D. Irwin, Inc., 1965.

Heady, E. O. *Economics of Agricultural Production and Resource Use.* Englewood Cliffs, N.J.: Prentice-Hall, Inc., 1952.

Knetsch, J. L. and Parks, W. L. *Interpreting Results of Irrigation Experiments—A Progress Report.* TVA Report No. T 59-1 AE, Knoxville, Tennessee, August, 1958.

Knight, Frank H. *Risk, Uncertainty, and Profit.* Boston: Houghton Mifflin Co., 1921.

Luce, R. Duncan, and Raiffa, H. *Games and Decisions.* New York: John Wiley & Sons, Inc., 1957.

McKinsey, J. C. C. *Introduction to the Theory of Games.* New York: McGraw-Hill Book Co., Inc., 1952.

McQuigg, J. D. and Doll, John P. *Weather Variability and Economic Analysis.* Missouri Agricultural Experiment Station Bulletin 771, June, 1961.

Miller, D. W., and Starr, M. K. *Executive Decisions and Operations Research.* Englewood Cliffs, N.J.: Prentice-Hall, Inc., 1960.

Simon, Herbert A. "A Behavioral Model of Rational Choice," *Quarterly Journal of Economics,* February, 1955, pp. 99–118.

von Neumann, John, and Morgenstern, Oskar. *Theory of Games and Economic Behavior.* Princeton, N.J.: Princeton University Press, 1944.

[9] To paraphrase Miller and Starr who paraphrase John Monroe Clark. This discussion is based upon ideas presented by D. W. Miller and M. K. Starr, chap. iii.

	FARM ADJUSTMENTS
Chapter	IN A CHANGING
9	AGRICULTURE

The purpose of this chapter is to present some factual information about agriculture and illustrate the use of concepts presented in previous chapters. Only selected topics are included, and the discussions are brief; obviously a complete review of all the many social and economic forces affecting farms in the nation and within regions of the nation cannot be contained in one chapter. Rather, the topics were selected with the twofold purpose of providing subject matter of general interest and of illustrating the application of economic analysis to varied situations. While foregoing chapters present concepts which agricultural economists need to know, this chapter gives a glimpse of what agricultural economists do.

AGRICULTURAL LAND

Quantity and Value

In 1959, farmland in the 48 conterminous states comprised a total of 1,120 million acres, 58.9 percent of the land area of the United States. At the turn of the century, only 839 million acres were classified as farmland. Under the pressures of expansion to the West and the growth of the economy and population, acres of land in farms increased steadily throughout the century and attained a peak of 1,159 million acres in 1950. Perhaps a more meaningful measure than total land in farms is cropland harvested. Cropland reached a peak in 1929 when 359 million acres were harvested. By 1959, 311 million acres of cropland were harvested, a drop of almost 50 million acres from the 1929 peak.

The acre value of farm real estate since 1910 is depicted in Figure 9–1. (A profile for the United States in 1959 is depicted in Figure 9–2.) These values follow a far different trend than do the total land in farm statistics. From $40 per acre in 1910, land value increased to a peak of $70 per acre in 1920. Land in farms and number of farms also increased during that period. Famine in Europe with resultant exports and high agricultural prices undoubtedly affected the increase in value during that period. After 1920, farmland values decreased to a low of less than $30 in

FIGURE 9–1

VALUE OF FARM REAL ESTATE PER ACRE, THE 48 STATES, 1910–66

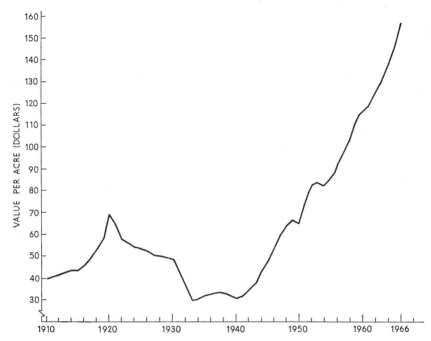

1932 and did not surpass the 1920 value again until 1951. The number of farms continued to increase until 1935, and as mentioned above, the amount of land in farms continued to increase until 1940. Land values have continued upward consistently since 1940 until in 1966 a value of nearly $160 per acre was attained, an increase of $120 above 1910.

From the standpoint of the economic theory of the firm, land does not differ from other inputs. In actual fact it is different, although an explanation of the reasons for that difference in the space available here may appear rather ethereal. Land is the most durable of all agricultural inputs. Although its fertility may be depleted as in any mining operation, the durability of land as pure space appears infinite, at least from man's viewpoint. Because all other inputs are less durable than land, it is natural to impute the residual earnings of agriculture, that is, the earnings remaining after all other inputs are paid, to land. Land prices would then seem to depend closely upon present and future expected earnings in agriculture. This was true until the decade of the fifties. In the 1920's, agricultural earnings dropped and land values declined (Figure 9–3). From 1930–50, agricultural earnings rose and land values increased,

FIGURE 9-2

AVERAGE VALUE OF LAND AND BUILDINGS PER ACRE, 1959

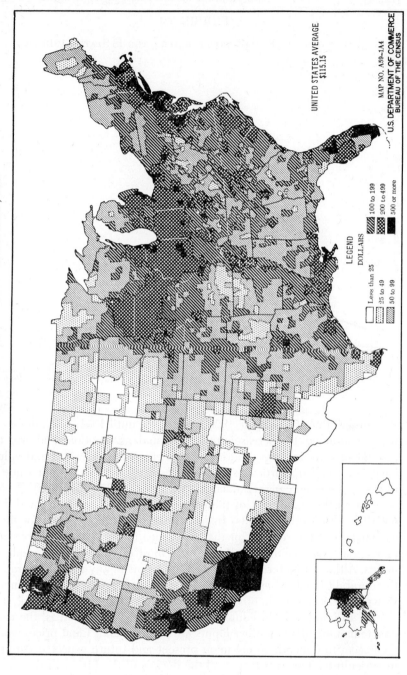

LEGEND
DOLLARS

Less than 25
25 to 49
50 to 99
100 to 199
200 to 499
500 or more

UNITED STATES AVERAGE
$115.15

MAP NO. A59-1A4
U.S. DEPARTMENT OF COMMERCE
BUREAU OF THE CENSUS

SOURCE: Map No. A59-1A4, U.S. Department of Commerce, Bureau of the Census.

FIGURE 9–3

TOTAL NET FARM INCOME AND TOTAL VALUE OF FARM REAL ESTATE, 1920–65

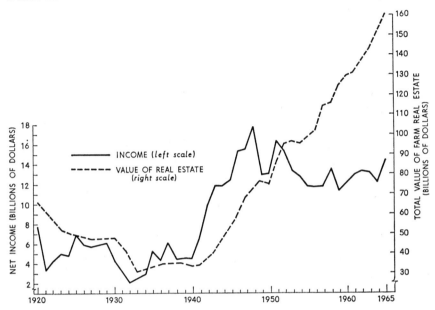

albeit at somewhat of a lagged pace in the forties. Since 1950, however, real estate values have doubled while aggregate net farm income has dropped.

The situation is depicted for recent years in Figure 9–4. In 1940, net

FIGURE 9–4

FARM INCOME AND REAL ESTATE VALUES

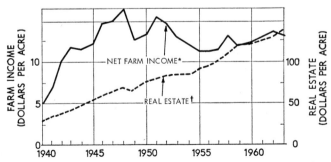

* Includes interest paid on farm mortgage debt and net rents to nonfarm landlords.

† Farmland and buildings. Value per acre, March 1 of the following year. 1963 preliminary.

SOURCE: U.S. Department of Agriculture, Neg. ERS 2105–64(7), Economic Research Service.

farm income plus interest paid on land and rent to landlords, a measure of the earnings to be imputed to land, was $5 per acre and land was valued at $32 per acre, i.e., land was valued at six times its earnings. In 1950, the land value-earnings ratio was still about six. In 1955, the ratio was not quite 9, and by 1963 it had risen to 10. As a matter of fact, net income per farm increased slightly in the late fifties and early sixties after substantial increases through the decade of the forties and a sizable drop in 1949. The modest increases in net income per farm do not, however, seem large enough to create an expectation for future earnings of the size needed to justify recent land value increases. Later in this chapter, forces other than income will be examined.

Distribution of Earnings

It is generally true that most inputs used in a productive process are complements. While inputs may substitute within limits, complete removal of one input from the process would usually stop production. This makes it impossible to divide any residual revenue among productive inputs. In practice, the manager looks at all costs and all revenue without actually knowing how much a machine or a particular day's labor added to total revenue or, more important, profits.

From the standpoint of economic theory, inputs are divided into variable resources, often called mobile resources, and fixed or immobile resources. Mobile resources are paid whatever is necessary to attract them into the productive process. Fertilizer, fuel, and other purchased resources are paid a price mutually agreeable to the dealer and the farmer. If not, the dealer won't supply them. Labor, other than family labor, is purchased at the market rate or not at all. Total payment to all these mobile resources comprises total variable costs. The residual amount, total revenue minus total variable costs, is imputed to the fixed resources—the ones that cannot move out of production in the short run. As the time period lengthens and resources fixed in the short run become variable, the owner must decide whether to reinvest or cease production. If he is satisfied with the residual imputed to the resource (when it is immobile), he will reinvest. Any amount accruing to him over and above the amount needed to keep the resource in production in the long run is termed "economic rent."

The concept of economic rent was developed by David Ricardo, an English economist. Ricardo applied it to agricultural land, hence the term "rent." Economic rent is not the same as the word "rent" used in the ordinary sense as rent to landlords.

Economic rent can be explained as follows: Suppose three classes of land—good, medium, and poor—exist in a country. Suppose that the demand for food is such that the product price received by the farmer is P_{y_1} (Figure 9–5). Then farmers with good land will produce amount Y_{1G}

per acre. (If the diagrams in Figure 9–5 are assumed to be drawn for a fixed input of one acre, then total production would be assumed to be the number of acres of good land times Y_{1G}.) P_{y_1} equals ATC, therefore the manager will keep his land in production in the long run but no economic rent accrues to the landowner. Suppose now that demand increases and product price rises to P_{y_2}. Farmers on good land will increase output to Y_{2G}, and farmers on medium land will commence production of amount Y_{2M}. Economic rent is now accruing to owners of the good land in an amount equivalent to AB per unit of output. The owners of the medium land are earning no economic rent. If product price increases to P_{y_3}, owners of the poor land bring it into production at the rate Y_{3P} per acre.

FIGURE 9–5

ECONOMIC RENT IN LAND USE

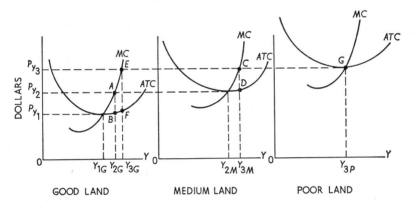

GOOD LAND   MEDIUM LAND   POOR LAND

An economic rent of CD accrues to the owners of medium land, and the economic rent on good land increases to EF.

Why is this concept called "economic rent"? Suppose you were interested in renting a farm. At price P_{y_3}, you would be indifferent to renting a good farm and paying the owner EF extra rent per unit of output, renting a medium farm and paying the owner CD extra per unit, or renting a poor farm and paying no extra rent. ATC by definition includes all costs which must be covered if you are to produce in the long run. Measuring your capital, management, and labor returns against returns in some alternative employment, returns at the points F, D, and G on the ATC curves must be the same. Therefore, you would be willing to pay the "economic rent" to the owner of the land. In fact, if you were renting good land and the product price rose to P_{y_2}, the landlord could extract amount AB per unit from you by offering to rent his land to someone considering renting medium land.

The type or quality of land brought into production at a particular product price is often called the "extensive margin" while the point at which product price equals marginal cost is called the "intensive margin." In Figure 9–5, medium land represents the extensive margin at P_{y_2} while Y_{2G} and Y_{2M} are the intensive margins on good and medium land, respectively.

Economic rent, if it exists in the long run, would have a persistent increasing effect on land values. If the supply of land were fixed and product prices continued to increase (or costs decreased), an economic rent would accrue to landowners thereby enhancing the value of land.[1] More will be said about economic rent and land values. For now we will turn to a discussion of land tenure.

Land Tenure

Tenure is the manner in which land is held by the operator. The two extremes in tenure are owners and tenants. In-between is an increasing group called part owners who both rent and own land. Trends in the percent of farms and land in farms held by each tenure group are presented in Table 9–1. The number of farms and land in farms controlled by tenants has been decreasing in this century. Surprisingly enough so has the percent of land controlled by full owners. In 1910, 53 percent of the farmers owned 53 percent of the land in farms; by 1959, full owners controlled approximately 60 percent of the farms but only 30 percent of the land in farms. As farms have expanded, some owners have rented more land while some tenants have purchased land. As a result, the part owner has controlled a larger portion of the farms and, more significantly, a larger portion of the farmland—approximately 45 percent in 1959. The data in Table 9–1 do not suggest the amount of rented land controlled by part owners, but it must be sizable. While land controlled by all tenants decreased from 18.3 to 14.5 percent between 1950 and 1959, gross rent due landlords increased $500 million during the same period, indicating a transfer of rental payments from all tenants to part owners.

Land Rental. Farm tenancy is a special case of a general problem that arises when the resources used by a firm are controlled by different people. Partnerships, corporations, and cooperatives represent vehicles through which individuals may pool their resources to produce a particular good or group of goods. Except possibly for some industrial jobs, even the hiring of labor causes some dilution of the management function. A hired worker has to decide how deep to plow or cultivate, whether to open the sieves on the combine, etc. The general problem of multiple

---

[1] Economic rent is a general concept which applies to inputs other than land. It arises in general when the supply function for an input is not perfectly elastic.

TABLE 9–1

Farms and Land in Farms, 1910–59

		FARMS			
Year	No. Farms	Full Owner	Part Owner	Manager	All Tenant*
1910.........6,361,502		52.7%	9.3%	0.9%	37.0%
1920.........6,448,343		52.2	8.7	1.1	38.1
1930†.........6,295,103		46.3	10.4	0.9	42.4
1940.........6,102,417		50.6	10.1	0.6	38.8
1950.........5,388,437		57.4	15.3	0.4	26.9
1959.........3,707,973		57.1	22.5	0.6	19.8

		LAND IN FARMS			
Year	Land in Farms (A.)	Full Owner	Part Owner	Manager	All Tenant*
1910....... 878,798,325		52.9%	15.2%	6.1%	25.8%
1920....... 955,883,715		48.3	18.4	5.7	27.7
1930†....... 990,111,984		37.6	24.9	6.4	31.0
1940.......1,065,113,774		35.9	28.2	6.5	29.4
1950.......1,161,419,720		36.1	36.4	9.2	18.3
1959.......1,123,378,059		30.8	44.8	9.8	14.5

* Includes southern croppers. In 1910, croppers comprised 17.5% of farms controlling 6.4% of land in farms. By 1959, croppers comprised 7.4% of farms and controlled 1.4% of the land in farms.
† Data for 1930 and subsequent years include Hawaii and Alaska.
Source: *Agricultural Statistics*, 1964, p. 432.

ownership in a firm gives rise to problems similar to those encountered in competition among firms (Chapters 11 and 12) or in more general theories of adversaries. While these general concepts can not be discussed here, some of the problems of farm tenancy will be outlined using previously developed theory.

Tenancy permits individuals to utilize resources and undertake productive activity which would otherwise be impossible for them. In general the inputs contributed by each member of the agreement are complements. Farm production cannot be undertaken without land or without labor, management, and operating capital. The tenant usually doesn't have the capital to both buy and operate land. The landlord does not have or otherwise chooses not to supply the labor, management, and operating capital needed for production. Therefore, they combine resources.

One of the primary interests of the economist is efficiency. To the economist, tenure systems as such are of themselves neither good nor bad but are undesirable only if they lead to inefficiencies. In the case of tenancy, the standard of comparison is the owner-operator. Given similar prices and production relationships, the tenure agreement should permit the tenant to use the same resources in the same manner as the owner operator, that is, to attain production efficiencies possible in the absence of binding tenure agreements.

Two common rental methods are the cash rent and the crop share rent. Some rental agreements include both: a crop share may be paid on cropland while a cash rent is paid for pasture. In many areas, livestock share leases are common, but because of space limitations and because the problems involved are of the same general nature, only crop leases will be discussed here.

One important consequence of renting is that risk may be shared. A cash rental requires a fixed sum be paid each year; a share lease permits the landlord to be paid a fixed portion of total product. Given perfect certainty, a renter would be indifferent to the two methods of leasing only if the payments over time are identical. Otherwise, he would prefer the one resulting in the smaller payment. In fact, however, perfect certainty is absent and the cash rental places all risk on the operator. In that situation, the operator would rationally only accept a cash lease if it resulted in lower payments over time, the size of the differential being a function of the risk in that particular farming area.

It is instructive to investigate the effects of cash rent on the renter's income variability. Suppose that the net income (including all land costs) from an acre of land over a 4-year period is $8, $14, $6, and $12, respectively. The average is $10 a year. A measure of variation could be defined by subtracting the four-year average from each annual value, squaring the differences so obtained, and then summing the squares. This gives a number that is positive or zero—zero if the annual earnings are identical, i.e., no variation exists. For our example the measure of variation is computed as follows (Table 9–2):

TABLE 9–2

Year	Income	Subtract Mean	Square Deviations
1...............	$ 8	−2	4
2...............	14	4	16
3...............	6	−4	16
4...............	12	2	4
Sums...........	$40	0	40

The measure of variation is 40. Suppose that the landlord charges $5 per acre cash rent. The tenant's income is then $3, $9, $1, and $7 per acre each year. His average income per year is $5, but the variation, computed again by summing the squared deviations from the mean of $5, is still 40. Thus the tenant's income is half that of the owner-operator but has the same variation. If the tenant's risk preference is such that he will assume added risk only at the prospect of an increase in income, he is in some sense "worse off" than he would be as an owner-operator when the cash rent exceeds the costs of land ownership. Because in the long run the landlord would not rent at a rate less than the cost of land ownership, the cash tenant can never be better off than the owner-operator.

The question next arises: What cash rent should be charged? Cash rent is a fixed cost to the operator, and he will purchase and allocate resources exactly as an owner-operator (assuming, of course, he expects to be on the farm a period of time sufficient in length to insure the complete utilization of the resources' services). The average variable cost and marginal cost curves will be identical for the cash tenant and owner-operator (Figure 9–6A). At product price, P_y, both would produce

FIGURE 9–6

Tenure Problems

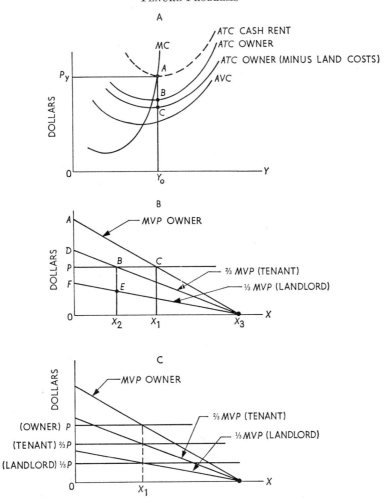

a total output of Y_0. If the owner-operator had an average total cost of ATC, there would accrue to him as a landowner an economic rent of amount AB. The landlord would thus want to charge a cash rent at least equivalent to the economic rent. But the owner-operator's ATC also includes the costs of land ownership. If he did not own land, there would exist a lower ATC curve excluding ownership costs which would represent the minimum-cost level at which he would stay in business in the long run. That is, the lower ATC curve includes as costs all imputed returns necessary to keep all nonland resources in farming. The landlord would thus want to charge the economic rent, AB, plus the costs of land ownership (including a return on land investment sufficient to keep land in production) represented by BC, or a total of the distance AC. When he does, the cash renter's costs will rise to ATC cash rent. If the farm were on the extensive margin, AB would be zero.

With a crop share lease the tenant and the landlord both assume a share of the risk, but conflicts may arise when costs of variable inputs are not also shared. Figure 9–6B depicts a situation in which the tenant pays all the costs of a variable input, X, and the landlord receives one third of the output. With input price, P, an owner-operator would use X_1 amount of X and make a profit represented by the triangle (APC). The tenant, however, would only apply amount X_2 and would thereby profit (DPB)—by so doing he would also earn a profit for the landlord, represented by the area $(OFEX_2)$.

Returns to the landlord are maximized when the tenant applies X_3 amount of input. At that point, the marginal product of X is zero and equal exactly to the cost of the input to the landlord. Thus, the landlord and tenant have opposing interests. The analysis would be similar when the landlord pays for the input and the tenant shares in the output.

The solution to this conflict is to share costs in the same proportion as returns. Such a solution is shown in Figure 9–6C. The tenant, paying two thirds of the cost, equates $\frac{2}{3}$ P to $\frac{2}{3}$ MVP. The landlord equates $\frac{1}{3}$ P to $\frac{1}{3}$ MVP. The optimum amount of input, to which they both agree, is X_1, the amount an owner-operator would use. Notice however, that while the tenant's profit is increased by cost sharing, the landlord's profit may not be, particularly if he can convince the tenant to use more than amount X_2 in Figure 9–6B. Thus while cost sharing provides for the most efficient use of resources, it may not be the most profitable for one of the two parties.

The above analyses presume a short-run situation and do not analyze the effects of cash leases or share leases on farm size or possible expansions. The commitment of capital funds and the conservation of resources comprise another important problem in leasing. Tenants are reluctant to make improvements of a durable nature when their lease is uncertain. Conservation practices which decrease present income in favor of future returns are not attractive to a tenant with a one-year lease. This is particularly true of soil treatments, but it may also be true of investments needed for livestock production, especially when the landlord receives no benefit from such investments. One suggested solution to this problem is to have the tenant invest in the durable assets he needs (with mutual approval) and then have the landlord or next tenant reimburse him the discounted value of the future earnings of the assets should he have to leave. A second solution is for the landlord to build the structure and charge the tenant a cash rent.

Space does not permit a complete analysis of tenure problems. The examples presented here should be sufficient, however, to demonstrate the use of economic logic to solve practical problems.

Land Ownership. The right to own land and treat it as they pleased was one of the most important freedoms sought by immigrants to the United States. This desire, despite its possible irrationality in some situations, is still a strong factor in today's agriculture. As a result, ownership by the farm operator is traditional in agriculture. Each farmer is expected to purchase land and other assets needed in agricultural production while also providing for the family expenses. This system is much in contrast to the corporation, one of the predominate methods of financing outside agriculture. The corporation is a legal structure in which ownership and management is completely separate and in which the outstanding debt (value of stocks held by owners) is never to be repaid by firm earnings.

At one time land could be acquired by homesteading. After all virgin land was claimed, farms could only be obtained by transfer of ownership. As mentioned earlier, the amount of land in farmland has decreased slightly since 1929. While urban expansion, airports, highways, and other nonfarm uses capture an increasing portion of farmland each year, the amount of farmland can reasonably be regarded as fixed for recent decades. (This is not true in local areas, such as in California, where urban expansion has removed a large percentage of the total available land from farm production.) Given this fixed total quantity, land available for purchase by farmers, prospective farmers, or others depends upon the willingness of owners to sell. This willingness has been decreasing.

Before World War II, land was readily available, but money for purchasing it was not. In 1947, a year of peak agricultural income, voluntary sales of farms averaged 58 per thousand farms across the United States. By 1964, this figure was 30 per thousand, almost a 50 percent drop. This decreasing supply coupled with increasing land values and interest charges, requiring large down payments and increased interest payments, have increased the difficulty of land purchase and hence entry into farming via that method.

If total income to farming is dropping and land values rising (Figure 9–3), who buys farmland and why? The first question is answered by Figure 9–7. Farmers buy two thirds of the land offered while nonfarmers account for the other third. The percent of tenants purchasing land has declined steadily since 1950, reflecting the decrease in numbers of tenants as well as the difficulty of purchasing land. The number of owner-operators buying land has increased while purchases by nonfarmers have remained reasonably constant.

Owner-operators buy additional land to expand the size of present units. The percent of land transfers for farm enlargement has increased

FIGURE 9–7

Who Buys Farmland

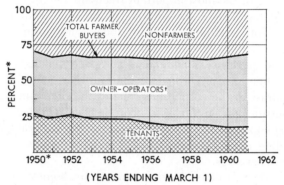

(YEARS ENDING MARCH 1)

* Years ending March 1.
† Voluntary transfers.
‡ Includes a few retired farmers.
Source: U.S. Department of Agriculture, Neg. ERS 535–61(91), Economic Research Service.

from slightly more than 20 percent in 1950 to about 55 percent in 1965. Farm enlargement transfers for 1955 and 1965 are presented in Figure 9–8. Pressure for expansion has been largest in wheat growing areas where large-scale mechanization has increased the amount of land that can be farmed by a family and where acreage reductions due to government programs have made the "wheat base" of additional farmland extremely valuable. The next largest increase occurred in the Corn Belt. In all areas the increase is striking, however. By enlarging farms and thereby more fully utilizing new technologies, farmers have managed to offset declining total farm income by increasing net income per farm.

One of the whys of land buying (farm expansion) has been answered. A second reason is capital appreciation. Farmland on the average has increased from $30 to $160 an acre since 1940. At the same time a steady rise in prices has occurred in the economy, causing a

FIGURE 9–8

FARMLAND PURCHASES FOR FARM ENLARGEMENT

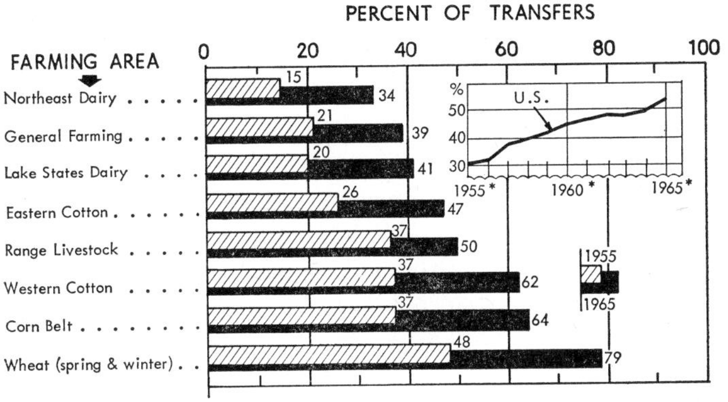

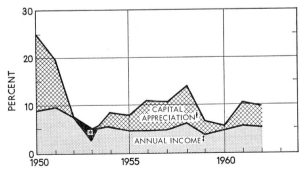

PERCENT OF TRANSFERS

* Years ending March 1.
SOURCE: U.S. Department of Agriculture, Neg. ERS 4519–66(5), Economic Research Service.

decline in the purchasing power of the dollar. During such times land is a good hedge against inflation. In fact, between 1950 and 1962, the capital appreciation of farmland exceeded the annual income from farm production five times (Figure 9–9). Such gains create expectations of similar future gains among farm and nonfarm buyers alike.

FIGURE 9–9

U.S. FARM REAL ESTATE
Production Income and Capital Appreciation as Percentage of
Current Market Value

* Capital loss.
† March to March change in value per acre.
‡ From farm production, after allowances for returns to other factors.
SOURCE: U.S. Department of Agriculture, Neg. ERS 1832–63(3), Economic Research Service.

A third reason, more nebulous but no less real than the others, is the value placed on farmland ownership in and of itself. In this sense, ownership is a consumption item. Many urban dwellers have farm backgrounds. Employment and wages have been high in nonfarm employment, providing a base of affluence for those who are inclined to pursue their farm heritage. As a result, some people purchase farms for rural residences with no intent to depend upon the income earned by the land, while others purchase farms with a view towards supplementing nonfarm income. A third group purchases land as an investment for funds earned elsewhere.

Ownership pressures are equally strong for farmers. Land ownership carries a certain prestige not associated with tenancy. Owners are thought to be more stable, more interested in building a better community, etc. These nonmonetary aspects of ownership exist but are largely unmeasurable, and their impact cannot be easily assessed.

CAPITAL AND CREDIT

The capital invested in a business is the total value of all assets. Capital is usually acquired through savings of the operator, borrowing from an outside source, or inheritance. Borrowing or inheritance becomes possible, of course, only when some other person or group of people are willing to save. When asset prices vary through time, capital can be acquired through increased market values (appreciation) or lost through decreased market values (capital, rather than use, depreciation).

Capital Requirements of Farming

The importance of capital (and credit) in modern agriculture can scarcely be overemphasized. The total value of assets in farming now exceeds $220 billion. Figure 9–10 lists the value of assets needed to produce $1,000 of net farm income for selected types of farms across the United States. The net income measure used in Figure 9–10 is the return available for management, operator and family labor, and capital payments. If the opportunity cost of capital is 5 percent, $500 would be needed to pay the capital costs for each $10,000 invested. Thus, farms requiring $10,000 of assets to earn $1,000 income would have $500 of income remaining for payment of family labor and management. Farms with over $20,000 investment required per $1,000 of income would have negative earnings imputed to these inputs.

Farm income is highly variable both for farms of a given type within one year and for the same farm over a period of years. The data in Figure 9–10 are averages for only three years and do not necessarily reflect long-run trends. Livestock prices in particular are variable and subject to cyclical variations, while in recent years, dairy and crop prices

FIGURE 9–10

COMMERCIAL FARMS
Market Value of Assets per $1,000 Net Farm Income*

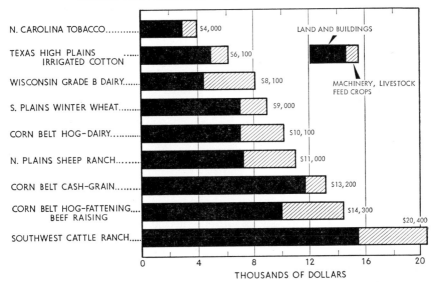

* 1960–62 averages: Net farm income is net return available for operator and family labor, management and return on capital.
SOURCE: U.S. Department of Agriculture, Neg. ERS 2397–63(10), Economic Research Service.

have been stabilized by government action. Nonetheless, the data in Figure 9–10 suggest returns in agriculture have not been high even for crop farms, given the present values imputed to assets.

Credit Use in Farming

The use of credit, borrowing money, is similar in one respect to renting land. By renting, a farm operator is able to use productive assets otherwise unavailable. By combining his limited amount of capital with another man's land, he is able to attain a farm organization and resulting income which would otherwise be impossible. In fact, he may attain a higher income level by renting an adequate sized unit than he would as a debt-ridden owner-operator of a small farm. In the same way, credit enables the operator to purchase land or other inputs needed in production. Because major inputs are complementary, judicious use of credit by the operator may permit him to utilize superior production techniques resulting in more income at lower risk.

At one time the use of credit was considered evil. This might have stemmed from the time when human rights and justice had not attained its present status (in the United States) and debtors could be thrown in

FIGURE 9–11

NONREAL ESTATE LOANS
(Held by Banks and Federally Sponsored Agencies)*

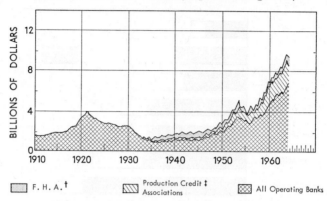

F. H. A.†   Production Credit ‡ Associations   All Operating Banks

* January 1 and July 1 data, excluding loans held or guaranteed by Commodity Credit Corp.
† Includes emergency crop and feed and R.A.C.C. loans.
‡ Includes federal intermediate credit bank discounts for other lenders. Alaska and Hawaii not included.
SOURCE: U.S. Department of Agriculture, Neg. ERS 150–64(4), Economic Research Service.

prison. Mothers at that time more than likely taught children to stay out of debt with the ultimate aim of keeping them out of prison. At any rate, long after the threat of prison was lifted, the abhorence of debt was incorporated into the minds of the people.

In recent decades, however, the use of credit in both consumption and production has become more prevalent. Reasons for this include a changing attitude towards credit by society and an increase in the amount of money available for lending. As society became more affluent and savings increased, for example by means of investment in insurance programs and time deposits in banks, those who loan money found they had more to loan. The increase in credit use resulted from encouraging people to borrow, changing the image of lending institutions, offering credit on a wider variety of purchases, and developing more flexible and useful credit plans.

The use of credit in agriculture has increased substantially since 1945. Trends in nonreal estate and farm mortgage debt since 1910 are shown in Figure 9–11. The relationship between assets and debt are contained in Table 9–2 for selected years. Farm mortgage debt increased until the early 1920's and declined thereafter until 1946, when it reached a low of $4.8 billion. Then a steady increase began until by 1964 the total farm mortgage debt was $16.7 billion, a threefold increase from the low.

Nonreal estate loans follow approximately the same trend as mortgage debt (Figure 9–11). The upward trend in these loans started

FIGURE 9–11 (Continued)

Farm Mortgage Debt Held by Major Lenders

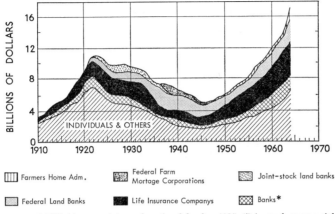

* 1910–14 open state and national banks. 1935–47 insured commercial banks; 1948—all operating banks; 1960—includes Alaska and Hawaii. Data for 1964 are preliminary.
    SOURCE: U.S. Department of Agriculture, Neg. ERS 149–64(4), Economic Research Service.

earlier, in the mid-1930's, due in part to an impetus by the newly established FHA and Production Credit Associations. By 1964 nonreal estate loans (held by lenders listed in Figure 9–11) had increased to 10 billion, over 250 percent above the previous high in 1921. Thus, nonreal estate loans have increased relative to real estate loans.

While debt or, to put it another way, the use of credit has increased

TABLE 9–2

ASSETS AND DEBTS IN AMERICAN AGRICULTURE
(Billions)

	Real Estate			Nonreal Estate		
	Debt	Assets	Debt as Percent of Assets	Debt*	Assets	Debt as Percent of Assets
1920........	$ 8.4	$ 66.3	13%	....	....	....
1930........	9.6	47.9	20	....	....	....
1940........	6.6	33.6	20	$ 3.4	$19.4	18%
1950........	5.6	75.3	7	6.9	56.3	12
1960........	12.1	129.9	9	11.8	69.6	17
1964†.......	16.7	152.0	11	16.1	74.2	22

* Includes debts held by banks and federally sponsored agencies plus holdings of dealers, merchants, finance companies, individuals, and others.
    † Preliminary.
    SOURCE: Agricultural Credit and Related Data, Agricultural Committee, The American Bankers Association, 1964, Table 16.

in absolute amounts, indebtedness relative to asset values has not spiraled. In 1940, real estate debt was 20 percent of assets. During the profitable war years debts were retired; by 1950 debt was 7 percent of real estate assets (Table 9–2). In spite of the tripling of debt, total real estate debt had increased to only 11 percent of asset value by 1964.

More striking is the increase in nonreal estate debt. By 1964, nonreal estate loans were the highest percentage of nonreal estate assets for the period of record. Also, this category almost equaled real estate debt in magnitude, suggesting again the increasing importance of nonreal estate credit in agriculture. As farm size and value of the assets needed for modern methods of production have increased, farmers have increasingly used credit in their efforts to maintain income.

The Economics of Credit Use

Except for its role as a common denominator, a function which theoretically could be performed by any input, borrowed capital is not uniquely different from other purchased inputs. Each dollar added to the productive process will result in a change in total product. Thus, a production function for capital can be visualized for any enterprise or firm. The interest rate is the cost or price per unit of capital; the manager will purchase capital and add it to the production process as long as the added profit exceeds the interest rate. That is, a dollar invested must return, after all other costs, a dollar plus the interest on the dollar. A limited amount of capital is allocated among enterprises in such a way that the marginal earning of a dollar are equal in each enterprise.

Two important concepts often encountered in agricultural economics literature are internal and external capital rationing. Capital is available to the farmer from several sources. Real estate mortgages usually represent the lowest cost loans. Interest rates are then higher for bank loans secured by productive assets, production credit loans, second mortgages, and usually even higher for personal loans or loans from finance companies. Thus, the capital supply curve faced by the farmer would appear as a "step" function (Figure 9–12A). The cost of a dollar is $\$(1 + i)$, where i is the interest rate. In Figure 9–12A, $0A$ amount of money is available at the lowest interest rate, and CD at the highest rate. After total amount $0D$, no more capital can be borrowed.

External credit rationing is depicted in Figure 9–12B. Here the operator desires to equate the MVP of capital to its cost. He finds, however, that he can only borrow $0A$ capital at the lower interest rate and AB at the higher rate, a total of $0B$. He would like to borrow more (at any interest rate which would intersect the MVP within the arc labeled C) but lending agencies will not extend the credit.

The farmer, when deciding to use credit or any other input, is faced with all the technical, institutional, weather, and other uncertain-

FIGURE 9–12

INTERNAL AND EXTERNAL CAPITAL RATIONING

A

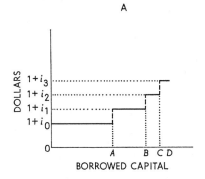

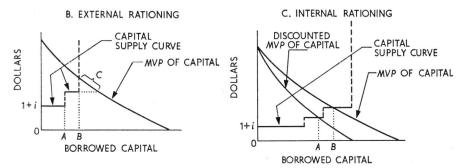

ties described in Chapter 8. The lending firm making the loan must weigh the same uncertainties plus additional uncertainities associated with the farmer himself, including the farmer's ability to use the added capital effectively and his general reputation. The lending firm wants to stay in business, and to do so must be sure it can reclaim its money. Thus, in the absence of sufficient security (mortgagable assets) or knowledge of the operator, the firm will not supply all the farmer's needs and external credit rationing exists.

Internal credit rationing occurs as a result of expectations or attitudes on the part of the farmer. In Figure 9–12C, the farmer's supply curve for capital intersects the *MVP* of capital and amount 0*B* should be borrowed. But in this case the farmer subjectively "discounts" the *MVP* of capital and borrows only amount 0*A*. What accounts for this discounting? First, the farmer may have the aversion to debt mentioned earlier. As the debt grows, his aversion and the discount increase. Second, he may also believe that uncertainty increases with the size of debt and may often be correct in this belief. Thirdly, due to the principle of increasing risk, capital losses on the farmer's owned capital (equity) increase as debt and size of operation increase. For example, if a farmer possessed $10,000 and borrowed another $10,000, a 10 percent loss would leave him with $8,000 after repayment of the loan. If he borrowed $90,000, a 10 percent loss would wipe out his equity. This can occur even though uncertainty, as measured by the percentage loss, does not change as borrowing increases.

In general, given the goal of efficiency in resource use, the economist would like to see credit extended on a basis which would maximize efficiency in production. A lending institution with a given amount of capital should therefore follow a set of lending criteria designed to allow capital to flow where it is most limiting, i.e., where its *MVP* is the highest. While the old saw that "in order to get a loan from a banker, you must first prove you don't need it" is perhaps unfair, it is probably true that loans to users with high *MVP*'s are considered more risky by the banker than loans to firms more amply endowed with capital. Or to restate it, if a farmer has good security in the form of assets or capital, he can easily obtain loans and consequently the *MVP* of capital in his business is approximately equal to cost per dollar.

Care should be taken to distinguish between capital "needs" and capital earnings. A small or poorly organized farm may "need" capital badly if it is survive, but the earnings of that farm may never be high; on the other hand, a loan to a well-organized, well-financed farm may result in large earnings. Right or wrong, the efficiency criterion would allocate capital where its earnings are the highest.

Interest rates on loans vary only within narrow ranges around prevailing rates determined by financial and governmental institutions. Moreover, maximum rates are established by law in many states. Lenders are thus not able to vary interest rates with the uncertainty of the loan. In the absence of restrictions, the lender would presumably regard interest rates and security as substitutes. A loan thought to involve a given amount of uncertainty might be made at a low interest rate if security (mortgagable assets) is ample or at a higher interest rate when less security is available. A very high rate might be charged when security is completely lacking; the farmer would then have to decide if the capital would earn more than it costs. Present lending techniques do not allow this type of lending. Therefore when the amount of security drops below that the lender believes to be needed for the man and investment involved, he simply will not extend the credit.

It is often argued that because of the uncertainty involved in agricultural production the repayment of farm loans should be scheduled to depend upon farm earnings. Large payments would be made in good years and small payments in poor years. In this way, a portion of the uncertainty is transferred to the lender who, in turn, would probably be reluctant to accept such uncertainty except for increased earnings—

higher interest rates—or increased security through mortgage of assets. The farmer would then have to decide if the increased costs of such loans were justified.

Other interesting and important aspects of agricultural credit will not be discussed here because of space limitations. The references at the end of the chapter should be pursued by those interested.

TECHNOLOGICAL CHANGE

One of the most striking features of the American economy has been its rapid rate of technological innovation. Agriculture has partici-

FIGURE 9–13

INDEX OF FARM OUTPUT AND FARM INPUT, 1934–65

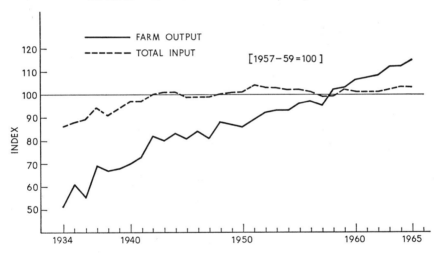

pated in this advance. The index of agricultural input stood at 86 in 1934 (1957–59 base), increased to 101 by 1943 and 103 by 1965, 22 years later. For the same base period, the index of farm output was 51, increased to 82 by 1942, to 102 by 1958, and reached 115 by 1965. These indexes are presented in Figure 9–13.

Agricultural productivity, the ratio of farm output per unit of input, is presented as an indexed series in Figure 9–14. Since about 1935, productivity has increased at almost a straight-line rate. As a result, farm productivity has almost doubled in 30 years.

This increase in productivity stems from two factors: (1) public and private investment in agricultural research, and (2) the farmer's willingness to adopt new techniques. A substantial amount of research

FIGURE 9–14

AGRICULTURAL PRODUCTIVITY—INDEX NUMBERS OF FARM OUTPUT PER UNIT OF
INPUT, 1910–65

has been devoted to improving agricultural production techniques. Much of this work has been done by the agricultural experiment stations established within land grant universities, and much has been done by the United States Department of Agriculture either directly or by providing funds to the experiment stations. Contributions have also been made by industrial firms supplying agricultural inputs, that is, by machinery companies, chemical and fertilizer companies, feed and seed companies, etc. These firms are continually attempting to develop and sell products better than those of their competitors. The ability to market a new product first, such as a self-propelled combine or a new feed additive, can mean the difference between success and failure in the farm supply market. By pursuing their own profit-motivated objectives, farm supply firms have contributed directly to agricultural efficiency.

Technological advances have touched every part of agriculture and include chemical fertilizers, sprays, better feeds and feed additives, improved and new types of machinery, high yield crop varieties, improved strains of livestock and, most important but perhaps immeasurable, a substantial improvement in managerial skills of farmers. All of the types of technological improvements and the resulting impacts upon farm production cannot be discussed here. Rather, the economic concepts presented in earlier chapters will be used to present the elements of an economic analysis of technical change.

Impact of Technology on the Firm

Technological change can cause old products to be replaced by new ones, can create new inputs or improve old ones, and can otherwise affect the production process. Some technological developments, chemical fertilizers for example, provide a new input while others, hybrid corn varieties as an example, represent an improvement in an established practice. When the technological development is a new input, this input would have a production function and a unit cost—the manager would thus equate the marginal value product of the input with unit cost. In this case the result of the technological change would be an increase in output and costs, revenue and profit.

If the new input were a replacement for an input previously used in the production process (and any change caused by a technological innovation can be regarded as such) and if it has exactly the same production function as the old input, the new input would be utilized (as a replacement for the old) only if it costs less. In such a case the input would be called a "cost-reducing" technology. If output remained constant, costs would be lowered and profits increased.

Output would not remain constant, however. As shown in Figure 9–15A, the new input, X_T, has a lower cost and the manager will use the added amount of DE, will increase profit by the area under the MVP curve and between the two price lines (center diagram), and will increase output by FG (right-hand diagram). Perhaps in a very short period, for example when appropriate adjustments in durable resources cannot be made, the new inputs will reduce costs without increasing output. In general, however, the manager will adjust as quickly as possible to gain the added profit. Thus, cost-reducing technological improvements tend to increase output, given constant prices for output and other inputs.

Suppose the new input shifted the production function upward as shown in Figure 9–15B. For any given input amount, output is increased and the production function slopes more steeply, indicating an increase in marginal productivity. In this case the new inputs, X_T, will be used to replace the old, X_o, even if it (X_T) costs more. The criteria is, of course, that profit using the new input must equal or exceed profit using the old input. If the inputs are identically priced, an additional amount HI will be used (center diagram) resulting in increased output JK (right-hand diagram) and an increase in profits. In fact, output and profits will be increased for all prices of the new input equal to or less than $0K$ (center diagram, 9–15B) and even for some higher prices (why?). Thus, a cost-increasing technology can also result in increased outputs and profits.

A third effect of a technological change might be to increase output

FIGURE 9–15

Technological Change and the Production Function

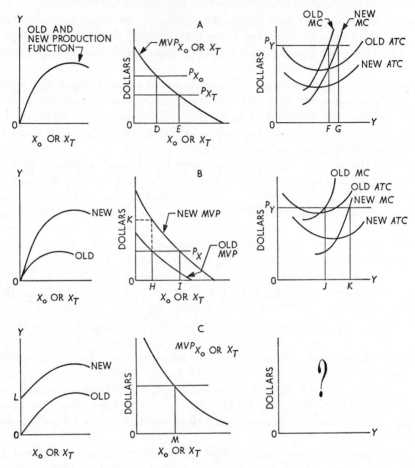

at each input amount while leaving marginal product unchanged. In this case the production function would increase a constant amount at each input level but its slope would remain unchanged. This situation is represented in Figure 9–15C; the production function shifts upward a constant amount and the MVP_X curve remains unchanged. As long as profits using the new input exceed those from using $0M$ amount of the old, the new technology will be adopted and an amount more or less than $0M$ (center diagram, Figure 9–15C) will be used depending on the unit cost of the new input.

Assuming for the moment that the new input costs as much or more than the old input, then an equal or smaller amount will be used. An increase in production has resulted without an increase in the amounts of other inputs. Additional resources are not attracted to the firm, and some may even be freed for use elsewhere. Also, output has increased. Thus, a technology having the effect demonstrated in Figure 9–15C would appear to be ideal—output and profits increase while the price mechanism diverts resources to other uses. Such a conclusion is fallacious, however, to the extent that "fixed" inputs are present and thus can be regarded as valid only in the short run. The technology increases the profits accruing to the "fixed" inputs—which, of course, are not actually fixed—and the manager will thus seek to acquire more of this "fixed" asset. Also, economic rent is increased and additional firms may enter production. Thus only in a time period so short that fixed assets cannot be expanded will this technological innovation fail to attract new resources into the business. (The effect of this type of technological change upon the average and marginal cost curves is left to the student as an exercise.)

Technology and Farms

If the assumptions of the preceding section are accepted, the conclusion is that technological change increases the farm's output. Because farmers are pure competitors and regard prices facing them as set by the market, the individual farmer can benefit from innovation. By adopting a new technique, a farmer can reduce costs and/or increase profits in the short run. As more farmers use the technique, total aggregate output of the commodity will increase and without a comparable increase in aggregate demand will cause product prices to fall. Thus, because of the competitive nature of agriculture, the technique will be adopted and aggregate output will increase regardless of the action of an individual farmer. It is therefore to the benefit of the individual farmer to adopt new technologies as quickly as possible, thereby capturing returns possible before others follow. Hence good managers are innovators.

Technological changes such as hybrid seed corn require little added capital investment, while changes such as those taking place in Grade A dairies (including milking parlors, milking machines, and bulk tanks) not only require substantial investment but also put a lower limit on enterprise size. A modern Grade A dairy cannot be established for a herd of two or three cows. With notable exceptions, technological change has increased the capital needed for farming.[2]

The same types of comments may be made about technology and risk. While new technologies at first represent an unknown to be mas-

[2] The question of whether the cost per unit of useable input has increased is begged because of lack of knowledge. That is, tractors cost more, but they are also more powerful, economical, and durable. Costs can be assessed, but returns cannot. Who knows what the value of the added timeliness of operation might be to agriculture as a whole?

tered by the manager, ultimately they may result in a reduction of risk for the good manager. For the poor or average manager, new technologies, because of the added capital investment and increased farm size, may tend to force the manager past his natural management abilities and thereby increase risk for him.

Land is a residual claimant of agricultural earnings. Thus, to the extent that technological change increases profits, it will also increase the economic rent accruing to land. According to the analysis above, this rent increase will increase the inherent value of land and tend to bring additional land into production. In fact, however, the total amount of farmland in the United States has decreased slightly in recent years. Acres of cropland have also dropped. Given these decreases, the increase in rent caused by new technology would tend to increase the value of land now in production and cause land values to rise. This in turn increases owners expectations of further earnings (or capital appreciation) and makes the acquisition of additional land more desirable. The causal effect may be reversed; farm enlargement also comes about to permit the use of new, large-scale technologies.

Technology benefits the good manager. If equal management ability were to be found on farms of different size, then technology would probably be most beneficial to farms of above average size simply because these farms have the land and other resources often needed to fully benefit from a new technique. Management, however, remains the single most important resource in agriculture and technological change is increasing its importance.

REFERENCES

Due, John F., and Clower, Robert W. *Intermediate Economic Analysis,* chap. xix. 4th ed. Homewood, Ill.: Richard D. Irwin, Inc., 1965.

Ferguson, C. E. *Microeconomic Theory,* chap vii. Homewood, Ill.: Richard D. Irwin, Inc., 1966.

Heady, Earl O. *Economics of Agricultural Production and Resource Use,* chaps. xviii, xix, xx, xxi, and xxvii. Englewood Cliffs, N.J.: Prentice-Hall, Inc., 1952.

Recent issues of the *Journal of Farm Economics* contain many articles discussing the topics considered in this chapter.

Data presented in this chapter, except when otherwise noted, are taken from recent copies of *Agricultural Statistics,* United States Department of Agriculture.

Chapter 10

THE PRODUCTION OF MARKETING SERVICES

The function of a market is to bring together buyers and sellers. The purpose of this confrontation, of course, is to facilitate an exchange of money for goods. A market is termed "efficient" if all buyers can purchase the good for the least price any seller is willing to accept and if all sellers can sell the good for the highest price any buyer is willing to offer. In the perfect market of the early economic theorists, efficiency was guaranteed by assuming (1) the process of exchange is without cost, (2) complete information by all traders of all price transactions, (3) the number of buyers and sellers are of such a magnitude that no one buyer or seller can influence price, (4) homogeneous products, and (5) complete indifference among sellers and buyers, that is, any trader is willing to deal with any other trader. As the reader can imagine, perfect markets are impossible to find in practice, although some markets, such as the New York Stock Exchange, possess many of the attributes of a perfect market.

Agricultural marketing deals with more than markets. Historically, agricultural marketing has been broadly defined as encompassing all economic activity through which an agricultural product flows from the time it leaves the farm and until it reaches the consumer.[1] Thus, agricultural marketing includes all transportation, processing, warehousing, and retailing functions associated with agricultural products. During its conversion from a raw form product to a finished consumer good, the agricultural commodity may pass through the hands of several business firms and be exchanged through several markets in the economic sense, as defined above.[2]

Agricultural marketing studies are concerned with the efficiency of the markets through which agricultural goods flow as well as the productive efficiency within the various firms which process, store, transport,

---

[1] For example, see R. L. Kohls, *Marketing of Agricultural Products* (New York: The Macmillan Co., 1961), p. 6.

[2] While the term "agricultural marketing" refers to an entity much broader than the economic market, it also differs from the usual definition of marketing in business schools, i.e., the problems encountered by retail firms in the selection and sale of goods to consumers.

and sell agricultural products. They are concerned with the structure of the industry in which these firms operate, that is, the number, size, and location of firms and the degree of competition among them. In an aggregate sense, agricultural marketing is concerned with the ability of this entire "marketing" system to transmit the desires of the consumer through the system to the farmer. Just as an electrical engineer studies a receiver to determine its ability to intercept accurately signals from a distant transmitter, the agricultural marketing specialist studies the marketing system to determine whether the price "signals" received by the farmer are actually those sent by the consumer. In summary, agricultural marketing is the study of efficiency in agricultural markets, efficiency of nonfarm firms handling argicultural products, and problems associated with the final sales of agricultural goods to consumers.

Chapters 11 through 17 discuss industry structure, market efficiency, pricing policies, and aggregate concepts of market performance in agriculture. The purpose of this chapter is to introduce some of the typical problems of individual nonfarm agricultural firms and demonstrate the impact of these problems on firm decision processes. First, the production line is defined and some of the corresponding theoretical concepts are discussed. Next, problems processing firms encounter when obtaining needed agricultural inputs are discussed, with special emphasis on the uncertainties encountered. Finally, the problem of moving finished goods to retail markets is mentioned.

Because the differences among firms is a matter of degree, many firms face similar problems and the examples presented here are not wholly unique to firms handling agricultural commodities. Further, because of the diversity of firms within the agricultural marketing milieu—transportation firms range from a local trucker to railroads and air freight service and processors from local creameries to giant corporations selling nationwide and worldwide under a common brand name—the problems of such firms are similar to many industrial firms found throughout the United States.

PRODUCTION WITHIN PROCESSING FIRMS

An understanding of the production process for processing firms involves extensions and refinement of production principles presented in previous chapters. As the refinement continues, the problems brought into focus gradually shift from those of importance to the economist to those of importance to the engineer and others interested primarily in technical efficiency. That is, the economist usually assumes that the most efficient production process is used by the firm and then concerns himself with determining the firm's reaction to changing economic conditions. The fundamental problem of management science, on the other hand, is to determine the most efficient production techniques. To the extent that the firm's reaction to economic stimuli are in part dependent upon management problems (problems of technical efficiency), such problems become of interest to the economist.

The Production Line

Production activity within a processing plant takes place along a production line, i.e., a continuous sequence of manufacturing, assembly, or processing operations that culminate in a finished product. Each production line may be subdivided into a series of "stages." A stage is

FIGURE 10–1

EXAMPLES OF PRODUCTION LINES

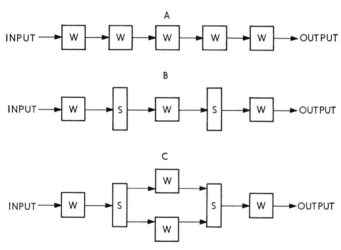

typified by the performance of a single operation after which the product is passed to a succeeding stage. Stages are of three types: The work stage performs some physical alteration of the product and usually but not necessarily involves an agglomeration of complementary durable inputs, that is, machines of various types. The transportation stage involves movement of the unfinished product between work stages (space alteration). The storage or bunker stage receives, holds, and transmits unfinished products between work and transportation stages (time alteration). The storage stage is defined to include only storage of in-process products. ("Stage" has a different meaning here than on page 51.)

Alternate schematic examples of production lines are presented in Figure 10–1. In the figure, each square represents a work stage, each rectangle a storage stage, and each connecting arrow a transportation stage. Figure 10–1A depicts a block line with no in-process storage—product flows continually through such a system. Figure 10–1B represents a line with some storage stages—such a line might become feasible when work stages operate at slightly different rates of output. Figure 10–1C pictures a line in which some stages are so slow that they must be duplicated—such stages are often termed "parallel." In general, production lines may be much more complex than the simple examples in Figure 10–1; a more complicated flow pattern is illustrated in Figure 10–2.

The concept of a production line can be viewed in different ways.

FIGURE 10–2

A COMPLEX PRODUCTION LINE

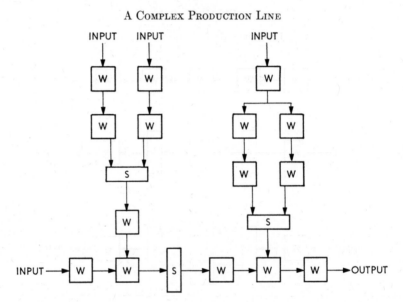

Unfortunately, some of these characterizations quickly become complex. For example, one might be interested in evaluating the dependability of a block line (Figure 10–1A). Using concepts from probability theory, it can be shown that such a chain is weaker than its weakest link. In fact a line such as depicted in Figure 10–1B is only as strong as its weakest link when the storage stages have very large capacities. While such problems cannot be approached here, they are solvable, and interested readers should refer to literature cited at the chapter's end. We now turn to a series of relevant concepts which can be attacked with tools at hand.

The Stage Production Function. Each stage is characterized by a production function uniquely its own. In fact, a stage has been defined as ". . . all productive services—durable or nondurable—that cooperate in performing a single operation or group of minor but closely related

operations."[3] To the extent that the assumptions of the production processes presented in earlier chapters apply, then the concepts presented in
those chapters also apply. When divisible, variable inputs are applied to
fixed inputs, perhaps machines, and the logic of previous chapters leads
to the correct solution. However, production stages often utilize indivisible inputs (lumpy inputs whose services must be purchased in large,
discrete units), and it is to these problems this section is addressed.

Assume that stage production is carried out with two indivisible
inputs which are both limitational and that neither can be substituted for
the other. Note that these inputs need not be durable—for example, labor
hired on a daily basis—and may be variable—number of workers hired
may be increased or decreased. The inputs, even when durable, need not
be those giving rise to fixed costs. The stage may be housed in a larger
building which would need to be heated, illuminated, cleaned, insured,
etc., regardless of stage production.

An isoquant map depicting output per unit of time under these
assumptions is presented in Figure 10–3. Output is denoted by Y and
inputs by X_1 and X_2. The isoquants are represented by the right-angle
array of dots. In this case the appropriate combination of the two inputs
is one to one regardless of input prices (why?). The inputs are complements—an increase in one results in no increase in production unless the
other is added also (in discrete units of one). Output, on the other hand,
is continuous. Given one man and one machine, output can be zero per
unit of time and increased to 10—the maximum possible with this input
combination—by increasing either the rate of output or time in production *within* the basic time unit.[4] In this case, the production function for
the minimum-cost combination of inputs is linear as shown in Figure
10–3.

The cost function for this process is also depicted in Figure 10–3.
TVC is constant for output ranges bounded by multiples of 10 (fixed
costs omitted). Thus, once the inputs are purchased, they will be operated at full capacity whenever possible. In a production line, the stage
will operate at that rate which insures optimum flow of product through
the line. For the sake of exposition, however, or if this were a one-stage
production process selling an output in pure competition, a total revenue
curve would be imposed upon the cost functions as in Figure 10–3. As
drawn, *TR* increases more rapidly than *TVC*, the "firm" would continually increase output, and firm size would be limited by other than
internal factors. The important lesson here, however, is that marginal

---

[3] B. C. French, L. L. Sammet, and R. G. Bressler, "Economic Efficiency in
Plant Operations with Special Reference to the Marketing of California Pears," *Hilgardia*, Vol. XXIV, No. 19 (July, 1956), p. 545.

[4] In general, this assumption would not have to be made. Also, the assumption
of constant returns to the inputs is not necessary.

FIGURE 10-3

PRODUCTION RELATIONSHIPS FOR PRODUCTION STAGES

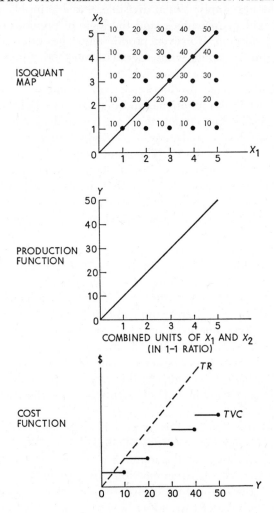

revenue is not equated to marginal cost. In fact the latter is zero except at each multiple of 10 where it equals the summed cost of buying one more unit of each input.

The stage production example just presented is often referred to as "fixed proportions" or "fixed coefficients." The first term is suggested by the fact that the same ratio of inputs is always used and the second by the fact that at maximum output the ratio of output over input is constant—at 10 in this example. When the inputs can only produce at one level of output, i.e., a machine is either on or off and produces at only one rate when one, then the term "fixed coefficients" truly applies.

The fixed-coefficient model and the model with divisible inputs that are substitutes represent the two extremes possible. Obviously many variations are possible within these extremes. One alternative is to assume one indivisible input (X_2) and one divisible input (X_1), both limitational, and then to assume that output increases linearly as the divisible input is combined with the indivisible input until a maximum output is reached after which output stays constant as more divisible input is applied.[5] That is, there exists a ratio of the inputs above which the indivisible input is limitational but below which it is not. The isoquant map for this stage production process is presented in Figure 10–4. The ratio of divisible to indivisible input above which output cannot be increased is assumed to be one to one. The expansion path appears as a stairway (why?). The production function resulting from the use of the input combinations on the expansion path (cost minimizing) is also shown in Figure 10–4 along with the total cost function. Total costs increase linearly as the use of the divisible input increases but jump each time an additional indivisible input is purchased. The distance of the jump, of course, is equal to the cost of the indivisible input. Because of these discontinuities in cost, if the production process depicted in Figure 10–4 were for a firm rather than a production stage, the profit maximizing output will not necessarily occur where marginal cost and marginal revenue are equated. In fact, with a linear *TR* function, the firm would always choose to operate where the inputs are used in a one-one ratio. Again, when profit is a nondecreasing function of output, factors other than internal production must limit firm size. (The student should draw average and marginal curves for the models presented in this section.)

The Identical Machine Problem. A special case of the stage production process resulting from the use of one indivisible input and one or more divisible inputs might be termed the identical machine problem. In this case, several identical machines are available for use. Each machine has the same production function and the same cost functions. The problem is to determine the amount of divisible input to combine with each machine to produce a given output at a minimum of cost.[6] Output amounts vary continuously from zero to the sum resulting when all machines produce at the maximum output.

Assume that output response from each of two machines follows the

[5] Hans Brems, "A Discontinuous Cost Function," *The American Economic Review*, Vol. XLII, No. 4 (September, 1952), pp. 577–86.

[6] This is, of course, the same problem as maximizing total production from several fixed (indivisible) input quantities, such as acres of land, given a limited amount of variable input.

FIGURE 10–4

PRODUCTION RELATIONSHIP FOR DIVISIBLE AND INDIVISIBLE INPUTS

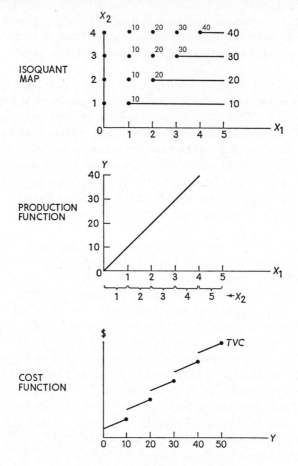

classic production function and hence the resulting total variable cost function is also of the classical shape. The problem is to decide how total production is to be divided among the two machines, I and II. The solution to the problem is illustrated in Figure 10–5A. A straight line is drawn through the origin intersecting the *TVC* function at the desired output, Y_o. Now, the question is: Should Y_o be produced on one machine or two? The answer is found by examining the relative costs at $\frac{1}{2}Y_o$. The height of the straight line at $\frac{1}{2}Y_o$ determines the total variable cost of producing each half of Y_o when Y_o is produced on one machine. The height of *TVC* at $\frac{1}{2}Y_o$ indicates the cost of producing $\frac{1}{2}Y_o$ on each machine. Thus, when the straight line falls below *TVC* at $\frac{1}{2}Y_o$, production can be carried on more cheaply on one machine than on two.

FIGURE 10–5

THE IDENTICAL MACHINE PROBLEM

A

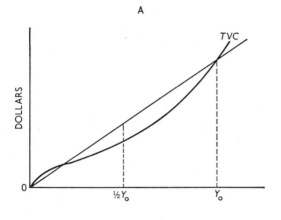

B

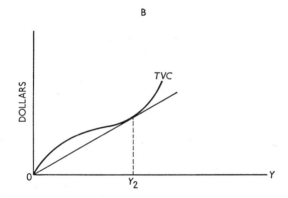

This graphic solution assumes that either all output will be produced on one machine or one half on each. Is this the appropriate
criterion? When marginal cost is increasing and exceeds average variable
cost for both machines the answer is yes. Moreover, consider the output
amount Y_2 on Figure 10–5B. For total outputs equal to or less than Y_2,
the straight line lies below the *TVC* function. Therefore, all of Y_2 will be
produced on one machine. Any other allocation of Y_2 between the two
machines will result in a higher total variable cost. Thus, output amounts
from 0 to Y_2 will be produced on one machine and outputs of $2Y_2$ or more
will be produced by dividing output equally between the two. Outputs
between Y_2 and $2Y_2$ will be allocated marginally assuming Y_2 will always
be produced on one machine. If output needed is Y_1 ($Y_1 > Y_2$), then the
difference, $Y_1 - Y_2$, will be allocated to one machine or the other (or

divided between the machines) depending upon where the *TVC* of producing this difference is a minimum. The specific solution will depend upon the functions in each case.

Time and Timing of Production

All production takes place in time. Inclusion of time in a production theory is necessary if a general theory is to be developed. Timing is important in production line problems and enters in two ways. First, through the rate of output of each stage and, second, through the time coordination of the entire production line.

Time coordination of production is important on farms as well as in processing plants. The difference lies in the fact that farm production is biological in nature and timing of operations (stages) at least in large part is not controlled by the manager. Production lines of processing plants, on the other hand, are subject to close scheduling and supervision.

The stage production function is determined per unit of time. Stage output can thus be increased by increasing output rate per unit of time (applying more variable input, X, to the fixed factors) or operating at a given rate per unit of time for a longer time period. The stage production function thus appears as in Figure 10–6A. The function is linear in the time dimension; when time is doubled, output is doubled when X_1 amount of variable input is used in each time period; resulting output is Y_1 in one time period, $2Y_1$ in two time periods, $3Y_1$ in three time periods, etc. This function could be graphed as a surface as in Chapter 5; when so done, the surface would appear perfectly straight (linear) in the time dimension.

Time and rate isoquants determined from this production function would appear as in Figure 10–6B. An isoquant depicts all the combinations of rates and times that result in a given output—the isoquant slope represents the marginal rate of substitution between units of time and rate per unit of time. The maximum output occurs at point b where the stage machinery is operated at maximum rate for the maximum number of time units, i.e., for an 8-hour shift or a 24-hour day.

A stage is usually organized timewise for a specified period of time, such as an eight-hour work shift. Once workers and other time-related inputs are procured for the shift, time within the shift becomes a free good. Rate of output per unit of time can be increased only by increasing variable input rates per unit of time. Under these assumptions, the cost of a given output level for a stage is minimized by always using the maximum amount of time. The ridgeline ab in Figure 10–6B becomes the appropriate expansion path. If this model were considered representative of a firm rather than a stage in a production line, the most profitable

FIGURE 10-6

STAGE PRODUCTION FUNCTION FOR TIME AND RATE INPUTS

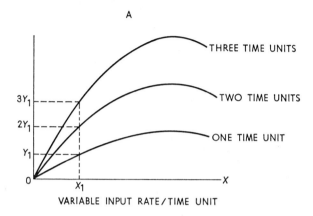

A

THREE TIME UNITS

TWO TIME UNITS

ONE TIME UNIT

VARIABLE INPUT RATE/TIME UNIT

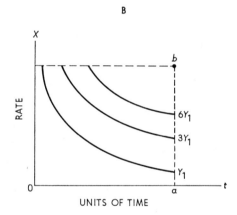

B

UNITS OF TIME

output would fall somewhere on the line *ab;* the resulting output would be the same as the most profitable output per unit of time multiplied by the number of units of time.

A more realistic problem is encountered when the manager is planning the production period. Assume for simplicity that a variable input (X) is used to increase the rate of output per unit of time and that labor is hired to increase units of time. Both labor and the variable input are assumed perfectly divisible.

An isoquant reflecting the output needed during a day (24 hours) can be derived from the stage production function (Figure 10–7A). The combination of variable input and labor that would minimize the cost of daily production is then determined by the tangency of the isoquant and isocost lines. Thus, $0C$ of variable input and $0D$ hours of labor would be used to produce output Y_1.

FIGURE 10–7

ISOCOST LINES FOR OVERTIME LABOR
CHARGES

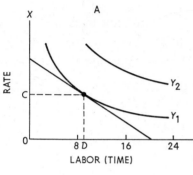

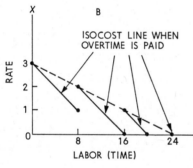

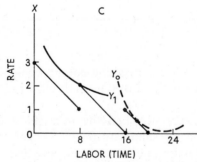

Suppose, however, that labor can be hired only in eight-hour shifts and any partial shifts must be paid overtime at increased hourly rates. Then the isocost lines would appear as in Figure 10–7B. The rationale underlying this isocost line is as follows: A total amount of money is available to purchase labor or the variable (rate) input. When this is all used to purchase the input, three units can be purchased. Or when labor is paid at the 8-hour rate, 2 units of X and 8 hours of labor, 1 unit of X and 16 hours of labor, or no X and 24 hours of labor may be purchased. These points are connected by a dashed line to indicate the position of the isocost line when overtime need not be paid. To purchase labor in amounts less than eight-hour shifts, however, overtime must be paid. The actual isocost line thus slopes downward more steeply (as determined by the overtime rates) than the dashed line until any multiple of eight hours is reached. At these points, labor can be purchased more cheaply in regular eight-hour rates and the isocost line jumps upward. At eight hours, the same amount of labor can be purchased either by paying overtime or by paying regular eight-hour shift rates. The manager will choose the lower labor rate and hence be able to purchase more X without purchasing less labor.

The presence of overtime charges tends to make labor a lumpy input used only in eight-hour shifts. For example, given the isoquant labeled Y_1 in Figure 10–7C, the output will be produced at least cost for a stage when one 8-hour shift of labor is hired in each 24 hours. Further, because of its nature, this solution (use of an eight-hour shift) is not sensitive to changes in hourly labor rates. A second solution (in Figure 10–7C) is represented by the tangency of the isoquant Y_o with the isocost line; this solution involves overtime. (Often, tangency solutions using overtime may not be cost minimizing. For example, consider an isoquant tangent to the isocost line at two units of X and 4 units of [overtime] labor but with a value less than two units of X when labor equals eight. The quantity of output represented by the isoquant can then be produced more cheaply using eight units of labor and less than two units of X. Depending upon the relative magnitudes of overtime and regular time, the eight-hour shift will tend to dominate the overtime solutions.)

A third type of time problem arises when a limited amount of time is available to produce a unit of output. Production occurs by passing the product through a time sequence of stages. If time were not of the essence and assuming labor and related inputs are purchased in eight-hour units, each stage would use the maximum (eight hours) time available. Total time elapsed used to produce each unit would thus be $8n$, where n is the number of stages. When time is limited (less than $8n$) then the rate of production per unit of time in each stage must be increased. Assuming that costs of production increase as time decreases, how should the total amount of time be divided among the stages to achieve the needed production in the limited time at a minimum of cost? The answer is found using the usual marginal principles applicable to the allocation of a limited resource. Under the assumption that each stage has hired inputs for eight-hour shifts, time has no direct cost as such. But it does have an indirect or opportunity cost in each stage; if time of production is to be reduced in a stage, the rate of output per time unit must be increased and this increase comes only at a cost. The needed output from each stage can be represented by a time-cost isoquant. The solution occurs, as outlined in previous chapters, where the marginal rate of substitution of time for cost is equal in each stage and the sum of the times used in each stage equals the total amount available.

The solution is illustrated in Figure 10–8 for a three-stage process. The raw input first goes to Stage I, then Stage II, and finally III. The isoquant for each stage represents all combinations of times and costs (rates) needed at each stage to produce an intermediate product which eventually is used to produce total final output. The times used for each stage must add to the total time available. The cost minimizing solution is illustrated at t_{1_1}, t_{2_1}, and t_{3_1} for the three stages, respectively, where the slopes of the isoquants are equal and $t_{1_1} + t_{2_1} + t_{3_1} = T$, the total time available.

The rationale underlying this solution has been presented in previous chapters. However, an intuitive argument can be presented by affecting a shift from the optimum. Suppose time in Stage I is reduced

FIGURE 10-8

THE TIMING OF PRODUCTION

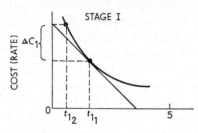

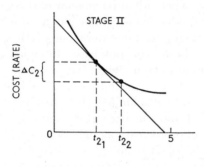

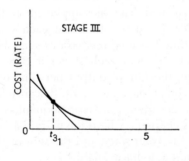

from t_{1_1} to t_{1_2} and time in Stage II increased a similar amount from t_{2_1} to t_{2_2}. Then the costs in Stage I are increased by ΔC_1 and the costs in Stage II decreased by ΔC_2. Because ΔC_1 exceeds ΔC_2 (by the slope of the isoquants), the total costs added over the three stages are increased by the movement from the optimum.

PROCUREMENT OF INPUTS

Typical agricultural processing firms are represented by dairy processing plants, poultry processing plants, fruit and vegetable canning plants, flour mills, egg-breaking plants, etc. In each case, these firms purchase a raw agricultural product and transform it into consumer products, such as fresh milk, butter, broilers, canned fruit, or products used ultimately to produce consumer products, such as liquid and frozen eggs or bread flour. To produce, these firms need management, labor, physical facilities and capital equipment, electricity, water, and a host of other inputs used by any factory. Common to all, however, is that they need a raw agricultural input—a commodity which is a farm output. The procurement of other inputs by the processing firm is likely to be similar to procurement problems of any industry; the procurement of the agricultural input presents a more unique problem. A discussion of these problems is the purpose of this section; broader aspects of the problem are discussed in the chapters on agricultural marketing.

The uniqueness of the procurement of an agricultural commodity, an input for the processor but an output for the farmer, depends in part upon the degree to which the market for that commodity resembles the perfect economic market described in the introduction. The processing firm wants an assured supply of quality input and, because of its profit maximizing motive, desires to purchase it at the lowest price a seller will accept. Many buyers and sellers assure the processor of any quantity he wants at a price determined in the marketplace, where price information is available to all. A homogeneous product assures him of at least a known quality of input, if not the quality he would prefer. Indifference among buyers and sellers assures him that sellers will deal with him if he offers the market price.

Some of the markets for raw agricultural commodities meet enough of the conditions of the perfect market to permit effective operation in practice. The wheat market is perhaps one of the best examples. Wheat is grown throughout the Great Plains and to a lesser extent in the Corn Belt. Quality is measured by weight per bushel and, in the case of hard wheats, protein content. Prices for each quality level are established daily and broadcast as public knowledge. While small price differentials and preferences among buyers and sellers exists locally, these differences do not prohibit large flour millers and other users from meeting their needs on a national level. In addition, wheat is readily stored and shipped—thus, time and space dimensions are easily added to the market for wheat.

The market for other agricultural crops, widely produced, widely demanded, easily stored and transported, is similar to that of wheat. Barley, soybeans, corn, and other feed grains are all examples. Departures from this type of market occur as products become more perishable, when production is limited to a small area, when there are few buyers and sellers, when processing costs or output quality are dependent upon input quality, when production of the agricultural good requires unique managerial skills, etc. For example, livestock markets are less perfect than many crop markets; poultry markets (white meats) have generally departed more widely from the norm than have swine and cattle (red meat) markets. Livestock, when taken to market, must be slaughtered; delay means added handling and feed costs, making "storage" before slaughter undesirable. Shrinkage encourages the slaughter of livestock and especially poultry fairly close to the area of production.

Perishable fruits and vegetables are much like poultry with the additional qualifications that production is highly seasonal, often limited to small geographic areas and thus subject to local weather variability, and often characterized by few sellers and more often few buyers. The market, in the traditional sense, usually functions very poorly for these commodities, although from the farmers' viewpoint, the market for fresh fruits and vegetables may approximate the traditional market more closely than does the market for processed foods.

Firm Size and Supply Area

A food processing company must determine where to locate processing plants and the capacity of these plants. One researcher has suggested that a multiple plant processing firm might pose the following questions:[7]

> How many plants should we have?
> Where should our plants be located?
> How large should each plant be?
> Where should raw material processed in each plant be obtained?
> What customers should be serviced by each plant?

The first two and the last questions are too broad to be analyzed here (but are discussed in the reference cited). The answers to such questions depend upon the location and density (volume of business per unit of the supply area) of the producers of the agricultural input, transportation costs of raw and finished products, location of consumers, plant site costs, production costs at proposed locations, as well as other cost and noncost factors associated with location.

Given plant location, the optimum plant size can be determined. Suppose that a given agricultural commodity—an input to the processing firm—is grown uniformly throughout the supply area surrounding a plant.[8] One important cost facing the processing plant is the "assembly" cost, the cost of traveling to the farm, loading the commodity, returning to the plant and unloading. If the price paid by the plant for the commodity is constant throughout the area, then assembly costs for a given volume of the commodity are minimized when the plant chooses to purchase in a circular area centered by the plant. The reason for this is as follows: Given uniform product density, an (additional) unit of commodity can be obtained by traveling a given distance from any point on the periphery of the supply area and the cost of traveling this added distance will be the same only if all points on the periphery are equidistant from the plant. Of course, uneven commodity density or the presence of nonuniform transportation facilities, road grades, highways, or rivers would cause the supply area to become noncircular. The average variable assembly cost per unit of commodity will increase with the quantity purchased but at a decreasing rate because the area of the circular supply region increases as a function of the square of the radius. To secure a given marginal increment of commodity, the radius of a large circle has to be increased less than the radius of a small circle.

The average at-farm cost of the commodity (purchase price), the average assembly cost, and the average processing cost can be added to

[7] John F. Stollsteimer, "A Working Model for Plant Numbers and Locations," *Journal of Farm Economics*, August, 1963, pp. 631–45.

[8] The following discussion was presented by J. C. Williamson, Jr., "The Equilibrium Size of Marketing Plants in a Spatial Market," *Journal of Farm Economics*, November, 1962, pp. 953–67. Also, see B. D. French, "Some Considerations in Estimating Assembly Cost Functions for Agricultural Processing Operations," *Journal of Farm Economics*, November 1960, pp. 767–78.

obtain the average total cost per unit of commodity processed (Figure 10–9). All of these cost curves are long run. Economies of scale cause average processing costs to fall. Increases in assembly costs eventually offset falling processing costs and average total costs begin to rise.

The cost curves presented are computed in units of commodity input. Assuming the plant can sell its output at a constant price and a fixed ratio between commodity input and product output, a "value of output per unit of input" can be determined and plotted on Figure 10–9.

FIGURE 10–9

Cost and Revenue Functions for a Processing Plant

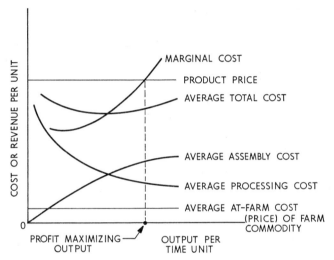

The optimum size of plant is determined by the intersection of this "value of output" and the marginal cost curve derived from total costs, i.e., the sum of at-farm costs, processing costs, and assembly costs. The firm should build a plant of a size indicated by the equilibrium amount of commodity input as long as (long-run) profits are zero or positive at that point.

If positive profits exist and persist, other firms will be inclined to build plants in the area. If the production of the farm commodity is sufficiently dense over a large enough area, additional plants would probably locate so that their supply areas do not overlap those of existing plants. As entry continues further, circular supply areas will overlap and plants competing for the farm commodity will bid up at-farm purchase prices and supply areas will take noncircular shapes depending upon relative assembly costs, processing costs, and revenue functions of the plants. Many times, because of location of the market for the finished product and availability of labor or other inputs, new plants will locate adjacent to old plants, perhaps in the same urban area, and both will compete within a given supply area. In this case, plant survival will depend upon efficiency in cost reduction as well as strength (high prices and good sales volume) in the markets for its outputs. An extension of the discussion and analyses of more complex situations can be found in the references cited at the end of this chapter.

Input Procurement and Vertical Integration

When the market for an agricultural commodity departs substantially from the conditions of the perfect market, processors of agricultural commodities are often faced with considerable uncertainty concerning the quantity, quality, and price of raw inputs. This uncertainty often grows to such a magnitude that the processor either ceases production or seeks an alternative method of obtaining needed supplies.

One set of alternatives to the open-market system has come to be known as vertical integration. Integration in general refers to some degree of coordination or control between firms which formerly operated independently. Horizontal integration is the combination of like firms, such as the merger of two railroads. Vertical integration applies when a firm coordinates with another second firm which either supplies inputs to the first or purchases the outputs from the first. The term "vertical integration" is at present quite widely defined in agricultural economics and ranges from simple forward contracts of a crop for a year to complete joint ownership of farm, processing, and retailing facilities.

Examples of vertical integration in agriculture are:

1. The processor agrees to buy, at some time before harvest, the production of a specified number of acres (or number of units of product) at a given price. Similar contracts may be executed for livestock or poultry.
2. The processor agrees to process and market the farmer's product and share in the return realized from the eventual sale of the product.
3. The processor sells supplies to the farmer, buys his product, and offers technical assistance, but the entrepreneurial risk (gains or losses) remains with the farmer.
4. The processor sells inputs to the farmer, buys the product, makes all management decisions, and guarantees the farmer a return.
5. Complete ownership of farm, processing, and marketing facilities and complete coordination of production planning within the firm.

Some of the problems of input procurement will be discussed here; later chapters will evaluate more fully the reasons for vertical integration and its impact upon agricultural marketing (and retailing) processes. The problems of obtaining inputs are different for each industry; thus the following discussion emphasizes problems that are illustrative rather than all-encompassing in nature. The type of product considered will in general be one that is perishable and harvested once a year. Problems associated with such a product will have both similarities and differences when compared to (say) milk or eggs. A more complete discussion is presented in Chapter 16.

The procurement of inputs by processors does not usually function as smoothly as suggested by the simplified assumptions of the previous section. In general, processors want adequate total quantities (enough to supply their markets) of a suitable quality input and they would like to process that quantity at a minimum of cost. The grower, on the other hand, wants to sell his product at the maximum gain to him. For both, uncertainty becomes a problem.

Consider first the processor's concern with obtaining a quality input in sufficient quantities. With many buyers and sellers, none of whom can affect price, the structure of the market creates no problem. Each seller can market all he wishes, each buyer can obtain his needs and the market will determine the price. Often, however, there are only a few buyers, with one or two comprising most of the market, and perhaps even a few sellers. Quantity uncertainty arises to complement price uncertainty. Growers simply do not know whether one of the few processors will need his product while processors cannot depend upon being supplied by any grower.

Under these circumstances there exists a strong tendency for both parties to favor preharvest commitments. In some cases, the grower may prefer to enter into a contract before planting and by so doing remove uncertainties associated with farmland leases, credit availability, etc. The processor may prefer such a contract because it enables him to control cultural practices, variety selection, harvesting dates, and general quality of the product. When some processors enter into contracts, the prospect of an open market existing at harvesttime is reduced and other processors will follow. The same is true of growers. The grower, of course, is particularly anxious to avoid being left with large stocks of a perishable product at harvest.

Next consider the processor's desire to obtain the needed quantity of input (the grower's product) and to process it at a minimum cost. Each processor has a production target (tonnage) he would like to meet each year. Because contracts are usually by the acre, the processor would like a stable acreage-tonnage ratio from year to year. In this way variations among years can be reduced and the most efficient production methods can be planned and used. Even when assured a reasonably constant total amount of input each year, the processor has not necessarily solved his volume problems. Volume peaks will occur within a season. If peak deliveries exceed processing capacity, stocks of perishable inputs will build and the processor will be faced with their loss or quality deterioration. These uncertainties again stimulate the processor to arrive at some type of contractual agreement with growers.

To minimize processing costs the processor will tend to build the smallest possible plant, i.e., the size that would adequately process all inputs when operated at full capacity over the length of the harvest period. It is, therefore, to his benefit to extend the harvest period to a maximum length. This can be done in a given producing area by in-fluencing (1) the cultural practices of growers and hence the date of maturity of their product and (2) the size of crew and the rate growers' harvest mature crops; it can also be accomplished by purchasing from widely scattered producing areas.

Ideally, as demonstrated above, the processor would prefer to buy all of his raw material input as close as possible to the plant. Hauling costs would then be minimized. Other costs arise, however. Crops in one area are possibly subject to the same weather, disease, and insects. The processor who receives all his input from one area might thus expect a high variability of input from a constant acreage. Further, crops in one area tend to mature simultaneously, contributing to peaks at harvest. To reduce year-to-year variability, the processor may decide to purchase inputs from producing areas not immediately surrounding his plant. This will be particularly true if the bounds (time and distance) within which the perishable product can be transported include producing areas with significantly different weather conditions from the standpoint of crop culture. Increased transportation costs are incurred in the hope of reduc-ing annual tonnage variability while maintaining the same tonnage aver-age and thereby enabling the processor to meet production goals at lower cost.

Buying from outlying areas will also help flatten peaks and troughs in the day-to-day rate of input flow to the plant. If cultural practices and harvesting rates aid in avoiding peaks in producing areas contiguous to the plant, they will provide even more flexibility when aided by weather differences in outlying areas. Once again hauling costs are increased, but this time to extend the harvest period and again reduce the size of plant and hence costs.

In summary, price, quantity, and quality uncertainties existing in the market between growers and processors cause their profits to become interrelated. Careful coordination of cultural practices, harvesting, and processing is necessary if the two parties are to avoid inefficiencies and resulting losses in profit. Furthermore, if each followed an independent profit-maximizing path, the result might not be optimal for either party or for the ultimate consumer of the product. A high degree of coordination among growers and processors is needed if the quality of product, in the quantities demanded, are to be supplied to consumers. In the case of some (but not all) agricultural products, vertical integration has provided the answer.

ORGANIZING THE PRODUCTION AND DISTRIBUTION OF FOOD

Consumers in the United States spent $69.8 billion on food in 1964. This vast sum was spent upon thousands of food items of varying size, shape, color, quality, etc. Each of these food items had to be assembled from farm production points and, after processing, redistributed to consumers. The physical movement of goods through channels of procurement and distribution is in general referred to as "physical distribution" or "logistics." The exact cost of physical distribution as a part of the total food bill is unknown, but transportation costs alone in 1964 were estimated to be $5.1 billion, almost 11 percent of the total marketing bill.[9] When handling, ordering, processing, protective packaging, and other related costs of distribution are added, the total cost of physical distribution must be substantial indeed!

The expense incurred in physical distribution is large, and savings from increased efficiencies can also be large. For example, an estimated five billion cases of grocery products are moved each year from warehouses into food retail stores. If the time needed to handle each case could be reduced by one minute, the estimated annual savings in food handling costs would be $160 million.[10]

Ideally, the food processing firm would like to proceed as follows: The quantity of product to be supplied at the end of the production period (day, week, etc.) would be accurately forecast at the beginning of the period. Then the processes of input procurement, production planning and scheduling, inventory (stocks on hand) of finished product, and distribution to wholesalers or other points of distribution would all be planned simultaneously in such a way to minimize the total cost of meeting the estimated demand. These processes can be visualized for purposes of analogy as similar to the production line described in a previous section. Input procurement leads to production which in turn leads to inventories and final distribution. Each part can be visualized as a subsystem or component of the total system.

A word of warning. Generalities can never apply to all situations, and food processing and distribution problems are extremely diverse.

---

[9] *Food from Farmer to Consumer,* Report of the National Commission on Food Marketing, June, 1966, chap. iii.

[10] Paul Shaffer, John C. Bonna, James J. Karitas, and Gordon Flynn, *Handling Groceries from Warehouse to Retail Store Shelves,* Marketing Research Report No. 473, Transportation and Facilities Research Division, ARS, USDA, April, 1966.

Perishable agricultural inputs must be processed as they are delivered to the processor. If the processors' product is also perishable, meat for example, it must also be marketed as produced. Inventory and production policies may rationally differ widely, and all such differences cannot be reviewed in this short discussion.

Historically the management of each component of the total system has been separated from each of the other components. If each component is minimizing costs, it was thought, then the total system is minimizing costs. This is true only if the components are independent with respect to all major inputs. In fact, for most businesses the costs of the various components are related. Production costs may be reduced by following a production schedule that unduly increases inventories and storage costs. On the other hand, small inventories may result in shortages at retail outlets and loss of sales. Transportation costs may be reduced by moving large volumes of product by the cheapest mode of transportation —but all the while substantial amounts of the firm's capital are invested in goods slowly moving to market, thus increasing capital costs.

The modern logistics concept recognizes that all components of the total system are related with respect to time and costs. (A similar problem was solved for the production time. See Figure 10–8.) The key to minimizing total costs—subject of course to meeting the firm's operating standards—is to balance the system analytically by means of a technique called "trade-offs." A trade-off is the offsetting of higher costs incurred in one component of the system by resulting lower costs in one or more of the others. Trade-offs are possible when the firm is not in equilibrium—in the sense of the classic economics—and therefore often occur in practice. (The cost changes, ΔC_1 and ΔC_2, in Figure 10–8 are "trade-offs.") An example of a trade-off might be found in protective packaging and cost of transportation. Usually packaging costs increase as transportation costs decrease. If the increased cost of premium transportation is exceeded in magnitude by the reduction of packaging costs, a feasible trade-off results. A trade-off may have a chain reaction. Premium transportation may also result in fewer shortages at retail outlets and a smaller inventory at the factory.

That trade-offs exist is a fact. Finding and implementing them is another matter. The traditional organization of business firms often does not lend itself well to the integrated decision making required of the total systems concept. Experts in firm logistics are now concerned with the manner in which management can coordinate the integrated system. Detailed information about production, inventories, and sales must flow freely through the system. Orders arrive and products must be shipped. Decision-makers must have relevant information concerning some or all phases of the firm's business activity in previous days. Much of this is being done through reorganization and the use of electronic data processing equipment. Operations research techniques are used to coordinate production scheduling, inventories, and distribution.

The Pillsbury Company of Minneapolis, Minnesota, has implemented a modern logistics system. Pillsbury is one of the largest flour millers in the United States and ranks high in the sale of consumer food mixes, refrigerated dough products, flour, and formula feeds. Pillsbury's experience with the coordinated logistics concept has been described as follows:[11]

Prior to implementation of the logistics concept, Pillsbury operated from 33 branch offices, each performing accounting, credit, and office processing functions. The operation was also characterized by a product supply network through which shipments were made from plant warehouses direct to customers, with out-of-stock items often being filled from nearly 100 small field warehouses. No plant produced the entire grocery line, and since it was required to provide mixed carload service to all customers, each plant warehouse had to stock products produced at other plant locations. The plant production control group controlled plant warehouse inventories and stock replenishment, whereas branch office managers controlled field warehouse activity.

Today Pillsbury has effectively implemented a logistical subsystem which includes all components (except possibly procurement) under one executive. Salesman's orders are now transmitted directly to one central logistics center. After editing, a computer checks inventory status, prices the order, checks against customer credit limits and outstanding receivables, adds the transport routes and other instructions to order. A communication computer then transmits these instructions to one of 14 distribution centers (replacing plant and field warehouses) where the message emerges as a loading order and bill of lading for next day shipping.

Generated sales forecasts are analyzed in light of production constraints. Production schedules by packaging line are developed centrally and allocations made to distribution centers in light of the forecast and as the direct product of the immediate updating of computerized inventory status records after order processing.

In a recent statement, a Pillsbury vice president summed up their accomplishments as "Management by Perception." He stated their centralized system gives management the complete state of the business as of 5:00 P.M. one day, at 8:00 A.M. the next day. Their system has allowed a manager to "stretch horizontally" to incredible dimensions in his effective direction span and have merged many successive elements in the administrative pyramid into a single integrated function. Several echelons in the chain of command disappeared and the executive level found itself nearer the field of action.

As computer operations expanded the manager's "theater of command," there was concern whether enlargement of the sphere would dilute the effectiveness of his direction. But it was found that he was more thoroughly in

[11] K. U. Flood, "The Business Logistics Concept," unpublished manuscript, July, 1966, pp. 12–14.

charge than before. A manager could count on better execution of his plans and decisions—far superior to that given him by any supporting staff in the past.

REFERENCES

BREMS, HANS. "A Discontinuous Cost Function," *The American Economic Review,* Vol. XLII, No. 4 (September, 1952), pp. 577–86.

COLLINS, N. R.; MUELLER, W. F.; and BIRCH, E. M. *Grower-Processor Integration.* California Agricultural Experiment Station Bulletin 768, October, 1959.

FLOOD, K. U. "The Business Logistics Concept," unpublished manuscript, July, 1966.

Food from Farmer to Consumer, chap. iii. Report of the National Commission on Food Marketing, June, 1966.

FRENCH, B. C.; SAMMET, L. L.; and BRESSLER, R. G. "Economic Efficiency in Plant Operations with Special Reference to the Marketing of California Pears," *Hilgardia,* Vol. 24, No. 19 (University of California, Berkeley, July, 1956).

FRENCH, B. C. "Some Considerations in Estimating Assembly Cost Functions for Agricultural Processing Operations," *Journal of Farm Economics,* November, 1960, pp. 767–78.

FRISCH, RAGNAR. *Theory of Production.* Chicago: Rand, McNally & Co., 1965.

HENRY, W. R., and RANNIKOR, R. "Integration in Practice—The Broiler Case," *Journal of Farm Economics,* December, 1960, pp. 1265–74.

———; CHAPPELL, J. S.; and SEAGRAVES, J. A. *Broiler Production Density, Plant Sizes, Alternative Operating Plants, and Total Unit Costs.* North Carolina Agricultural Experiment Station Technical Bulletin No. 144, June, 1960.

HOLT, C. C.; MODIGLIANI, F.; MUTH, J. F.; and SIMON, H. A. *Planning Production, Inventories, and Work Force.* Englewood Cliffs, N.J.: Prentice-Hall, Inc., 1960.

KOENIGSBERG, ERNEST. "Production Lines and Internal Storage—A Review," *Management Science,* Vol. V, No. 4 (July, 1959), pp. 410–33.

KOHLS, R. L. *Marketing of Agricultural Products.* New York: The Macmillan Co., 1961.

SHAFFER, PAUL; BONNA, JOHN C.; KARITAS, JAMES J.; and FLYNN, GORDON. *Handling Groceries from Warehouse to Retail Store Shelves.* Marketing Research Report No. 473, Transportation and Facilities Research Division, ARS, USDA, April, 1966.

STOLLSTEIMER, JOHN F. "A Working Model for Plant Numbers and Locations," *Journal of Farm Economics,* August, 1963, pp. 631–45.

WILLIAMSON, J. C., JR. "The Equilibrium Size of Marketing Plants in a Spatial Market," *Journal of Farm Economics,* November, 1962, pp. 953–67.

PART III

The Theory of Markets

Chapter 11

COMPETITION AMONG THE MANY

The detailed complexity of a market economy can never be understood in its entirety by any one individual. Precisely how are x million hogs produced by one million farmers, transported to n markets, slaughtered and processed in m plants, distributed to k supermarkets, and sold in rather even day-to-day flow to 200 million consumers? Multiply this example by a thousand other commodities and complicate it by much more intricate systems of processing and manufacturing in many cases and you glimpse the immensity of a national market economy. Yet the fantastic amount of coordination implicit in such a process somehow gets done.

The market economist devotes his efforts to explaining how the system works and/or evaluating how well it works. He is concerned with what products are produced; how the product designs are determined or what grades are set up; the procedures by which products are sold; the quantities sold; and the prices paid. He is interested in the ways in which the market system adjusts to various "disturbances" as well as its possible position if it were in static equilibrium. He is interested in the answers to these questions as they are affected by the type of "market structure" of a particular industry.

We shall concentrate our attention on *how* the system works rather than *how well*. Evaluation of the *how well* of "market performance" is a difficult and complex task. The reader is cautioned to avoid the temptations of quick and easy judgments based on partial knowledge and understanding.

How nice and simple it would be if we could confine our competitive theory to the supply and demand analysis we learned in the Principles course! Supply and demand are fundamental to all market analysis, and they are in no sense superseded by the chapters that follow. However, we soon find that we must go behind the forces of supply and demand to discover the vast differences in supply and demand and to connect the industry supply and demand to the decisions of real-life firms in that industry.

In Figures 11–1 and 11–2, we see that comparable shifts in demand have no effect on price in 11–1 but a big effect in 11–2. What is the

263

FIGURE 11-1   FIGURE 11-2

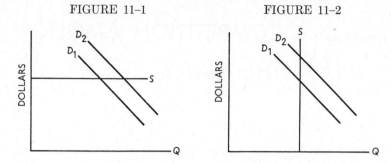

justification for one supply curve being *perfectly elastic* (horizontal) and the other supply curve *almost perfectly inelastic* (almost vertical)? Suppose we were to find that both of these curves are for the same industry but 11-1 is in the long run and 11-2 is in the short run. We must go behind the supply curve to the industry firms to understand what is meant.

We shall use the conventional *definition* of market structure as those characteristics of a market which significantly affect the competitive behavior of the firms in it. There are several important structural characteristics and some variation between markets in their relative significance. Degree of product differentiation (see next paragraph) and the ease with which new firms may enter are invariably important. The number and size distribution of buyers are important. A distinction of first importance is the number and size distribution of sellers in the market. This chapter is concerned with those competitive situations in which the numbers of buyers and sellers are large; the next chapter with those situations in which the number of sellers is small, although the number of buyers is large. This chapter combines material often found in separate chapters on pure (atomistic) competition and monopolistic (imperfect) competition.

THE NATURE OF COMPETITION AMONG THE MANY

Substitutes and Differentiation

If you deposit a dollar bill in a savings bank, you don't expect to get the same bill back when you make a withdrawal later. Any other dollar bill is a perfect substitute for the original one. One bill may have been crisp and new while the other is old and soiled, so that they were not identical in appearance but they were identical *in value*. Likewise, two products are often identical in value to a buyer because one is a perfect substitute for the other, even though the products may not be identical in appearance or chemical structure. On the other hand, two products that are identical in appearance or chemical structure may differ in value to a particular buyer because of different brand names, or different reputations, or different guarantees of quality. Products are said to be "differentiated" whenever two closely competing products differ in value to some or all buyers, regardless of the reasons of the buyers. If many buyers regard Smith brand candy bars as better than Jones brand candy bars, this attitude is a fact of economic importance. Obviously, it is important to Smith, but why to the economist or to society? Because any loyalty of buyers to Smith brand candy bars isolates Smith to some degree from his competitors. How Smith is isolated depends upon the dollars and cents loyalty that buyers possess. If Smith bars can be raised in price from 10 cents to 15 cents without materially reducing sales while Jones bars remain at 10 cents then most buyers obviously regard the two bars as very imperfect substitutes. We observe that most candy bars are pretty good substitutes in the minds of most people, so that prices for similar sized bars are generally similar.

Agricultural products are often perfect substitutes between units: Brown's Grade A milk is indistinguishable from Smith's Grade A milk; both may sell for identical prices. The imperfect substitutes in agriculture arise from quality differences which may or may not be associated with particular producers. These quality differences are often "graded" in agricultural markets so that all units within a grade are perfect or near perfect substitutes. The theory of grading is discussed in Chapter 17. The differences between grading and conscious product differentiation by processors and manufacturers are substantial enough to justify separate consideration.

Product Differentiation and Competition

Competition among sellers is defined as the rivalry to sell "substitute products" in the same market. Since purchasing power of buyers is limited, it can be argued that all products are substitutes—that a sale of golf clubs may reduce the amount of steak that can be sold. The bit of truth in this conjecture is too small to be very enlightening to a study of competition. The sporting goods retailer is more concerned about the sales of competing brands of golf clubs than he is about the sales of steak in the community.

We can recognize the significant variations in degree of substitution between products and still have an operational concept if we *define* x and y as "substitutes" when increased sales of either one in a market during a given time period "ordinarily" reduce the sales of the other. The modifier "ordinarily" was slipped in the definition to exclude exceptional conditions such as a special promotion when greater sales of x might excite interest in both x and y and lead to greater sales of y as well as x.

Let's return to our definition of competition among sellers as the rivalry to sell substitute products in the same market. Although only two sellers are *necessary* to rivalry, two are not *sufficient* because they may choose not to compete. One hundred sellers are very likely to be sufficient for competition. While any number of sellers might agree not to compete, the many complications of obtaining and implementing such an agreement among many sellers lead most economists to feel that competition is more likely as the number of sellers is larger. Therefore, modern economists have found it useful to distinguish between competition among many sellers and competition among a few sellers.

It should be obvious from our discussion of substitute products that numbers of sellers is not the whole story. Competition among 5 sellers of identical products might be as intense as among 10 sellers of nonidentical (but substitute) products. In fact, a major contention of the "theory of monopolistic competition" was that competition among many sellers of nonidentical (but substitute) products is different than competition among an equally large group of sellers of an identical product.

Characteristics of the Large Group

In the late 1920's Professor Edward Chamberlin developed a theory of competition of firms with slightly imperfect substitutes which he called "monopolistic competition." The central concept was that each product has slight monopoly elements unique to it and yet the limited significance of these elements exposed the firms to most of the rigors of competition.

The "large group" is a large number of firms each of which has such a small influence upon the sales of any other firm in the group that each firm can act without fearing retaliation from the other firms. If all but one firm were in equilibrium, the movement of that firm to equilibrium would not disturb the positions of the other firms. The key concept of the large group is the lack of interdependence between any pair of firms. This lack may be so large that two firms hardly regard each other as competitors even though they sell strikingly similar products or services in the same market. Large numbers of firms are often associated with such a lack of interdependence. If my neighbor and I each produce 0.1 percent of industry output of hogs, then even such an extreme action as his doubling his output has such a minor impact upon total output that it is of little interest to me. However, the reader should be warned that numbers alone can be deceptive. Within an "industry" of 1,000 firms, it is possible that a few firms are highly interdependent with each other so that actions of one of the few do directly and significantly affect the other. In such a case, shall we say that the industry is a large group or not? It contains both a small group and a large group. Most firms, say 995, may operate in a large group with its impersonal type of competition, while a few firms, say 5, in the same industry may operate in a more personal type of direct competition which will later be defined more carefully as competition among the few.

An important aspect of competition within the large group is the helplessness of the individual action when it is counter to the group. Suppose Jones thinks that a lowering of industry output by 50 percent would not reduce total receipts and would increase profits greatly. Suppose Jones, who produces 1 percent of industry output cuts his own output by one half but nobody else in the industry changes output. Then the effect of Jones' action on industry output and price is hardly perceptible, and Jones has accomplished nothing except the lowering of his own gross revenue by one half. If everyone in the industry had imitated Jones, his anticipations about industry benefits might have been realized. However, the lesson to Jones is that the industry did not go along and that his unilateral actions hurt him alone. The next logical step is for Jones to conclude that his interests and the industry's interests are different and that he must take care of himself rather than worry about industry interests. Such selfish reasoning is accurate, although it need not go so far as to preclude trips to the annual conventions of the industry or the giving of pep talks to others about the virtues of industry cooperation.

The Firm

When there are many firms, each is "small." May it be logically assumed that firms in a large group have cost limitations on the maximum size of the firm? If they do not have a U-shaped cost curve at reasonably small size, then why are they still small firms—i.e., "small" relative to industry output. This implication is generally accepted as justifying the assumption of the U-shaped cost curve for firms in atomistic (pure) competition. That is, since there are no constraints on the demand faced by the firm in *atomistic competition,* the equilibrium size of the firm must be limited by its cost curve. However, in the *large group selling imperfect substitutes,* each seller does have a slightly sloping demand curve stemming from some slight loyalties of some customers. Thus, it is possible that the declining sales curve of the firm might limit its growth. It is, of course, not logically necessary to assume cost constraints upon the size of firms if demand constraints already exist. But by the same token, it is logically *possible* for both cost and demand constraints to be hampering the growth of an individual firm (Figures 11–3, 11–4, 11–5). For example, farm firms face horizontal demand curves, and the limits on their size are U-shaped cost curves. On the other hand, the limits on the size of a barbershop or drugstore in a city may be either U-shaped costs or a declining demand or both.

Firms in atomistic competition differ from their counterparts in monopolistic competition in several ways. First, the negative tilt of the

FIGURE 11-3   FIGURE 11-4

COST CONSTRAINT   DEMAND CONSTRAINT

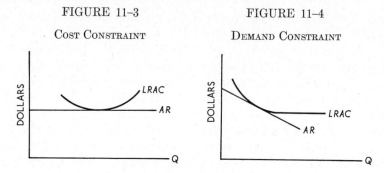

FIGURE 11-5

COST AND DEMAND CONSTRAINTS

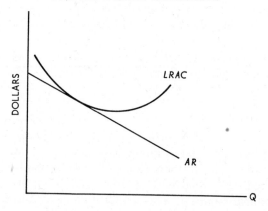

sales curve facing the monopolistic competitor contrasts with the horizontal slope of atomistic competition. This tilt requires a pricing policy since the firm has some price leeway; it causes a divergence between price and *MR* where there is none in atomistic competition. The leeway implicit in the demand curve tilt could be easily overestimated, as it is generally agreed that the slope usually deviates only slightly from the horizontal.

Second, the monopolistic competitor has an incentive to expand efforts in promoting his product and services, developing improved models, etc., in hopes of making his little niche in the market more secure, more profitable, and larger. Since the atomistic competitor's product is identical to that of the entire industry, it is pointless to advertise, promote, etc., except possibly in cooperation with other firms at the industry level. Therefore, the monopolistic competitor has a special class of decisions to make about advertising, product design, etc., which does not concern the atomistic competitor. Both competitors—monopolistic and atomistic—are in large group competition, as we have defined it, but they "play the game" somewhat differently. In many cases, however, the results of the game are quite similar.

DERIVATION OF THE INDUSTRY SUPPLY CURVE

The supply curve is defined as the relationship between the price of a product and the quantity that will be supplied. Any firm in atomistic competition will equate price to marginal cost and supply the corresponding quantity. As various price possibilities are considered and equated to marginal cost, it becomes obvious that the supply curve of the firm is traced out by the *MC* (marginal cost) curve.

The concept of an industry supply curve in monopolistic competition faces two difficulties. First, some economists question the meaningfulness of adding together the supplies of differentiated products as if they were a homogeneous product. How can one add the supplies of Wheaties and Corn Flakes? However, the products within an industry are substitutes, and there are meaningful uses for an industry supply curve—even one for breakfast cereals. Second, a firm facing a sloping demand curve does not itself have a supply curve. This absence seems strange until one recalls the definition of a supply curve for a firm. The supply curve indicates the precise Q that will be supplied for each and every P; Q is related to P through equating P to MC. But with a sloping demand curve there is no unique Q to be related to each and every P because MR, not P, is equated to MC. Such a firm could derive an MR–Q curve, but that is not the P–Q curve called supply. This second difficulty can present analytical problems sometimes. Therefore, the discussion of industry supply applies to atomistic competition and not completely to monopolistic competition. However, the same basic forces affect monopolistic competition in very much the same way. The reader will find it useful to consider the similarities.

The short-run supply curve of the atomistic industry is found by summing up the quantities offered by each firm in the industry at various alternative prices, *ceteris paribus*. Sometimes everything else may not be equal, as far as significant changes in industry output are concerned. The simultaneous increase in output of many firms involved in reacting to a rise in product price may bid up the price of a variable input and thus shift up the MC curves of the firms. In a free agricultural market, the prices of feeder cattle and even feed grains are often bid up when inflated prices of fed cattle lead many cattle feeders to try to expand their numbers on feed. In this case of an external diseconomy, the supply curve of the industry is steeper than the ΣMC (sum of the marginal costs) of the individual firms (Figure 11–6).

FIGURE 11–6

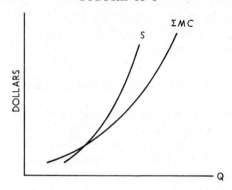

Here we have again a warning against the fallacy of composition. While one firm in atomistic competition can vary its output sales and input purchases without affecting the price of either, all firms in the industry may not have such freedom, even in the short-run.

Short and Long Run

We can go no further without reminding you of the *definitions* of short and long run. In the long run, all inputs can be varied, whereas in the short run, an input called "plant" is fixed. (See latter part of Chapter 7.) The crux of the matter is whether plant is variable or not because of its effect on costs and on amount supplied. These are not calendar time concepts except in the sense that plant is not varied as readily as other variables. Since plant adjustments involve sizable capital outlays, they tend to be infrequent; during much of the calendar time of a firm's life, plant is static and only short-run adjustments are being made.

The *firm* is in short-run equilibrium when its $MR = MC$ (which in atomistic competition also involves $P = MC$). The *industry* is in short-run equilibrium when all firms are in short-run equilibrium.

The long-run industry supply curve is more complicated to build since the number of plants (and firms) may vary. In a long-run period of adjustment, a higher price will bring in more plants until price is no longer any higher than the minimum AC of the prospective entrant. The firm is in long-run *equilibrium* when its total revenue (TR) = total costs (TC), or, to say it another way, when $AR = AC$. "Normal profits" in the opportunity cost sense are assumed to be included in TC, so that a situation of $TR = TC$ indicates normal profits such that the firm has no motivation to exit. The *industry* is in long-run equilibrium when all firms are in long-run equilibrium and there is no entry of new firms.

Since the conventional supply curve is a static concept, we cannot refer to P and Q relationships during a period of adjustment of all inputs.

Instead we compare the P and Q to be supplied at *one long-run equilibrium* with the Q at some different price in a *new long-run equilibrium*
after there has been time for all input adjustments. The detail of these
adjustments are indicated later. However, it should now be apparent that
the industry supply curve at any given long-run equilibrium is the sum of
the quantities produced by the firms that are *then* in the industry when
each firm is producing its long-run optimal quantity. That optimal quantity is at the minimum point of the firm's $LRAC$ curve. Therefore, the
concept of the LR supply curve is very different from that of the SR
supply curve.

The conventional LR supply curve is a very unexciting horizontal
line in the absence of external economies or diseconomies. Output
changes as the number of firms changes, and costs remain constant unless
some costs are a function of total output of the industry. The full
explanation of the conclusion can wait until the next section, but the
external economies and diseconomies need discussion now. These economies or diseconomies refer to decreases or increases, respectively, in the
AC (average cost) of production generated by changes in industry
output. They arise from forces *external to the firm*—hence the term
"external"—but internal to the industry. Shifts in AC arising from inventions or other developments *unrelated* to industry output are not considered "external economies or diseconomies" since they constitute a once-
and-for-all shift in the supply curve rather than forces affecting its slope.

Pecuniary and Technical External Economies and Diseconomies

Pecuniary external economies (diseconomies) arise when an expansion in industry output reduces (increases) input prices and thus shifts
the entire AC curve of each firm using that input down (up). *Nonreversible pecuniary* external economies are fairly common—mass production
in a growing industry often leads to all kinds of cost-cutting discoveries.
However, they are often nonreversible in the sense that the cost advantages remain if output is later reduced. For purposes of analysis and
prediction, it is important to separate nonreversible external economies
from the other kind. In fact reversible pecuniary economies seem relatively scarce. Most lists include these possibilities:

1. More productive labor relative to wages.
2. Trade journals and other means of market information.
3. Raw materials produced at decreasing costs by "quasi-monopolized"
   supply industries.

Pecuniary external diseconomies are regarded as fairly common and
as arising from a growing scarcity of one or more inputs. As noted
previously, they may arise in the SR as well as the LR. The larger the
industry's demand for that input relative to total demand for it, the more

likely that price will be bid up by output expansion. Hence, we expect that the *LR* supply curve of every industry eventually would slope upward because of net pecuniary external diseconomies. These are ordinarily reversible. With given technology, almost any agricultural enterprise—feed grains, hogs, soybeans—will encounter pecuniary external diseconomies with a significant change in output.

An external *technical* economy (diseconomy) arises when an expansion in industry output increases (reduces) the efficiency of the production functions of the individual firms. Convincing examples are not easy to find.

ADJUSTMENTS

Change

Ours is an economy of change: change in the number, quality, and amount of products produced; change in the occupations of people; change in the number and size and product mix of firms; change in employment opportunities and wages; change in the price of assets. Economic theory has developed classifications of changes and factors involved in change which help one to understand relationships and to foresee the "working out" of certain processes of change. The private advantages to the reader of such understanding may be extra capital gains on properly timed investments, a position in an area of rapidly rising pay, etc. Or the public advantages to the reader may be, as a citizen, in evaluating the factors affecting public welfare and in leading society to take *timely* actions.

We necessarily ignore many aspects of change in order to focus on a few that seem most important to the economist. Moreover, we use a partial equilibrium approach of looking at things from the point of view of equilibrium for a firm or an industry. From this vantage point certain forces are regarded as disturbances and causes of change, which would be regarded as effects of still more fundamental causes if we were looking at the whole economy. For example, a change in the demand for frozen cherries is a cause of adjustments in cherry production and processing. We could assume a change in demand for cherries and examine its implications for the cherry processing industry. It is just as interesting a question to explain why the demand for cherries might change or what the impact of such a change is upon the price of peaches, but we leave all of that to the other parts of the book and to other books.

We want to examine these types of "disturbances" to an industry:

1. Change in demand for the product.
2. Change in input prices.
3. Technological change which alters optimal scale of plant or firm.

As if these promised explanations were not ambitious enough, our theory is also designed to explain some differences in the working out of these disturbances which relate to the market structure of the industry concerned. An increase in demand may have somewhat different effects in a monopolistic competitive industry than in an atomistic one. Likewise, the variety of methods of competitive conduct are much greater in monopolistic than in atomistic competition in which there is really only one way to play the game.

Moreover, our theory is designed to give a time dimension to our explanations so that both short-run and long-run effects can be traced out and equilibrium positions can be described even though they may not be reached. The time dimension in economics is a special one, of course, and the reader must be ever wary of confusing it with calendar time.

LR Equilibrium as a Starting Point

The theory of monopolistic competition was modeled after the theory of atomistic competition. Both models assume that there are zero profits ($TR = TC$) for all firms at the point of long-run equilibrium and that these zero profits prevent either entry or exit of firms. In each model, there is a point showing *a* quantity that would be supplied by the industry at *a* price in this particular *LR* equilibrium.

A difference between the two theories of competition is in the revenue-cost relationships at *LR* equilibrium. In atomistic competition, the horizontal demand (sales) curve is tangent to the minimum *AC* of the firm; in monopolistic competition, the slightly sloping demand (sales) curve is tangent to the *AC* curve of the firm at a point to the left of the minimum (Figure 11–7). This famous tangency solution in monopolistic competition showed monopoly without "monopoly profits" but with inef-

FIGURE 11–7

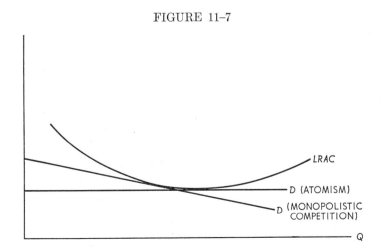

ficient operation—i.e., equilibrium at higher than minimal AC. The efficiency aspects of the LR equilibrium conditions were compared and commented upon endlessly in the 1930's. We will devote our main efforts to comparing the two competitive models as to adjustments to disturbances.

Adjustments in Atomism to an Increase in Demand

Suppose these curves exist *for a firm in atomistic competition* and that identical curves exist for all N firms (Figure 11–8). Differential rents to factors lead to identical costs. The LR equilibrium price is P_1, and the firm output is Q_1. It follows that *industry* demand is such that $N \cdot Q_1$ clears the market at price P_1.

Assume a shift to the right of industry demand so that $N \cdot Q_2$

FIGURE 11–8

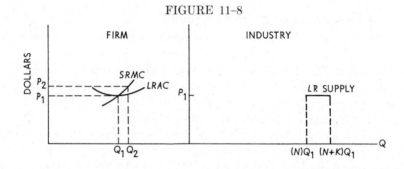

quantity would clear the market at price P_2. What are the effects of this disturbance?

1. The SR tendency is for each and every firm to expand up its $SRMC$ toward P_2 and Q_2. *Sizable SR* profits are attained.
2. Will firms tend to expand their existing plants? There is a temptation to do so because of the juicy profit margins now existing in the industry, and undoubtedly this ill-advised expansion often takes place in real life. However, the smart thing to do is to build more plants of the optimal size (output Q_1). These will be built by existing firms or by new ones. It's very reasonable to ask if a firm in atomistic competition can be assumed to have more than one plant and even to insist that there are very definite limitations on the economies of scale of the *firm* in atomistic competition. We shall assume that the economies of scale are such that most plants are held by single-plant firms without digressing into the interesting questions raised by such an assumption. The reader should distinguish clearly between economies of scale of a plant and a firm.
3. As new plants enter, industry output expands and price falls from the lofty P_2 height.
4. At the end of the adjustment period, there are $N + K$ firms producing $(N + K)Q_1$ output at price P_1.

5. The new equilibrium price is identical to the previous equilibrium unless external economies or diseconomies were encountered. As indicated above, a sufficiently large change in industry output will lead to at least moderate external diseconomies and therefore a rising *LR* supply curve. Many changes in real life are not that big.

In summary, this disturbance did lead to *SR* changes in output of firms and the industry; to *SR* changes in product price, production costs, and profits; and to *SR* changes in the relative employment of fixed and variable factors. The reader will find it useful to summarize the *LR* changes in each of the above categories. He may also find it useful to trace through the adjustments to a *decline* in demand.

It is always tricky to find practical examples. There have been many cases in American agriculture in which rising demand led to a rising output and a multiplication of the number of firms. The expansion from 1800 to 1900 in national wheat production is an example. Another is the increase in the number of Grade A dairy farms around areas like Chicago and St. Louis as they grew from small to great cities. However, technological change has always been at work so that the price and scale effects were not exactly as described in this theoretical model.

In the practical affairs of men, it is important to anticipate correctly the amount of calendar time involved in making such an adjustment from one *LR* equilibrium to another. It may vary from a few months to many years. Likewise, it is very important for would-be entrepreneurs to anticipate correctly whether there is still "room" for the output of another new plant. Perhaps even more important is the need for new businessmen to realize that they must plan for a plant that can cover costs at price P_1 rather than at the currently higher *SR* price. Incorrect anticipations are rather frequent—particularly if the calendar period of adjustment takes a few years—and they often result in such dynamic phenomena as the alternate overexpansion and overcontraction of plant capacity. Another mistake that is easily made during the temporary period of high prices is to expand one's plant beyond the optimal size. The resultant higher *AC* will lead to persistent losses as soon as entry of new plants forces price back to its old level. Again, timing is important. If it will require several years for entry to force price back to its old level, then there may be situations in which the temporary profits of a plant expansion will be sufficient to justify it.

Adjustments in Monopolistic Competition to an Increase in Demand

Now let's compare the same adjustment situation in monopolistic competition. Suppose these revenue and cost curves (Figure 11–9) exist for a firm in monopolistic competition and that identical curves exist for N firms. The *LR* equilibrium price is P_1, and firm output is Q_1. It follows that industry demand is such that $N \cdot Q_1$ is sold at price P_1. (Note: In following this symmetry assumption of Chamberlin, we would warn that costs and prices and outputs tend to differ a bit among firms in monopolistic competition. However, interdependence is so high that they tend to adjust in much the same fashion as if they were identical.)

Now assume a shift to the right of industry and firm demand so that the firm would maximize its profits by selling Q_2 quantity per market period at price P_2 (see Part B, Figure 11-9). What are the effects of this disturbance?

It is quite possible to argue that the results are essentially the same as in atomistic competition. Firms do compete fiercely for the bigger market. The possible effects of external economies or diseconomies on input prices apply in the same fashion as in atomistic competition. No firm has

FIGURE 11-9

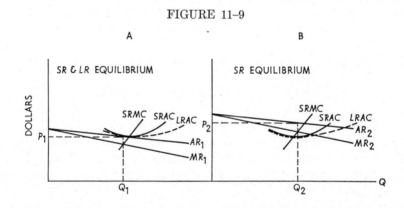

monopoly powers. While agreeing with the main import of this argument, there is point in us examining some aspects of the potential differences.

Some industries which may resemble the model of monpolistic competition include service industries such as real estate brokers, insurance agencies, barber shops, resorts around a large lake or along the seashore, motels, hotels and restaurants in a large city, dentists, lawyers, service stations, etc. In any of these industries, you may think of a few firms which are apart from the main group because they or their products have special characteristics which set them clearly apart. There are special hotels and surgeons with such reputations that they have very little competition from others in their groups. For the reasons indicated earlier, we must confine our analysis of the large group to those firms whose products or services are highly substitutable one with another. Among this large group an expansion in demand is almost equally accessible to each firm. For example, the rapid growth of a community provides potential customers for all real estate brokers, insurance agencies, dentists, surgeons, and barbers. Or the rapid growth of demand for outdoor recreation in a particular lake area provides potential customers for all resorts and restaurants in the area. However, observation of such situations indicates three points. First, some real estate brokers and restaurants, for example, appear able to respond more adequately to a new demand and to benefit proportionately more than others. Second, the *LRAC* cost curves of many such firms may have a wide, flat bottom so that the existing firms can expand plant capacity considerably without raising their *LRAC*. Third, the difficulties of securing a part of the market *may be* a little difficult for an entrant in monopolistic competition so that entry of new firms *may be* somewhat slower than in atomistic competition. This third conclusion does not apply to all situations because entry into some industries such as barbershops is easier than into an atomistic industry like commercial cotton production. Therefore the following sequence of adjustments is quite possible in monopolistic competition:

1. There is a general increase in demand.
2. Some firms respond much more readily than others and do expand considerably their operations at approximately the same level of *AC* as at the old equilibrium.
3. There is limited entry of new firms who obtain only a fraction of the increased output.
4. The new equilibrium involves a larger output at approximately the same cost-price relationship as the old equilibrium. The similarity of size distribution of firms has been reduced.

Inferences from empirical observation to a theoretical situation can be misleading. How can we say that firms were in equilibrium initially if they seem capable of substantial expansion of output at the same *AC?* If some firms could secure most of the new demand, why couldn't they pull most of the old demand away from competitors? Is there instability inherent in any equilibrium of the large group if some firms have the potential of increasing their market positions at the relative disadvantage of other firms? Let us, therefore, agree that while the theoretical adjustments in monopolistic competition to an increase in demand are essentially the same as in atomistic competition, it is wise to expect some variations of the type mentioned above when attempting to predict the working out of such a disturbance in the real world.

Adjustments in Atomistic and Monopolistic Competition to an Increase in the Price of a Variable Input

Assume an increase in the price of a variable input, such as labor, while there is no corresponding change in the productivity of that input. What are the adjustments in atomistic and monopolistic competition?

Some substitution of cheaper factors for the now more expensive factor will occur (see Chapter 7). Since short-run costs are higher at any combination of inputs than previously, the old equilibrium output and price cannot continue. *SRMC* has shifted upward and to the left, so firms will reduce output slightly. Whether the resulting increase in price is sufficient to cover the new higher *SRAC* depends upon the elasticity of industry demand. That is, the reduction of total output in atomistic competition increases the price equating industry supply and demand and thereby raises the sales curve facing each firm (Figure 11–10). If the new *SR* price falls below the new *SRAC*, then there will be exit eventually and price will rise to equate minimum *SRAC*. In the long run, this factor substitution may include a higher capital investment in plant and equipment.

FIGURE 11–10

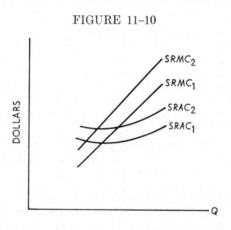

In somewhat like manner, the reduction of output by each firm in monopolistic competition reduces the total supply of competing substitutes for each firm and thereby raises the sales curves facing some and perhaps all firms. If demand is so elastic that the price rise due to *SR* reorganization of inputs is not sufficient to cover costs, then there must be some exit of firms before a new *LR* equilibrium is reached.

We have just seen the procedure by which some part of a cost increase is passed to consumers via a higher price for the product. This passing on of a cost increase was not entirely painless to the firms. If we were to assume that the cost increase affected some firms more than others, then those firms most affected will bear the brunt of the output adjustment and any exits are likely to be from their ranks.

Another consideration also applies in monopolistic competition. If we allow some variations in the elasticities of the individual demand curves facing the firms, then those firms facing the most elastic demands will have the most difficulty in reorganizing their operations to absorb the price increase of the input.

The student will want to examine the effects of an assumed price *decrease* of a variable input.

Adjustments in Atomistic and Monopolistic Competition to a Change in Optimal Scale of Plant

Assume a technological improvement which doubles the optimal scale of plant. What are the adjustments?

In both atomistic and monopolistic competition, the impact of this sort of disturbance comes gradually rather than immediately as in the previous cases. There is no *SR* response, since the very nature of the change is a *LR* change in plant. New optimal plants are built. Conventional theory is not and cannot be very informative as to who builds them—existing firms or entrants. These plants can be built by many firms—both inside and outside the industry.

In atomistic competition, new technology then leads to new plants, and it usually leads to increased output and to a lower price. If the new, larger plants achieve no lower minimum costs then the old plants, then the change in scale of plants would be very slow because any expansion of output by adding new plants would put pressure upon profits and would discourage the capital commitments in new plants. If, however, the new larger plants can achieve lower minimum costs, then there will be a profit incentive to the building of new plants. The old plants will remain in use as long as *AVC* can be covered, and doubtlessly longer in some cases as some managers do not give up easily.

The new equilibrium will be at an industry output the same as or larger than the old one, depending upon whether lower *LRAC* were achieved (Figure 11–11). The number of plants will be one half the former number, or more, since we assumed a doubling of optimal plant size. If the original firms were single-plant firms, then there is at least as great a decline in the number of firms. The number of firms must be presumed to remain large if our competitive models are to be maintained. It is this type of disturbance which when repeated enough times turns a large group of firms into an oligopoly.

This type of disturbance is a very common one in the American economy and a rather trying one for businessmen. There is usually considerable technical uncertainty at the outset; not everything that is bigger is really more efficient. Besides there is the very real question of how much bigger—50 percent, 100 percent, 1,000 percent. Yet there are possible innovational profits contrasted with likely losses for those firms who do not adapt. Sizable capital commitments are made at a time of what is hopefully regarded as temporarily depressed prices. Some new plants are found to be larger than the capabilities of their managers. A rather high proportion of exits is finally required. Moreover, in real life these technological developments may come in a steady stream so that it is years or decades before anything resembling a new equilibrium appears. The student should compare these atomistic adjustments with those that would occur with a decline in demand. Note in particular the impact on short-run profits of all firms.

The adjustments to a scale change are much the same in monopolistic as in atomistic competition. However, the tendency of each competitor to have something of a little submarket of his own makes him a little more wary of doubling his output to take advantage of enlarged econo-

FIGURE 11-11

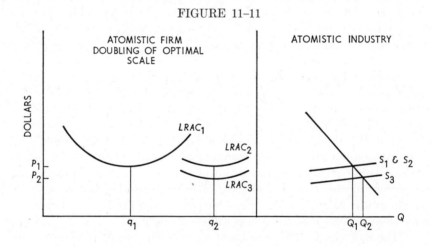

mies of scale. Where will he sell the extra output? Must he revise his entire marketing procedure? These problems are not likely to prevent size adjustments from being made, but they may delay them. Exits will finally be required.

The firm and industry adjustments to a change in optimal scale and to reduced costs have been and are very common in the American economy. Many industries, including agriculture, have gone through a shake-out period in which many early firms exited as others expanded.

The reader should be aware of the large amount of uncertainty in real-life situations as to which disturbances are at work and what are their magnitudes. Likewise the very existence of disturbances makes entrepreneurs seek more flexible and secure positions than if they could act in confidence that no more disturbances would be forthcoming. The point of our classifying disturbances and comparing equilibrium is to develop skill in sorting out what is going on in reality so that general consequences may be anticipated somewhat correctly. Unfortunately disturbances do not come neatly labeled as to nature and magnitude nor do they often come separately.

A SUMMARY LOOK AT EQUILIBRIUM AND ADJUSTMENTS

An equilibrium occurs when the firm or industry involved is at rest—it has no motivation to change. An equilibrium in the long-run sense also requires a short-run equilibrium. However a firm or industry may be in short-run equilibrium and not in long-run equilibrium (see Figure 11–12). It should be emphasized, however, that revenue and

FIGURE 11–12

CONDITIONS WHICH CAN EXIST SIMULTANEOUSLY

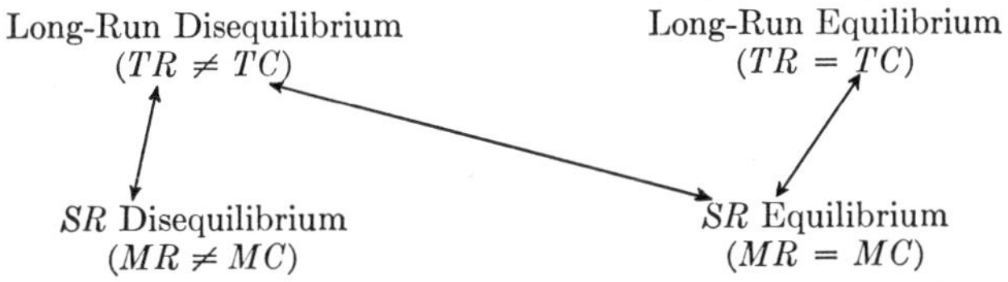

| Long-Run Disequilibrium | Long-Run Equilibrium |
| $(TR \neq TC)$ | $(TR = TC)$ |

| SR Disequilibrium | SR Equilibrium |
| $(MR \neq MC)$ | $(MR = MC)$ |

especially costs take on different dimensions in a long-run than in a short-run sense since plant can be varied in the former. Therefore a firm might conceivably be in a SR situation in which $SRTR = SRTC$, but it would still be motivated to change plant size to improve the relationship of $LRTR$ and $LRTC$.

Adjustments—particularly plant adjustments—require calendar time. We have looked briefly at some situations in which firms and an industry move through several periods of short-run adjustments and a period of plant adjustments as they move from one long-run equilibrium to another. At various times during this "long-run adjustment period," many or all of the firms may have arrived at a short-run equilibrium only to have it disturbed again by plant changes. We have emphasized that long-run equilibrium is rarely achieved—that it is not equivalent to the conditions occurring most of the time.

What are the forces which move *a firm* away from its LR equilibrium?

1. A change in price of its product. This change requires SR adjustments and *perhaps* LR. Would a shift in the demand schedule cause *every* firm to move into a new LR firm equilibrium different from the old?
2. A change in technology propels the firm into SR adjustments. Does it also compel LR adjustments?
3. A change in the prices of one or more inputs requires SR adjust-

ments—and may require *LR* adjustments. Could prices of product and inputs change together as part of a general inflationary movement so that there were only minor *SR* adjustments and no *LR* adjustments?

4. In monopolistic competition, a firm may lose sales to a competitor who is engaging in a new form of price or nonprice competition. This loss can lead to *SR* and perhaps *LR* adjustments. Is there any comparable disturbance in atomistic competition?

Agricultural economists have been quite concerned with explaining the amounts supplied of one or all agricultural commodities. Consequently, their analysis of "supply response" go considerably beyond the analysis in this chapter as they include other influences such as expectations, risk, redistribution of assets, and weather. Their analyses lead to predictions of next year's wheat or peach crop or next fall's hog marketings.

Chapter 12

COMPETITION AMONG THE FEW

THE OLIGOPOLY PROBLEM

An oligopoly exists when a few firms are so highly interdependent that one's actions directly and significantly affect another's. For example, evidence of oligopolistic interdependence would be the finding that A's profits are affected significantly by the volume of B's sales. These few firms may constitute the entire industry or they may be a subset of firms within the industry.

This interdependence of oligopoly has led to a very different type of market theory than is used for competition among the many. A stable market solution is not determined by a few individual firms maximizing profits in terms of their sales curves. An oligopolistic firm cannot locate a sales curve because its location depends upon the actions and reactions of its rivals. For example, A thinks that he can increase his total revenue

TABLE 12–1

BLUE'S PROFITS UNDER FOUR COMBINATIONS OF MERCHANDISING STRATEGIES

Blue's Strategy	Red's Strategy	
	A	B
A	5	4
B	3	6

10 percent by cutting his price 3 percent. Whether he can actually realize such a gain depends upon whether firms B and/or C and D meet such a price cut or ignore it.

The mutual dependence of a "duopoly," or industry composed of only two firms, is demonstrated in Table 12–1. For simplicity, we make the unrealistic assumption that the *combined* profits of the two firms—Red and Blue—are always $10 per unit of time. In this table we take the shortcut of only showing the profits of Seller Blue. Red's profits

283

are obviously 10 minus Blue's profits. Therefore, Blue wants to maximize the numbers in the table while Red wants to minimize them. These profits depend upon joint actions taken by Red and Blue. For the moment, we will say that A and B define any alternative sets of relevant actions. For example, A and B may represent different prices or different outputs thrown upon the market or different advertising strategies.

The tantalizing aspects of duopolistic interdependence are clearly evident. Blue finds that he can make $6 per unit of time by choosing his policy B *if* Red will choose his policy B. But if Red should choose A instead of B, then Blue would only realize $3 profit by choosing B.

Duopolistic (and oligopolistic) competition is much more complicated than suggested by the little table, which illustrates the interdependence problem and little more. There are ordinarily hundreds or thousands of alternative choices to be made rather than two (A and B of the table), and the nature of these alternatives change over time and in relation to previous occurrences. Moreover, relative strengths and weaknesses of the various firms in terms of market position, customer loyalties, and net worth, etc., affect the choices made. Likewise the vigor with which one enters today's battle is tempered by a vision of the endless string of tomorrows and one's expectations about the influence of today's results upon tomorrow's "battle lines." Moreover a considerable fog of ignorance as to the exact consequences of either one's own choices or of the combined choices (e.g., Red's A and Blue's B) not only produces some unexpected results but also likely leads to a more conservative playing of the game than would otherwise hold.

Oligopolies are usually classified as homogeneous or differentiated. Products and therefore prices are identical in a homogeneous oligopoly. Products are less than perfect substitutes, and therefore prices need not be identical in a differentiated oligopoly. It is difficult to imagine a completely homogeneous oligopoly in which buyers find no differences in the product nor in the conditions of sale. However, a homogeneous oligopoly is a useful model because there are industries such as basic raw materials (coal, iron ore) and intermediate products (steel sheets, aluminum extrusions) which closely approximate homogeneity.

Supply curves in many-seller competitions are traced out by passive reactions of firms to price changes. There are no such supply curves in few-seller competition because the firms are actively involved in price making. One firm may stay with an announced price through wide swings in demand and physical sales, while another firm in another industry may change price frequently. The same general set of economic forces influences amounts supplied as in many-seller competition, but these influences operate within a different type of price-making framework, and the results can vary considerably with the type of competitive behavior within the small group.

To summarize so far, oligopolies are interdependent and cannot be analyzed in terms of demand and supply models with determinate solutions. The price and output results of an oligopoly can vary widely depending upon how the firms play the game. We will indicate several of these possible ways to play the game after we examine a bit more the where and how of oligopolies in the American economy.

THE BIG FIRM AND OLIGOPOLIES IN NATIONAL MARKETS

Giant firms are not necessarily oligopolists but they usually are. The most visible and the most important oligopolies on the American scene are those composed of giant firms. The automobile and steel industries are the usual textbook examples.

The annual *Fortune* magazine survey of the top 500 industrial corporations is a likely place to start the hunt for giant oligopolists. Automobiles, steel, oil, and electric manufacturing have crowded the lists of the top 10 firms for many years. General Motors sales have exceeded $10 billion annually for many years—a sum greater than the national income of a majority of the countries in the United Nations! In 1957 some 37 firms had sales exceeding $1 billion, and almost every year another firm joins this exclusive Billion Dollar Club.

What are the basic forces explaining the giant firm—whether oligopolist or not? Such a question can be answered in many ways. One force is the motivation of the decision makers of the firm. In some sense they wanted and sought size—often over a half century or more of growth. Bigness may be sought for the power, prestige, and security it gives to management. Firms in the Billion Dollar Club do not escape all the rigors of competition, and they do occasionally lose money. However, these club members come fairly close to immortality, and their managements reap many rewards—nonfinancial as well as financial.

Economies of scale are ordinarily cited as the chief cause for big firms. Economies of scale need to be examined in terms of production, distribution (marketing), financial and managerial factors, as the *LRAC* curve of each factor tends to differ. In certain industries the *LRAC* curve is flat or declining over an enormous range of output, *allowing* growth of the big firm.

We need to pause to define the difference between a plant and a firm. The early chapters of this book are concerned with a plant and with a single-plant firm. We *define* a firm as a decision-making organization and a set of one or more plants managed by that organization. The economies of scale of plants and firms usually differ because only production and some physical distribution economies are a function of plant size, while economies of promotion, finance, and management are a function of size of firm.

The firms in the Billion Dollar Club are multiplant firms. They are multiplant firms because the *LRAC of production and/or physical distribution* turns up soon enough that production and physical distribution can be accomplished more cheaply from several plants than from one. A *firm* can avoid certain *diseconomies of scale* (rising *LRAC*) by adding more plants. It seems likely that the *LRAC* function of advertising and merchandising in a national market may be horizontal, or probably declining, for an enormous range. Large firms are not likely to experience increasing difficulties of finance as they become still larger, so the financial *LRAC* curve is not likely to turn up. Therefore, all these factors point toward the possibility of almost unlimited growth of the multiplant firm. Is there no limit?

Management capacity is sometimes the factor limiting the growth of the big firm. However, developments in communications and in management science have greatly enlarged management capacity in many situations so that we really don't expect to find many members of the Billion Dollar Club collapsing from the weight of an overburdened management. Of course, it would take a great amount of study to determine which firms are experiencing sufficient managerial scale diseconomies to slow their growth materially.

Joe Bain concluded from a detailed study of 17 moderately or highly concentrated manufacturing industries that distributional and merchandising economies of scale were much more important than production economies. A typical giant firm could be split into many firms (as many as it has plants) without hurting its production efficiency, but its distributional and sales efficiencies would be hurt sometimes.[1]

How much oligopoly do we find in the national markets? There is not complete agreement on the answer because of the difficulties of definition and measurement. For example, what is the percentage of industry sales sold by Coca Cola? Do we define the "industry" as the soft-drink industry or do we include competing drinks like beer—or even tea and coffee? Sometimes the industry boundaries have to be drawn rather arbitrarily because there is no precise demarcation and/or because the Census or other industry data available makes a certain boundary most expedient. Suppose that you define an industry and obtain data showing that the top eight firms produce 45 percent of industry sales. Is this an oligopoly? What if they produce 85 percent?

Two respected authors have measured what they call Type I and Type II oligopoly:[2]

Type I—First 8 firms have 50 percent of industry sales and first 20 have 75 percent or more.

[1] Joe S. Bain, "Advantages of the Large Firm: Production, Distribution and Sales Promotion," *Journal of Marketing*, April, 1956, pp. 336–46.

[2] Carl Kaysen and Donald F. Turner, *Antitrust Policy: An Economic and Legal Analysis* (Cambridge: Harvard University Press, 1959), pp. 24–43.

Type II—First 8 firms have 33 percent of industry sales and first 20 have less than 75 percent.

Using these definitions, Kaysen and Turner found that a majority of manufacturing industries were Types I or II oligopolies and that about one third were Type I oligopolies.

Fletcher found that about 75 percent of the volume of farm inputs originate in industries having Type I oligopolies. About 25 percent of the volume of farm output is processed in industries having Type I oligopolies.[3]

These data indicate the indisputable importance of oligopolies in the national market, but they do not indicate that oligopolies are everywhere and controlling everything.

THE LITTLE FIRM AND HOMETOWN OLIGOPOLY

Market boundaries are difficult to put on maps. We speak of a national market because there are tariffs and other politico-economic boundaries around a nation, but many times there is an international market for commodities—wheat, sugar, autos, airplanes, transistor radios. Thus, even the nation's boundary may not be a large enough boundary for a market in which the forces of demand and supply are at work.

Within the nation, there are many smaller markets which are sufficiently isolated from other markets that it makes sense to draw some boundaries. For example, the males of Columbia, Missouri, will ordinarily obtain their haircuts within that city. Therefore, the barbers of Columbia are in a separate market from those in Chicago. Assuming no legal barriers, barbers can move from Columbia to Chicago or vice versa—and customers can go out of town for haircuts so that these two markets are not *completely* separated. However, it is no surprise that the price of haircuts may vary considerably between those two cities, and it is useful to consider them as two different markets.

Likewise consumers buy many other services (legal, medical, beauty-aid, entertainment, banking, auto repair, appliance repair) and many goods (food, clothing, hardware, etc.) in essentially local markets.

In the early development of this country, these markets were very small—about the radius that a farm family could drive a team and wagon in half a day. The farm and town families as consumers and the farm firm as an industrial buyer and seller usually faced local oligopolies. At best, there were two or three grocery stores, barbers, physicians, grain elevators, livestock buyers, and banks; and at worst, there was one. Better transportation has greatly widened the market areas, but sometimes the

---

[3] Lehman B. Fletcher, "Market Structures and Market Power," in *Farmers in the Market Economy* (Ames: Iowa State University Press, 1964), pp. 82–117. Fletcher uses the measure of 50 percent by top 8 firms but doesn't include an additional measure for the top 20 firms.

concurrent demise of firms has developed another group of oligopolies. Two small banks or barbershops can face some of the same duopoly problems in the County Seat that General Motors and Ford face in the national auto market. These little firms lack the great resources of management and capital and the infinite life expectations of the corporate giants, but oligopolies they are. As we discuss the defensive and offensive strategies of oligopolies and various possible outcomes, it would be well for the reader to ask himself which of these apply to the national markets and which to the little oligopoly in his hometown. How does the difference in ease of entry, for example, influence the two kinds of oligopolies and their behavior?

DEFENSIVE STRATEGIES

"Survival and growth are implicit goals of every behavior system, including most particularly those which operate in the market place."[4]

The oligopolist must select strategies and tactics. His choices are determined in a very complex situation. The results of his strategies and tactics vary with those chosen by his competitors. Consequently, there are many oligopoly models and many so-called solutions. The reader's hope that one model or solution will prove to be superior to all others in explaining firm behavior is understandable but unrealistic.

Oligopolists can cooperate so closely that market results resemble a monopoly or they can compete so fiercely that profits are nonexistent. Neither extreme is common, but where a particular oligopoly falls between these extremes depends upon the strategies of the participants. We shall discuss some classes of strategies which we call defensive and offensive. These classifications should be applied quite loosely. In general, an industry dominated by defensive strategies arrives at "solutions" closer to monopoly than does an industry dominated by offensive strategies.

We will discuss only four defensive strategies: collusion, quasi-agreement, full costs, and the kinked demand curve. Each is geared to avoiding the rigors of aggressive price competition, but success in that endeavor varies with circumstances.

Collusion

Collusion has much to recommend itself to those managers seeking a defensive strategy. It appears that survival is not only assured but the maximum total industry profits can be obtained and shared among the firms. Competitive problems can be eliminated by agreeing not to compete.

[4] Wroe Alderson, *Marketing Behavior and Executive Action* (Homewood, Ill.: Richard D. Irwin, Inc., 1957), p. 1.

The theoretical appeal can be shown quite simply. Assume four firms selling a homogeneous product make up an industry. Weary and confused from several rounds of vicious price warfare, their top managers talk business while playing a round of golf one afternoon. An economist who is caddying for the group outlines the situation to them as follows: Each firm has a total variable cost curve (*TVC*) representing its particular plant, labor, market, and management situation. (Figure 12–1). From these, a combined *TVC* curve can readily be drawn which

FIGURE 12–1

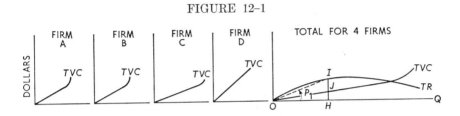

allocates any output to the plant where it adds least to total costs. Then, the golf caddy economist muses that the industry total revenue situation can be represented by *TR*. It then follows that the four firms should charge the price represented by the arc P_1, which will sell amount *OH*. Furthermore the firms should divide up production among the firms so that combined total cost is only *HJ*. Profits of *JI* are to be divided in "an equitable fashion."

Each of the four managers ponders the proposed collusive agreement. Assured profits would be a most welcome alternative to throat-cutting price warfare. But there are doubts. For one thing, in several countries including the United States, collusion is illegal; if convicted, top management can go to jail and affected customers can sue for triple damages. The damage payments of the American electrical manufacturers in the 1960's ran into the hundreds of millions. There are other doubts. Manager D has an old, inefficient plant, which probably should be closed down completely in a few more years. But once it is closed, what *real claim* would firm D have to any profits? Manager C has a very efficient plant which would produce about one third of the scheduled industry output. He thinks that "equitable sharing" of profits means one third to his firm rather than one fourth, but will the others agree?

Assume these managers overcome their doubts and form a "centralized cartel" which operates as projected above. Certain problems arise. At the relatively high price P_1, a small firm enters the industry. The cartel can lower its prices and drive out the new entrant, but losses temporarily replace profits. After about the 10th such entrant is driven out, serious analysis is made of the hypothesis that a lower price would be more

290 · Economics of Agricultural Production, Markets, and Policy

profitable if it did not attract any entrants or, at least, not nearly as many.

Other stresses on the collusive agreement are likely. Consumer demands shift, and manager A believes that their volume could be greatly increased by producing a low-priced, stripped-down product. It appears that it would be most efficient to confine its early manufacture to one plant, and manager A demands the right to do it, while keeping his share of the market of the original product. The other managers fear that the new version of the product might be so successful that firm A will maneuver itself into virtual control of next year's market.

As another possible problem, firm D decides that it will drop out of the cartel before its old plant is phased out, so it abandons its old facilities, builds a small efficient plant, and sells at essentially the same price as the cartel. By aggressive merchandising it cuts just a bit more into the cartel's market than its old "share," but it is careful not to antagonize the cartel too much. The cartel dislikes this dropout, but it has no legal basis for action, since cartel agreements are usually legally unenforceable where they are not illegal. It may or may not decide to punish the dropout by price warfare in the marketplace.

Will the cartel survive? Perhaps it will survive for a decade or more. However, in a dynamic, growing market, the self-interests of the individual firms tend to break down the cartel. In a legal environment hostile to cartels, such as in the United States, cartels seem likely to be much more of a compromise patchwork than the clear-cut maximization model shown above.

Phosphate and synthetic ammonia are two important components of fertilizer, and they provide interesting contrasts in their recent pricing behavior. The Justice Department filed suit in February, 1964, against eight phosphate producers who mine and produce about 75 percent of industry output, alleging fixing of the price of domestic rock phosphate.[5] In contrast the two prewar giants—Du Pont and Allied Chemical—have completely lost their domination of the synthetic ammonia industry, as there has been postwar entry by many firms. While there was in the early 1960's a list price for ammonia on each side of the Rockies with a delivered price that was supposed to be list price plus freight costs from the nearest plant, actual prices varied from 15 to 30 percent under list.[6]

Quasi-Agreements

Homogeneous oligopolies must have identical prices. Moderately differentiated oligopolies must have very similar prices. These "facts" appear to be generally recognized and accepted. The price level can be determined by various means in a manner that produces a mutually acceptable price level. An industry over time can find that there is a

[5] *Chemical Week*, February 22, 1964, p. 25.
[6] *Oil and Gas Journal*, February 3, 1964, p. 65.

certain price-cost range that is acceptable. The industry may accept a
price leader who performs "barometric pricing." That is he leads exactly
where he is convinced that the group will go. There are many subtle
ways by which communication is achieved without resort to written
memoranda. These agreements are not nearly as complete as the cartel
case. Individual firms may compete very aggressively in merchandising,
service, product design, and in everything but price. This is a parallel to
nations' competing and even warring with all weapons except nuclear
ones.

Industry examples of quasi-agreements would seem to include the
cigarette industry, which has avoided price competition almost completely except for a brief period of the 10-cent brands in the depression.
U.S. Steel was long the price leader in the steel industry. The auto
industry has a long historical pattern of models and prices. International
Harvester and Deere & Company were recognized price leaders for many
years in the farm equipment industry.

Close observation of the economy will indicate many more cases of
quasi-agreements or partial collusion in which price warfare is avoided.
There will be other industries in which conditions fluctuate so that there
are alternate periods of defensive and offensive strategies. Gasoline retailing is a prime example in many areas where price warfare occasionally occurs when surplus gasoline is on hand or when a particular
company "gets out of line."

Full-Cost Pricing

Businessmen are often impatient of talk about setting $MR = MC$
because they argue that they cannot quantify either. Sometimes they
argue that they can quantify AC and that they simply obtain "full
costs" by adding a profit margin to AC to get price. A range of full-cost
prices is possible, only one of which would be a profit maximization
point. In Figure 12–2, P_1 is the $MC = MR$ price, while P_2 or P_3 could be
full-cost prices, depending on the amount of full cost and the output

FIGURE 12–2

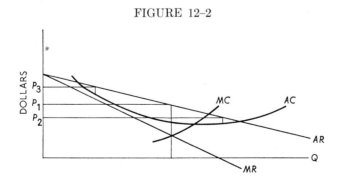

position of the firm. What happens if one firm in the oligopoly chooses P_2 while another chooses P_3? Unless the two firms' products are exceptionally well differentiated, such divergent prices cannot coexist, and competition will force them closer together. Full-cost pricing cannot be strictly independent in any oligopoly, and the more homogeneous the products the less the range for individual decisions on price. Moreover, the more divergent are average costs or even firm's estimates of their average costs; the less workable are likely to be full-cost prices.

However, when viewed as a business practice facilitating the obtaining of quasi-agreement on price, the method may often work. Consider three clothing retailers in Hometown County Seat. The input costs of the three firms are quite similar. Average costs and volume sold at a particular price level are fairly predictable on the basis of previous years' experiences. There are a great many different items to be priced from handkerchiefs to belts to expensive suits. From industry publications and from regular communications from manufacturers, each retailer "knows" that a fair profit is x percent on belts and y percent on men's best suits, and he is fairly confident that his competitors believe the same. Hence, each retailer has a *simple* method of pricing which keeps him in line with his competition, which leads to acceptable profits, and which guides him on how much to change prices if his costs change. In other words, if a defensive strategy of quasi-agreement is sought by the industry, some form of full costing or of retail markups may be an acceptable tool under certain conditions.

The Kinked Demand Curve

The oligopolist's sales (demand) curve shows the functional relation between his price and the quantity he can sell—*given the prices of his competitors.* In Figure 12–3 the curve DD' shows the sales of firm A if the prices of his competitors remain constant, while dd' shows the sales if the prices of his competitors rise and fall in lockstep with his own price. The high interdependence of oligopolists makes it reasonable for many of them to assume that price will be matched and that dd' is the relevant sales curve. In numerous oligopoly situations in which firms strongly prefer the status quo, another pricing assumption about one's competitors seems reasonable. The kinked demand model assumes that they will meet any price cut but will not follow any price increase above the present price level. Graphically this means that a firm's demand curve is now the kinked curve DOd'. The kinked demand curve dictates

FIGURE 12–3

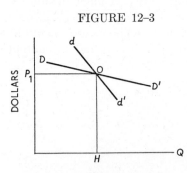

a strategy of few changes in prices. As indicated in Figure 12–4, this kinked demand curve generates a kinked total revenue curve that makes price P_1 clearly superior to any higher or lower price. The reader can imagine many kinds of changes in the height and slope of the total cost curve due to changes in technology or input prices which would not change the firm's determination to charge price P_1. However, an upward shift in "industry demand" would raise DOd' and the kinked TR which would encourage firms to increase price above P_1. While the model permits price adjustments to changes in industry demand, it is generally viewed as a theory of price rigidity.

FIGURE 12–4

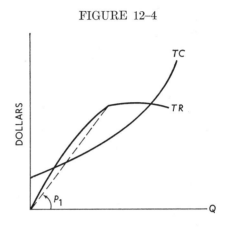

The kinked demand curve is a bit inadequate as a "solution" of the oligopoly problem. It fails to explain how the firm got where it is or much about how it somehow moves on. However it shows remarkably well the reasons why some oligopolies change prices quite infrequently. And it shows equally well the motivation for a defensive strategy of preserve the status quo—don't rock the boat—live and let live.

NONPRICE COMPETITION

Nonprice competition occurs in differentiated oligopolies. To the extent that it is adopted to avoid price competition, it appears to be a defensive strategy. However, a firm can employ nonprice competition in a very aggressive way and occasionally with results almost as destructive to one's rivals as price competition.

Modern oligopolists typically expend tremendous sums in selling efforts that vary greatly as to specific application. Auto companies build dealer organizations, guarantee performance, bring out new models annually after spending millions on product redesign and even spending thousands on researching the name for a new model. Of course, these firms spend more millions on consumer advertising. Most sellers of consumer products will spend large amounts in TV and magazine advertising, in contests and giveaways, and in fancy packages or product design. On the other hand, sellers of industrial products such as forklift tractors or complex gauges and meters strive to impress potential industrial buyers with their technical competence, prompt service, product reliability, and even occasionally with "Christmas gifts."

One principle of interest to business economists is the importance of a match between the product, its price, and the promotion. Whether one is trying to sell widgets to teen-agers or mink coats to dowagers, the product, its price, and the promotional efforts should create a single image that appeals to that particular market. Undoubtedly one reason that one aspirin company convinces people that its aspirins are better is *because* they are higher priced.

A subtle and powerful motivation for nonprice competition is now solidly entrenched in American business. The justification for advertising departments, research and development departments, product engineering departments, and public relations departments is the gain from nonprice competition. When one has a team on his payroll, he hardly questions the need to play the game.

The effects of the competitor's countermoves tend to be less obvious in nonprice than in price competition. Hence, a firm manager can easily underestimate the extent to which he must run hard in order to stand still.

Selling efforts usually generate counter selling efforts, which may or may not neutralize the initial firm's efforts. Nonprice warfare is usually safer for the participants. The costs are more predictable and less likely to escalate out of control than is probable in price warfare. Moreover, the long-range effects of selling efforts may build demand, while price warfare may spoil the market or increase demand only at very low prices. While much cigarette advertising must largely be self-canceling, it must have been a chief factor in the long-time growth in industry demand. There have been a few spectacular gains and losses in market shares of particular cigarette brands, which illustrate the potency that selling efforts sometimes have. For example, the Camel brand captured 35 percent of the market within four years after its introduction in 1913. Lorillard (Kents) nearly doubled its initial 5 percent market share between 1956 and 1965 while the share of Liggett & Myers declined by more than one third. Both firms were spending approximately the same amounts for advertising—$30 to $35 million annually.[7]

Selling efforts and especially advertising are widely discussed and sometimes criticized in economic literature and the popular press. Important issues can be raised. The reader is cautioned to go slow in his appraisal. Any firm which is really consumer oriented and trying to satisfy today's and tomorrow's consumer wants rather than simply peddling the same commodity today that it sold yesterday must become deeply involved in product design and product merchandising. It must design and redesign to maximize attractiveness as tastes change, and it must determine the right methods and channels for exposing its products

[7] An unpublished paper by Douglas Erickson, "An Analysis of the Cigarette Industry," University of Missouri, 1966.

to consumers. But beyond this essential consumer orientation lies an area in which consumer wants may be more manipulated and misled than satisfied. In such an area, advertising and counteradvertising, design and counterdesign may produce an arena of confusion and waste. It should be obvious that the "good area" is not easily distinguished from the "bad area."

OFFENSIVE STRATEGIES

Strategies are not easy to classify, and classifications should not be taken too literally. Firms and industries change strategies from time to time. We are going to look now at some situations in which one or more firms are aggressive and have enough productive capacity and market power to affect materially the oligopoly results. When a single strong firm is aggressive, it disturbs the whole group. Anybody can declare war; peace requires unanimous consent.

In general, we assume that the offensive firm has good economic reasons for its aggression. There is something in the market situation which motivates it. Perhaps the firm has a cost advantage or a product preference.

One type of cost advantage is the obvious one of lower AC (Figure 12–5). Another type is the less obvious one of having much overcapacity

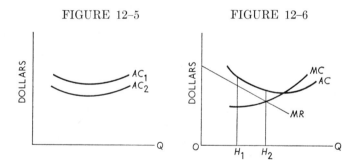

FIGURE 12–5   FIGURE 12–6

and lower $SRMC$, so that a gain in volume of OH_1 to OH_2—even at fairly low prices—would spread overhead and greatly reduce losses, or increase profits. (Figure 12–6). Perhaps it has a joint-product or by-product situation which lowers its costs compared to its rivals. Perhaps the offensive firm has a different time perspective or a totally different outlook on how products and prices must be changed to develop future markets. Warfare may sometimes be resorted to in order to teach a rival a lesson or to scare away potential entrants.

We will look at three models. The Cournot model shows how firms acting independently but in a very specialized manner can fight their way to a mutually acceptable outcome containing a price that is neither monopolistic nor zero profit. The second model describes a set of very aggressive situations and can best be labeled as warfare. The third model describes the importance of a pacesetting firm which keeps things stirred up. Such a firm may or may not stimulate a "hot war," but it is aggressive enough to stimulate a great amount of competition.

The Cournot Model

Our first example is a classic oligopoly case developed long ago by a Frenchman named Augustin Cournot. It assumes two competitors who pursue rather aggressive attempts to maximize their own profit with the conviction that the rival will not react. Each rival is a rather simple-minded profit maximizer. The chief fascination of the Cournot case is that the two rivals by certain independent actions will eventually arrive at a mutually acceptable solution. This solution of price and output is fairly close to monopoly for a duopoly situation but approaches atomism as the number of participants is increased.

Cournot assumed two noncolluding sellers of a homogeneous product (mineral water) with many buyers and perfect communication within the market so that only one price was possible. The gross and net revenue of each is a function of the sales of both sellers. Each seller can supply enough water alone to force the market price to zero, so some restriction of sales is necessary to maintain a profitable price. Such long-run considerations as one rival buying out the other or the entry of new competitors are ignored.

Each seller is assumed to conjecture that his rival's physical sales will remain constant. Then market price, which is a function of total physical sales of both sellers, is assumed to be stable except as a firm varies his own output. It follows that a seller can then vary his own output in such fashion as to maximize his own profits if the rival's output is constant. The complication arises in that neither output is constant. Each adjustment of one firm to a maximum profit position changes the market opportunity of the other firm and leads, in turn, to its readjustment. The problem can be solved algebraically or graphically by determining the "reaction functions" of each seller and then determining the particular pair of outputs which satisfies both reaction functions.

A reaction function indicates the most profitable output of one seller for each and every output of his rival. Assume A is alone in the market, maximizing profit at A_0 when B enters (Figure 12–7). While B would much prefer that A produces nothing and he produces B_0, this best of all solutions for B does not exist. The hard realities are that A is producing A_0. The curve B_0A_1 is the reaction curve for B showing his best outputs given A's. Therefore B sells a small output B_1 which puts him at position 2. Then A finds that the market is "flooded" by the combined output of A_0 plus B_1 and so cuts back to the new optimum output for A which is position 3, etc., until an "equilibrium" is reached at the intersection of the curves.

If we had assumed that the problem "began" at point 5, then the necessary series of adjustments would have been much smaller. Moreover, it would have been easier to believe that the two sellers might cling to their assumption of constancy of rival's output through a much smaller range of maneuvers.

FIGURE 12–7

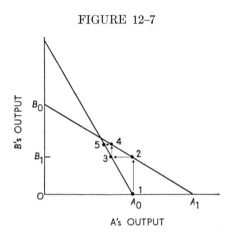

Cournot's solution showed a duopoly producing a larger output at a lower joint profit than was obtainable if the two firms colluded and maximized joint profit. As the number of firms increased, the equilibrium price was progressively lower. Therefore this type of aggressive strategy produced lower consumer prices and lower industry profits than a defensive strategy such as collusion might have produced.

The Cournot solution is as limited as its special assumptions. There is no attempt to deal with technological developments, successful attempts of one or the other rival to differentiate his product or to legislate the other out of business, etc. One might assume that one rival salts away his profits in a Swiss bank while the other squanders his at the Riviera, until the day comes when the former buys out the latter, and our duopoly becomes a monopoly. In fact, real-life conditions do change, and the behavior that arrives at a solution under one set of conditions may not be adequate for another.

Warfare

Wars may be limited or unlimited. Price cuts may be across the board and highly advertised or selective and almost secretive. Price cuts can be quietly given, for example, through absorbing freight charges or giving special advertising allowances. The victor may demand minor spoils or unconditional surrender. The mission of the aggressor may vary from a little adventure and profit to total destruction. The conditions of warfare among firms parallel those of nations.

A Brookings study in the late 1950's found evidence that A&P had rather consistently set a goal of maintaining and/or improving its market position by consistently low margin pricing. The authors found that this determination to price low had greatly influenced food retailing in the 1940's and 1950's. This was an aggressive strategy that had limited objectives, but these objectives made price competition generally quite rigorous in food retailing.

At the other end of the scale is the warfare by which James Duke conquered the cigarette industry in the 1880's. Using the latest production technology, aggressive promotion, price cutting, and "fighting brands," he speedily gained industry dominance and finally combined in 1890 the five principal manufacturers into the American Tobacco Company with James Duke as president.

Any analysis of warfare centers on the ability of the rivals to give and take punishment. The firm which can generate profits at very low prices; the firm which can supply an extremely large part of the market at such low prices; and the firm with great financial strength is the probable victor in any prolonged warfare.

The lowest cost firm has a very obvious advantage, and it must eventually win *if* it can stay in the field. However, such a firm may go bankrupt and/or find itself bought up by a competitor with higher costs but better financial assets. Whether it's a giant national firm or a small hometown oligopolist is obviously important here.

Warfare to the death is likely to be discouraged by public policy whenever one or more of the rivals are large, highly visible firms. Competition requires the continued existence of competitors.

The Pacemaker

J. M. Clark has strongly emphasized the dependence of the intensity of competition upon one or more pacesetters. A&P in the example cited above was a pacesetter for a long time in high-volume, low-cost food merchandising. In general, a pacesetter is a firm which has both the incentive and the capacity to adopt offensive strategies of various sorts in both price and nonprice competition and in both a short-run and long-run framework (see the final section of this chapter). A pacesetter is essential to the active process of moves and countermoves which characterize our more dynamic industries.[8]

---

[8] John Maurice Clark, *Competition as a Dynamic Process* (Washington, D.C.: Brookings Institution, 1961), pp. 471–76.

Pacesetting may be related to or stimulated by disturbances from outside the industry, such as the introduction of new technology or the entry of new multiproduct firms from other industries. Clark emphasizes that *the diversity* of rival firms as to size, costs, long-run interests, product mix, and elasticities of demand is essential to the development of one or more pacesetters. The Volkswagen is a symbol of the pacesetting done by foreign auto makers in the late 1950's. From the safety of their own markets, they introduced the compact car design and other concepts to the American automobile industry.

COMPETITION OF THE FEW AMONG THE MANY

Many industries appear to be a combination of an oligopoly and monopolistic competition. A few large firms may produce a half or two thirds of the output, but many small firms produce the rest. Shall we call such industries oligopolistic or monopolistically competitive? It appears the behavior may approach either of these models, depending upon the cost and demand conditions within the industry. The cost comparison is shown in Figure 12–8. Assume that DD' indicates industry demand facing a fairly homogeneous oligopoly and that S_2 represents the amounts that will be supplied in the long run by the "many" at varying prices. Assume that P_1 represents a zero-profit level for the "few" while P_3 represents the price level which the oligopoly would prefer. Clearly, the oligopoly must yield OH of the market to the many if it charges price P_3. This share may be acceptable to the oligopoly. However, if the supply curve of the many were not S_2 but S_1, then P_3 would most likely not be a feasible price. Instead the oligopoly would be pushed perilously close to their rock-bottom price of P_1. A price of P_2, for example, would give about two thirds of the market to the many. One answer to our initial question is then: The market power of the oligopoly depends upon the elasticity of supply provided by the many in relation to the supply function of the few.

The possible market power of the many as shown by S_1 may seem very strange to the reader. After all, couldn't one or more of the giant firms destroy any or even all of the many small firms in economic warfare? Perhaps so. It is well to remember that firms small in a particular industry may be parts of very large firms primarily engaged in other industries. For example, a few years ago, several of the large oil compa-

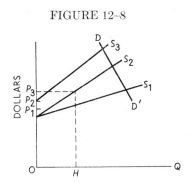

FIGURE 12–8

nies were small entrants in the synthetic ammonia (fertilizers) industry. Du Pont, one of the giants, had no illusions about destroying these small rivals. But suppose we disregard the multi-industry firms and consider only the single-industry small firms. By price cutting or other forms of economic warfare, the firms in the oligopoly could probably destroy their many rivals. However, (1) the financial costs would be very high— sometimes prohibitive; (2) the risks of antitrust intervention might be high, and (3) the probability of entry of more small firms seems high, and (4) unless the oligopoly has the best of internal communications and understandings, any warfare against the many may lead to suspicions and battles among the few.

Let's turn to alternative situations. Assume that this industry of the many and the few has large economies of scale and that the supply curve of the many is S_3. It would appear that the many are no longer a serious market threat and that they survive on the fringe as "window dressing"—to provide evidence that the industry has many firms and is "quite competitive." This may be true in a homogeneous industry. However, in a differentiated industry the many may have a more secure position than it first appears if they have found secure "niches" or "differential advantages" in the market. This niche is due to some aspect of product differentiation—perhaps personal service or some other circumstance of sale. Very often the niche may be a locational advantage that the small firm has in some small submarket near it. "Space is the best friend of little business." Therefore, these firms might be very hard to dislodge except by more extreme price cutting than is suggested by the position of S_3 in Figure 12–8. Continued coexistence of the many and the few seems likely. Doubtlessly, the few will keep an anxious eye on the supply curve of the many, lest it become more elastic in some long-run period. Would it be surprising if members of the few regularly bought out several of the many?

OUTSIDE DISTURBANCES AND LONG-RUN CONSIDERATIONS

Long-Run Plant Changes

By definition, plant sizes and numbers can be adjusted in the long run. Such size and number adjustments in oligopoly may be part of an active strategy to enlarge the firm's markets rather than a reaction to an already enlarged demand. The firm that builds plant capacity faster than its rivals has the competitive edge if the market should expand. In many service industries from barbershops to cotton gins and from service stations to feed mills, sales volumes over a long period are a fairly reasonable function of physical capacity, and the firm which would expand sales must expand capacity. Firms may adopt a deliberate strategy of keeping the market covered with plant capacity so that there is no easy gap tempting potential entrants.

Even though the *LRAC* curve of a typical oligopolist may be horizontal over a long range, its plant curve is U-shaped, and it must choose a particular plant size (Figure 12–9). In the long run, it can choose again, but plant construction costs are hardly cheap enough that firms can exercise this option very frequently. Therefore choices must be made infrequently about a plant size that will exist into the future. It is not surprising that five years later some choices were quite wrong. It seems quite possible that in an industry of one or more pacesetters, some or all of the firms will overbuild for the future. Consequently, each will

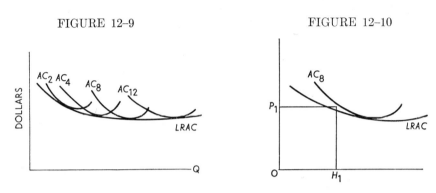

FIGURE 12–9   FIGURE 12–10

have overcapacity (Figure 12–10) and will have strong pressures either to compete vigorously for present markets *or* to reach some sort of quasi-agreement which will raise price sufficiently to cover the variable and inflated overhead costs. Again, J. M. Clark reminds us of the "public need" for enough diversity in the industry that some firms will find it more profitable to choose the competitive path rather than the collusive one.

Entry and Exit in the Long Run

By definition, these adjustments only occur in the long run. Bankruptcy or near-bankruptcy is not a necessary condition for exit—nor is it a sufficient one. Since bankruptcy of a large firm does not necessitate its death, it is not a sufficient condition for exit. Many railroads have been bankrupt, but they have rolled on through one or more financial reorganizations. Many other insolvent firms with complex patterns of capital investments, dealer organizations, brand acceptance, etc., have far more value as "going concerns" than as an unrelated collection of nuts and bolts. Therefore financial reorganization is probable in the unlikely event that hard times strike. As already emphasized, our giant oligopolists tend to be immortal.

On the other hand, firms will often voluntarily leave an industry that begins to lose its profit or growth potentials. Giant firms are usually multi-industry firms and can shift their resources fairly readily in the long run. Some giants, such as Du Pont, with strong R & D departments, rather expect to innovate, reap innovational profits, and then, as often as not, phase out as the industry becomes crowded. Thus exit becomes more of a voluntary strategy than is usually assumed.

Capacity also expands when there is entry of new competitors. Entry may be by firms larger or smaller than existing firms. Entry by new, small firms is often hindered and even prevented in some industries by such barriers as customer loyalties built up by existing firms, economies of scale sufficiently large to make operation of small firms very uneconomical, absolute cost advantages such as favored access to raw materials, and capital rationing which makes financing more expensive for entrants.

Joe Bain has written a great deal about conditions of entry.[9] Condition of entry is defined as the degree of advantage which existing sellers have over entrants as to product prices obtainable and/or production or marketing costs incurred. In a study of 20 manufacturing industries he found that product differentiation (established customer loyalties) was the most significant advantage of established firms. He found it to be very important in the following industries: automobiles, liquor, cigarettes, typewriters, tractors and complex farm equipment, and high-priced fountain pens. He found product differentiation to be moderately important in soap, petroleum, tires, metal containers, flour, higher priced shoes, and certain canned fruits and vegetables.

Product differentiation is often as dependent upon strong advertising as upon research and development, and in a few industries product differentiation *is* advertising. In such industries the gaining of market acceptance of an entrant's new brand might cost millions.

Large economies of scale may be a very effective barrier to entry. On the one hand, the infant firm cannot finance the big economical plant (and distribution network), and it cannot obtain low enough costs to compete in the size plant that it can finance. On the other hand, the giant multi-industry firm can afford an economical plant, but it may calculate that such a plant would increase industry output by say 10 percent, and this would reduce prices and potential profits sufficiently to make entry no longer attractive. The reader will realize, of course, that prospects are often better than just suggested and that entry can and does occur where the profit opportunities are inviting.

In recent years such small group industries as steel and autos have felt the impact of entry by importers. Foreign competitors have some important disadvantages in entering a market—lack of dealers (for

---

[9] Joe S. Bain, *Industrial Organization* (New York: John Wiley & Sons, Inc., 1959); and Joe S. Bain, *Barriers to New Competition* (Cambridge: Harvard University Press, 1956).

autos), import regulations and duties, slow consumer acceptance, etc. However, they have the advantage of a home base away from the foreign market, so that they may compete vigorously in a foreign market without risking their entire business in it. They may achieve economies of scale through total sales in both markets that they could not possibly achieve in the new market alone.

Entry may come vertically from a firm buying or selling to the oligopoly. Such entry may be motivated by perceived gains from making a product rather than buying it at a high price from an oligopolist. For example, a cannery set up its own can factory. Such entrants have the advantages of a protected home base, specialized experience in a related area, and an assured market or source of supply.

Entry of differentiated products is a matter of degree, and it may come from "outside" the industry in another way. New and different products may be developed which compete quite effectively with the industry. A dramatic case in point was the demise in the 1950's of the powerful motion-picture producers as their markets were ruined by television. Those who argue that oligopoly is held in check by such interindustry competition claim too much. But such new outside competition has been an important disturbance to the tranquility of a number of oligopolies including the railroads (by trucks), the bottlers (by cans and other packages), and the terminal livestock markets (by auctions and direct buyers).

In summary, entry and exit are possible but not automatic in oligopoly. We cannot confidently postulate a long-run equilibrium in which $TR = TC$ for each and every firm. With entry barriers, TR may exceed TC in the long run. In the less likely case of TC exceeding TR, then TC may be scaled down through financial reorganization as a possible alternative to exit. Entry into an oligopoly is capable of threatening the routines of business as usual. Sufficient entry, of course, can transform the small group into a large group. More likely is entry of only a few firms. However, these entrants must establish niches for themselves, and to do so they must compete more aggressively than the existing firms. Whether to discourage such aggression actively or passively becomes an important question of "industrial statesmanship."

Demand Shifts

Important disturbances to the mode of living together of oligopolists can come from changes in relative demand for the various differentiated products within the industry. Demand may switch within an oligopoly to the particular gain of one or more firms. This switch may or may not be due to some action of the favored firm(s). In either case, the switch changes power relations within the group and threatens the modes of living together developed in the context of the old relative demands. For example, in the mid fifties the market acceptance of Chrysler Corporation fell drastically, purportedly because of errors in styling and product design. Several smaller auto companies experienced somewhat similar difficulties and left the auto industry for other fields.

Our industry analysis can lead us into a trap in our thinking, just as a too-narrow industry orientation can trap a firm's management. A firm can conceive of itself as: (1) a business organization ready to engage in almost any potentially profitable line of commerce, or (2) as a business organization identified with a particular area of consumer or business demand, or (3) as the seller of a particular product or service in a specific industry. As an example, the N.Y. Central Railroad might consider itself as (1) a business firm looking for opportunities or (2) in the transportation business using rails, trucks, pipelines or rockets, or (3) in the railroad business. A firm with the narrowest concept of itself, whether it is railroading, or commission selling of hogs in the St. Louis terminal market, or manufacturing Model T Fords, will have the greatest number of drastic adjustments to make in response to shifts in demand. The firm with the broadest concept will often make its shifts in resource use well ahead of demand shifts, and will tend more to make the trends than to buck them.

Aggregate demand may also change with or without accompanying changes in relative demands. A decrease in aggregate demand can tempt each firm to cut price and fight to maintain sales. If the decrease is viewed as temporary, the repercussions upon oligopolistic behavior are likely to be far less than if it is viewed as long standing. An increase in aggregate demand also has repercussions. In atomistic competition, such an increase leads to short-run over expansion of some firms, extra utilization of existing plants, and eventual entry of new firms. Oligopolies are viewed as commonly facing horizontal or declining $LRAC$. Therefore, an increase in LR demand may be efficiently met by expansion of existing firms rather than entry of new ones. However in the nitrogen fertilizer market, the market expanded so fast that a tight little oligopoly rather quickly became an industry of more than 40 independent firms.

Technological Change

This great disturber of the status quo is no respecter of oligopolies. Perhaps the most disturbing change is a decrease in the economies of scale. Such a change can open the door to entry of many smaller competitors who chip away at the existing markets of the few. If the few are slow about adopting new technology and allow the entrants to obtain cost advantages, the oligopoly may be transformed into a large group over a rather long period of time.

Assume the typical oligopolist in industry has a long-run average cost possibilities curve as shown by $LRAC_1$ in Figure 12–11 and has built a plant having average operating costs of AC_{12}. Then assume that new technology removes some of the advantages of scale and changes the long-run average cost possibilities to $LRAC_2$. Then entrants who formerly could not finance a plant of even one half the size of AC_{12} can now build a plant one sixth the size of AC_{12} and compete on an even basis. Even more disturbing, of course, would be the technological displacement of $LRAC_2$ by $LRAC_3$ which would give a cost *advantage* to the much smaller plant. Are such displacements possible? The displacement of $LRAC_1$ by $LRAC_2$ is quite possible; the displacement of $LRAC_2$ by $LRAC_3$ is possible but less likely. The change from $LRAC_1$ to $LRAC_3$ would probably be due to changes in the technology of both production and physical distribution. If output OH can be produced in a plant at cost OC_1, cannot an output four times as great be produced at cost OC_1 by simply adding three or more such "plants" on adjacent building lots? On the other hand if OC_1 includes the costs of producing and distributing to a surrounding market area, then distribution costs may increase at an increasing rate as sales rise from OH to $4(OH)$. The reader might ask himself whether sharp-witted oligopolists could largely forestall entry by rapidly replacing their AC_{12} plants by four or five times as many plants of the new optimum size.

FIGURE 12–11

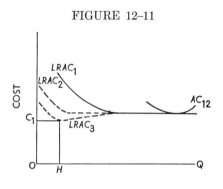

The meat-packing industry went through a shift in economies of scale somewhat similar. The weasel words "somewhat similar" reflect the fact that many types of changes occur in reality, and it is very difficult to unravel all the threads and determine that anything was exactly like a hypothetical model.

In the early 1900's, meat packing was dominated by an oligopoly. The output of each firm came mainly from a small number of large, multistory plants built adjacent to the large terminal livestock markets. These plants, built mainly prior to 1900, needed large amounts of power, heat, refrigeration, and labor. Moreover, it was desirable to keep these plants very near the livestock markets to avoid further movement shrink, and on major railroad lines to move the meat to market. Apparently, these reasons justified the large plants that were built. Animals were typically driven to the top floor and slaughtered. Then the carcasses moved largely by gravity flow down through several stages of disassembly and processing to the holding coolers and the railroad cars.

There has since occurred a whole complex of technological changes which transformed the meat-packers oligopoly into competition of the few among the many, with the many demonstrating more collective muscle than the few. What is especially interesting is that many of these technological changes occurred outside the packing industry and must, at first, have seemed of no interest to the oligopolists. In fact, our account will probably unintentionally miss some. Foremost must have been the development of modern trucks and highways. No longer did livestock have to come by rail to terminal markets; they could be hauled by trucks to any point on the highway system. No longer did meat have to be shipped by rail, although much of the long haul is so shipped. Then developments in power and in machinery reduced the manpower needs in meat packing, eliminated the old gravity flow economies of the multi-story plant, and made smaller refrigeration and heating plants more efficient. And so it came about that smaller one-story plants came to be built out in the country away from the big labor areas and the large terminal markets and railroad yards. Many of these new plants were built by entrants who carved out local or regional markets. The new plants operated more cheaply than the old. It is doubtful that the *production* costs of a new plant of X size would have been any lower than a *new* plant of $10X$ size. However the combined total of production, assembly, and distribution costs undoubtedly were lower for X size than for $10X$ size.

There were other changes, of course, including antitrust action and a famous Consent Decree against the Big Four packers of 1920. There were changes in federal grading and in the size and market power of retailers which likely made life more difficult for the original oligopoly. There may have been some deficiencies in management of the top firms. Yet, technological changes reducing the economies of scale must retain top billing as a destroyer of the old meat-packing oligopoly.

A technological change which increases the economies of scale considerably beyond and below the old minimum $LRAC$ may reduce the number of firms which can survive in the industry. Again, the firms which are slow to react are likely to suffer. However, before speedy action is praised too highly, recall that knowledge is imperfect. Speedy action to adopt a technology which turns out to be cost increasing rather than cost decreasing is a very real possibility.

An oligopoly can absorb technological change with less disturbance than atomistic competitors can, although it may not necessarily do so. The oligopolist does not blindly increase his capacity and his output without regard to its impact upon total supply; the atomistic competitor does.

Chapter 13

COMPETITION AMONG AGRICULTURAL MARKETING FIRMS

INTRODUCTION

Agricultural marketing consists of heterogeneous firms performing a heterogeneous variety of services in order to match heterogeneous supplies with heterogeneous demands. We will only sample this diversity; we cannot encompass it in a chapter.

Services for Sale

Most agricultural marketing firms produce services, not goods. These services are generally just as essential as the farm production of the product, but they should be distinguished from the products. The point is that a packer has no control over the supply of hogs or pork, and in a very real sense, he sells packing-house services, not pork. Likewise the retailer sells a retailing service in competition with other retailers rather than selling pork or apples.

Marketing has another sector of rapidly growing importance. Firms in this sector may be considered as producers of goods. In fact, some of them design products and develop merchandising campaigns in a fashion quite similar to General Electric or Standard Oil. At the production end some packers have integrated back to the farm and actually produce hogs. At the other end, some marketing firms have developed manufactured, branded products which bear so little relation to the original agricultural raw material that it is best to consider these firms as product producers. General Foods, for example, produces Post Toasties, and its sales have no relation whatsoever to the annual corn crop.

The older marketing texts emphasized services and tended to ignore the firms which produced them. The classic text by Clark and Weld, *Marketing Agricultural Products*, bears not the slightest relation to Chamberlin's *Monopolistic Competition*, although they were published almost simultaneously. In more recent years, economists have tried to treat marketing services in terms of the real world of powerful firms.

This chapter describes the marketing process within a conventional functional framework. Then it describes within the analytical framework of market structure the competitive process taking place among real-life

307

firms in performing each of these marketing functions. We then analyze the vertical interdependence among firms within the marketing channel and again examine competition as it occurs vertically. Finally we develop further the contrast between selling services and selling your own branded products by case studies of structure and competition in marketing hogs and in manufacturing and merchandising breakfast cereals. The contrasts between pork and Post Toasties are very informative.

Marketing Services or Functions

Marketing services need to be defined carefully, both to understand the complexities of the marketing system and to understand the diverse sorts of things done by firms called agricultural marketing firms. There are various sets of terms and definitions that say much the same thing. We like the following:[1]

1. Exchanging goods and titles.
2. Assembly and accumulation.
3. Sorting out.
4. Processing.
5. Allocation.
6. Assorting.

The postal exchange of Christmas cards illustrates most of these functions. It is a process by which items of value (sentimental) are exchanged. The postal system performs a tremendous task of *assembling* and *accumulating* hundreds of millions of cards from millions of letter boxes into thousands of post offices. In each postoffice the cards are *sorted out* so that the cards going in the same direction and by the same rate (airmail or first class or second) go into the same mailbag. Then this supply at each postoffice is *allocated* (i.e., shipped) to the proper offices across the land and thence to millions of other mailboxes, where eager householders watch their *assortments* of cards grow. Like all analogies, this one was stretched pretty thin in a few places, but it should demonstrate some basic functions of the marketing system.

We will now try to define these terms more clearly. Farmers produce a wide variety of products of varying sizes and qualities from coast to coast, and from January 1 to December 31 these products are assembled by a vast array of marketing firms. Simultaneously, there is a process of sorting out into fairly homogeneous groups—not only pigs from steers but also lean, choice 600-pound carcasses from wasty, choice 600-pound carcasses. Accumulations are built up for shipment in economical lots—carton or truckload or carload or even trainloads. Once these "big piles" of homogeneity are accumulated, they are then allocated or broken down

---

[1] Wroe Alderson, *Marketing Behavior and Executive Action* (Homewood, Ill.: Richard D. Irwin, Inc., 1957).

into shipments to various "markets" or to various intermediate buyers. Finally, the products reach retailers who generally build up an assortment—a pattern of different products with appeal to the shopper. In today's supermarket, this assortment is said to number six to eight thousand different items. The retailer assortment reflects the consumer's fundamental demand for a vast array of different goods to be made conveniently available to her.

All of these marketing services occur within a marketing system composed of tens of thousands of firms. What determines how many of these services are performed by a single firm? What determines how many firms play significant roles in the livestock-meat-market channel or in cranberry or frozen strawberry marketing? What determines the marketing margin for slaughtering turkeys or storing wheat? What determines whether a "homogeneous lot" is all beef carcasses or all choice grade beef carcasses or only choice grade 600-pound, lean carcasses? We shall need to look in some detail at each marketing service and at the competitive process by which it is performed. We will also look at the firm economies of scale in performing services, ease of entry, degree of service (product) differentiation, etc. (see Chapter 12, Competition among the Few).

EXCHANGING OWNERSHIP

The irreversible flow of agricultural products to consumers requires an enormous number of sales transactions. For example, how many total changes in title per year are involved in transferring, say, 80 million hogs from 1 million producers to 1,000 meat-packers, who then sell hundreds of millions of pounds of cuts and sausages to thousands of retailers who resell them to 50 million households? Imagine the labor and expense involved if every single transaction required 30 minutes haggling! The simple, efficient transfer of ownership from farmer to consumer is one of the great, unseen accomplishments of marketing.

Even if there were no *physical* functions of storage, transportation, and processing, we cannot imagine consumers buying their pork directly from farmers. The exchange inefficiencies of 50 million housewives shopping and buying from 1 million farmers is staggering. Marketing intermediaries make exchange much more efficient by reducing the number of transactions among many sellers and many buyers.

Most marketing firms buy and sell in conjunction with the performance of other marketing services. However, some firms specialize only in exchange. Commission firms receive products and sell them for the consignor without taking title. Such firms are typically rather small and relatively few in number in any given geographical area. In the heyday of the terminal livestock markets, some commission firms occupied very important sales positions and entry of new firms was difficult because of producer loyalties, market exchange entrance rules, etc. Other firms, called brokers, specialize in negotiating sales or purchases—they neither take possession nor title but they perform a vital function. Examples are brokers on the East Coast who sell midwestern beef carcasses to the local eastern trade or who sell western fruits and vegetables. These are typically very small firms in a very competitive (more nonprice than price) business where development of contacts and confidence is all important.

It is very difficult to generalize about market structure in the performance of the exchange function. Structures varying from the few to monopolistic competition are present in various commodity channels and in particular geographic areas. The competition between different types of firms—e.g., auctions, commission firms, dealers, and cooperatives—and among firms from different geographical areas makes very difficult any comparison to textbook models of competition.

A modern example of a firm specializing in the exchange of ownership is the sale of livestock by telephone auction. Some midwestern cooperatives sell feeder pigs at a weekly telephone auction. Buyers and the auctioneer at various "squawkbox" phones communicate as easily as if they were in the ring. The only handicap is the necessity of the buyers depending upon description of the pigs rather than visual inspection. The big advantage is a transfer of ownership accomplished without expensive and time-consuming trips of buyers to the auction and the avoidance of the expense, stress, and shrink of moving the pigs through the auction ring. A feeder pig auction in which pigs from many small sellers are sold to many small feeders is probably the best example of atomistic competition *on both sides of the market* found anywhere in agriculture. The cooperatives in most cases have represented forward integration by feeder pig producers. As a marketing firm per se, the cooperative, or any firm which arranged such telephone sales, was selling a sales service on a commission basis. The competition *to provide such services* is never atomistic. Scale is unimportant, and entry depends upon obtaining customer (and cooperative member) confidence.

Buyers and sellers in a subarea of a market must have current news as to supply and demand pricing conditions prevailing in the rest of the market. Otherwise there is pricing inefficiency with some buyers paying "too much" and others paying "too little." If these buyers and sellers are many and small, then any efficient system of market news is likely to be publicly provided. If some of the buyers or sellers are very large, they may prefer a market in which they provide their own internal market news and hope to capitalize on their superior knowledge. If these products are not homogeneous as to value, then there needs to be a system of generally understood grades which are related to the market news (see the grading chapter). These "if . . . then" propositions "explain" the development of public market news and grades for many agricultural products in the early 20th century.

ASSEMBLY, ACCUMULATION, AND SORTING

We turn now to the assembly, accumulation, and sorting functions of marketing. Changes of title will ordinarily also be involved. For the moment, we will ignore the many parts of marketing in which these functions are also integrated vertically with processing. Our prime examples occur in those product lines such as eggs and fresh fruit and vegetables in which there is no processing. The California Citrus Exchange is a typical example of a large cooperative which assembles, sorts, and ships a large proportion of California citrus.

Most assemblers at the farm level are small firms, although they might be "hometown oligopolists" (see Chapter 12, Competition among the Few). Entry may be rather difficult for new firms and may be of no interest to large, established firms because the market is too small to be worth the fight for it. Service differentiation is a matter of credit policy and the many rather personal aspects of the services rendered, and it may range from a virtual invitation to entry to a very high barrier against entry.

Prior to 1950, the Midwest was covered with a vast network of Farmer's Exchanges and elevators which were the first step in assembling farm produce from the general farms of the area. Through these exchanges came eggs, frying chickens, old hens, hides, wheat, soybeans, feed grains, cream, and wool. Some firms were private and some were cooperative. Many were also in the feed business or farm supply sales, etc. In the preauto era, these local firms often had considerable monopsony or oligopsony (i.e., oligopoly in purchasing) power arising from the great difficulties of local farmers selling elsewhere. The recognition of that geographically generated market power led to the creation of many local cooperative Farmer's Exchanges and Farmer's Elevators.

Most of the perishable products no longer go through this network because their production has been concentrated by farm and by area. Or should we say that perishable production was concentrated by farm and by area to obtain a more efficient marketing system than this old network? Like many things in economics, there was some mutual dependency. There were both production and marketing economies to be gained by specialized farm and area production. We will note this interdependency of marketing and production again in Chapter 16. A farm with 100,000 layers has as many eggs *already assembled* on it as the network of exchanges in a whole county could assemble in 1945. This assembly on that one farm takes place much more cheaply and much faster, since there is no exchange of ownership, only brief storage, only a single handling, and no over-the-road assembly transportation. Thus, precious freshness of perishables such as eggs can be preserved in a production and marketing system of big, specialized units that was never possible under the old general farming of midwestern agriculture. Since the big production unit performs certain marketing functions of assembly and even sorting, it is no surprise that it has superseded the old marketing unit and often sells directly to the chain-store buying organization. However in 1964 there were still more than 8,000 handlers of fresh eggs, and only a few of them handled as much as 10,000 cases a week.[2]

There are still discrepancies in size and number of buyers and sellers and a geographical dispersion in the Midwest that leaves a vital assembly role for the local elevator, milk plant, cotton gin, and livestock marketing association. To the extent that products are bulky and expensive to transport in relation to value but yet are produced in a geographically dispersed fashion because they are "tied to the land," then there is a local assembly function and that function tends to be performed by one or a very few firms per locality. As trucks and roads have improved, the "locality" has become a much larger area, but it does and will continue to exist. Thus something akin to oligopsony exists from locality to locality in the performance of these marketing functions, although the ability of sellers to turn to buyers in other geographical areas somewhat limits the market power of the oligopsony.

Geography and the economics of assembly determine how many assembly points are available to farmers, but not how many different assembly firms.

Principle: As long as the assembly function is expensive relative to postassembly transport, the assembly point nearby the farmer has a cost advantage. The reader should examine this principle closely before he accepts it. Suggested examples include transportation of cotton in trailers to the gin and in bales on truck or rail from the gin; transportation of wheat from combine to local elevators in trucks and trailers versus transportation by rail or barge from the elevator (there's also a time factor in harvest transportation as well as a cost one).

What determines the number of *firms* involved in such an assembly function as that performed by elevators? The reader will note that our transportation costs model explains the economies of many receiving *points or plants* distributed over any vast production area such as the Cornbelt or the great Plains; it does not indicate any economies in each being a separate firm or in all of them being owned by one firm. In fact, if one firm owned all the wheat acreage and elevators in Kansas, that firm would operate many elevators, although likely not as many as now exist.

[2] National Commission on Food Marketing, *Organization and Competition in the Poultry and Egg Industries*, Technical Study No. 2 (Washington, D.C.: U.S. Government Printing Office, 1966).

On the other hand, as long as the Kansas wheat acreage is owned by independent farmers, they would not likely tolerate the ownership of all elevators by one firm. Nor is there any convincing evidence that the economies of scale are such that an independent elevator cannot survive, although these economies allow rather impressive strings of elevators to be controlled by a single firm or cooperative.

Thus far, technology has not been a powerful force in generating really large economies of scale in assembly in contrast to its dominant role in processing. Giant size is more likely to be generated by a push for market power and/or as a subsidiary operation of processing firms. Some large firms are engaged in the marketing services of assembly, accumulating, and sorting such commodities as wheat, feed grains, cotton, livestock, and certain fresh fruits. For example, the capital requirements are considerable for engaging in the nationwide assembly of wheat for milling and export. However, barriers to entry generally tend to be low; and with a few exceptions, market power is not especially impressive.

Price Setting

The market power of the local assembly firms are often overestimated because they are few and because they appear to set price. Let's

FIGURE 13–1

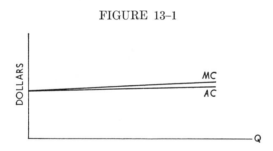

analyze the actual independence that a local elevator has in setting price. We assume the elevator to be an oligopsonist with a relatively small influence on price. Purchase price is assumed to be a single price paid to all selling wheat at any given time. Purchase prices for wheat in that locality will generally be the same for a given quality, although there may be slight and temporary variations. The buyer chooses one price among the alternatives with the knowledge that volume purchased will be a direct function of price as shown in Figure 13–1 by *AC*. Average costs (*AC*) of the purchased product obviously equal the purchase price. The marginal costs of the input (wheat), as indicated by *MC*, rise twice as fast as the linear *AC*.

How shall the firm maximize? It equates *MC* to *MR*, like any maximizer does, except that we have to define a different kind of *MR* (marginal revenue). Why? Because operating costs of the firm other than for buying the wheat haven't been accounted for. The elevator firm's manager will reason: I can sell another bushel of wheat for X cents. To buy and handle that marginal bushel through resale will cost Y cents. Therefore the *real MR* of another bushel of wheat is $X − Y$ cents. I will maximize my profits by pushing my purchase volume—and price—up to the point where the *MC* (which is greater than the purchase price) of wheat $= X − Y$ cents.

Our economically sophisticated elevator manager *derived* his real *MR* by subtracting the marginal costs of operation, so we will call it *DMR* for derived marginal revenue. Choose output where $DMR = MC$. Thus our maximizer should set price P_1 and buy amount *OH* (Figure 13–2). The marketing firms equating of *DMR* to *MC* is equivalent to the

FIGURE 13–2

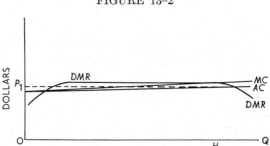

farmer equating the marginal value product MVP_x of fertilizer to the marginal factor cost (*MFC*) of that input (see Chapter 4).

How stable are *DMR* and *MC* of purchasing wheat? They fluctuate from day to day with every change in short-run expectations as these expectations influence the national markets—and hence *DMR*—and as they influence local farmer willingness to sell—*AC* and *MC*. The price discovery process goes on continuously. Prices set by the local elevator are largely barometric readings of supply and demand. Even oligopsonists elevators cannot control the price paid over time, nor the amount they buy.

The oligopsonists can neither control price nor quantity over time because they have no control over either the supply of or the demand for wheat. However, they do control the *supply of elevator services* in this area, and therefore, they can set buying price from day to day or week to week in such relation to selling prices as to set their margin (the difference between buying and selling price of wheat) and produce nice profits. Even if buying price has to be reset once a week or more often as the *AC* curve and/or the *DMR* curve fluctuates, the analysis is the same as if the curves were stable for an entire season. Now the reader should perceive more clearly the comments early in the chapter that many marketing firms compete in the selling of services, not products.

How high a margin the oligopsony is able to maintain depends upon all the factors discussed in Chapter 12, Competition among the Few. In the late 1800's when strings of line elevators were built by the powerful millers along the railroads opening up the West, the market power and the margins of the assemblers were probably quite substantial.

PROCESSING

Processing is the manufacturing phase of agricultural marketing. It becomes increasingly important as consumers demand, and as technology permits, more and more convenient and table-ready foods.

Large economies of scale came in the late 19th century in processing as in much of manufacturing. The moving belt disassembly line in meat-packing that took the work to the worker and permitted minute specialization of labor was developed long before Henry Ford's auto assembly line. The Big Four meat-packing firms which dominated the industry by 1890 had been built in the short space of 30 years by dynamic, aggressive leadership, which capitalized upon new technology to achieve economies of scale never before dreamed of in meat-packing. The successful refrigerator car was the major innovation which allowed these aggressive firms to slaughter at midwestern livestock centers and out-compete eastern slaughterers shipping in livestock. However, use of the disassembly line and development of profitable uses for by-products also contributed to the economies of scale.

The leading grain millers of the 1890's were built by aggressive development of new technology. Curiously, the leaders were Minneapolis millers, which seemingly faced severe handicaps in the 1860's because the area's hard spring wheat made inferior flour. Development of new milling processes led to a superior technology which gave industry leadership. The average capacity of Minneapolis mills increased more than sevenfold between 1876 and 1890, indicating the response to growing economies of scale. The Minneapolis millers organized subsidiary companies to build lines of elevators along the railroads and tried unsuccessfully to organize a buying cartel to purchase for all the mills. By 1890, four milling firms controlled seven eighths of the milling capacity of Minneapolis (and the Northwest).[3]

---

[3] Harold F. Williamson, *The Growth of the American Economy* (Englewood Cliffs, N.J.: Prentice-Hall, Inc., 1944), pp. 440–41.

Economies of plant size depend upon economies in assembly and distribution as well as in processing. Most agricultural processing involves some processes such as cutting, cleaning, cooking, canning, heating, cooling, etc., in which mechanization and even automation is feasible (see Chapter 10). Therefore, economies of scale of plant size are considerable. Very often the limits on plant size are the diseconomies of assembly or distribution rather than manufacturing diseconomies. Thus, a change in assembly or distribution costs can make a big change in economies of scale. Two industry examples illustrate how such changes can work either way: (1) The economic size of milk bottling plants increased many times as soon as the lightweight, nonreturn plastic-coated cartons were substituted for glass bottles. (2) The economic size of meat-packing plants decreased when short-haul truck transportation of livestock to market replaced long-haul rail transport. (See a full discussion at the close of Chapter 12, Competition among the Few.) The reader might ask himself which one of these changes seems more likely in other industries today.

Scale in Turkey Processing Plants

Turkey processing is a relatively simple operation. A recent study of economies of scale found such economies at each larger capacity of plant. Plant capacity was measured in terms of hourly output and ranged from 200 to 4,000 per hour (see Figure 13–3). The economies of scale

FIGURE 13-3

HEAVY YOUNG HENS—PROCESSING COSTS BY PLANT SIZE AND CAPACITY
Ten Model Plants Operating 144 Days

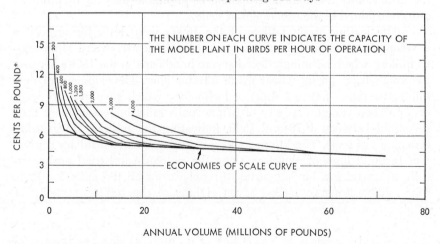

ANNUAL VOLUME (MILLIONS OF POUNDS)

* Ready-to-cook basis.
SOURCE: U.S. Department of Agriculture, Economic Research Service.

curve (*LRAC*) continued to decline over the full range of the plants studied. Should every processor rush out and build a 4,000-per-hour-capacity plant? It depends on the supplies available or potentially available in that location. A 4,000 plant used at only 40 percent of capacity cannot process turkeys as cheaply as a 2,000 plant used at 80 percent of capacity (see Figure 13–4).[4]

If processing firms were single-plant firms, none would probably be large enough to be on *Fortune's* list of the top 500 industrial corporations. Multiplant processors are common because there are important

FIGURE 13–4

HEAVY YOUNG HENS—PROCESSING COSTS BY PLANT SIZE AND USE OF CAPACITY
Ten Model Plants Operating 144 Days

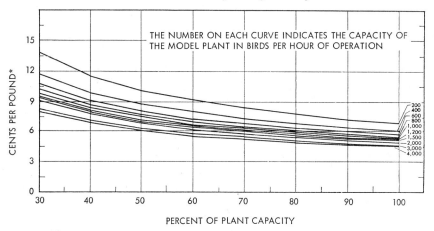

* Ready-to-cook basis.
SOURCE: U.S. Department of Agriculture, Economic Research Service.

advantages of scale in merchandising and advertising. In 1965, *Fortune* reported five food companies: Swift, Armour, National Dairy, General Foods, and Borden among the top 40 industrial corporations. A study showed that the manufacturers of food and grocery products represented the largest single group of advertisers in 1965. Some 21 food companies spent $690 million to promote their product—even more than the soap and detergent companies spent.[5]

Oligopoly, monopolistic competition, highly effective product differentiation, no product differentiation, high barriers to entry, no barriers to entry—all of these can be found in food processing. In fact, various parts of the business of a large diverse company like Swift may be found

[4] *Costs and Economies of Scale in Turkey Processing Plants,* USDA Marketing Research Report No. 627, September, 1964.

[5] *Supermarket News,* September 5, 1966, p. 8.

to fit into each of these situations. Concentration ratios for 1963 or 1964 reported by the National Commission on Food Marketing are shown in Table 13–1. National market power is not excessive in processing with a few exceptions. However, within the differentiated product lines, there is probably more market power at the national level in processing than in any other part of agricultural marketing, except retailing. The reasons lie in the great barriers to entry associated with large economies of scale and effective product differentiation.

TABLE 13–1

PERCENTAGE OF NATIONAL BUSINESS ACCOUNTED
FOR BY THE FOUR LARGEST FIRMS

Commercial red meat processing	29%
Young chicken slaughter (F.I.)	18
Turkey slaughter (F.I.)	24
Fluid milk	23
Ice cream and ices	37
Fruit and vegetable canning	24
Fruit and vegetable freezing	24
Flour milling	24
Baking	23
Breakfast cereals	85
Crackers and cookies	62

SOURCE: National Commission on Food Marketing, *Food from Farmer to Consumer* (Washington, D.C.: U.S. Government Printing Office, 1966), p. 138.

ALLOCATION AND ASSORTING

The consumer has a tremendous food inventory problem. To maintain balance and variety in the family diet and minimize the number of times an ingredient is "out" when recipe or meal preparation is contemplated, the consumer must maintain a very large number of items—foods, ingredients, spices, beverages, etc. The limitations of spoilage (or quality deterioration), space, and money keep this inventory "low." In the prerefrigeration and preauto days, the urban housewife shopped everyday to meet this problem. We now take for granted the weekly shopping trip to the shopping center.

Much of the structure of food retailing is geared to the consumer's shopping patterns and inventory limitations. In terms of our previous definitions, retailing is geared to providing the kinds of *assortments* which enable the consumer to save time and effort in maintaining her assorted inventory. In an affluent society, the ratio of goods purchased to shopping time must rise because the length of the day is fixed and consumers tend to restrict total food shopping time. The reader may consider how much these same ideas go to explain the big retail assortments in drugs, hardware, etc., versus the lesser assortments in some other lines.

Allocation refers to the process by which products like hams are distributed from a thousand packing plants to many thousand retail supermarkets. In a country with as many people and square miles as ours, the physical job is a staggering one. Many people and firms are involved, including trucking firms, warehouses, wholesalers, brokers, chain-store distribution centers, and retailers. There are at least as many market channels through which these products move as there are products.

In an oversimplified view, processors have allocation problems and retailers have assortment problems. The big packer has many carloads of beef to sell; the big supermarket wants a dozen sides of beef, other specific kinds of meat, 10 cartons each of specific kinds of fruit and vegetables, and a dozen cartons each of various kinds of dry groceries. The wholesaler has been the traditional intermediary who purchased the beef, hams, breakfast cereal, flour, and toilet tissue by the carloads and broke into smaller shipments for regular delivery to retailers. Food wholesaling firms at one time typically were large, powerful organizations compared to their customer retailers. Food wholesalers possessed some oligopoly power by virtue of the spatial characteristics of a city or market area. When supermarkets came into being, the process of selecting and buying each of 6,000 items became a staggering task. The chain supers reduced the task per supermarket by organizing a simple purchasing unit for a whole group of supers—typically a division covering a big city and its hinterland. The next step was to routinize the transactions by the chain integrating backwards to its own wholesale unit so that changes of ownership were no longer required between the purchase of the carload lot and the consumer purchase at the check-out lane. The independent wholesalers and retailers had to counter with an alliance that drastically routinized their transactions in order to survive (see Chapter 14 on food retailing). In summary, the building of retail food assortments for consumers and of wholesale assortments for retailers is a big business that is incompatible with atomism.

While the allocation and distribution of many food products takes place within a national or near national market, some products tend to be more localized with a relatively small amount of intermarket shipments. Most of the fluid milk products, for example, are sold in local markets, which bear a general relation to the 80-odd federal milk order markets. The four largest local fluid milk dealers had a 73 percent share of volume processed within such local markets in 1964.[6] *Local concentration* in fluid milk was three times as great as national concentration.

VERTICAL INTERDEPENDENCE

Agricultural products are shipped down a one-way channel with the possibility of many firms or only one firm being involved in the market channel functions of accumulating, sorting out, processing, allocating, and assorting. There is an absolute dependence of each function or stage upon the other.

Competition takes place vertically as well as horizontally. Just as labor and management have both complementary and competitive interests, so do processors and wholesaler-retailers or processors and assemblers. In each market channel there is a total revenue pie to be sliced and the size of one's slice is related to the size taken by one's neighbor. For example, consumers pay X amount of money this season for canned tomatoes, tomato soups, pastes, juices, etc. That total money was divided among those relevant firms from the tomato grower to retailer. It was generally divided on an ex ante or anticipatory basis—i.e., each firm had been paid for its function before the particular can of tomatoes went in the shopping cart. Every decision was made on a derived basis. The retailers on the basis of the supplies available had to estimate prices at which the product would readily move, deduct their margin (as related to their operating costs), and thus derive a maximum price they were willing to pay. Each firm down the line to the canner processor made the same type of derivation.

Suppose that over a period of three years very efficient, new methods of processing cut the processing costs in half. What happens to the cost savings? If processors were a monopoly or a tightly run oligopoly with closed entry, they might keep the extra savings as profits. If processors are quite competitive, the processing margin will be bid down to match the new cost level and the savings will be passed down to farmers and up to the other elements in the channel. Just how these savings are finally distributed depends upon supply elasticities. It's safe to generalize that most savings eventually are passed to consumers in lower prices or more service and better quality products. However in the short run (which may last several accounting periods) firms up and down the channel benefit. This "sharing" is one of the things we mean by saying competition is vertical as well as horizontal (see Chapter 16).

Market power may be dominant at some juncture of the market channel or may be somewhat evenly spread throughout. "Market power"

---

[6] National Commission on Food Marketing, *Organization and Competition in the Dairy Industry*, Technical Study No. 3 (Washington, D.C.: U.S. Government Printing Office, 1966), p. 75.

is used very loosely these days. We *define* it here as the power of a firm to influence price or other terms of exchange. Obviously the possession of market power is a continuum varying from zero power in the case of an atomistic seller facing a monopsony to total power in the case of that monopsony.

One is impressed in any study of business history with the way that market power has shifted about. For example, the big meat-packers of 1890 had much more market power than either farmers or retailers or any other segment of the channel. Now it is widely argued that big retail chains—both voluntary and corporate—have more market power than any other part of the livestock-meat channel. When supplies are plentiful, those who can "control" demand—retailers or processors with very effective productive differentiation—tend to have the market power. However when supplies are scarce, the producers or those furnishing the scarce supplies reap the larger gains. Thus in an era of agricultural abundance, we have seen large processors—who were built on large economies of scale of processing undifferentiated agricultural products—turn aggressively to merchandising and product differentiation techniques which would give some "control" over demand. The market channel is a power structure.

Concern for power can unite firms at a particular level of the marketing channels. When threatened, firms at one level will unite in political or economic action against another vertical level. Even the auto dealers have gone to Congress for relief from the alleged oppressive hand of the auto manufacturers. The long-time tight supply control of tobacco production has been justified by pointing to the great market power of the tobacco processors and distributors. Negotiation between vertical levels of a market occasionally may take on some of the aspects of labor-management negotiations. These negotiations can become the bitter quarrels of those who must live together, although they would much prefer not to. The market channel is a power structure.

Firms may adjust their operations to others strictly through price negotiations. Or they may choose to achieve some degree of vertical integration—either by ownership or by some sort of contractual arrangements. As we have seen, there is ownership integration of the wholesale and retail functions in national chains and various kinds of ownership and contractual integration of these functions in the voluntary chains. Some meat-packers own feedlots; others own cattle which they hire a custom feedlot to feed for them; a few have contracts with assembly organizations to provide so many slaughter livestock per month on a price formula basis. The typical broiler integrator owns the feed mills, the feed, the broilers, and the processing plant, so he is a producer as well as a processor and assembler. He may even own the hatchery for the broiler chicks.

Vertical integration is a much studied and discussed problem in agricultural marketing and policy. Vertical integration means the control by a firm of two or more stages of production or marketing where a salable product is available at each stage. (See the section on vertical integration, Chapter 16.) Many special factors can be causes of vertical integration; we shall remain with the basics. The degree of interdependence of production functions at adjacent vertical levels is basic. Tomatoes cannot be canned until grown, picked, and delivered to the cannery; if a two-day supply of picked tomatoes is already waiting at the cannery door, there is little point in picking more ripe tomatoes. In the case of numerous perishables there is a high interdependence of production functions, and contractual or other types of vertical integration are typical. The economic interdependence of particular canners and particular vegetable producers is typically made even stronger by the spatial production patterns which restrict the number of canners to which a producer can go and vice versa.

There is probably some degree of interdependence in production functions of any adjacent levels, but many times it is not sufficient to encourage vertical integration. For example, the quality of spinning cotton is affected by the variety of cotton, its maturity and moisture when picked, and the quality of the ginning. Yet there has been no move for spinners to buy gins or cotton fields. In part, the spinners can communicate their quality specifications by means of market prices without resorting to vertical integration. Moreover, spinning, ginning, and cotton production each require complex and very different operational and managerial skills, so that the problems of ownership integration would be formidable.[7]

The degree of discrepancy of assortment has been emphasized by Alderson. Vertical integration of food retailing and wholesaling achieved real economies because the assortments were the same and substantial costs associated with selling to the retailers were eliminated. But vertical integration of Swift and A&P would be a different matter because their assortments do not match. Swift produces many items that A&P could not merchandise in retail supermarkets. Likewise, A&P must merchandise several thousand items that Swift doesn't produce. Even the products like beef and pork which both Swift and A&P handle would frequently be located geographically so as to be economically inaccessible so that Swift could make more by selling to Safeway, or A&P could buy at a lower price from Armour. This is not to argue that A&P and Swift could not merge. Stranger combinations of firms are about and apparently doing very well. But the point is that the product relationships of these two

[7] Jesse Markham, "Integration in the Textile Industry," *Harvard Business Review,* January, 1955, pp. 74–88.

firms are not a strong incentive to merger. The reader might ask himself how closely related are the concepts of interdependent production functions and of discrepancy of assortments.

A third factor in vertical integration is the grab for market power as illustrated in the broiler industry. During the early and rapid growth of the industry, some large growers began to mix their own feed. At the same time, or perhaps in response, feed dealers began to contract with growers to supply feed on credit. Credit was typically short in this mushrooming business. In self-defense, other feed dealers resorted to contracts to protect their own feed markets. Integration, once begun, became self-sustaining until more than 95 percent of the industry was vertically integrated.

Higbee tells of a visit to a Georgia broiler processing plant during the glutted broiler market of 1961 when chickens costing 15 cents a pound to grow were bringing 10 cents.

It did not make sense to the visitors that one of the largest processing plants in the world was in trouble because it was too small. Just who is big in this business, they wondered. The supervisor proceeded to explain the facts of life: "We're an independent; that's our difficulty. We're alone. We have only five feed mills and five hatcheries in our organization. We have to take whatever the market will pay. We are not A&P or Safeway. There's a war on right now—Quaker Oats, General Mills, Ralston Purina, and a few other big grain dealers are trying to kill each other off. They're selling below cost and we're caught in the middle. We'll go broke before they will—you can believe it. They know that too. They're waiting for us to fall in their lap. They all have other lines to make up their losses. We are in broilers; that's all."[8]

Like most tools, vertical integration can be used as an offensive or defensive weapon. Vertical integration contributes to the acquisition, or preservation, of horizontal power as it is used to acquire, or defend, markets—for example; the feed companies in the broiler industry; and the independent food wholesalers who organized voluntary chains around them. Vertical integration of atomistic firms would not produce market power. It would be of no consequence if some citrus growers individually integrated with some roadside fruit stands. However, vertical integration in conjunction with horizontal power compounds the market power. A giant feed company which dominates feed sales to individual broiler producers in an area as well as controlling through contracts the feeding of as many more broilers in the area is in an excellent position "to play both ends against the middle."

We now turn to case studies of the marketing of pork and breakfast cereals. We shall examine the horizontal and vertical competitive proc-

---

[8] Edward Higbee, *Farms and Farmers in an Urban Age* (New York: Twentieth Century Fund, 1963), p. 32.

esses in the two market channels. We shall point out the important competitive differences between marketing firms which attain market power over their own effectively differentiated products and marketing firms which sell marketing services.

STRUCTURE AND COMPETITION IN THE MARKETING OF HOGS AND PORK

It is an admitted restriction to study hogs and pork rather than all livestock and meat. However, there are so many variations among the three major livestock species as to area of production and marketing channels used, that this simplification seems necessary. Hogs are not to be considered as particularly typical of the livestock industry. In fact, there has probably been less postwar change in this industry than for sheep and cattle.

About 85 percent of the nation's pork supply is produced in the North Central States plus Kentucky. We will restrict most of our discussion to this major area. In the late 1950's, there were 26 terminal markets, about 1,000 auctions, several thousand dealers, about 500 slaughterers, and several hundred local markets in the region.[9] Since hogs are often hauled more than 50 miles to market, it seems obvious that each of the 870,000 farmers selling hogs had access to several buyers. Assembly and accumulation at the 500 slaughtering plants and changes of ownership were accomplished by several devices. One third of the hogs was purchased directly by packer buyers at the plants or at the farms. Another third was sold for the farmers by commission firms operating on the terminal markets. These firms took possession but not title to the hogs; to the extent that several buyers competed to buy from the commission firms, there was competition. Another sixth of the hogs were sold to local markets or concentration yards who in turn resold to packers in the region or in other regions. Dealers purchased the remaining hogs and in turn resold to packers or sometimes to other dealers.[10] The four largest packers purchased 35–40 percent of the hogs marketed.[11] The next 16 largest packers purchased another one third of the hogs. Thus there was considerable concentration in ultimate buying at the processing level. At intermediate stages, buying and performing of assembling services was in the nature of a large group monopsonistic competition, but at the

[9] Richard R. Newberg, *Livestock Marketing in the North Central Region*, Ohio Research Bulletin 846, December, 1959.

[10] A more recent study shows some further decline in the share of marketings through terminal markets: National Commission on Food Marketing, *Organization and Competition in the Livestock and Meat Industry*, Technical Study No. 1 (Washington, D.C.: U.S. Government Printing Office, June, 1966).

[11] Nationwide, the percent of U.S. pork production accounted for by the four largest packers fell from 38.8 percent in 1956 to 34.1 percent in 1964. *Ibid.*

processing-purchasing level, the situation resembles more the model of competition of the few among the many.

The reader will recall from Chapter 12 that the market power of the few depends upon the elasticity of supply of the many in relation to the supply function of the few. In the past half century, the market share of the few packers has fallen from one half the market down to one third. There has been considerable entry into the packing business, and there have been many successful expansions of smaller firms. Economies of scale of slaughtering are not large; it is not necessary to have a national or regional distribution system. Competition is ordinarily quite intense.

Since hog and pork supplies are not controlled by the packers, hog and pork pricing by packers is a continuous series of adjustments to clearing the market of two perishable products—hogs and pork. The packer *derives* the buying price for hogs from the expected selling prices of pork products via the cutout test which indicates the physical and value yield of products. In accord with the old saying of "sell it or smell it," perishable pork products are sold by packers at the going wholesale prices, regardless of whether the prices of those particular products covered costs.

The ability of packers to maintain a satisfactory *average* margin between pork and hog prices is related to competitive conditions within the packing industry and to the swing in hog supplies. Since the supply of hogs, in effect, constitutes a demand for *hog packing services,* increased hog marketings utilize more of the packing industry capacity and generally increase earnings while a decline in hog marketings tends to cut packers' earnings. This effect is due to the variations in utilization of industry capacity and would be expected to be true even if the packing industry were atomistic. Seasonal, cyclical, and other fluctuations in agricultural products are a most important problem to any marketing service firm. Such fluctuations affect capital commitments, industry capacity, operating costs and procedures, and the competitive process.

Farmers sometimes ask why the prices of hogs *fall* with increasing supplies while the "prices" (margins) and earnings of packers *rise*. The question arises from a confusion as to what packers supply. We repeat: it is not hogs or pork but rather hog marketing services that packers supply. Hogs constitute a *demand* for packing services not a *supply* of them.

The corporate and voluntary retail chains and their integrated meat warehouses constitute the major part of the rest of the channel. Buying is generally centralized by chain-store division or by voluntary chain regional headquarters. The typical buying office annually buys several million pounds of pork. Buyers are generally able to canvass the market very carefully for the best deals and possess a great deal of market information about packer inventories, costs, etc. There is general agreement that the growth of large-scale retail buying has intensified the price competition at the packer level because the large buyers are much more knowledgeable and price conscious than the independent retailers of the 1920's. The National Food Commission found that many small packers sold as much as 25 percent of their output to one large retailer, while several large packers have adopted a policy of restricting sales to any retailer to a maximum of 5 percent.[12]

Wholesale price discovery is complicated and obscure enough that its efficiency is often challenged. Buyers and sellers explore alternatives via telephone and other personal contacts. "Facts" are available via private and public market news wires and sheets as to certain price transactions recently made by others in the market, although the *exact* relevance of these facts is not always obvious. What is the relationship between the product qualities and prices of reported and unreported transactions? Some buyers and sellers attain physical exchange efficiency by contracting to exchange certain amounts of product regularly; they usually link their prices to reported prices of others. There are many debates as to the effect of such formula pricing upon the pricing process. Product similarity pressures each buyer to try to obtain prices as low at least as his competitors do, and vice versa for sellers. But in the present exchange system, information is hardly adequate for insuring the consistent attainment of those goals.

Significant amounts of fresh and cured pork are also sold to restaurants, schools, U.S. Armed Services, and other institutional outlets. Some fresh and frozen pork is sold to sausage and other manufacturers who in turn resell to the retail and institutional trade.

Large meat-packers used to be accused rather regularly of "sharing the market," i.e., purchasing a constant percentage of livestock receipts in a particular terminal market. Nicholls showed that the shares of livestock purchases of the Big Five—and then the Big Four—packers remained virtually constant at each of a number of terminal markets through a 34-year period starting in 1913. Week-to-week percentages were also quite constant.[13] Such constancy of market shares can be explained by conscious noncompetitive behavior designed to avoid short-run price competition and preserve comfortable packing margins. However, it can also be explained by the existence of fixed facilities located at the markets and by *competitive* efforts not to lose their share of the market.

In recent years, other practices have gained attention. The relative decline of certain terminal markets, the closing of some Big Four plants, and the entry of many new firms and plants in the country have thoroughly disrupted traditional market shares and changed the market

[12] *Ibid.*

[13] William H. Nicholls, *Imperfect Competition Within Agricultural Industries* (Ames, Iowa: Iowa State University Press, 1941), pp. 4 and 5.

organization of meat-packing. Now more concern is directed toward direct buying practices, packer or retailer integration into production via contracts or ownership, etc. In the mid sixties, hog production is still in the hands of more than a million farmers. However, the centralization of control of farm production and marketing has made such inroads in other areas that even hog producers and marketing agencies are looking nervously over their shoulders. If centralized control is ahead, who will exercise the control?

Why hadn't there been much more vertical integration in hog production and processing by the mid 1960's? Applying our three tests of (1) interdependence of production functions, (2) discrepancy of assortments, and (3) quest for market power, all three factors appear to offer mild encouragement for vertical integration. Perhaps the biggest barrier has been the lack of success of very many large hog production units. The would-be integrator must still deal with hundreds or thousands of producers. If and when hogs can be produced readily in ten-thousand or fifty-thousand units, then vertical integration of some sort appears more likely. Whether it is to be "forward integration" by producers, "backward integration" by packers, or "both-ways integration" by marketing agencies remains to be seen.

STRUCTURE AND COMPETITION IN THE MARKETING OF BREAKFAST CEREALS

Grocery manufacturers are a very different kind of agricultural marketing sector than most of the agencies marketing hogs. Many "dry grocery" products have well-established brand names and their sales— both volume and price—have almost no relation to the farm products which comprise their ingredients. A number of such product lines have highly concentrated market structures like the Type I oligopoly of Chapter 12. Examples include breakfast cereals, cake mixes, candy bars, coffee, crackers and cookies, salad dressings, and soups. As an illustration, we will examine briefly the breakfast cereal industry which markets small parts of our corn, wheat, rice, and oats; cheers our breakfast tables; and sponsors the kiddie programs on T.V.

The 4 largest manufacturers of breakfast cereals had 84.6 percent of the $580 million sales in 1964, the next 4 had 11.9 percent, and 50 other companies divided up the remaining 3.5 percent. Number of firms has been quite stable for the past decade, and entry has been practically nil.[14] Prices and profits indicate that the Big Four do much better than the rest

[14] The entire description of this industry is based upon National Commission on Food Marketing, *Studies of Organization and Competition in Grocery Manufacturing*, Technical Study No. 6 (Washington, D.C.: U.S. Government Printing Office, 1966).

of the industry. In short, industry structure resembles a differentiated oligopoly with a not-very-competitive fringe and high barriers to entry.

The larger firms are such large conglomerates that breakfast cereals are a small part of total business. The large ones include such household names as General Foods (Post Toasties, Grape-Nuts, Alpha-Bits), General Mills (Wheaties, Cheerios), and Kellogg (Corn Flakes, Froot Loops, Raisin Bran).

A cost breakdown (as percentage of sales) for 1964 for the top four firms indicates much about the industry:

20.0%	Cost of ingredients
14.4	Cost of containers
18.2	Other manufacturing costs
52.6%	Total manufacturing costs
28.0%	Total selling expenses
4.2	Administrative and general expenses
7.4	Federal income tax (minus other income)
7.8	Net income after income tax
100.0%	

Since wheat is only one ingredient of Wheaties, since ingredient cost is only 20 percent of the sales dollar, and since only about 1.7 percent of wheat goes into Wheaties and other wheat cereals, it is obvious that ordinary fluctuations in wheat harvests and prices have no relevance to the sales of Wheaties.

Advertising is the largest single component of the 28.0 percent selling costs. It is generally believed that the consumer demand for breakfast cereals is highly inelastic. Price competition is almost nonexistent because of industry structure and the inelasticity of demand. The main elements of nonprice competition center on attracting consumer demand via advertising and maximum shelf space at retail. These two are not unrelated.

Procter & Gamble salesmen are probably the most admired and feared in the entire packaged goods business. "They're always gentlemen to the core," says a Princeton, N.J., retailer. "But when they walk in with their soft-spoken ways, you know they are always carrying that big advertising stick. When they bring in a new product you just have to take it. Otherwise with all that advertising, the women start coming in here screaming 'where is this? where is that?' "[15]

While cereals can be "sold" by T.V., they must be constantly resold, as strong brand loyalties are unusual. Moreover, there seems to be a consumer desire for variety and for the new. Consequently, there is considerable effort to introduce new products and even two or three

[15] "Behind P & G's Marketing Success," *Dun's Review and Modern Industry*, May 3, 1963, p. 88.

versions of the old. There were 27 "new" ready-to-serve cereal products introduced between 1955 and 1964, and by 1964 they had acquired 23 percent of the total markets.

Breakfast cereals may appear very simple to us at 7:00 A.M. However, the introduction of a new one generally requires two to three years and costs a great deal. For example, almost a million dollars is often spent in test marketing a new cereal. The advertising costs necessary to launching a new product may run as high as one half of the sales revenue the first year. Profits on a new product are rare before the third year after introduction.

Economies of scale at the production plant are said to be L-shaped. One plant produces over 10 percent of industry output. A plant producing more than 1 percent of national output should be competitive. Multiplant firms are justified on the basis of distributional savings, and not on any gains in manufacturing efficiency. The number of plants per firm for the big firms ranged from one to six. There are some economies of size in selling. The larger advertisers receive quite significant discounts from the networks and advertisers.

Breakfast cereals are a bulky product, which must be kept dry and clean and should move to the consumer in six months or less. The *allocation* or distribution ordinarily occurs from manufacturer plant or distribution center to chain warehouse. General Foods has pioneered a system of regional distribution centers with automated handling of orders (both the order information and the products). It reduced delivery time from 15 days to 2 or 3.

Profits, either as a percentage of sales or as a return on stockholder's equity, have been better in the cereal industry than in most manufacturing. Why have they not attracted entry? Presumably because entry is difficult in relation to the absolute amount of profits to be gained—after all, the industry is a small one. Entry is expensive and risky enough to deter smaller firms. Not everyone is willing and able to "take on" the massive power of General Foods or Ralston Purina. Entry is made difficult by product differentiation. The market is so fragmented that only a few branded items each have as much as a 5 percent share of the market. Hence a rather successful new entrant with one branded item might achieve annual sales of only, say, 2 percent of $580 million, or $11.6 million—not a very impressive figure, considering the break-in risks involved.

Vertical integration is relatively minor. Some processors own grain elevators, but this ownership appears related more to other facets of their business than to any incentives as cereal manufacturers. Retailers have not integrated into cereal manufacture, and only 1 percent of cereal sales are private (retail) brand. The discrepancy of manufacturer and retailer assortments is one obvious barrier to such vertical integration. The heavy dependency on advertising and the same fragmentation of branded items which discourages entry also discourages retailer integration.

The balance of market power in manufacturer-retailer relations is probably tipped in favor of the manufacturer by his advertising-induced customer demand. However, the big chain with its control of shelf space and its ability to allocate such space among several competing firms is not powerless.

Since it is generally accepted that most customers buy several brands of cereals, the retailer desires the *assortment* that will maximize his profits. Exactly what should be that assortment cannot be answered accurately and cheaply; obviously shelf space is expensive and many items cannot be carried. Each manufacturer, of course, wants to influence that retail assortment to his own advantage. In the 1950's several packages were widened to give the maximum amount of visual, "pick me off the shelf," impact. Then retailers began laying cereal packages on their sides to reduce display space. Consequently, packages have been reduced in height and width in order to regain better shelf display. The battle for standing room is ths grand finale of nonprice competition.

PORK VERSUS POST TOASTIES

From processing through retailing, the marketing functions are similar for pork and breakfast cereals, but most other things are different.

Market structure is a tight little oligopoly in the processing and distribution of breakfast cereals; the little firms on the fringe apparently present no significant competitive challenge. On the other hand, the pork slaughterers and processors are not nearly as concentrated and the smaller firms are very much of a competitive threat. Entry appears very difficult in cereals and has not occurred in recent years. Entry is easy in meat packing and occurs very frequently.

Pork pricing is on a market period basis. The fluctuations in daily and weekly supplies and demands of this perishable product determine hog and pork prices. Except for minor branded items, price is entirely a barometric reading of supply and demand. Today's hams must be sold on today's market regardless of the costs incurred "yesterday" in procuring and curing them. While pork can stay in the cooler a few days or in the freezer a few months, storage is expensive, and consequently the market period supply curve is very inelastic.

In contrast, breakfast cereal prices are found on long-lived published lists. The cost of grain and other raw materials is only 20 percent of the sales dollar rather than 75 percent or more as in pork processing. Both grains and breakfast cereals are much less perishable than hogs and pork so that supplies are much more stable. Pricing is truly administered, and supply (factory production) is geared to product movement. In effect, there is no market period pricing. Retailers, faced with many sellers and rapidly fluctuating pork prices, are always trying to bid down wholesale pork prices in order to make certain that they buy as cheaply as other retailers. Retailers, faced with few sellers and published, stable prices of breakfast cereals, are reported to make no attempts to bid down wholesale prices.

Technological change has affected the meat-packing industry much more than the industry of breakfast cereals. The changes which reduced optimal size of meat plants and shifted location were indicated in Chapter 12. These changes literally revolutionized the meat-packing industry. No such changes have occurred in cereals. There have been new patents issued and significant engineering improvements within the industry, but these have not affected materially the optimal scale. Bulk handling of flour and other ingredients and palletization of product handling and shipping has likely contributed to a larger optimal size plant. The developments already described in distribution have reduced costs significantly.

Markets for both pork and cereals are expanding as population increases. As children and older adults are relatively greater consumers of breakfast cereals, their market has jumped considerably in the 1960's. Industry expansion has not been via an increase in the number of plants or firms as would occur in atomistic competition. It has come through increases in plant and firm output and through an expansion of brands, as each firm tries for a larger share of this growing market. Expanding pork markets have contributed to more meat plants and more firms, by the process described in Chapter 11, Competition among the Many.

Chapter

14

COMPETITION AMONG
FOOD RETAILERS

Food retailing is big business. We measure its national volume in millions of tons and billions of dollars. The typical supermarket has 20,000 square feet of space,[1] almost as large as half a football field. In 1963 more than $52,000,000,000 of food were moved in and out of 245,000 grocery stores, through the efforts of 1,080,000 employees.

Competition in retailing can be considered nationally or regionally or locally. We shall begin at the most important level, the local. We begin with the story of a fairly typical retailer in a typical competitive environment. The names are fictional, but the resemblance to reality is intentional.

COMPETITION AS THE SUPERMARKET OPERATOR SEES IT

Johnny Affiliate owns and manages a modern supermarket in Typicity, a bustling suburb of Megalopolis. Typicity's population is 60,000, and it is growing at about the same rate as most urban areas. There are 9 modern supermarkets in the city and about 25 much smaller food stores, including a specialty meat market, a retail bakery, and a dairy store or two.

Pricing

It is Thursday afternoon, and Johnny is thumbing through the grocery ads in the *Typicity Evening Star*. He quickly appraises the specials being offered by each of his three major competitors. Of course, all 31 of the food stores are competitors, but the 3 supermarkets nearest him—each about a mile away—give him his chief competition. Johnny has a location on a main street with good access. He knows that some of his customers drive all the way across town, but he estimates that half of his customers live within one mile of his market. Two of his "competitors" are units of national chains—Easyway and E&P. The other competitor

---

[1] National Commission on Food Marketing, *Organization and Competition in Food Retailing*, Technical Study No. 7 (Washington, D.C.: U.S. Government Printing Office, 1966).

is another affiliate, but affiliated with *DGA* rather than his own organization, *CG*.

Johnny is quietly satisfied as he lays the paper aside. No competitor has exactly the same group of price specials as he. Easyway has strong specials this weekend on hams, flour, and coffee. E&P is using mayonnaise, margarine, and sirloins as leaders; while DGA is pushing coffee, chuck roasts, and lettuce. Johnny feels that his really attractive prices on broilers, lettuce, and prune juice will match the customer attractions of any of his competitors. Occasionally, he or one of his competitors happen to hit on a specials list that draws several customers away from other stores, but usually the new customers that Johnny attracts for his specials are about offset by the customers drawn elsewhere after other items. Of course, there are a few "cherry pickers" who go from store to store buying only the specials at each.

Competing

Johnny reflected upon his conversation last night with his college student son about specials. John, Jr., had asked why specials instead of a general price cut? Johnny had had trouble explaining it. Johnny felt that specials weren't nearly the same as the kind of open-price competition and possible warfare resulting from a general price cut. The purposes of specials were to create an image of "bargains," to create some excitement, and to make a special appeal each week to a slightly different group of shoppers. Some prices were moved up at the same time that others were cut, so that the general price cut for the weekend was much less than implied by the ads. The objective was a mix of special prices which generates the sales volume and of higher prices to maintain profits. After all, even if a consumer can remember 100 or 200 prices, there are 6,800 items on his shelves. Price specials were so much a part of retailing that Johnny was shocked by Junior's question. How else would Johnny have the flexibility to push seasonal items? How else could he attract customer attention every Thursday evening in the *Star*? Johnny found it difficult to follow Junior's distinction between price and nonprice competition. To Johnny, price specials and the weekend ads were an integral part of a whole policy of promoting an image of quality products, friendly personnel, cleanliness, and many services at reasonable prices. He was convinced that the successful manager must provide a satisfactory shopping experience. Such an experience would not be defined exactly the same by all customers, so that what appealed to some would be unattractive to others. Moreover, the package called a satisfactory shopping experience was a constantly evolving thing that kept a good manager always searching. But as of now, some fundamentals include "quality"; some bargains; such services as fast check-out, air conditioning, music, carry-out boys, and adequate parking; and trading stamps.

Stamps

Johnny has had the popular Green Stamps for several years. Stamps were a great inconvenience to handle, and they cost a healthy 2 percent of sales. He had been the second food retailer in Typicity to purchase trading stamps. He had lost 8 percent of sales during the first month that Easyway had them, and that was long enough to convince him. His sales actually increased above normal levels for several months after he had stamps. However, they were now back down to about normal. Johnny had not believed that stamp salesman's spiel about stamps increasing his volume enough to pay for the stamps. He had foreseen that stamps at all stores would probably cancel each other out so that margins would have to rise. He added stamps because he couldn't afford the sales volume decrease which would result without them. He suspected that there might be enough customers in Typicity who preferred 2 percent lower prices to stamps and that they would have exceeded his normal volume if he could get all of them to shop at his store. But how could he possibly convince those potential customers that he really had 2 percent lower prices? He knew he couldn't. Stamps are highly visible; slightly lower prices are not. His neighbor affiliate, DGA, had been so slow to adopt stamps that no nationally popular ones were still available. After a short and frustrating experience with a little-known stamp, DGA finally saved his skin by introducing a very popular giveaway game.

Johnny wonders if stamps are here to stay. He had a friend in another city who decided that the higher margins created by stamps gave him an opportunity as a price discounter. So he dropped stamps and cut average prices about 5 percent. He cut prices only on the faster-moving items so that the price cuts appeared considerably larger than 5 percent. Johnny's friend was confident that these price cuts were big enough to be visible. And they were. His business increased 25 percent. Then his competitors reacted—some with double stamps and Bingo, but some with price cuts of their own. While their price cuts weren't as big as Johnny's friend because of their 2 percent stamp costs, these cuts were big enough *on selected items* to match his. His image as a truly cut-rate store rather quickly deteriorated. Soon sales were back to normal; he added Bingo and dropped the discount idea. Perhaps if he had had just a bit more cost advantage or if the city had been "overstored" enough that a full-utilization rate would have been unique to him, then perhaps the discount idea would have worked. Certainly it worked for the chains in the 1910's and for the supermarkets in the 1930's. However, in both cases, the discounting was associated with a new method of merchandising with significant cost savings to absorb the lower margins. Even in the mid sixties, there were quite a number of successful "discounters" in operation. One of the fascinating and tantalizing aspects of retail management was the lack of sufficient information to "know" why an approach worked successfully for one manager but not for another.

Margins

Johnny spent most of the following Tuesday afternoon with the management troubleshooter from his CG organization. They had examined the most recent margin and expense figures for his operation from the CG computer. His gross margin (difference of food costs and food sales) as a percent of sales was running at 19 percent with operating expenses of 16.8 percent and profits of 2.2 percent. Store labor made up 7.7 points of the 16.8 expenses; advertising and promotion, 2.5. Johnny took professional pride in the way that he had managed to hold store labor costs down while wage rates had risen steadily in the postwar period. Labor costs had risen only 0.4 of a point 1958 to 1963. However, advertising and promotion costs had increased from 1.7 points to 2.5 in the same period. Johnny saw this jump as a measure of increasing competition in recent years. Total operating expense had moved steadily upward—from 15.0 percent in 1958 to 16.8 percent in 1963. Johnny felt that consumers were getting more for their extra money—merchandise variety, for example. The number of items he handled had risen from 5,500 to 6,800. He had added air conditioning, music, free check-cashing services, and had extended shopping hours by 10 a week. During the same period profits as a percentage of annual sales ranged from 2.6 percent to 1.6 percent.

Margins, of course, varied tremendously by items and considerably by departments. Groceries were the traditionally low major department with a margin of 16.8 percent this year contrasted to 21.9 percent in meat and 29.0 percent in the produce department. Some margins on some products were high or low for obscure historical reasons and were preserved—like hair styles—because everybody else priced that way. But there was a rhyme and reason for most margins:

1. Slow-moving items tend to high margins.
2. New items tend to high margins.
3. Items with low unit price (the five and dime) tend to a high percentage margin.[2]

Expansion

Should Johnny expand? The really serious question which Johnny and the CG consultant discussed that day was the possibility of his opening an additional CG affiliate super in Typicity. Leases were being let in a new shopping center on the other side of town. It *appeared* to be

---

[2] Ralph Cassady, Jr., *Competition and Price Making in Food Retailing* (New York: Ronald Press, 1962), pp. 114–17.

a choice location. New subdivisions were being built and others planned within easy access. Johnny knew full well how essential to success was a good location.

Were the risks too great? Johnny had thought long and hard about the capital and risks involved in another store. Assuming that it would cost about $21.50 per square foot for the land, buildings, and equipment for a new store, another 20,000-foot store meant a lot of money. Of course, much of that could be financed. He would rent the land and building from the shopping center developers. The CG wholesale organization would finance a large share of the equipment and of the $70,000 inventory. It appeared that he could swing the necessary capital, but if he should hit a couple of unprofitable years in opening, it would be touch and go. One of the big risks was people risk—could he find and hold a top-notch manager for the new store? Could they find and train the new people necessary to operate it? The CG representative pointed out the employee training program which they could provide him—at a price. The one significant economy that Johnny could visualize with an additional store was in advertising. Here was a place in which "two could live as cheaply as one."

Could he get a lease? Johnny appreciated more than ever the advantages of the wholesale affiliate organization at a time like this. He would have had no chance of obtaining a shopping center lease without the backing of the CG affiliate. Even so, he knew that he had less than a 50:50 chance of winning the lease away from some national chain.

How big is too big? Johnny and the CG consultant reviewed again the problem of size of store. The shopping center at this stage had from 15,000 to 30,000 square feet available. Johnny had to admit that the thoughts of running the largest super in town tempted him to ask for all 30,000 feet. However, Johnny and the consultant agreed that there were no economies of size in going from 15,000 to 30,000 feet. What is much more important are the economies of utilization. Store expenses could be expected to be 17 cents out of each sales dollar at average sales volume (about $3.50 weekly sales per square foot), but they would jump to 20 or 21 cents at half that volume. A 30,000-foot store with sales at half volume for two years or more would be disastrous. There was always the possibility of a competing supermarket opening nearby at about the same time. Many management and advertising complications could be avoided if Johnny kept both stores about the same size with about the same items carried. The neighborhoods of both areas had much the same socioeconomic status, so similar stores seemed feasible.

As the CG representative left that afternoon, he reminded Johnny that a university retailing extension man would visit him the next morning to develop plans for remodeling the back room. Although few consumers recognize it, tons and tons of merchandise move through a supermarket each week. The physical handling costs of unloading, storing, moving, locating, etc., are considerable. University and USDA researchers had developed some new layouts and handling techniques which had reduced back-room labor costs by 25 percent in several places in Megalopolis. Johnny had agreed to be a demonstration store in Typicity for the extension specialist. Here was an area in which he and his competitors would cooperate.

RETAILER-WHOLESALER MARKET STRUCTURE

National Level

In 1963 the "chains" had a 47.0 percent share of national grocery store sales, the affiliated had 43.9 percent, and the unaffiliated had 9.1 percent. (*Definitions:* A chain is a grocery firm with 11 or more stores. An affiliated is a group of independently owned retail stores attached to a supplying wholesaler or distribution center by contracts or ownership.) The chains and the affiliated each had about one third of the market in 1948; they grew equally fast at the expense of the unaffiliated.

At the national level, there are some retailers with market power, but there is no oligopoly. A&P leads the race with one tenth of the grocery store market. A&P and the next 19 chains had the rather impressive fraction of one fourth (26.9 percent) of the market in 1948. They increased this share to one third (34.1 percent) in 1958, but then their growth stabilized. However, the stability was due to the faltering of their leader, A&P, which lost 1.7 percent of the growing U.S. market in five short years.

The chain was an early innovation of the 20th century in the United States. Chain-store numbers skyrocketed from 2,000 in 1910 to 80,000 in the mid thirties. Their meteoric rise alarmed more than just their competitors and led to political attacks and special chain-store taxes. The chain stores learned public relations, cooperated together, and weathered the storm. The efficiency of the chains with their integrated wholesale operations and modern management methods seemed to make the chains unbeatable. But where politics had failed, two significant economic changes were to slow the chains.

First to shake the chains were huge, low-margin, self-service independents called supermarkets introduced in the Great Depression. The chains were unable to beat the supers, so they took over the idea. As one-stop shopping and an affluent society developed after the war, the supermarkets' share (chains, affiliates, and independents) of the grocery business soared to 69 percent in 1963 (see Table 14–1). The small stores of both the chains and independents fell before the supermarket. The number of chain stores fell from the 80,000 peak in the mid thirties to one fourth that number, while sales rose. However, this tremendous growth of the supermarkets has slowed; there are still niches in the vast American market for convenience stores and other small stores.

The second economic change which prevented market domination by the chains was the rapid growth of the affiliates. The affiliates gained most of the chains efficiencies by copying their organization, their wholesale-retail integration, and many of their operating and merchandising

TABLE 14–1

Sᴜᴘᴇʀᴍᴀʀᴋᴇᴛs' Sʜᴀʀᴇ ᴏғ U.S. Gʀᴏᴄᴇʀʏ Sᴛᴏʀᴇ Bᴜsɪɴᴇss Sᴏᴀʀs

Size of Annual Sales of Supermarket	1948	1954	1958	1963
More than $1,000,000	11.9%	32.6%	45.5%	52.7%
$500,000 to $1,000,000	15.9	16.1	15.7	16.1

techniques. An important difference between affiliates and chains was that local stores were operated by owner-managers—like Johnny—rather than hired managers. This difference was usually an advantage to the affiliate. Considerable numbers of these owner-managers came up through the ranks of a chain and then joined an affiliate in order to own their own business. Competition is not only for market share but also for personnel, and he who wins the latter race is well on his way to winning the race for market share. As indicated by the national market share figures, the postwar race between chains and affiliates has been a draw,

TABLE 14–2

Sʜᴀʀᴇ ᴏғ U.S. Gʀᴏᴄᴇʀʏ Sᴛᴏʀᴇ Sᴀʟᴇs, 1963

	Chains	Affiliates
Top 4 firms or groups	20.0%	6.2%
Top 40 chains and 30 groups	38.7	16.2*
All chains or groups	47.0	43.9

* Top 30 affiliate groups.

although the national figures cover up the many victories and defeats that have occurred at the local level.

Thus far the affiliate groups are much less concentrated than the chains (Table 14–2). However, one seventh of the affiliate sales in 1963 were handled by the top four groups.

The affiliate groups have many more small stores proportionately than do the chains. In 1963 about 55 percent of the stores of the top 40 chains had annual sales of $1 million or more while only 11 percent of the top 30 affiliates' member stores were that large.

A recent Bureau of Labor Statistics study showed that chain-store supermarket prices averaged about 1 percent below affiliate supermarket prices but about 3 percent below the prices of independent small stores.

Several affiliated groups also own directly some stores and thus are defined as chains as well as affiliates. The present clear distinctions between affiliates and chains may gradually diminish.

Certified Grocers of California has been a leading retailer-owned wholesaler. It is a cooperative with one member-one vote, patronage dividends, and identical prices to all members regardless of size or purchase. Its membership includes neighborhood Mom and Pop's and large local chains in the Los Angeles area. Its basic function is to purchase, warehouse, and allocate to its members at the lowest possible costs. However, it also provides all of the management services received by Johnny Affiliate—and more. In 1964 Certified carried 15,694 items including 6,453 nonfoods. To satisfy the customer demands of its retailer owners, this cooperative wholesaler carried 57 kinds of toilet paper, 326 baby food items, and 196 food items for the canines and felines.[3]

Mergers. The principal method for a large chain to expand its sales is to add another store(s). In other words, this firm's best method of expanding its demand is by adding another "plant"—an interesting contrast with the atomistically competitive model in which the demand expansion leads to the *LR* plant expansion rather than vice versa. The firm desiring to add stores may usually choose between building new stores and buying those already built.

Mergers have been very important in the growth of large chains. Of the top seven chains in 1930, excluding A&P, about one fifth of their stores had been purchased from other firms. From 1949 to 1964, the 20 leading chains purchased stores with more than $3 billion in sales! The leading acquirer, National Tea–Loblaw, purchased one-half billion in sales. The big merger movement, 1949–64, has been primarily large chains buying smaller ones. In the main the buyers have not bought out next-door neighbors but rather have bought their entry into new market areas. Even the biggest chains are not nationwide and do not operate in many major cities. From 1948–63, the 9 leading U.S. chains entered a total of 126 new metropolitan areas, an increase of 32 percent. Entry by purchase is likely the best way to enter a metropolitan area some distance removed from a chain's existing distribution centers. To service its stores economically, a chain may desire a distribution center and enough stores to sell more than $25 million a year. There are few markets in which an

---

[3] Testimony of the Vice-President of Certified Grocers before the National Commission on Food Marketing, May 5, 1965.

entrant could add that many new stores without ruinous competition. Instead, a chain may choose to minimize disturbance by buying much of its needed volume in a new metropolitan area and then building the rest.

"On October 11, 1955, the company purchased the Fred Montesi Supermarket Chain in Memphis, Tennessee. This provided us with a new branch of operations in the Memphis area, comprising nine modern supermarkets and a food distribution center with office and warehouse facilities of 150,000 square feet. We plan to operate eventually from 40 to 50 stores in the Memphis branch territory. . . ."[4]

Within 4 years, National Tea's original 15 stores in the Memphis district has expanded to 37.

Mergers appear to have increased materially the market share of the largest 20 chains, to have reduced the number of national competitors, and to have reduced the number of potential entrants in local markets. It has increased the market contacts of the largest firms. For example, such giants as National Tea and A&P competed in only 18 metropolitan areas in 1948 but in 47 such areas in 1963. The National Food Commission and especially the Federal Trade Commission have questioned the social usefulness of continued growth by merger of the larger retailers.

Vertical Integration.   Some of the reasons for vertical integration have been discussed in Chapter 15. The interdependence of the wholesale and retail functions, the almost perfect matching of assortments, and the economies in buying for many stores requires vertical integration of wholesale and retail mass food merchandising. It is, for example, a tremendous job to buy for a retail supermarket handling 6,800 separate items. The job is very little larger to buy for 30 or 300 supermarkets. The integrated retail store manager seldom sees a salesman; he orders from the distribution center by checklist. Perhaps in a few years a computer will order most items automatically on the basis of a running inventory of retail stocks. The manager's decisions in this area will be confined to items to be specialed, new items, and items to be discontinued.

The predominant chain pattern is a distribution center in a large metropolitan area serving a large group of stores in that area—and often other stores within two or three hours' travel radius outside the city. These distribution centers are typically very large and efficient. In 1963 distribution centers with annual sales of $25 million or more turned their inventory an average of once every 26 days. As another rough measure of efficiency, average tons handled per man-hour in the warehouses of distribution centers rose from 1.85 in 1954 to 2.26 a decade later. Distribution centers need an annual volume of at least $75 million for

---

[4] Statement from National Tea to Federal Trade Commission, cited in National Food Commission Technical Study No. 7, p. 374.

maximum efficiency. Vertical integration of food retailers into food manufacturing is another important development. It is discussed later in this
chapter.

Local Market Structure

Competition for the shopper occurs at the local level. This level is
often smaller than the entire city, as illustrated by Johnny's reference to
three main competitors. Most of our statistics are for standard metropolitan statistical areas (*SMSA*), and so the statistics underestimate the
concentration at the customer level. Even so, these *SMSA* figures show
far more concentration in food retailing in those areas than at the
national level. In 1963 the largest 4 firms in each of 218 metropolitan
areas controlled an average 50.1 percent of the grocery sales—an increase in share of 4.7 percentage points in 9 years. The Big Four market
share ranged from 23.5 percent in Fresno, California, to 75.6 percent in
Great Falls, Montana. The large national chains are often among the top
four at local level. In one half the metropolitan areas in which they
operated, each of the top nine national chains had 10 percent or more of
that market. However, it appears very difficult for any firm to hold a
market share above 20 percent. Moreover, the overall increase in local
concentration is due more to the growth of local and regional firms than
national firms.

Do we have oligopoly in food retailing? We certainly have an
oligopolistic-type structure in most metropolitan areas and even more so
at the customer level. There is evidence of price leadership and of other
types of oligopolistic behavior in a number of markets. However, some
economists are very reluctant to speak of retailing as an oligopoly. Their
reluctance stems from the rather large number of firms in the unconcen-
trated part of the market—the "many" in a very large"competitive
fringe," and the conviction that food retailing seems to operate as much
like monopolistic competition as like oligopoly. We should not be surprised that the realities of this dynamic industry do not nicely fit any of
our little models.

Local Market Competition. Several factors contribute to oligopolistic relationships. Because of the heavy concentration of firms and the
spatial network of locations, supermarket managers can and do identify
their chief competitors. There is generally a careful avoidance of direct
price competition—except on a bare handful of specials; in the exceptional case, two or three rivals have had price wars. There is a very heavy
emphasis on nonprice competition.

There are other factors contributing to a type of monopolistic
competition. There is a strong fuzzing of direct price relationships because of the thousands of items and the variable price merchandising
followed. It is virtually impossible for the average customer to tell which

of two stores has average prices 2 percent below the other. There is reasonably easy entry. The *LR* average cost curve is so flat over such a wide range that many sizes of firms can compete on fairly even terms.

There is oligopolistic interdependence among the big neighbors, but the "competitive fringe" is so big and has such an elastic supply function that the oligopoly can hardly unite and reap large oligopolistic returns (see Chapter 12). The nature of the many items, the weekend pricing process, and the consumer acceptance of many services makes it easy to avoid direct price competition. Thus, food retailing is circumscribed by limitations discouraging aggressive price competition on the one hand and collusion or quasi-agreements on the other.

Above all, there is diversity in competition with varying intensity of competition from one market area to another and over time. It was found in a Federal Trade Commission case involving the National Tea Chain that its gross margin and net profits were directly related to its market share; i.e., the larger its share of a metropolitan market, the higher its gross margin and net returns. Another researcher reported that differences in price levels among many midwestern cities were not associated with the degree of market concentration but, instead, were associated with such factors as new entries, rapidity of market growth, and goals of independent firms.[5] Another author confirms that the intensity of competition (nonprice as well as price) is related to:

1. The presence of one or more aggressive competitors (A&P and Safeway used to have low price policies; their "pacemaking" materially influenced price levels in their areas).
2. New entrants fighting for a niche.
3. Overcapacity of stores.
4. Drastically new competitive methods.[6]

Cassady indicates that an intensely competitive situation—caused say by a new competitor across the street—may cause competition to become quite direct. Strategies of pricing and promotion will be aimed directly at that competitor. Each will try to find out how the other is fairing. One possible source of information is a milk or bread salesman-driver who calls on both. Total sales may be estimated on the basis of the crude functional relationship of $50 total sales per $1 of bread sales.

Chains have often been accused of such predatory practices as price cutting their way into a new market while subsidizing their losses from an area where they are well established. The National Food Commission found evidence of such activity in a few cases—particularly in the earlier period when chains were largely competing with small inde-

---

[5] Hiroshi Mori and Wm. D. Gorman, "An Empirical Investigation into the Relationship between Market Structure and Performance as Measured by Prices," *Journal of Farm Economics*, August, 1966, Part I.

[6] Cassady, *op. cit.*, pp. 110–11.

pendents. Now that chains are rather frequently competing with other chains or large affiliates, such predatory price cutting holds fewer attractions. Of course, one of the "insurance features" of a large regional chain is the probability that losses in any one area will be balanced by better conditions and profits in other areas. A chain's large financial strength, its buying power, and its continuity are more important competitive advantages than its use of predatory price cutting.

NONPRICE COMPETITION

The difficulties and disadvantages of intense price competition and the importance of high sales volume in reducing operating costs have led to a tremendous emphasis upon other means of attracting customers. These have included a vast variety of services including bag carry out, check cashing, free cups of hot coffee, air conditioning, etc. While some of these additions are later dropped if they don't appear to pay, many are built into the system. Promotional devices such as trading stamps and prize-winning games have attracted the most attention. Food retailers began to use stamps in the mid fifties, and a decade later stamps were going into one half the bags which left the check-out counters.

Trading stamps are big business. About 364 billion trading stamps were issued in 1963, and about one eighth of these were used by food retailers. Some $817 million of merchandise were "purchased" with the 327 billion stamps *redeemed* in 1963. It is estimated that 83 percent of all U.S. families were "saving stamps" in 1963.

What do retailers expect to accomplish by buying trading stamps? Some may expect to substitute them for other promotional and advertising costs with the hopes of maintaining, or increasing, total sales without increasing operating expenses as a percentage of sales. The early purchasers hoped to increase their sales sufficiently so that the costs of stamps would be more than covered by the increased sales and lowered average costs. (Remember that average costs are directly dependent upon utilization.) Some retailers may have expected that the attractiveness of stamps would allow them to raise prices the necessary 2 percent to cover stamp costs without losing sales. Various combinations of all three of these possibilities may have been anticipated.

Experiences vary. SMI (the Super Market Institute) surveyed its members in 1957 and again in 1962 and found that about 60 percent of those markets using stamps had experienced sales increases large enough to absorb their costs. But a survey by *Progressive Grocer* found such substantial sales gains for those giving stamps only in 1954 and 1955 and not in later years when stamps became more common. Compared with 1958, in 1964 twice as many SMI members were convinced that stamps "were here to stay."

A USDA study in the mid fifties found that stamps could be a bargain—that average prices in stamp stores were only 0.6 percent more than in nonstamp stores, so that saving and redeeming the stamp meant real savings. However, as the use of trading stamps has saturated most markets, it is now generally agreed that most of the value of stamps is being reflected in higher retail prices. It is, of course, no condemnation of trading stamps to say that they aren't free. When redeemed they have value in economic goods, so how could they be free?

The fascinating things about stamps (and other sorts of economic goods and services used to promote retail sales) is that there is a time period within which they can be free. Let's analyze the problem. We recall again the fact that any retailer who has room for many more customers in his store can reduce average operating costs considerably *if* he can fill that store. Therefore this retailer can afford to *give away* considerable economic goods or services (stamps, hot coffee, air conditioning, etc.) *if* those gifts will produce sufficient sales in his store. Customers who shop there receive free this good or service as long as the above two conditions are met. However, if and when other retailers neutralize the first retailer's offering by giving the same or comparable services, then the second condition is not met. It is clearly impossible for *all* retailers to achieve larger sales by any sort of promotion or giveaway. Yet there are competitive forces which lead almost all retailers to try. Therefore, the *free gift time period* ends when enough retailers are in the act to restrict the individual market's gains in sales and thereby prevent sales gains from absorbing any significant part of the costs of the "gift."

Now we can look at the oft-debated question: Do consumers "want" trading stamps, or free hot coffee, or bag carry out? It is quite obvious that most consumers do accept such services as free gifts. But do they want them enough to pay for them? Very often the market system never presents a very clear opportunity for consumers to answer this question. Because of the *delayed price rise* described above, consumers usually received stamps in the beginning as a free gift. Then later if and when all stores had stamps and margins had risen, all consumers found themselves paying for stamps. If each consumer had convenient access to two stores which were equally attractive except that one had stamps and 2 percent higher prices, then each consumer could make a clear-cut choice. An even better choice would be a choice at the check-out counter whether to take stamps or a 2 percent discount. Such a choice is rare indeed, whether the promotional service involved is stamps or music.

Therefore, it is difficult to generalize from consumer behavior as to whether consumers "want" a particular individual service which is part of a whole bundle of goods and services provided in the supermarket. If a service isn't attractive to many people even as a free gift, it will probably be dropped; for example, Kiddy Korners and in-store bakeries each have had their ups and downs and have never become a standard part of the supermarket package. But a service or "prize" which is attractive as a free gift and is a minor cost (say 2 percent or less of total package) is likely to become a standard part of the shopping experience.

There is likely to be an upper limit to how many promotional extras can be added in. If the competitive system were to build in enough services and prizes that a discounter could move in at say a 5 to 10 percent lower price level with a stripped-down package of services, then there might well be significant groups of consumers who would buy from the discounter. The supermarkets did just that in the 1930's and the discount stores are trying it again in the mid sixties. The presence of the discount alternative is likely an important limit on how much the conventional stores will spend on stamps, "contests," giveaways, etc.

The issue of how much the "extras" cost and whether they are desired seldom attracts general public understanding and concern. An interesting exception was the so-called "Housewives Rebellion" of the fall of 1966. Spontaneously organized groups in many cities protested rising food prices with picketing of chain stores and other publicity. In Phoenix, Arizona, the Housewives Voice for Lower Prices had the slogan: "Speak now or forever pay the price." Chain spokesmen reacted by sometimes blaming general inflation, sometimes running rather dramatic cut-price sales, and even occasionally admitting that prices could be several percent lower if some extras were eliminated. Apparently consumers are most sensitive to the extras when the general level of food prices is rising.

Is all this nonprice competition good or bad? Economists are generally rather skeptical of the merits of nonprice competition—although they believe in it when selling their own services! They generally argue that efficiency will be increased by lessening nonprice competition and thereby increasing price competition. Thus the National Food Commission took a hard and rather frosty look at trading stamps. Other authors have argued that straight price competition would be intolerable, given the industry structure. Hence the presence of considerable nonprice competition allows a niche for the discounter who emphasizes price. With the coexistence of price and nonprice competition, retailing has something for everybody.[7] The major disagreements concern the desirable degree of nonprice versus price competition; it is largely accepted that we will have both. Perhaps the student should conclude that he will be very cautious about value judgments when experts disagree.

"Bantom stores" sell a small range of products at higher prices. Yet they have very significant market niches across the United States and are expanding. Their success is due to total stress on one basic appeal—

---

[7] Eugene R. Beem and A. R. Oxenfeldt, "A Diversity Theory for Market Processes in Food Retailing," *Journal of Farm Economics,* August, 1966, Part II.

convenience. Convenient location, quick service, and long hours make them the place to stop by for a loaf of bread or a carton of soft-drinks, etc. The number of such stores expanded from 1,500 in 1960 to 6,000 in 1965 and to sales of $1 billion that year. The 7–11 chain (open 7 A.M. to 11 P.M.) had approximately 1,200 stores in 1965. These convenience stores are an impressive example of effective selling of specialized retail services to meet special demands.

BUYING POWER

Farmers and processors, but especially farmers, have often expressed considerable concern about the degree of concentration in the purchase of food store products. It has been argued that this concentration has provided large retailers with a market power which has been used to hold down the manufacture and/or farm prices of food products. While such an exercise of power is theoretically possible in the short run, it is difficult to obtain empirical evidence as to whether this power exists or not, and as to its extent. Galbraith popularized the idea that retailer power was used to "countervail" the power of strong manufacturers, but other economists cite evidence that such power was more often used against the weak than against the strong.

How much buying power exists? Its amount is related closely to the amount of concentration of purchases of retailers. At first glance, one would assume that concentration of purchases and of sales is identical. It is not. Many purchases are made by chains at the regional or divisional level, so these purchases are more segmented than suggested by the national size of the chains. On the other hand, several of the chains have a joint buying office called Topco which purchased $160 million of mainly private brand goods for them in a recent year. An affiliate group buys as a unit; each member store sells independently; therefore, there is much more concentration on the buying side. Like the chains, the affiliates have further centralized certain purchases through special regional groupings, but their total purchases are relatively small.

The share of the total food store sales of the 40 largest chains and 30 largest affiliates rose from 31.7 percent in 1948 to 51.4 percent in 1963. There is some concentration of buying power when 70 firms represent one half the national market!

Power Confrontation

Consolidated Foods is a large food manufacturer and food retailer. In early 1965, it operated seven supermarkets in Chicago in competition with National Tea and other retailers. In mid-April its retail stores launched a major promotion of "miracle prices" billed as cross-the-board cuts. National Tea is reported to have immediately stopped its purchases of Sara Lee baked goods—one of Consolidated's most important and profitable manufactured lines. Shortly afterward Consolidated stopped its retail price cutting and, a bit later, sold its seven Chicago supermarkets. The National Food Commission staff summarized the episode as follows: "The recent Consolidated Foods–National Tea confrontation also demonstrates the buying power of large chains. Consolidated Foods presumably capitulated and withdrew from food retailing in Chicago rather than lose the National Tea account."

Price Discrimination

There is nothing new about quantity discounts. The Robinson-Patman Act prohibited such discounts if they exceeded differences justified by reduced cost in the manufacture, sale, or delivery of such larger quantities. However discounts larger than justified by costs were allowed if they were "made in good faith to meet an equally low price of a competitor." Each of the 9 largest chains were cited by the Federal Trade Commission as recipients of unlawful discriminatory preferences from suppliers in a total of 68 different occasions 1954–65. In some cases the customer solicited the discriminatory deal, and in some cases the supplier did. It is significant that the larger buyers are most often the recipients of these discriminatory concessions.

One documented case shows the extent of these price discriminations, even though the FTC complaint against the supplier was dismissed on grounds that he acted in good faith to meet competition. In 1958 National Tea had a 24 percent share of the Denver market and two other chains had another 47 percent. Beatrice Foods had been supplying National Tea all its dairy products at a discount of 7 percent. Then in 1958 in response to a cut-price offer to National from a new entering dairy company, Beatrice increased its price discount to National to 10 percent on its manufacturer brands and 12 percent on its private-label milk. Kings Soopers, the second largest purchaser from Beatrice, received discounts of only 4.6 percent even though its very substantial purchases were one third as large as National's. These discounts prevailed for three years and provided a significant cost advantage to National over its smaller rivals.

PRIVATE (RETAILER) BRANDS AND VERTICAL INTEGRATION

Private Brands

Some of our agricultural products are sold in their original form: apples, eggs, and fresh vegetables. But most are processed or manufactured: bread, breakfast cereals, canned fruits and vegetables, TV dinners, meats, macaroni, gelatin desserts, baby foods, condiments, etc. Before these products can be sold to consumers, they must be *defined*, quality controls on processing must be developed, they must be transported to distribution centers and stores economically but without quality deterioration, and they must be sold to the retailer.

The large national manufacturers perform these marketing functions for many products with well-known household names: Wheaties, Del Monte, Wonder Bread, Heinz, Gerbers, etc. But alongside these brands on the supermarket shelves often appear retailer brands of similar products. The retail distributor performs most of these functions of product specification, distribution, and selling for his own brands.

Multiunit supermarkets (chain or affiliate) are necessary to the success of private labels. One-stop shopping in today's supermarket focuses the consumer's attention on the store and on items in general rather than on a specific branded item. The supermarket can, and often does, stock both the nationally advertised brands for those who desire them and also private brands.

The large chains have had the incentives and the necessary volume for private label items. The incentives have been some combination of reduced product costs, reduced distribution and selling costs, and—most important of all—to build consumer loyalty to the chain and its exclusive line of private label products. Chain purchasing and sale of private label products eliminate many costs: the national advertising of the manufacturer, salesmen's salaries, coupons, etc. Moreover private label processing usually costs less because there are enough smaller processors in the act to make it quite competitive. However, the costs of introducing and gaining market acceptance of a new private brand can be very significant.

The competitive battles between private and manufacturer brands show little sign of ending. Two different distribution systems are competing: (1) the larger chains and affiliates and the smaller processors and the chains' own processors form one system, and (2) the smaller chains and independents and the national manufacturers are the mainstay of the other system. However there is overlapping of systems because even the largest chains are obliged to sell many of the more popular manufacturer brands. The first system excels at economical merchandising of well-accepted products. The second system probably cannot distribute as economically, but it excels in introducing new products and in promotion. In an affluent society, there seems to be room for both systems. The independent operator or even the small chain could hardly dream of operating without its grocery shelves laden with many highly advertised and well-known brands. Customers want to know the quality inside that can or box, and many depend on national brands for that quality assurance.

The success of private label varies greatly by products. Private label frozen vegetables and bakery and dairy products are top sellers which

have about one half the sales of those items in retail chains. About one
third of the coffee, wieners, and canned fruit sell under private brands.
Less than 1 percent of breakfast cereals are private label! The reader
might ask himself what factors favor private brands of some items more
than others.

The National Food Commission investigation found evidence that
private brands are often a bargain. On the average, the advertised brand
was priced 20 percent higher than a comparable quality private label.
Does this figure suggest anything about the power of national advertising
and promotion? The retailer might seem to have all the advantage in this
competition, since he controls his shelves and sets the prices. However,
many manufacturer brands are presold so well that retailers feel that
they must stock them; and they find that they must price their own
brands significantly cheaper to obtain good sales. In some items like
bakery products where manufacturer advertising and distribution costs
are very high, many retailers can price their brands below the advertised
brand and still obtain quite satisfactory operating margins.

Vertical Integration

Food chains have often "integrated back" into manufacturing. Two
retail chains are among the top 50 food *manufacturers*. Some 35 of the
top 40 chains did some manufacturing in 1963. As a group, they manufactured about one sixth of their sales of manufactured foods, and the trend
was up. Food manufacturing is closely associated with the size of chain;
the top 4 chains manufactured as much as the next 36. The affiliates have
done very little manufacturing.

Vertical integration into manufacturing is highly related to private
brands. After a private brand becomes successful, the chain faces the
question of whether to continue to buy it or to make it. Sometimes it is
more profitable to make it because there are efficiencies in a close
coordination of production and distribution, or because high distribution
costs can be shaved, or because there are noncompetitive profits in the
manufacturing sector. For example, distribution costs have been reduced
greatly in bakery goods by vertical integration. Occasionally private
brands cannot be obtained except by vertical integration. During World
War II, there was integration into meat-packing and even cattle feeding
to assure supplies.

Large food chains have the power to enter many sectors of manufacturing, so their entry ordinarily depends upon the degree of incentive.
The magnet of high, noncompetitive profits is a strong incentive. Cost
savings are also an incentive, although such savings can often be secured
by contracting for private brands without the managerial complications
of ownership vertical integration. The discrepancy of assortments is an
important consideration in decisions concerning vertical integration. If

an economical size plant for making widgets produces as many as 500 average supermarkets can sell, then a chain with only 250 markets faces the problem of manufacturing inefficiency, or selling widgets to 250 other retail markets, or contracting for widgets rather than owning the plant. Retail sales of $100 million seem essential for a firm to integrate into the manufacturing of many food products. It is estimated that to integrate into shortening and margarine, $1.5 billion retail sales are necessary!

A COMPETITIVE RESUME

Food retailing more closely resembles competition of the many among the few than any of the other models described in Chapters 11 and 12. In particular, it resembles that model in which the economies of scale curves for both plants and firms have broad, flat bottoms; entry is moderately difficult in some areas; and the many firms have an elastic supply curve that is reasonably competitive with the few. Retailing provides an extremely favorable environment for nonprice competition. Competition in retailing has often been greatly affected by the presence of aggressive pacesetters (see Chapter 12).

In an economic sense retailers are suppliers of retailing services. Their returns are related to the supply and demand for such services. These services are very perishable in the short run as each day's potential ends at the evening closing. Many of a store's costs are committed for the duration of the store whether x or $2x$ customers per week shop the aisles. A few *operating* costs such as trading stamps and income taxes vary directly with volume; many more are partly related to sales (such as payroll and sometimes rent); but many others such as utilities, real estate taxes, depreciation and interest, management overhead, insurance and operating licenses are unrelated to sales volume. In atomistic competition the presence of large fixed or committed costs and low variable costs can lead to drastic short-run price reductions in any case of oversupply. In retailing, the road to a greater short-run sales volume is paved with promotions rather than price cuts. Thus low volume can encourage intensive nonprice retail competition in the short run.

In the long run the big firms compete for sales by acquiring more stores. A tremendous number of supermarkets have been built in the 1950's and 1960's in response to rapidly rising population demand (more babies) and because supermarkets have forced out many Mom and Pop stores. If long-run building campaigns lead to "overstoring," then competition (price and/or nonprice) is very aggressive in that area until demand catches up or there is exit. Conversely, to the extent that an area may be "understored," sales volumes will be high and competition is likely to be lax.

The food retailing industry has adjusted to very dynamic shifts in demand and in technology:

—affluence, autos, and supermarkets;
—metropolitan distribution centers with conveyors and forklift trucks;
—mass merchandising and ordering by computers.

In a generation, the economic size of stores jumped from a few thousand square feet to 20,000. Thousands of tons of food move through a modern distribution center.

Economies of scale of the firm and the plant are much different. The rise of the affiliate system permits the continuation of the one-plant firm. At the other end of the scale, the largest chain had twice the total sales of the 215,000 single-store grocery retailers. The multiunit firm in an area has substantial economies of scale in advertising. The large chain also has advantages in obtaining *popular* stamps, in obtaining admission to new shopping centers, in purchasing, in manufacturing, and in the capital markets. The chain can afford to make a mistake in store location; the individual independent cannot. The minimum size of a chain in a metropolitan market is related to efficient warehousing, distribution, and advertising. The maximum size chain in the national market is limited by the capabilities of management, and perhaps by the observed difficulties of holding more than a 20 percent share of any local market.

There must be a closely coordinated *system* to perform efficiently the *processing, allocating,* and *assortment* functions (see Chapter 13) required in the modern-day food industry. This system is presently obtained under chain ownership and under wholesaler-retailer affiliation. While both *systems* might continue for a long time if *efficiency* is the only criterion, there is some concern that the affiliates will gradually lose out in the likely *power* struggles. The voluntary group cannot significantly subsidize the member store which is in trouble the way the chain can. Nor can the affiliate "buy its way" into new metropolitan markets the way chains can, and do.

Each big chain which pushes its private brands is trying to differentiate further its retailing services and expand its market position and profits. In so doing the interests of the chains and large, national manufacturers directly conflict. Neither has come close to winning this battle so these vertical competitors must cooperate even as they compete. A decisive victory by either side would substantially affect retail market power.

Food retailing is a huge and complex industry. It is impossible to comprehend all of its many facets or all of the forces for change impinging upon it. While we expect tomorrow's industry to look much like today's, it would be foolhardy to try to project accurately the coming changes in this dynamic business. Food retailing is a crucial link in the agribusiness chain between farmer and consumer. Farmers and consumers will likely continue to observe it with a mixture of pride and concern. Many college graduates will continue to find it a challenging area for developing their managerial careers.

REFERENCES

Current information concerning the dynamic food retailing industry is available in such trade journals as:

Chain Store Age
Food Topics
Progressive Grocer

A very useful index of supermarket articles is published annually by Super Market Institute.

Chapter 15

COMPETITION AMONG FARMERS

Farming furnishes most of the oft-cited examples of atomistic (pure) competition. What product is more homogeneous than wheat or eggs? What industry has more numerous producers, each too small to influence market demand or price? What industry has such easy entry and exit? While the similarities of real-life agriculture to the atomistic model are striking, there are differences that should not be ignored. These differences are more significant than the inevitable but inconsequential differences between any simplified theory and the accompanying reality.

You will recall that among the basic attributes of the atomistic model are the following:

1. No participant can influence price.
2. In a *LR* equilibrium, price equals average cost for each firm.
3. Free entry and exit permit ready adjustment back to *LR* equilibrium after any disturbance.

This chapter indicates:

1. Ways in which competition among farmers is more complicated than suggested by any simplified model.
2. How the long length of the production period relative to the marketing period and the sequence of cost commitments leads to price-cost relationships often very unsatisfactory to farmers.
3. How continuous disturbances lead to depressed factor returns, increasing scale of firm, and other changes which many farmers dislike.
4. Consequently, how farmers have struggled to modify the atomistic nature of their competition.

THE COMPETITORS

In our discussion of competition among farmers, we omit those who are outside commercial agriculture. We are discussing the several hundred thousand farmers each producing more than $10,000 annually and together producing more than 90 percent of the economy's farm output. There are some giants within this diverse group of farmers. As early as

1959, 20,000 farms (less than 1 percent of all commercial farms) produced five billion dollars or 17 percent of all farm production. Such a concentration ratio is a far cry from oligopoly, but it also contradicts sharply the usual image of the average farmer producing only a "trace" (4 parts per 10 million) of total output. Most of midwestern agriculture still fits the family-farm model of sales per farm below $100,000. But "superfarms" (producing over $100,000 annual sales) have become very important in the specialty crops and in many phases of California agriculture. Such superfarms produced 47 percent of the nation's output of vegetables in 1959 and 58 percent of its sugarcane, 25 percent of its rice and 24 percent of its cotton. These superfarms fed 24 percent of the cattle but only 2 percent of the hogs, 30 percent of the Irish potatoes but only 2 percent of the corn.[1] In some areas and for some products, superfarms are important and growing more so. Present data indicate no clear general trends, except that average size of farm is growing. Many experts now consider superfarms as a real threat to the family farm in major parts of agriculture. It is possible that atomistic competition will disappear by 1980 in a few of the very specialized crops, even as it has already disappeared in broilers.

The capital-income ratio in agriculture is much higher than in most business. Compare the $243 billion of agricultural assets in 1964 with the $42 billion of gross farm income. This high ratio in excess of 5:1 has two important implications. First, entry into farming is becoming impossible or unattractive for a sizable segment of the population. Whereas it was once necessary for an entrant to have only a lease, a team, and a wife, entry now requires assets so sizable that they must be inherited or acquired from outside agriculture. As participation in full-time commercial agriculture is gradually restricted to those who can gain control of at least one half million dollars of assets, the public attitudes toward agriculture will change, and so will the attitudes and aptitudes of the farmers. Second, this high capital-labor ratio makes it quite possible for changes in the value of the capital to overshadow current income. It is quite possible for farmers to "live poor and die rich." (See Figure 9–9, Chapter 9.)

For a number of reasons, including especially the structure of our tax laws, capital appreciation is often sought more aggressively than current income by those with considerable income and/or assets. The tax laws have permitted nonfarmers to engage in various farming enterprises in such manner as to maximize their capital appreciation. If and when finally realized, these capital gains are taxable at a much lower rate than if they had been current income. One way to do this has been the

---

[1] U.S. Department of Commerce, Bureau of the Census, *1959 Census of Agriculture*, Vol. V, Part 7, Special Report.

purchase of farmland and the obtaining of capital appreciation via industrious improvement of the land and the generally rising land market. As indicated in Figure 9–7, Chapter 9, about one third of land purchases are by nonfarmers. A more complicated way has been the leasing of land and livestock by Mr. City Man and the capital gains sale of offspring from these rented cows as breeding stock. The on-farm operation need not be profitable for the total operation of Mr. City Man to be very profitable to him—and correspondingly unproductive for the Collector of Internal Revenue. Suppose $20,000 a year rental costs are offset by $20,000 a year in capital gains. In effect "farming" has enabled the investor to transfer $20,000 a year from a high tax bracket, say 50 percent, over to the lower capital gains bracket, 25 percent.

Various industries become especially competitive whenever some of the competitors don't have to cover average costs *in that industry* in order to be able and willing to remain in it. We shall see such examples later in vertically integrated industries, but they also occur in other multi-industry firms. Farmers are likely to face increasing competition from outside the farming sector.

LONG-RUN EQUILIBRIUM AND FACTORS DISTURBING IT

Modern agricultural economists have never seen anything approaching long-run equilibrium in most of agriculture and never expect to. In a society like ours with changing technology, increasing population and incomes, and changing tastes, we economists would be surprised to find many industries in long-run equilibrium at any given time. However, agriculture has been among those industries most out of equilibrium in the mid 20th century with many major disturbances on both the supply and demand side. Both the demand and supply functions for most agricultural products are on the move and, consequently, so are the price-output results emerging through time. All of the disturbances listed in Chapter 11 are at work. Size of farm is changing rapidly in a way that suggests important changes have occurred and probably are still occurring in economies of scale. The "probably" in the previous statement reflects the possibility of a considerable time lag between changes in optimal and actual scale due to the deterrences of inadequate capital, management, and risk taking. At the same time technological developments in purchased inputs are shifting costs in ways which vary with size of farm unit, type of land resource, weather conditions, and half a dozen unknown factors. Technology is a disruptive force, and its adoption spearheads a process of creative destruction with many significant, widespread, and often unexpected impacts upon agriculture and agribusiness. More commodity specialization is developing, and methods of producing broilers and fed cattle have undergone drastic changes.

Atomistic competition tends to be rough on the participants when supply is outrunning demand. Atomistic competition tends to be disruptive of established and conventional methods, organizations, and firms when technology is introducing radically new methods and economies of scale. Thus, it is not surprising that farmers have struggled to modify the atomistic structure of farming. They have obtained through political action such modifications of supply and—to a lesser extent—of demand that it is sometimes claimed that "farm prices are made in Washington."

Farmers have also found irksome and puzzling the process by which daily prices are determined for their products, and the sizable price fluctuations which occur from day to day and week to week. Some of their political activity has led to motivational changes in the marketplace which modify the price-making process. Part of the difficulties arise because of the biology of farming. Agricultural production is typically a very time-consuming process with a fairly continual expenditure of inputs over several months, or several years in the case of tree fruits. Some of the inputs like weather tend to be random so that amount of output cannot be controlled completely. Most agricultural products are quite perishable in a physical and/or economic sense. Thus, it is not unusual for farmers to sell their products at a price which did not cover their "costs," as they measure costs. We turn now to a discussion of these market price problems in agricultural atomism.

BARGAINING AND MARKET-PERIOD PRICE DISCOVERY

Every great city used to have a large wholesale produce market. Here, items such as fresh fruits were offered by various brokers and other wholesale merchants to the hundreds of retailers seeking their daily supplies. The extreme perishability of many such items made it economically imperative that the sellers clear the market on a daily or other short-period basis. When market intelligence was poor, transportation to the markets quite variable, and coordination among shippers almost nonexistent, then supplies and prices of particular items often varied greatly from day to day or week to week. Price was established by bargaining between individual buyers and sellers, and it inevitably varied somewhat from one transaction to another. The bargaining of each seller and buyer was influenced not only by his own stocks and/or needs but also by his appraisal of total market stocks and total market demand.

This process of arriving at price through individual bargaining against the backdrop of rapidly varying supplies and demands has been called the process of price *discovery*. The more perishable the product, the shorter the market period, and the more urgent was the bargaining process. It is difficult to find in the economy another industry like fresh fruit and vegetables which pour out a most-perishable output in a great erratic stream without prior orders and with low or nonexistent reservation prices.

The market period is an important constraint on price making of many agricultural products even if physical perishability is not a pressing problem. Since the market period is defined as a period when stocks are fixed, then the long periods between harvests of crops like wheat, cotton, and feed grains a set of market periods with stocks decreasing through time. These "nonperishables" are sold in a market that strongly resembles the produce exchange, although in a broader market as to space and time. The bargaining within these markets is affected by the maximum supplies physically available, expectations as to demand and next year's crops, and the usual economic incentives to avoid more than minimal carryovers into the next season.

Bargaining between many parties within a market is usually assumed to result in a very narrow price range for a homogeneous product. Each party fears to withhold its purchases or sales at any acceptable "going price" because of the likelihood that the available offers will be preempted by one's rivals. While price is independent of any single participants actions, no participant has assurance as to whether tomorrow's market price will be more or less advantageous than today's price. Market news as to available supply and demand becomes vitally important in the discovery of the "going price."

Reservation and Bargaining Prices

It is useful to distinguish between "reservation price" and "bargaining price." A farmer's reservation price is *defined* as the minimum price at which he will sell, regardless of the prices his rivals accept in the short term. Thus, the reservation price is just above the point of indifference between selling and not selling. In the case of a perishable crop ready for harvest, the reservation price may be assumed to be no lower than per unit harvest costs. Otherwise, why harvest? The market period supply curve of a farmer for apples is shown in Figure 15–1. The horizontal section at P_1 is just above the net costs of picking and marketing the apples and indicates the farmer's reservation price. The vertical section reflects the physical limit on size of harvest. The line at price P_2 indicates a possible asking price or bargaining price. A farmer's bargaining price is *defined* as the price he is presently asking for his product. This asking price is subject to immediate changes. The two prices are not ordinarily the same; the exception occurs when excessive stocks force the bargaining price down to the reservation price. In the free market, the whole intent of participants is to find the bargaining price satisfactory to both buyer and seller.

In terms of atomistic theory, the seller's reservation price will just cover AC in a long-run situation and AVC in a short-run situation. In a

FIGURE 15–1

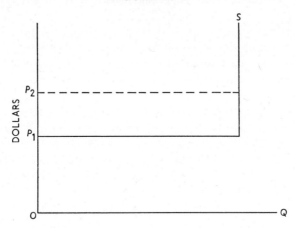

market period of fixed stocks, the reservation price depends upon the seller's ability and willingness to hold for his own use or for sale in another market (Chicago rather than Kansas City, or next spring rather than this fall). Since the stocks are already produced in the market period, sunk (already expended) production costs have little or no relevance to reservation price.

In terms of Figure 15–2, the reservation price of a farmer for apples would be P_3 in the LR, P_2 in the SR, and P_1 in the market period. If the number of apple trees in the industry is small relative to consumer demand for apples, then the market price may be higher than P_3 for a number of seasons. On the other hand, a "surplus" of trees, which forces the price down toward P_1, may also last for a number of seasons.

Price determination on the basis of existing stocks is a very unsatisfactory way of pricing for sellers because it is not related to production costs. Most nonfarm sellers avoid this problem by producing on order or producing on a very low inventory basis that can be closely tied to current receipt of orders. The advantage of producing on order is a near guarantee that firms in the industry will not produce unless price covers AVC, at least. On the other hand, if goods are produced prior to sale and price determination, then a firm has almost no assurance as to how low his competitor's reservation price may fall.

In contrast, farmers usually produce before they sell. A peculiarity of agricultural production is the extent to which price is determined after production—i.e., on the basis of already produced stocks. The discontinuous, seasonal nature of crop production and the livestock breeding-growth-feeding cycles contribute to this situation. Inputs are combined over a period of months or years to produce a crop harvest of wheat or

FIGURE 15-2

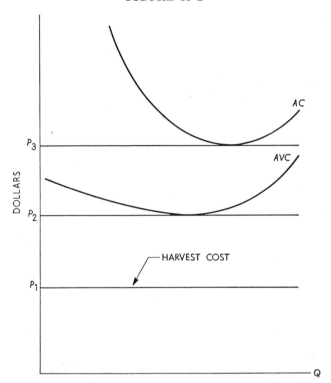

peaches which then is marketed more or less quickly as determined by the costs of holding. Costs of producing a particular crop are irrelevant to *its* sale price, although the relation of these costs to current prices will affect future output and prices. As already indicated above, the *harvest costs* of a perishable crop can become relevant to market price, but these costs are relatively low for most products and therefore an effective limit on price only in cases of extremely large harvests and low price.

Principle of Uncommitted Costs

An agricultural production process has an economic inertia all its own, so that once started, it is difficult to stop. In general, efforts to produce a crop or to feed out livestock will continue as long as the anticipated revenue exceeds uncommitted variable costs (and sometimes only the cash part of these costs). Before production is begun, all variable costs are uncommitted; but gradually as planting, tending, etc., proceed, the *uncommitted* costs become smaller and smaller. Therefore, even if anticipated revenue falls rapidly during the production season, it is not likely to fall fast enough to halt production. The principle of uncommitted costs is illustrated in Figure 15–3. Suppose an Iowa farmer is feeding out feeder pigs purchased at 100 pounds average weight. *MC* indicates after purchase all of the uncommitted marginal costs for feeding out the pigs to slaughter weights. As long as anticipated price is 12 cents, it is obviously economical to feed the hogs until they weigh about 220 pounds, (where $P = MC$; we assume away real life complications that *MR* falls below *P* when heavier weight hogs are penalized in price. See Chapter 7 for the solution if the farmer maximizes per unit of time rather than per bunch of pigs.) This maximization weight of 220 pounds holds true regardless of whether the 100-pound feeder pigs were purchased at 15 cents or 20 cents or 25 cents or any other figure. As indicated

FIGURE 15–3

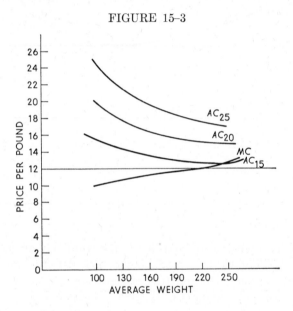

by the three alternative *AC* curves, the farmer will lose money (his *AC* won't fall below price) if he paid even 15 cents for pigs. The point is that once the pigs were bought, the cost for pigs was committed, and it should have no effect whatsoever upon the farmer's decisions concerning feeding them out. However, the total profits or losses may have some effect on how readily the farmer bids on his next bunch of feeder pigs!

The principle of uncommitted costs applies to the *producer* of feeder pigs in a special way, since he is producing an *intermediate* product. Suppose at the time of the farrowing of the spring pig crop, it becomes apparent that pig numbers are up sharply instead of being normal as anticipated. Suppose, moreover, that the pork market is weak and prices of fed hogs are falling. Both producers of feeder pigs and potential buyers will immediately revise downward the expected prices for feeder pigs. The producers will go ahead and raise the pigs as usual, since anticipated revenue is almost certain to be more than uncommitted costs, regardless of whether it covers the total of uncommitted *and* committed costs. The prices of the feeder pigs will fall sufficiently that hog feeders are willing to purchase. In this case, the pig producers not the hog feeders bore the brunt of the change in market anticipations because it occurred while the pigs were owned by the producer and before the hog feeders had committed themselves. Moreover, a very substantial revision downward in hog prices made as early as six months before slaughter will have no influence upon the number of hogs marketed six months later (although it may affect weights), because the production process is underway and committed costs are written off. The reader should ask himself whether feeder pigs would likely be slaughtered at birth, even if it were widely understood that the pig crop was so large that price would not even cover the uncommitted costs of the pig producer. In such extreme cases, the economics of the decision may be overridden by a moral principle against the destruction of animals or even of food supplies.

Consider the problem of a Cornbelt cattle feeder who has a load ready for market when the price falls, say $2. Shall he accept the lower price or shall he commit more inputs in feeding the cattle longer? Feed costs per pound of gain rise at heavier weights. On the other hand, a price recovery of even $1 would pay for a large amount of feed. The decision would be easy if one only knew what market price would do. Sometimes cattle are held for too long because of overly optimistic anticipations about price.

Pricing Results

Is the importance of market-period, fixed-stock pricing in agriculture a matter of concern? After all, supply and demand still determine price, and supply over the years will have some average relationship to costs of production, even if it has none in any given market period.

One result of the peculiar importance of market-period pricing in agriculture has been farmer efforts to protect their market position via the support of public, central markets and the government regulation of agencies and practice thereon; regulation of speculation in agricultural products; development of cooperative marketing organizations; attempts like the *Sapiro* Cooperatives in the 1920's and later the NFO to influence prices; and development of federal market news and outlook; etc.

Another result of farmers living with the perturbations of a derived demand and a near-vertical supply has been concern about marketing margins—i.e., the spread between consumer demand and derived demand at farm level (see next chapter).

A third result is the suspicion with which farmers have traditionally viewed processor activities on the production side such as packer feeding of livestock or canner production of fruits and vegetables. The concern has been that a buyer gains a bargaining advantage in the market period if he is also a "seller."

Another result is a concern of farmers that the extreme eagerness to sell of some farmers leads to lower prices than necessary to clear the market. This result is not possible in a well-organized market with atomistic sellers *and* buyers. But agricultural markets are not always so well organized, particularly those for perishables, and the number of buyers is sometimes so small that competition between them might be somewhat limited. It is possible for a relatively few buyers of lettuce or tobacco or peaches to exercise a price leadership in establishing a market price in full knowledge that there is only X amount of crop available and that it can be as readily shared among themselves at price P as at some higher price.

The key to raising bargaining prices is to reduce the fear and fact of being undersold. Assume in a free market with an inelastic derived demand, an attempt of three-fourths of the sellers to raise the general level of bargaining price. Assume the sellers choose to raise price to a level P_1 at which they realize that only about two thirds of the total crop will be purchased. In a free market, this attempt is customarily wrecked by those other sellers who hope to obtain more total revenue by selling *all* of their crop at a price of, say, three-fourths P_1. Thus the fear of being undersold holds bargaining prices down to the level at which buyers will accept the total crop for sale and, perhaps, below that level in some cases. That fear is reduced in a number of ways ranging from the obvious one of a government supported price to the much greater subtleties of certain market orders.

Consumers as well as producers appreciate the merits of orderly markets. A chaotic market in which price fluctuates greatly and supplies are nonexistent one day and in surplus at almost any price on another day is an inefficient market. Thus, farmers have been able to obtain political acceptance of certain institutional modifications of the traditional price making in an atomistic market. These modifications are discussed only briefly here, as they are covered more thoroughly within the context of other government policies in Chapters 20 and 21.

Market Orders

Market orders are excellent examples of the modification of the market environment involved in attempting to raise the bargaining reservation prices of all farmers. A marketing order is a program regulating certain aspects of the marketing of an agricultural commodity under the supervision of the USDA. Such orders are voted into being according to procedures specified in the Agricultural Marketing Act of 1937 (see

Chapter 21). Market orders are common in the area of fresh fruits and vegetables. In that area, reservation prices were low, supplies varied rather rapidly, and markets often became chaotic. It was argued—and often with persuasion—that a falling market reduced both the bargaining prices of farmers and the derived demand prices of buyers below the level justified by orderly supply and demand conditions. In a situation in which farmers are persuaded of the values of cooperating to maintain a higher bargaining price, the market order provides a mechanism for an equitable sharing among producers of the unsold stocks, or of stocks diverted to secondary outlets at lower prices. The market order does not set price, except for minimum prices in the case of milk. Instead, when prices are anticipated to be below parity, those administering the order agree on certain procedures which either physically reduce supplies (quality or quantity limitations on shipments) or which may raise the bargaining prices of farmers.

The raisin marketing order is a very interesting example of manipulation of "free" supplies which is aimed at raising the bargaining prices of individual farmers. The buyers may anticipate from past performance that they will get as large a share of the total crop as they demand at a price level established in the early buying from hundreds of growers. This price level is responsive to size of crop, but it is also affected by the marketing environment. Raisins are pooled in the sense that the same percentage of every grower's crop will be diverted to the secondary market, so no grower can sell all his crop on the better market by shading his bargaining price. A significant fraction of the total crop is insulated from the initial "free" market in "reserve" and "surplus" pools. Thus the amount of product which can be purchased from weak bargainers[2] is significantly reduced by the fraction of their crop insulated from initial sale. The "free" price will eventually cover the price that a hard core of farmer bargainers think is reasonable. In the raisin case, the influence of a large marketing cooperative is probably important in guiding the bargaining of farmers. Such a lack of precision of results may be very unsatisfactory to the analyst, but it appears to describe the situation.

Market prices of raisins are *not* "set" by a physical limitation of supplies. Market prices are determined by a bargaining process between several buyers and many sellers; the crop is already harvested; the costs of production are already sunk; domestic demand is presumed to be inelastic; the secondary market demand is elastic but not usually as renumerative except in marginal terms.

Raisin prices have apparently been higher than they would have been without an order. However, raisin prices appear to have been quite

---

[2] Such weak bargainers are willing to sell cheap because of anticipations, a pressing need for quick cash, or other reasons.

reasonable as compared to prices in the secondary market and to preorder prices. It is possible that a considerably higher price just below parity (parity is the legal maximum *with* pooling) could have been obtained in all years of small crops if the growers had bargained more diligently. How much growers are influenced by long-run considerations, by a consensus of a "fair price," by conversations with buyers, by comparison with last year's price, etc., is not at all clear.[3]

Bargaining Associations

A bargaining association is a voluntary organization—usually a cooperative—of farmers established with the aim of improving their terms of trade. While price is determined in some bargaining associations by multiple party bargaining, as in raisins, some California processed fruit and vegetable bargaining associations bargain as a collective unit with individual buyers.[4]

The contracts of bargaining associations with canners may provide that the canner will not pay any outside grower a higher price than is paid those in the association. It seems clear that a *well-run* bargaining group, representing a large share of a crop, could effectively curb the willingness of farmers to accept very low prices. In other words, it can prevent weak bargainers from setting a price which is lower than is required by the current supply and demand. However, the other limits of potential supply expansion and buyer resistance probably severely limit the price-raising potential of many of these bargaining associations. "If the long-run welfare of the industry, growers, and canners is considered, the price attained must be an economic price; that is, one that is justified in terms of the economic conditions of the time."[5]

A number of the bargaining associations have failed and others have had very difficult problems because they thought they were somehow immune from the market forces of supply and demand. Some other associations have been so unskilled in bargaining that they never achieved anything in price level and very little in fringe benefits. Such benefits include more stable prices, reduced price discrimination among sellers, better fieldmen services, more adequate harvesting supplies and equipment, etc.

Both market orders and bargaining associations have been generally confined to fairly small geographical areas—ordinarily a few coun-

[3] Norman Townshend-Zellner, "The Effect of Marketing Orders on Market Structures and Some Consequent Market Developments," *Journal of Farm Economics,* December, 1961, pp. 1357–65.

[4] Sidney Hoos, "The Role of Cooperative Bargaining Associations in the Integration of Agricultural Marketing," University of California mimeo, April 6, 1960, p. 13.

[5] *Ibid.,* p. 8.

ties or less. However, there has been a rapid rise in interest in broader use of somewhat related types of farmer bargaining. A proposed national marketing order for turkeys was defeated in a national referendum in 1962. The National Farmers Organization has campaigned for collective bargaining for farmers. The American Farm Bureau's subsidiary, the American Agricultural Marketing Association, has organized group action in a number of commodity areas. The National Food Marketing Commission in 1966 recommended broader scope and powers for such self-help groups (see Chapter 21).

Price Supports

A third commonly used method of raising the bargaining reservation prices of farmers is the government price support program. The bargaining price of farmers eligible for price support loans will ordinarily closely approximate the price support level. If there were no political constraints upon the level of price supports, farmers might strive to obtain very high ones. However, the limited political palatability of price support activity commonly leads to a limitation of the support price to less than parity and to the limitation of farm output. Production control was used in the early 1960's not to give farmers bargaining power but to make the price support program less expensive to the government. The increment to farmers' bargaining power stemmed from the price supports rather than from the production restrictions. Control of supplies without support prices—say by a large Soil Bank—would be the case of a program in which farmer bargaining power stemmed directly from supply restriction. Under certain conditions farmers may be willing to accept lower free market prices; under other conditions they may prefer the higher prices with the marketing restrictions (see Chapter 20).

Quoted Prices

It is commonly said that supply must be restricted to raise price. This supply-restrictive behavior is customarily imputed to industrial firms. Yet it is known that industrial behavior might more precisely be described as follows. The firm stands ready to supply all that will ordinarily be demanded at the set price it quotes. That is, price is not raised by an unavailability of supply; rather production, or the volume that can be sold, is limited by the height of the quoted selling price. We have just reviewed somewhat comparable situations in agriculture in which price is set by sellers at a level at which they stand ready to supply more than is ordinarily demanded. In both cases, some of the pressures within the typical produce exchange "to clear the market" have been resisted. The differences between the agricultural and industrial situations lie in the market changes which must be made by government or by cooperative action of farmers in order to set such a price. In agriculture it is necessary to change from an entirely free market in order to change the willingness of individual producers to sell cheaper; in many of the more concentrated nonagricultural industries the recognition of interdependence is a sufficient curb upon price cutting (see Chapter 12).

SUPPLIES VARIABLE

Let's leave the market period and turn to the more fundamental relationships between amounts supplied and *anticipated* prices. The Marshallian distinction between short run and long run is not satisfactory for atomistic farm firms, but we will approximate it as closely as we can. The purpose of such distinctions is to examine the particular sets of variables that are at work in various situations. Our classifications are:

1. Shifts of given resources between products within a production period (including the planning period immediately prior to production.
2. Variations in total amounts of inputs (resources) but technology static.
3. Variations in total amounts of inputs and in the application of technology.

Observe that classifications 2 and 3 are likely to involve more calendar time than 1, as is the case with long run versus short run. However none of the classifications are based on calendar time.

Situation No. 1—Total Inputs Constant

First, we examine Situation No. 1, which applies to a planning-production period. Economists are fairly happy with the economic calculus applied by farmers as they choose among alternative uses of their resources for producing various crops and livestock. Occasionally, last-minute switches are possible as to alternative uses of an already produced product. Certain varieties of grapes can be sold fresh or to the wineries or can be dried for raisins. Likewise, the supplies of Grade A milk not needed for fluid consumption on a daily basis can be diverted into manufactured products. In general, however, we are thinking of those choices made at the beginning of a cropping season. Shall I plant this 100 acres in feed grains or soybeans? Shall I cull these five cows out of the dairy herd this year or next? Technical transformations become quite important in choices concerning the production of two or more products (see Chapter 6). The relative feeding efficiencies of hogs and cattle have become important in relation to anticipated prices in deciding how many of each to feed. Likewise the expected yields and production costs of corn and soybeans can be compared to expected prices of each in determining relative acreages. There is room for individual error, of course. Enterprise cost accounting is probably not very well refined on most farms. There are varying risks and uncertainties associated with anticipated costs and yields. Unexpected or large profits or losses encountered last marketing season may warp the price expectations for this season. Moreover some costs and benefits are easy to overlook because they are nonmarket in nature and extend to following production periods.

The possible supply adjustments within one planning production period are quite significant for most of the big items of American agriculture—feed grains, soybeans, cotton, hogs, and to some extent beef cattle and wheat. Such quick adjustments do not apply as well to items requiring specialized capital goods such as fluid milk or broilers, nor to products with extremely long production periods such as apples. The current trend in most of agriculture toward commodity specialization with the aid of specialized capital—cattle feeding in big lots, continuous corn production, etc.—is reducing the flexibility associated with intrafarm shifts of resources between products.

If we were to imagine static total supplies of farm inputs (land, labor, and capital), static technology of agricultural production, and a stable total demand for agricultural products, then it is quite likely that most variations in the demands for most individual agricultural products *could be met* within one planning-production period. While it is by no means obvious that the varying demands *would be met* because of the potential errors stemming from incorrect anticipations, they could be. In such a world, the supply curve of each individual product would be fairly flat *over a normal range of variation* with an upward slope when less adapted resources were pulled in to increase greatly the output of some commodity like wheat or cotton. The student can test his understanding of the above paragraph and the recent validity of its conclusions by asking: What have been the price ratios between soybeans and corn over the past 10 years? What explains the year-to-year variations? Do the price ratios indicate any trend? The supply curve for all agricultural products in the aggregate is very different than the supply curve for any individual product such as wheat. This difference is particularly pronounced in the assumed Situation No. 1 in which total inputs are constant. The aggregate supply curve for all practical purposes is perfectly inelastic (vertical) for most prices, although it would slope off to the left for very, very low prices.

Situation No. 2—Total Inputs Variable

Our second classification includes variations in the totals of all inputs within agriculture, but technology is held constant. Farmers now compete on the basis not only of how well they manage their resources in production and how well they make the optimal product choices but also on how effectively they augment and recombine the resources of land, capital, and labor within their firms.

The supply curves for individual agricultural products will generally be more elastic then in Situation No. 1. The extra elasticity stems from the assumed ability of farmers to increase output by bringing in extra, well-adapted inputs rather than by having to rely entirely on shifting inputs from some other crop or enterprise as in Situation No. 1. Capital is the most important input in modern American agriculture, and it can be freely varied in Situation No. 2. Of course, we are still limiting our elastic supply curves to a reasonable or normal range of variation. With given technology, we could not expect to triple our production of wheat, or cotton, or hogs, or many other major commodities without encountering sharply rising production costs.

If farm inputs were homogeneous and if technology were static, then the optimal scale of firm would presumably be identical among firms and constant over time and space. However, ranchland in eastern Colorado is strikingly different from that of the rich cotton farms of the Missouri Delta as to soil and climate. The heterogeneity of management in American agriculture is probably equal to that of land. A 65-year-old poor manager cannot handle the same operation as a 30-year-old poor manager, and the two men combined could not handle an operation optimal for a good manager.

As soon as we acknowledge heterogeneity of inputs and the mortality of farm managers, then we admit that there will be constant changing of farm units because of entry and exit, firm growth and decline. The famous forest analogy of Marshall's comes to mind in which there is constant change among the trees within a forest of constant total size and constant average size and age of tree. By assuming technology constant, we assumed away the reason for any change over time in the *average* optimum scale of firm. The reader can argue about this last statement if he assumes that improvements in managerial abilities can occur even while technology is constant.

Competition in such a world would be less difficult from a farmer's point of view. It would still be true that the good managers will earn more income than the poor and the good land will yield more rent (see Chapter 11). With changing demands there will be mistakes in outlook and in investment and planning decisions. Farmers would still seek such institutions as market orders to obtain more orderly daily and seasonal markets. However the constancy of technology reduces the instability of supplies and makes the latitude for errors smaller. Yesterday is a good basis for tomorrow's farm practices and tomorrow's investments. A wrong decision is not so likely to put one behind forever when the pace of the race is slow.

If demand were falling, stable, or increasing very slowly, supplies might remain excessive in such a situation. There seems to be a tendency in atomistic agriculture for farmers to overcommit productive resources—particularly the more durable capital inputs. Imperfectly informed farmers who overcommit resources cannot completely correct those errors.[6] While this overcommitment has been associated historically with advancing technology and the purchases of that new technology as it is embodied in new models of equipment, etc., the same forces toward overcommitment might persist to a lesser extent in a situation of unchanging technology.

On the other hand, if demand would rise rapidly and for a long time due to a population explosion while technology were unchanging, we have assumed the Mathusian nightmare. Total output could only increase by augmentation of total inputs. Some augmentation is possible at fairly low costs—the amount of cropland could be increased by a third or more in this country, the use of fertilizer could be doubled or tripled, etc. Agriculture would be incurring external diseconomies as output was expanded to keep pace with an increasing population. Farm prices would rise. Owners of farmland would receive sizable capital gains (or their potential) as it became increasingly scarce. The aggregate supply curve for all agricultural products would rise to the right fairly steeply. Output would be increased by bringing in more inputs and by increasing the number of farms (firms), assuming existing firms are at optimal scale.

Any reader at all familiar with American agriculture will recognize the stark unreality of some of the conclusions just drawn (see Chapter 9). Total cropland has been falling rather than rising. Total number of farms has been falling rapidly rather than rising, while the average size of farm has been increasing. The aggregate supply curve has moved to the right so rapidly in the postwar period as to create a path of falling market prices rather than rising ones.

The differences are due to changing technology and the tendency of atomistic farmers to overcommit productive resources, and also partly, perhaps, to a run of good weather. While we might have assumed technology to be static for decades in the 18th century or in some underdeveloped countries today, it can hardly be assumed static for a year in this age. The reason for discussing a static technology situation was to point up the tremendous significance of technological advance.

Situation No. 3—Technology Variable

We can move fairly rapidly through the third situation of varying inputs *and* technology. It describes midcentury American agriculture. Technology typically increases greatly the optimal scale of farm while reducing minimum AC of the large-scale firm. As discussed in Chapter 11, the result is a strong incentive toward growth of firms and competi-

---

[6] Glenn L. Johnson, "Supply Functions—Some Facts and Notions," *Agricultural Adjustment Problems in a Growing Economy* (Ames: Iowa State University Press, 1956).

tive pressure on unadjusted firms. If the pressure is not too great, such backward firms can still remain in agriculture a long time if they are content with covering out-of-pocket costs.

The combination of rapid technological advance and atomism makes competition very difficult for many participants. First, there is normally a continuous downward pressure generated on price by the rising supplies, which squeezes the profits of all but the most efficient—and sometimes of them also. Only a very rapid increase in demand would suffice to offset the pressures of rising supplies. Second, all of the participants cannot and/or do not adjust equally well. The firms who make the right adjustments in technology and scale generate the incomes and assets and confidence to repeat their successful adjustments to the next round of technology—and to the next. On the other hand, the firms who fall behind in one round of adjustment often do not have the incomes nor the assets nor the confidence to adjust successfully to the next technological innovations. The fast obsolescence of machines, practices, and skills demands capital and a willingness to learn and to venture. In a traditional agriculture of few technological changes, the old man's decline in strength and in willingness to take risks was offset by his growing experience and wisdom, so that he competed on equal terms with the young and venturesome. But today the hare, not the tortoise, wins the race.

The supply curves of individual commodities tend to be more elastic over a wider range than in Situation No. 2. The reader should be able to explain why.

If we were to be unconventional and include technology as an input, the aggregate supply curve for agriculture would appear to slope down to the right. Both the uncertainties of the availability of technology and the usefulness of a timeless supply curve argue for a definition of the supply curve with technology static. Thus we return to the upward rising aggregate supply curve of Situation No. 2 and then quickly note that the curve has been shifting so rapidly to the right that the upward slope has been of little practical consequence. However, the intervention of any massive increase in demand, such as occurred in World War II, would make the upward slope of great practical consequence.

The policy implications of the long continuing shifts in technology are seldom appreciated by those with only a superficial knowledge of agriculture. After a paragraph analyzing "the farm problem" as too many resources in agriculture, very reputable economists recommend policies to adjust the excess factors out with the implication or even an explicit conclusion that it will only take a few years to reach equilibrium. Implicit in many of these recommendations is a concept of an outmoded agriculture in which output is a function of labor and land rather than of capital. Such recommendations have been made throughout the 20th century and probably will continue to be made for the rest of it. The hard fact is that rapidly accepted technology permits no equilibrium. The substitutability of capital for labor is so high that capital pours into agriculture and industry output continues to expand.

Exit of so-called "excess factors" from agriculture is peculiarly difficult, although it is never as easy from any industry as usually implied by our equilibrium models. The average age of American farmers is about 50 and the median age is higher. Men of this age are not highly mobile either as to occupation or place of residence. The decreasing demand for people to do unskilled work reduces even further their chances of profitable migration into industry. Nor is the future in small business much brighter for the 50-year-old ex-farmer with $50,000 capital but no experience in urban business; only a few such people will do well.

Capital items enter readily but exit slowly. A modern dairy milking parlor cannot be converted economically into a gasoline filling station, nor even into a farrowing house. In general even though the capitalized value of productive assets may fall rather low in times of low farm prices, this capitalized value will usually exceed the salvage value. Moreover, there is the same important distinction between committed and uncommitted capital expenditures as has been already discussed with relation to variable costs. Suppose the imputed interest return on a very large investment in land and equipment is only 1 percent. Also assume that an interest return of 6 or 8 percent is anticipated on a marginal addition of another 80 acres or of another tractor or baler or combine. The further investment is likely to be justified even though the enterprise already earns very low capital returns. If unanticipated price declines follow, the whole process is somewhat like that of a dog chasing his tail. Moreover, agribusiness firms are playing an increasingly important role in pumping capital into agriculture (see Chapter 16).

The cumulative effects of technology are often revolutionary. These cumulative effects have increased tremendously the interdependence of farmers and agribusiness. They have, in fact, created a huge and powerful agribusiness complex that is beginning to dominate certain parts of agriculture. Vertically integrated agribusiness firms have already met and out-competed farmers in broiler production. Farmers are asking: Who is going to control agriculture in the future? Some important new competitive forces are likely to affect competition among farmers in the near future (see Chapter 16).

Farmers may give up and move to town, but their farms do not. There is little debate that most productive land will stay permanently in agriculture regardless of the levels of farm incomes and farmland prices unless it is removed by government action. Land exits from agriculture for three reasons. First, a small percentage exits because of much more lucrative uses in highways, city lots, and building sites. However the exit percentage is much higher in urban fringe areas, and it is very high in certain intensive cropping areas of California. Second, a somewhat larger amount is reclassified as forests as the trees on it get taller. Third, some cropland is transferred to grazing, and some grazing land is abandoned as no longer worth grazing.

SUMMARY

How shall already produced supplies of agricultural commodities be priced? A monopolist would look at the elasticity of demand in the SR and LR and set a profit-maximizing price. Atomistic sellers sell all they have by letting a price be set which clears the market. Farmers have been reluctant to see their prices determined by market-period clear-the-market pricing. This reluctance has been particularly strong for producers of perishable items with traditionally chaotic markets. Consequently many have moved a short step away from such produce-exchange markets by obtaining market orders for Grade A milk and for many fresh fruits and vegetables. Bargaining associations have been formed for many canning crops and have been attempted or are being developed for many others. The hundreds of thousands of producers of the big-ticket items like soybeans, wheat, feed grains, cattle, and hogs have found it easier to obtain some price stability and support via government price supports, production controls, land diversion, and government purchase programs rather than through bargaining associations or market orders.

To what extent can farmers avoid competing atomistically? The motivations for the individual farmer to pursue goals detrimental to group welfare and leading to atomistic results are almost irresistible. The market orders work, when they do, because there is a legal compulsion voted by the groups that prevents the individual from maximizing at the expense of the group. Bargaining associations, lacking this legal compulsion, face a great deal of difficulty in obtaining and holding significant market control. This difficulty is especially great if the commodity buyers or processors are trying to discourage membership in the association. Farmers have modified atomistic competition by obtaining new institutional arrangements, and they are likely to obtain more.

To what extent can farmers avoid the *effects* of competing atomistically? Various methods of trying to avoid these effects have been listed. Various commodity groups have relied on varying methods. Limited success is quite possible. However, there are three basic limitations upon any attempt of farmers to improve their prices and incomes. One is long-term price elasticity of demand. While demand is almost always very inelastic in the short term, substitution possibilities for individual products can be significant in the long term. For example, there has long been a debate as to whether cotton price supports have aided synthetic fibers in capturing markets away from cotton. The second limitation is political acceptability. The atomistic nature of agriculture requires it to obtain explicit federal help. It is quite clear that the federal government will not help any segment of agriculture to transform itself into a monopolistic cartel exploiting consumers. The third constraint on market-period pricing is supply response in succeeding production periods. A market order committee which significantly increased real incomes by producing commodity X instead of Y or Z can generally rest assured that next season's supply increase in the volume of commodity X will make its job doubly difficult. Again, there are significant differences between commodities—supply response to an improved price may come in less than three months in broilers and require more than three years in certain tree fruits and nuts.

Creative destruction is both productive and destructive. Creative destruction based upon great advances in technology accepted by farmers has greatly increased the efficiency of food and fiber production. The result has been relative declines in farm prices and plentiful supplies—both clear gains to society. The result has also been a "destruction" in the producing and earning power of many productive factors, including both capital goods and individual farmers. New capital replaces old capital *and* old men. Farms must be consolidated to give the large acreages in which eight-row corn planters can operate efficiently. We will not attempt here to examine the inherent welfare conflicts in creative destruction. See the policy chapters beginning with Chapter 18.

Chapter 16

THE INTERDEPENDENCE OF FARMERS AND MARKETING FIRMS

A striking feature of the structure of the market for farm products is the crucial interdependence throughout all parts of it. The interdependence between the successive stages in the production and marketing sequence is the crux of the significance of marketing to agriculture. The farmer, who no longer sells his products to consumers, is critically dependent upon the intermediaries who do. But all market firms are equally dependent on the farmer for their supplies of raw products. No dependence in all the economy is more absolute than that between a market and its supplier, or between a supplier and its market. Each is essential to the other.[1]

The previous chapters on competition among retailers and among agricultural marketing firms have demonstrated the complexities of the marketing system. The functions of this complex interlocked system are: (1) to move products to consumers, and (2) to give coordination to the entire sequence of production and marketing decisions.

This coordination is obtained through the guidance of prices and through all kinds of cooperative arrangements among firms. Any industrial or agricultural marketing system is knit together with special working relationships between and among firms. "If any firm, no matter how large and powerful, suddenly found that all of its co-operative arrangements with other firms had lapsed and that it had to negotiate from scratch, it would probably be out of business as of that day. It would be beyond the capacity of the most able executive group to reconstruct a complete action system quickly enough to save the firm."[2]

Farmers and their input suppliers—of equipment, fuel, power, feed, fertilizers, chemicals—are as interdependent as farmers and those firms marketing agricultural products. However, for lack of space, only the latter interdependencies are treated in this chapter.

This interdependence among firms and among farm and marketing firms can be considered and observed at various levels. Interdependence

---

[1] Harold F. Breimyer, *Individual Freedom and the Economic Organization of Agriculture* (Urbana, Ill.: University of Illinois Press, 1965), p. 96.

[2] Wroe Alderson, *Marketing Behavior and Executive Action* (Homewood, Ill.: Richard D. Irwin, Inc., 1957), p. 134.

can be seen daily at the loading dock and the receiving rooms. It can be seen in the adjustment of the pace of daily processing operations to the volume of the harvest. Interdependence is implicit in every discussion of marketing margins and farmer's share of the consumer's dollar. Interdependence of another sort was made explicit when Congress directed the National Food Marketing Commission to include "the changes . . . which would be appropriate to achieve a desired distribution of power. . . ."

NATIONAL RELATIONSHIPS OF PRICE AND INCOME

Farmers consider themselves residual claimants on the consumer's food dollar. The relationships of farm prices to consumer prices of the same or equivalent products have been of long-standing concern to farmers.

Farmers do not ordinarily sell directly to consumers. Instead farmers face a demand curve of processors or middlemen which is derived from consumer demand. The *derived demand* for any given quantity is the consumer demand minus the per unit marketing charges of all involved middlemen. The discussion begins with these identities:

$FP \equiv CP - MM$; i.e., farm price equal consumer price minus the marketing margin.

$GFR \equiv CE - MB$; i.e., gross farm receipts equal consumer expenditures for farm products minus the marketing bill.

The interest of farmers and others in these relationships has led the USDA to estimate them on a continuing basis for a number of commodities and product groups. For example, the average retail cost to consumers for October–December, 1966, of a pound of choice grade beef was estimated to be 83.9 cents, the farm-retail spread (i.e., marketing margin) as 36.7 cents, and the net farm value as 47.2 cents. For the same period in 1965, the estimates were 82.9 cents, 36.0 cents, and 46.9 cents respectively.[3] In other words for this particular period, a 1-cent addition in retail price had apparently been divided 0.7 cent to marketing agencies and 0.3 cent to farmers.

With rapidly expanding markets, the total consumer expenditures for food have tended to increase more than $2 billion a year. As indicated by the identity, $GFR \equiv CE - MB$, this increase is divided between farmers and marketing agencies. The USDA estimates that civilian expenditures (CE) for domestically produced farm foods increased from $53.1 billion in 1955 to $77.6 billion in 1965. At the same time, the total marketing bill (MB) increased from $34.4 billion to $52.1 billion and the

---

[3] U.S. Department of Agriculture, *Marketing and Transportation Situation,* MTS–164, February, 1967, pp. 36–37.

farm value of these foods (*GFR*) increased from $18.7 billion to $25.5 billion.[4] In other words, the $24.5 billion increase in *CE* was divided: $17.7 billion to marketing firms and $6.8 billion to farmers.

The mechanics of arithmetic manipulation of these identities are quite simple: by holding one of the three terms constant and manipulating another, the effects on the third are direct and obvious. Unfortunately, practical inferences are seldom so simple because many real-life situations do not have a single, clear-cut effect on one, and only one, term of the identity. Before we furnish evidence for that pessimistic statement, we pause to examine the relations of gross receipts to net income.

The relation of gross farm receipts to net farm income decreases with "time." Within a market period, a change in gross farm receipts is associated with a nearly identical change in net farm income. Thus a change in the farm price for soybeans during August which persists through the marketing season will change gross and net farm receipts from soybeans by almost the same amount. If the changed demand persists through another production season, there will be an output response which will change the relationship of gross and net farm income from soybeans. In the very long run, the net unit returns from soybean production may be much the same whether 500 or 900 million bushels of soybeans are produced, as long as there is a long-run supply and demand equilibrium. However, it would be unrealistic to move from this conclusion to the inference that the size of gross farm receipts are of no interest to farmers. On the contrary, the short-run dominates real life. When gross receipts are rising, net income is ordinarily rising; when gross receipts are falling, net income is ordinarily falling. Today's gains or losses can be overemphasized because they won't last forever, but they cannot be ignored.

What is the relation of gross farm receipts and net farm income if all commodities are involved? Suppose, for example, a policy shift which results in a shift to the right in the derived demand at farm level for all farm products. In the market period, price would rise and gross and net farm incomes would rise correspondingly. In the following production periods, aggregate farm production would expand and farm prices will return at least part of the way to their former levels. The new price and output levels will depend upon the elasticity of aggregate supply (see Chapter 20). Gross income will be higher than formerly as a national total—as will per farm income assuming no change in number of farm units. If we had equilibrium adjustments of all factors in agriculture, net incomes should adjust to the same level as previously. Since we have a long history of disequilibrium, it seems quite likely that net incomes are

---

[4] U.S. Department of Agriculture, *Marketing and Transportation Situation,* MTS–163, November, 1966, p. 12.

long affected by moves to the right or to the left of the aggregate derived demand for all farm commodities.

Interdependence of Supplies, Demands, and Incomes

At any given time, there is a nearly fixed relationship between the quantity marketed of a farm product and the marketing services provided to market it. In effect, the demand for marketing services is a function of the supply of agricultural products. While this function is constant in the short term, it varies somewhat in the longer term for reasons of importance. Likewise the derived demand for farm products is a function of final demand and the marketing margin. The precise nature of these interdependencies will now be examined in several situations.

1. *Under what conditions do increases in marketing margins reduce gross farm receipts?* The answers depend upon (1) the effect on derived demand and (2) the length of time considered. Any shift to the left of derived demand will force adjustments on farmers.

When a marketing margin increases, the derived demand curve will shift to the left (Figure 16–1) unless the increase in margin promotes a sufficient shift to the right in final demand (Figure 16–2). In other

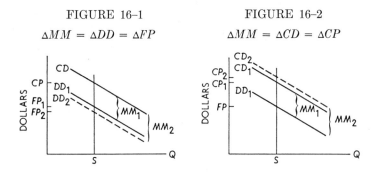

FIGURE 16–1   FIGURE 16–2

$\Delta MM = \Delta DD = \Delta FP$ $\Delta MM = \Delta CD = \Delta CP$

words, an increase in MM must decrease FP *unless* the increase in MM leads to a corresponding (or greater) increase in CP. As long as we consider individual commodities it is possible to find numerous situations in which demand-promoting measures such as prettier packages or trading stamps or additional processing may increase consumer demand (and CP) by as much or more than they increase costs (MM). However, even for the individual commodity, there have been numerous increases in input prices (labor, transportation, utilities, rent, etc.) in the postwar period, which had no possible effect upon final demand. Moreover, the aggregate picture of demand-increasing measures is much less rosy than that of individual commodities. Merchandising measures to increase pork demand tend to be offset by measures to increase chicken consumption, etc. The final result of many individual commodity promotional efforts is much the same as *everyone* in a football stadium standing up to see better on a fourth and goal play. However, the effects of such promotion cannot be entirely discounted; if our food marketing system contained no promotion and merchandising, it is highly unlikely that the demand for food in the aggregate would be as high as it is. Moreover, as farming becomes more specialized there are those who will support pork or beef promotion as long as there seems to be gains for that group regardless of the effects on demand for other foods.

Thus, during the market period an increase in a marketing margin is likely to be associated with some decrease—and sometimes an *equal* decrease—in farm price (Figure 16–1). The impact upon gross farm receipts and net income are correspondingly direct. In a longer period, this price reduction is partially or completely reversed by supply adjust-ment—if farm supply is perfectly elastic, for example, all the price reduction is eventually eliminated by a supply reduction (Figure 16–3). As indicated elsewhere, supply tends to be much less elastic in the aggregate than for individual commodities. It would appear, therefore, that the large postwar increases in marketing margins on most agricul-tural products have held down farm prices and gross farm receipts (Figure 16–4).

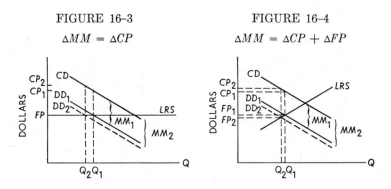

FIGURE 16–3

$\Delta MM = \Delta CP$

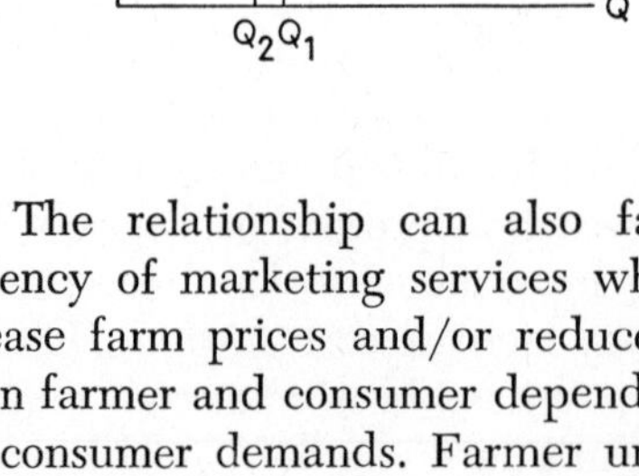

FIGURE 16–4

$\Delta MM = \Delta CP + \Delta FP$

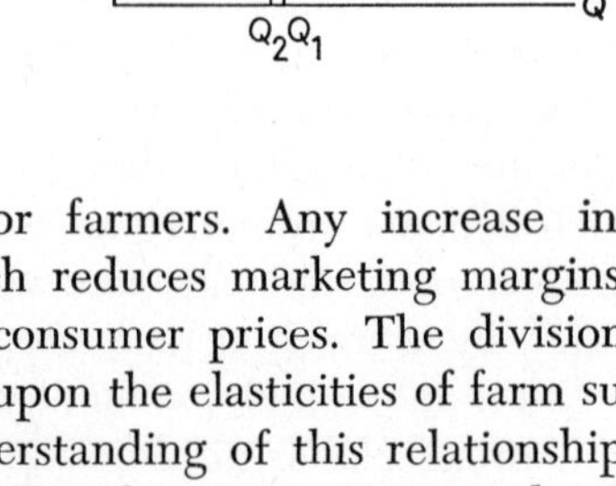

The relationship can also favor farmers. Any increase in the efficiency of marketing services which reduces marketing margins can increase farm prices and/or reduce consumer prices. The division be-tween farmer and consumer depends upon the elasticities of farm supply and consumer demands. Farmer understanding of this relationship has been responsible for some of their political activity. Farmers have ob-tained legislation aimed at helping marketing firms to operate more efficiently in the confidence that farmers' returns would ultimately benefit. The Research and Marketing Act of 1946, which has provided for millions of dollars of research and educational activity with marketing firms, was supported by farmers as well as business interests. Farmers have viewed with increasing concern the power of retailers to influence considerably the consumer demand for their commodities by varying emphasis upon displays, promotion, and size of margin. The National Food Marketing Commission set up in 1964 by the Congress and President to investigate the marketing of agricultural products was instigated by farmer interests who thought that it was time to change some rules of the game in order to limit the market advantages of retail chain stores.

2. *Under what conditions do changes in farm output change margins and incomes of agricultural marketing firms?*

First, it's useful to return to the pork versus post toasties distinction of the agricultural marketing chapter. Those firms which merchandise successfully differentiated manufactured products such as breakfast cereals or pancake flour or baby foods are isolated from farm supply fluctuations. The volume and price of these products are ordinarily dependent upon consumer demand, not upon farmers' output.

However, farm output is important to those marketing firms which sell marketing services. It is useful to break down our analysis according to the market structure of the marketing firms.

Large Group. Since the volume of farm output represents the "derived demand" for marketing services, an increase in that volume tends to be advantageous to marketing firms and a decrease tends to be disadvantageous. In the short run, if the volume change is relatively small, the operating costs and margins per unit are likely to be unaffected. Of course, both buying and selling price will be changed by the new farm product price, but *margin* need not be affected. In the short run, if the volume change is relatively large, operating costs per unit of marketing firms are likely to be increased by either an increase or decrease in volume. That is, assuming the firm initially is operating in the vicinity of the low point of its plant average cost curve, any significant change in volume forces up costs (Figure 16–5). To the extent that each marketing firm competes vigorously to maintain its own volume when farm supplies *are reduced,* then the marketing margin may stay stable or be bid down, even though short-run operating costs for each of the firms in the industry are higher. On the other hand, when farm supplies *are increased,* marketing firms are reluctant to increase their volume and costs except with higher margins; therefore, margins tend to be bid up readily. In the long run in such large groups, there will be an adjustment of factors and/or firms to the changed "derived demands." Assuming that there are no unexploited economies of scale before or after the adjustment and assuming competitive rather than full-cost pricing, then any change in "derived demand for marketing service" will ultimately lead to a change in the number of marketing firms. If a region's cotton crop were to decline year by year, the number of cotton gins would also decline. How closely related are these two trends would depend upon anticipations and other economic factors in both farming and ginning.

FIGURE 16–5

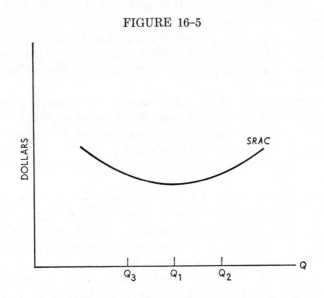

Small Group. When the marketing firms are few, what is the impact of a change in farm supplies and thus a change in the derived demand for marketing services? In the short run, a relatively large decrease in farm supplies has much the same effect of increasing operating costs as in the large group. A rather close-knit oligopoly will raise its margin to cover those extra costs; a more competitive oligopoly will likely hold down or reduce its margin in the same way as the large group. A relatively large increase in farm supplies is also likely to increase short-run oligopoly margins for the same reasons as in the large group.

In 1966, rather sharp increases in bread prices led to an *FTC* investigation. Some of its findings were:

The bread price increase followed the spring increases in wheat prices, which resulted from greater export demand and a smaller-than-usual wheat crop, the FTC found. Retail bread prices rose an average 1.7 cents a loaf in the 25 cities studied. The FTC said the cost of wheat and other ingredients accounted for 0.6 of a cent, bakers for 0.7 of a cent and retailers for 0.4 of a cent.

The higher cost of farmer-supplied ingredients had a rather uniform impact on bakers throughout the country, the FTC said. On the other hand, the end result on retail bread prices between January and August went up as much as 22.5% in Milwaukee, while in Los Angeles they declined.

The FTC's explanation was that bakers raised their wholesale prices most in cities where prices had been lowest in January and least in cities where January prices had been highest.

In cities where January prices had been lowest, bakers "had been earning very low profits or incurring losses" and these bakers used the "occasion of increased flour costs in June to raise their prices substantially in excess of their increased cost of ingredients," the FTC said. But where wholesale prices were high, some bakers absorbed the entire additional cost of ingredients, the commission added.

When wholesale prices increased, retailers passed the increases on to consumers it said.[5]

The baking industry is quite concentrated. If the FTC report is correct, the industry recognizes a "correct margin," which gets out of line from time to time. The change in wheat supplies and prices furnished a vehicle for margin adjustment. The real-life example gives us a picture of industry dynamics in motion rather than a shift from one equilibrium to another.

The oligopolistic long-run response to an increase in farm supplies will be an increase in factors employed and an increase in the number of plants. Unless there are external economies, the new margin is likely to be a bit higher than the old margin because additional factors have been bid into the industry. Industry growth may encourage entry of one or more new firms. What about the long-run response to a decrease in farm supplies? Factors of labor and capital are often fairly mobile. Some multiproduct processors can more readily divert emphasis from one product to another than can one processors with very specialized facilities. Margins will be depressed temporarily unless there is very close-knit oligopolistic control. While such a decline can put great pressure upon an oligopoly's mode of living together, there is strong motivation for cooperation and there is reduced danger of new entry. Who wants to enter a declining industry? The marketing margin may stabilize at a slightly lower figure than the initial one because the marginal factors (plants, firms) have left the industry.

In summary, significant changes in farm output do affect the margins and profits of agricultural marketing firms. In general the shorter the period and the greater the number of firms, the greater the impact. But even in market-period, large-group competition, margins are not likely to fluctuate as much as farm prices do. Marketing firms seldom have a sequential committing of variable costs such as that which leads a farmer to harvest and sell a crop even though price covers little more than

---

[5] *Wall Street Journal,* October 26, 1966, p. 8.

harvesting costs. In general *ceteris paribus,* farm prices and margins in the short term ordinarily change in opposite directions in response to a change in farm output.

3. *Can the market power of retailers reduce the prices paid for farm products in the short run?*

There are often claims that farm prices are hurt by the exercise of market power by retailers. We will not attempt to evaluate what *is being done* but rather what is possible. It is theoretically possible for retailers to hold farm prices in the short run below the levels which would be expected if these retailers competed like atomistic firms. Moreover the results need not show up in excessive chain-store profits if the gains are passed on to consumers through Bingo prizes or double stamps or lower prices. In terms of the identity, the reduction in *FP* is accompanied by a fall in *CP* or a rise in *MM*.

As shown before, atomistic farm price in the short run is determined by derived demand and the size of the crop. The derived demand is nothing more tangible than the anticipations of the middlemen, based upon their estimates of final demand, the available supplies, and marketing costs. Their estimates of final demand vary with how many special sales they decide to run, etc. There is evidence that each chain-store buyer is very concerned that he buys as cheaply as any rival. (See Chapter 14 and "Pork versus Post Toasties" in Chapter 13.) If there is any element of price leadership, it seems particularly possible that derived demand—and farmer returns—may be less than is justified by actual consumer demand.

The theory of price depression by aggressive buying practices is precisely the obverse of price elevation by aggressive selling practices. That is, some market orders are believed to raise the bargaining prices of farmers so that they do not bid down a going price even though they may not be able to sell as much volume as they would like. Likewise, it is conceptually possible for a small group of buyers to refuse to bid up the going price of a product even though they may not be able to obtain quite as much volume as they would like. Since market period supplies are fixed, they can as well share the total volume at price *P* as at price 1.2*P*.

The reader will note that the conceptual possibility that buyers aggressively bid down short-run price below the levels which could clear the market is not evidence that buyers actually do so. Such evidence is hard to come by. One point of interest would be the standards set by management for chain-store buyers. Are they strongly motivated to bid down farm product prices, or can they follow an easy route of buying at a "going price?"

Short-run prices and long-run sales of any farm quantity can be directly affected by the actions of the retail merchandisers. Retailers exercise considerable pricing flexibility on individual products as they "price the mix" of 6,000 or so items. For various reasons, one commodity may be assigned a quite high retail margin and another one a low margin. Broilers, for example traditionally carry much lower margins than other meats, and the consequent extra price differential at retail has promoted the demand for broilers. Likewise, some commodities receive much more merchandising push than others—bigger and more attractive displays, feature ads in the Thursday newspapers, etc. Thus producers observe that the consumer demand for some products depends more upon retailer policy than upon consumer income or other traditional variables influencing consumer demand. As farmers become more specialized in the production of a commodity, they observe a growing dependence upon retailer policies which affect them but which they cannot influence in return.

Interdependencies of Agricultural and Marketing Policies

Farmers have often demanded the regulation of marketing firms. Those firms have often supported certain agricultural policies opposed by many farmers and opposed other policies supported by many farmers. Some economists in the early sixties even talked of vigorous antitrust policies as an alternative to such farm policies as supply management. However, it is quite clear that the most vigorous antitrust and other regulation of marketing firms would have much less effect on farm prices and gross receipts than a moderate supply control program.

Our conclusions would be quite different if there were *monopoly* control of a marketing level. In this situation, a monopoly could greatly affect marketing margins and effective antitrust could have a major impact upon farm income. It is possible to show with simplified models that a monopoly at one stage or level of a marketing channel—at the processing level, for example—could have as much impact on consumer price as if the monopoly controlled all levels from farm production to retail.

Local agribusiness firms have sometimes felt rather severe effects from such programs as the Soil Bank which reduced production disproportionately in certain areas. Even at the national level, any effective supply control program for commodities such as wheat, cotton, or feed grains does reduce the demand for marketing services. With a few exceptions, such reductions have been relatively small, and so has been the impact on marketing firms.

Marketing orders are another form of agricultural program that has very limited effects on total supplies marketed. However, intraseasonal stabilization of supplies and prices may shift emphasis away from speculative buying and selling and toward efficient handling and marketing. For example, there is evidence that the canners of certain fruits and vegetables may hold back in buying for fear of a later break in farm prices which would allow competitors to build inventories at lower costs. The margins sought by such processors might be smaller if the price risks were reduced. Likewise, the amount of necessary handling facilities may be reduced if there is a leveling of the peaks and valleys of marketing. But the competitive forces fixing processing or retailing margins still remain internal to those levels and are not directly affected by market orders or bargaining cooperatives.

Some Influences on Price Elasticity at Farm Level

If there is a significant shift in the final demand for a commodity like fluid milk or eggs and if the marketing margin remains constant, then the full effect of the shift hits the derived demand curve. Moreover the full effect of any shift is *proportionately* larger at the derived demand level because the original magnitude is smaller there. For example, suppose that the farm price of fluid milk is 50 cents a gallon, the margin is also 50 cents, and the retail price is $1. Suppose an increase in milk supplies lowers the retail price 10 percent (or 10 cents a gallon). The fall in farm price of 10 cents a gallon is a 20 percent decline (10¢/50¢) rather than a 10 percent. If we suppose that the increase in milk supplied was 3 percent, then the elasticity of retail demand was 0.3 while the elasticity at farm level was only 0.15. The reader can easily determine that the larger the margin, the more inelastic (or, occasionally, less elastic) is demand at *farm level.*

This difference in proportionate effects has other implications. For example, farmers might argue for a government program to reduce milk supplies so as to raise farm prices 10 cents a gallon at farm level. Farmers could further argue that this 10 cents, which represents a wonderful 20 percent gain to them, will only be a 10 percent increase at retail and, therefore, neither very discouraging to total consumption nor very painful to the consumer wallet. In general, the larger the marketing margin relative to farm price, the more these arguments apply. Practical examples, such as comparisons of the tiny cost of the wheat in a loaf of bread, are often cited in farm policy discussions.

This subdivision of the consumer payment for a farm product into payments to the farmer and several middlemen usually leads to inelastic derived demands for the product or services *of each segment* even when final demand is elastic. Each segment—retailers, processors, and even the retail clerks union seeking a new contract—is tempted by the inelastic demand facing it alone; thus, actions result which have an impact upon each of the other segments in the market channel.

Demand at farm level tends to be very inelastic with respect to price because of the levered effect of marketing margins upon already inelastic retail price elasticities. It is generally agreed that retail food demand is becoming more price inelastic. Moreover, more food products are moving into the highly manufactured and differentiated categories where price stability is maintained by the manufacturer or retailer. Therefore, farmers face markets which are increasingly inelastic, where "minor" shifts in supplies cause "major" fluctuations in price. This aspect of interdependency is coming to be one of the more serious problems faced by farmers.

VERTICAL INTEGRATION

Vertical integration has been a common term in agriculture for more than a decade. (See the section on vertical integration in Chapter 13.) Definitions still vary a bit. Generally, it means the control by a firm of two or more stages of production or marketing, where a salable product is available at each stage.[6] Control may be contractual or by ownership. Most interest has been focused on a certain type of vertical integration—that which ties together an agricultural enterprise and some phase of agricultural marketing. On the other hand, such forms of on-farm "vertical integration" as a farmer raising feeder cattle and feeding them out arouse no interest and are generally not considered as vertical integration. The prime example of vertical integration is the broiler industry in which a number of feed manufacturers and food processors have obtained control of broiler production and processing and sometimes of hatching as well.

Vertical integration appears to be motivated by considerations of efficiency and/or market advantage and/or reduction of risk and uncertainty (see Chapter 13). The integrating is typically done *by* the marketing firm rather than by farmers. The much larger volume of the typical processor and the much larger financial strength are the reasons for the initiative resting with the marketing firm. In this case the dog wags the tail and not vice versa.

While most farm firms are too small to integrate forward into marketing, farmer-owned cooperatives often are not. Several fruit grower cooperatives in California including the California Fruit Growers Exchange in fresh citrus products and the Cal Can Corporation in canned foods have been notably successful in integrating into many marketing activities. Cal Can even manufactures its own cans.

---

[6] See Ronald Mighell and Lawrence A. Jones, *Vertical Coordination in Agriculture,* USDA, Agricultural Economics Report No. 19, 1963, p. 1; and Raphael Trifon, "Guides for Speculation about the Vertical Integration of Agriculture with Allied Industries," *Journal of Farm Economics,* November, 1959, p. 736.

The Cal Can success story is an impressive one:

Since 1958 our membership has increased from the original 473 to more than 1,100. It is important to point out that this has been a controlled expansion, with additions each year limited to anticipated market growth. For, as we will emphasize later on, Cal Can is a market-oriented company.[7]

Many cooperatives operate on the philosophy that since the growers own and control the business, they should therefore be entitled to produce crops in whatever volumes and varieties they desire. It is the function of the cooperative, they assume, to find a market *some* place for whatever quantity and quality of raw material the members deliver to the gate.

Cal Can takes exactly the opposite view. We begin with the market. We operate on the premise that Cal Can's professional management has been hired to analyze and develop markets which will give each grower the greatest return for the investment in time and money he puts into his crop. Therefore, we begin our analysis at the market level.

Twice a year our market analysts are required to submit projections of market requirements and potential. This is then related to our processing capacities and efficiencies and finally to raw product availability. Our growers' production is thus based upon market requirements and processing capabilities which will produce maximum returns. There is particular emphasis and enforcement regarding variety and quality factors.

We admit to membership only those growers who firmly understand and agree with this philosophy and procedure. Should a grower later disagree and fail to conform to the policies which have been set for the good of the whole, the board gives him the opportunity to cancel his membership. I should add here that we have had very few terminations.[8]

As a safety valve against unwanted surpluses in big crop years, we obtain only about 90 percent of our raw product requirements from member-growers. The balance we buy outside as a hedge against major fluctuations in market conditions and supply availability. But, unlike some cooperative associations, we do not feel any responsibility to sop up excess crop production.

Land O'Lakes is another very successful cooperative, which has integrated vertically into many phases of marketing.

From its humble beginning with a group of producer cooperatives banding together to pool and market butter, primarily to the eastern butter houses and distributors, Land O'Lakes has grown into a broad diversified market service cooperative which not only markets dairy products for its members, but in addition, processes and sells butter, cheese, dry milk powder, turkeys, poultry, eggs, mixed feeds and seeds, processes milk and cream,

[7] Robert R. Mauser, "The Cal Can Story," *Farmer Cooperative Success Stories* (Washington, D.C.: American Institute of Cooperation, 1965), p. 11.
[8] *Ibid.*, pp. 12–13.
[9] *Ibid.*, p. 13.

operates hatcheries, sells dairy equipment and creamery supplies, retails milk and ice cream, operates wholesale and retail milk and ice cream routes, and operates retail dairy stores under its Bridgeman Division.[10]

We sincerely feel that we have been able to make Mrs. Consumer pay a little extra for Land O'Lakes butter and other LO'L products. How has this been done? Partially by creation of demand for the products, through advertising and promotion, but also by making her feel that the Land O'Lakes brand is worth more because it is better than average. In this respect, Land O'Lakes record on butter is enviable, for it is not only the nations largest selling brand, but at the same time is priced the highest at both the retail and wholesale level.

Creation of demand through constant advertising and promotion, quality control of products through continuous supervision and inspection—all of these help to establish a consumer franchise for the Land O'Lakes brand. However, the servicing of today's larger buyers is much more complex, the requirements of the purchasers more exacting, the quantities of products required much larger, and the services demanded far greater than they were a few years ago.[11]

Despite these success stories, most vertical integration is not by farmer cooperatives. Even in the dairy industry in which cooperatives have been very successful, the most important vertical integration has been by chain stores which have integrated into processing and distribution of fluid milk and manufactured products.

Through integration, chain stores have been able to reap a number of benefits: (1) lower processing costs because the integrated plant has a dependable outlet for its production and frequently processes only a few items; (2) higher profits as a result of chains doing their own processing and distribution in States that fix the prices stores must pay for milk; (3) lower distribution costs as a result of delivering milk to stores with other perishable products and through the use of hourly-paid rather than commission-paid delivery men; (4) better control in the past over the quality and quantity of raw and finished manufactured products; and (5) lower-cost milk in a few instances where existing dairies have been unwilling to grant discounts for quantity delivery or private label milk.

In California, where both wholesale and retail prices of fluid milk are set, many local and national chains have integrated into dairy processing.

In 1963, 14 of the 40 largest food chains produced in their own plants 53 percent of their sales volume of fluid milk. Seventeen of the 40 largest chains produced 37 percent of their ice cream sales.[12]

---

[10] Owen K. Hallberg, "The Land O'Lakes Story," *Farmer Cooperative Success Stories* (Washington, D.C.: American Institute of Cooperation, 1965), pp. 2–3.

[11] *Ibid.,* p. 4.

[12] National Commission on Food Marketing, *Food from Farmer to Consumer* (Washington, D.C.: U.S. Government Printing Office, June, 1966), p. 45.

INTERDEPENDENCE OF PRODUCTION FUNCTIONS

The production functions of farmers and marketing firms are often interdependent. As already indicated, a high degree of such interdependence may be an important reason for vertical integration. Either highly interdependent production functions must be under a single managerial control, or close coordination needs to be obtained through some market mechanism. We want to look briefly at a few of these interdependencies in agriculture.

Interdependence is associated with timing. The one-way flow of products from farm to market sets up an obvious one-way interdependence in which products cannot be distributed until processed, nor processed until harvested and delivered to processors. Interdependence increases when the timing is crucial *both ways*. Farmers cannot long keep fluid milk or ripe tomatoes on the farm; their production is dependent upon the capacity and closely timed operations of processors and receivers.

Interdependence is associated with spatial economics. The economics of processing and transportation are such for many products that a production location close to a processor is highly advantageous. While there is a *national* market for canned fruits and vegetables, sugar, and beef carcasses, there really is not a national market for fruits and vegetables for canning, or for sugar beets or cane, or even for beef cattle. Even the wheat producer who would locate 500 miles from the nearest elevator is incurring a market disadvantage. In the Midwest, the commercialization of egg production in a relatively few areas has led lending agencies to refuse financing to proposed new egg farms outside of those areas. Likewise, the potential broiler or turkey producer who would locate many miles from a processing plant will receive strong discouragement. Sugar beet production is peculiarly tied to a nearby processing plant because (1) transport costs for any distance tend to absorb much of the value of the beets and (2) the control of output is managed through quotas to processing plants, which are in turn subdivided to farmers.

Some industries face interdependencies due both to spatial and timing problems. Such industries as fluid milk and canning of fruits and vegetables have resorted to a number of market controls to interlock the production functions of farm and market firm. Most Grade A fluid milk is sold through federal marketing order programs regulating the mutual obligations of seller and buyer and assuring farmers stable outlets during periods of flush production. The mutual obligations of farmer sellers and canner processors of fruits and vegetables are regulated by detailed contracts. Many canner contracts not only strictly control the delivery schedule to the canner but also specify varieties and other production practices related to the precise canned product specifications sought by the canner's customers.

The interdependencies are repeatedly affected by technological changes in farming or marketing. The development of quasi-automated "egg factories" led to a completely different production and marketing system for fresh eggs. Even the grading was affected. The old candling system was replaced by a sampling breakout procedure where eggs are handled under approved conditions. The advent of the mechanical cotton picker drastically speeded up picking and shortened the picking season. Ginners responded with more capacity and with some storage of seed cotton (unginned cotton). Modern developments in fast, refrigerated transportation allowed the concentration of almost all production of lettuce in a very few specialized areas with comparative advantage. Development of the disposable milk carton allowed bottling plants to expand their distribution areas by many times.

MARKET POWER

The role of power in American life is a curious one. The privilege of controlling the actions or of affecting the income and property of other persons is something that no one of us can profess to seek or admit to possessing.[13]

Despite this convention, which outlaws ostensible pursuit of power and which leads to a constant search for euphemisms to disguise its possession, there is no indication that, as a people, we are adverse to power. On the contrary few things are more valued, and more jealously guarded by their processors, in our society.[14]

There is a great concern in agriculture about power. Evidence can be found in the interest in farmer bargaining ranging from the N.F.O.'s use of "holding actions" to the bargaining programs of the Farm Bureau's American Agricultural Marketing Association. The National Food Commission was instructed by Congress to recommend changes appropriate to achieve "a desired distribution of power." Authors such as Galbraith and Breimyer have brought these power issues into academic as well as public discussion.

Power within the market is important because it affects economic efficiency. But it is even more important because power per se is a goal of individuals and firms. Power per se is important philosophically, politically, and socially. Atomistic competition was upheld as a standard by both economists and businessmen long after it was dead. One of its merits was that in it market power was fragmented and unimportant. The industrial economy has accommodated itself—sometimes uneas-

---

[13] John Kenneth Galbraith, *American Capitalism: The Concept of Counter-vailing Power* (2d. ed.; Boston: Houghton Mifflin Co., 1956), p. 25.

[14] *Ibid.* p. 25.

ily—to a nonatomistic type of competition in which economic power and power blocs are dominant. Not all the standards of atomism have been lost. Entry and exit are still reasonably easy in many industries; these are fairly effective safeguards against such abuses of power as fraud, coercion, and monopoly. Those without power—individual workers, independent food stores, local coops, etc.—have frequently found means of identification with power blocs which hopefully represented their particular interests. Balances of power exist in the market as well as in our legislative-executive-judicial system.

Atomism still prevails in agriculture, even though competition in agriculture can be quite different at times from the textbook models (see Chapter 15). But as farmers become increasingly an integral part of the economy, the disparities between "their atomism" and the structure of the rest of the economy becomes increasingly evident. Many farmers have lost their confidence in the uncoordinated production and marketing practiced in atomism and are looking for other market arrangements. At one and the same time, the inroads of vertical integration into agriculture are eliminating parts of its atomistic structure and further shaking farmer confidence. While changing economies of scale are greatly reducing the number of farms, they are not sufficient to eliminate atomistic agriculture within the near future. However, the power pressures from outside agriculture may accomplish what economies of scale cannot. There are a few who predict that the growing interdependency of agriculture and agribusiness will lead to a merging of the two and the eventual disappearance of agriculture.

Atomistic sellers, such as farmers and laborers, have always felt at a disadvantage in dealing with nonatomistic buyers. While labor has gone the group bargaining route, until recently, farmers have mainly emphasized market safeguards. Atomistic sellers supplied with dependable market news and dealing with buyers in open, noncollusive competition had some market power. The postwar breakdown of this system of price making has reduced the confidence of farmers as to the forces affecting prices and the comparability of a given price offer to other alternatives. When many or most market transactions go unrecorded; when the availability of supplies on a given market day can no longer be aggregated (because they are in feedlots or fields, not in public markets); and when many prices are being set by formula based on someone else's prices, then the workings of supply and demand are not readily observable. As individual bargaining replaces impersonal price discovery in the marketplace, farmers begin to seek improvements in the bargaining process rather than in the marketplace.

Interdependence is always an invitation to a contest for advantage. Wherever two or more economic processes are interlocked, there is an open invitation for one to gain some degree of control over one or more of the others. This is the heart of the reason for the great struggles for power that are taking place at various stages in the marketing and distribution of farm products today. The outcome of those struggles, together with the protective measures that may be taken by farmers and the surveillance that may be exercised by government, will do as much as any other single factor to determine the future economic organization of the agriculture of the United States.[15]

The old system of agricultural markets in which farmers were independent agents is beginning to fade away. Prices established in free markets are ceasing to be the instrument of coordination in some areas of our complex production-marketing system. There are several reasons: (1) Product differentiation as reflected in advertising, promotion, and "new" products has overshadowed price in much of manufacturing and retailing. (2) Marketing firms have learned the lesson of "pork versus Post Toasties" (Chapter 13), and almost all are seeking ways to sell their own products rather than selling marketing services. Vertical integration is replacing the vertical coordination of price in many areas. (3) Nonnegotiated or formula pricing is replacing market negotiation. Very large amounts of meat, for example, are traded by formulas on the basis of price quotations in a trade report, the "Yellow Sheet."[16]

The broiler story has been told in many ways (see the brief discussion, Chapter 13). Its complexity permits many views. In one sense the present integrated broiler industry represents a great achievement of American business. The old-fashioned, inefficient, seasonal production of farm chickens was replaced in short order by a modern, efficient, year-round production of broilers. Another view is that farmers, small farm cooperatives, and small marketing firms were decisively beaten by the power of large, conglomerate firms. There is much evidence for the hypothesis that a modern efficient system of producing broilers could have been developed within a more atomistic framework which preserved the market exchange system. Much of the drive for integration was a drive for market power and for a protection of investments in feed mills and processing plants.

Broilers, among the various farm products, are especially well suited to a system of the industrial type. Once such a conversion begins, unless it is halted arbitrarily, it is likely to proceed all the way. Integration carried to its logical conclusion would recast the make-up of agriculture, which would become industrial. It would be attended by contests between the different foci or power. Organizationally an effort would be made to build a partly protected

---

[15] Breimyer, *op. cit.*, p. 96.
[16] These points are made by Harold F. Breimyer in a paper, "Appraising Performance of a Marketing System," given at the Western Extension Marketing Conference, Salt Lake City, September 20, 1966.

market by the brand-naming route, and a series of mergers would probably ensue that would put a few firms in positions of strength. At the worker level the probably outcome would be group action, perhaps through unions. This is typical industrial experience in similar circumstances, and there is no reason to believe the pattern would be different in any part of agriculture that goes the industrial route.[17]

Who is going to control agriculture? Who is going to provide most of the risk capital and make most of the managerial decisions? These serious questions receive many answers as farmers and agribusiness firms strive to analyze the crosscurrents. While marketing firms demonstrated their overwhelming power in the broiler victory, there are some reasons to discount it. After all, the poultry business was largely a penny ante sideline enterprise. However, some big independent farmers were integrated in broilers and later in eggs and turkeys. It would require tremendous quantities of capital to integrate vertically the feeding of livestock. Yet with the continuing migration from the farm and the high average age of farmers, there is a tremendous flow of farmer capital off the farm via migration and inheritance. As demonstrated in broilers, once agribusiness invests large amounts in supplying the agricultural inputs and marketing the output of agriculture, it is quite ready to invest more capital *within the farm fence* to protect its initial investments outside the farm fence and/or to maximize its *total business* profits. As the technical and economic interdependence of farmers and their suppliers and marketing firms increases in an age of chemistry and electronics, can the average farmer be an able decision maker? What kinds of systems of sharing the risk and the management between family farmers and agribusiness are possible? Surely the only alternatives are not traditional family farms in an open-market economy versus an agriculture in which the decisions are made in a few hundred corporate offices and the work is performed by unionized laborers. If there are other alternatives, they must be forged within the complex networks of interdependence of agribusiness and farmers.

The increasing inflexibility of market outlets is another crosscurrent. As already discussed, the increasing price inelasticity at farm level places a heavier burden on farmers to keep markets in balance. The difference between too much and too little food production is very small. National concern can shift from food surpluses to food scarcity in a season—and back again in another season. Agricultural output is largely a function of the employment of agricultural capital. Any industry with a centralized ability to control its total commitment of capital has such power that our society generally requires some social surveillance of it. Thus, intermingled with the question of how power shall be shared

[17] Breimyer, *op. cit.*

among farmers and agribusiness is the question of how much power in what form shall be exercised by society (see Chapters 20 and 21). The National Commission On Food Marketing had these conclusions about this problem:

> The marketing and pricing problems in agriculture differ, sometimes dramatically, from those found in food processing and distribution. Contributing to the difference are the large number of farmers, the lack of product differentiation, the frequent oversupply resulting in part from rising farm productivity, unplanned variations in yields arising from weather and other natural hazards, and the extreme perishability of many products. Farm markets lacking the firming influence of group action are volatile, often depressed, and highly sensitive to downward pressures originating further along in marketing channels. Farmers as independent operators have not been able to coordinate quality improvement programs or to schedule more even flows of products to the extent demanded by today's food industry.

> We believe, therefore, that there is frequent need for group action by farmers to adjust sales more uniformly to market demands at reasonable prices, to improve product quality and uniformity, to negotiate with buyers, and to protect themselves against trade practices and abuses of market power to which they are otherwise vulnerable. We see three approaches by which this might be done.

COOPERATIVES AND BARGAINING ASSOCIATIONS

> The first is through producers' marketing cooperatives and bargaining associations, which already play a prominent part in food marketing. We believe that farmers do not yet fully appreciate the importance of cooperative action in marketing their products. We support all assistance government can reasonably give to producer cooperation.

MARKETING AGREEMENTS AND ORDERS

> The second and often complementary approach is through marketing agreements and order, which have been available for use for certain products for about 30 years.

> *We conclude that Federal marketing agreements and orders should be authorized for any agricultural commodity produced in a local area or regional subdivision of the United States.*

> Since marketing orders and agreements may outlive their usefulness, it follows that they should be periodically reviewed by the Secretary of Agriculture, and we think that the reviews should be made public.

AGRICULTURAL MARKETING BOARDS

> Producers frequently are not able to coordinate sufficiently their individual production efforts, or to negotiate effectively with buyers, by means of cooperatives or under the usual marketing order or agreement.

> *We therefore conclude that a third and new approach is needed. Legislation should be enacted enabling Agricultural Marketing Boards to be brought into being upon vote of producers for the purpose of joining in the sale of products as they first enter into channels of trade.*

By an Agricultural Marketing Board is meant a body having specific powers in group marketing activities in the farm sale of a particular commodity. Such activities should be the immediate charge of an Administrator appointed by and representing the Secretary of Agriculture. Powers that may be exercised under a board include those granted under Federal marketing orders and, in addition, regulating production or marketing and negotiating prices and other terms of trades. The board should also be empowered to engage in other activities necessary to accomplish these purposes.

While the main purpose of our proposal is to strengthen the bargaining position of farmers, we also see opportunities to increase efficiency in the marketing of farm products. Group action by producers permits advance planning of production, greater assurance for both farmers and buyers that enough but not too much product will be available, lower procurement costs for buyers, more control of quality and shipping schedules, and, in general, less disorganized marketing than now commonly exists.

To insure that the powers granted to a board are not misused, the body's membership should include representatives of handlers and the public as well as producers, and all policies should be subject to the approval of the Secretary of Agriculture. Criteria for boards should preclude their use by any group other than all growers of a product over a substantial producing area. Provision should be made for periodic public review of each board's purpose and operations.

PROTECTION OF THE RIGHT TO ORGANIZE

Special efforts appear necessary to protect the right of farmers to organize bargaining associations, to approve marketing orders, and to engage in other group efforts.

We believe that specific legislation should be enacted providing that all processors, shippers, and buyers of farm products, engaging in or affecting interstate trade, are prohibited from obstructing the formation or operation of a producers' bargaining association or cooperative, and from influencing producers' understanding of or voting on marketing orders or similar programs, by disseminating false or misleading information, discriminating among producers in any manner, boycotts, or other deceptive or coercive methods.

The enforcement of this statute should be assigned to the agency responsible for regulation of trade in perishable farm foods.

We expect that the foregoing proposals to strengthen the position of producers will have most application to the more specialized branches of agriculture, e.g., fruits and vegetables, poultry, and fluid milk production for local markets. Problems faced in types of production widely distributed over the Nation and engaged in by scores of thousands of producers must be approached mainly by other means.[18]

There is currently before Congress a bill to prevent the use of unfair practices by buyers and processors against growers belonging to

---

[18] National Commission on Food Marketing, *Food from Farmer to Consumer* (Washington, D.C.: U.S. Government Printing Office, 1966), pp. 110–11.

voluntary bargaining associations. The American Farm Bureau Federation general counsel testified in favor of the bill in 1966 and asked that it be broadened to include "threats as well as actual discriminations." He cited examples of alleged discrimination by tomato processors.[19] Although farmers and marketing firms must live together, we can rest assured that they often will not like it.

[19] "Official News Letter of American Farm Bureau Federation," July 25, 1966.

Chapter 17

GRADING AND QUALITY

STANDARDIZATION

BY GOVERNMENT

Buy a U.S. No. 1 apple at the supermarket and you dare to eat it blindfolded without fear of surprising a sleeping worm. Go to most supermarkets and you can buy butter or eggs or beef or poultry which carry federal grades. Aside from a possible fleeting thought that it must take many federal employees to mark all those graded products, you, as a young economist, have probably never given grades another thought. Grading seems too routine to be interesting and too technical to have much interest to economists. Grade standards are often associated with other standards such as official weights and measures. What honest trader could be against a standard size of a bushel?

On the contrary, grading involves many economic problems. Moreover it involves conflicts which sometimes can be settled only in the political arena. While some struggles concern very specific issues about the nature of a grade or grade boundary, there are struggles involving the very existence of grades and grading.

Two objectives are uppermost in this chapter. One is to examine carefully some theoretical fundamentals concerning the economics of grading. The other is to examine some practical problems and controversies in the grading of agricultural products in the present U.S. economy. There exist U.S. Standards for about 300 fresh, canned, dried, or frozen agricultural products, running the gamut from cotton to turpentine to fruits and nuts. Such widespread usage of grades is a powerful argument for their usefulness in our marketing system. As consumers, we often do not realize the extent of grading because many graded products do not carry grade labels at retail. Beef, lamb, butter, poultry, and eggs are the chief products carrying grade labels. Grades on many more foods are often utilized by agricultural marketing firms from processors to retailers.

Most fresh fruit and vegetables are packed and sold on the wholesale market on the basis of U.S. grades. There are standards for 72 different kinds. Thirteen "consumer standards" have been developed for use at the retail level but are seldom used.

The typical range of grades used at wholesale for fresh fruit and vegetables includes U.S. Fancy, U.S. No. 1, U.S. No. 2. . . .

Grades for fresh fruit and vegetables are determined on the basis of the product's color, size, shape, degree of maturity, and freedom from defects. Defects may be those caused by dirt, freezing, disease, insects, or mechanical injury. . . .

Only a limited amount of processed fruits and vegetables and related products are marked with the U.S. grade shield, which means that a Government grader has examined the product and certified that it is the quality stated.

Hundreds of processors, however, employ the grade standards in packing and selling processed fruit and vegetables. They may use the grade name, without the "U.S." in front of it, on their labels, even though the product has not been examined by a Government grader, as long as the quality actually is as good as indicated by the grade name.

If the quality does not measure up to the grade claimed, the processor is liable to prosecution under laws on mislabeling.[1]

Grading should not be confused with inspections of foods and food-handling facilities for sanitary and health requirements. Federal inspection is required in processing plants that ship in interstate commerce. Many state and local governments require inspection. Many products bear a label certifying such an inspection for wholesomeness.

Sorting and allocation to match specific supplies and demands are two of the largest tasks performed by agricultural marketing firms (see Chapter 13). There are many kinds of sorts. A restaurant buyer may want not just green beans but rather a certain variety and a certain sieve count in a certain size can. Grading is only one of several processes which indicate gradations in the marketplace. Apples are purchased by variety—Jonathan, Delicious, etc.—as well as by grade. As another example, distinctions are made between juice oranges and fresh market oranges. One variety of potatoes is superior to another for baking. Certain beef cuts are not suitable for broiling regardless of their grade. Somehow the marketing system must sort these various "gradations" so that supply and demand may be matched.

Grading may be defined as the sorting of a product into quality classifications by a disinterested third party.[2] But now "quality" needs to be defined. A horticulturalist and an economist would not be likely to define the quality of tomatoes in precisely the same terms because of their differing fields of interest. While agricultural economists are not unanimous in their definitions of quality, their definitions are oriented to the marketplace. Many agricultural economists would accept this *definition:* quality is the sum of the attributes of a product which influence its acceptability to many buyers, and, hence, the price they are willing to pay for it.

[1] U.S. Department of Agriculture, *Consumers All, the Yearbook of Agriculture 1965* (Washington, D.C.: U.S. Government Printing Office, 1965), p. 426.

[2] Grading is sometimes defined as the sorting of a product into quality classifications regardless of who sorts it. However a more restrictive definition is considered more practicable. Private sorting is discussed later in the chapter.

Grading is then the subdivision of a product such as tomatoes or wheat into classes which vary in acceptability to a significant group of buyers. Grades are useless unless they reflect differences in demand. Whether and how much these grade subdivisions are different in market price depends upon relative supply and demand. It will be shown later that certain market price situations depend upon certain preference and cost relationships.

THE BASIC MARKETING PROBLEM OF MATCHING SUPPLY TO DEMAND AND "SIMPLE SOLUTIONS"

Assume that there are varying qualities of a product being produced and being demanded. Then the task of the marketing system is one of matching supply to demand. One might imagine a system by which every unit of product—say tomatoes—is inspected by every buyer (housewife) in order to obtain the best possible matching of qualities produced with qualities demanded. But such a system is not even physically possible, and it would be fantastically expensive.

The market system has some shortcuts. Grading is one of these shortcuts. Assume that fresh tomatoes are subdivided into three grades. The market system can give each housewife her opportunity for choice by providing her these three grades rather than the infinite variety of all fresh tomatoes in the market system. In this case, has the market system greatly curtailed the buyer's choices in order to provide an economical workable scheme? Not necessarily. While it is probably true that no two tomatoes are biologically identical, it is entirely possible that all tomatoes in a grade are identical as far as the housewife is concerned. That is, the differences existing between the tomatoes in the grade are either (1) not differences in quality or (2) are quality differences too small to concern the buyer. Both cases are possible and both exist in reality. Recall our definition of quality as the sum of the attributes of a product which influence its acceptability to many buyers. It logically follows that minute differences in attributes which do not influence acceptability are not "quality differences" in any meaningful economic sense. We can state the nature of grading symbolically by saying that tomatoes have characteristics a through k and each of these varies from 1 to n:

$$a_1 a_2 a_3 a_4 \ldots a_n$$
$$b_1 b_2 b_3 b_4 \ldots b_n$$
$$\cdot$$
$$\cdot$$
$$\cdot$$
$$k_1 k_2 k_3 k_4 \ldots k_n$$

Grades are assigned according to the product variations important to consumers. Perhaps grade A is defined to include tomatoes with these characteristics: a_1, b_1 or b_2, c_m and c_n, d_2 to d_4, ..., and k_1.

Assume that the demand for tomatoes "differs" among housewives. Assume that the marketing firms or producers ascertain the criteria—the characteristics of tomatoes—by which consumers make their choices. Assume also that grades are then described according to the same criteria. Assume further that tomato production can *or* cannot be altered to affect the distribution of tomatoes with various quality attribute. Assume that the supply and demand factors balance out so that producers not only *can* produce all qualities demanded but also will find it profitable to do so. At any one of these points, the reader might well say, let's *don't* make that assumption until you show me why it makes sense. And if the reader is persistent he will find some instances in which the assumptions are unrealistic. In the process, he will prove to himself that some complicated economic conditions are involved in efficient, working grades. Among the crucial assumptions of this paragraph were these: The demand "differs," and the supply can or cannot be "altered" in line with those differences. These assumptions need to be examined in detail.

Homogeneous Demand

Demand for a product is *defined* as "homogeneous" when buyers agree as to ordinal variations in quality, although they may or may not entirely agree as to the relative prices they are willing to pay for these qualities. For example, all buyers agree that group I of tomatoes is superior to group II; some buyers would pay 5 cents a pound more for I than II while other buyers would pay 10 cents a pound more. This definition and example seems so commonplace that somebody is certain to suggest that all demands are "homogeneous." Not so. Demand for a product is *defined* as "heterogeneous" when buyers do not agree as to quality variations. For example, some buyers agree that group I of tomatoes is superior to group II while other buyers just as stoutly agree that group II is superior to group I. In terms of our model, all buyers might agree that characteristic a_1 is better than a_n and b_1 is better than b_n, but some buyers argue that c_1 is better than c_n, while other buyers find c_n to be more desirable than c_1. This disparity of views may stem from different uses of tomatoes, but it may also stem from differing attitudes for an identical use.

Thus, there are two ways in which demands may "differ": they may differ as to relative prices they will pay for qualities agreed to be good, better, and best; or they may differ as to which is better or worse. If demands of different consumers differ only with respect to relative prices, these demands are defined as "homogeneous."

The Alteration of Supply

The biological variation inherent in the production of most agricultural products has long been accepted as one of their more important characteristics. Even long after man learned how to guide and restrict this biological variation by control of breeding and of certain phases of environment, economists have often continued to accept natural variability as given and unalterable. Grading has been regarded as selection from within natural variation.

The second point I wish you to accept is that grading applies chiefly to *products of nature in essentially their natural state.* This is true because natural products are not subject to precise control of man; and because they vary in a continuous sequence that has no automatic cut-off points. Consider for example the thickness of wool fiber, or the freshness of eggs, or the tenderness of beef. For all three, if we examine thousands of samples we will find a continuous gradation from one extreme to the other. The wood of the chairs on which you are sitting similarly varies as to strength and freedom from imperfections. But any screws in those chairs are manufactured by design according to specified lengths such as ¾ inch or 1 inch or 1¼ inch. Grading is selection by arbitrary cut-off lines within a continuous range of natural product. It is sharply in contrast with manufacture of industrial products by specification.[3]

Perhaps for some products the supply of varying qualities is unalterable. More realistically, certain product characteristics may be unalterable over a short period of a crop season or even a decade. Likewise, it may be so expensive to alter certain product characteristics that they are unalterable in practice. Perhaps all variations from a_2 to a_n of characteristic a of tomatoes occur in nature, and there is no feasible way of controlling the distribution of tomatoes having a_1 or a_2 or a_n. On the other hand, through breeding or production practices, the proportion of tomatoes having any variation of characteristic b, such as b_2, can be varied feasibly from 90 percent of the crop to 10 percent. It is true that in the American agriculture of the 1960's, the supply of particular qualities of many products can be altered. The practical implication is that the way a product is sorted this year can affect the nature of next year's production. The economics of these effects will be discussed later.

Homogeneous Demand and Unalterable Supply

This situation seems to be the one assumed by several writers of the 1920's and 1930's. Quality has a single dimension in the sense that all buyers agree as to which is good, better, and best. Therefore, rank-

---

[3] Harold F. Breimyer, "The Purpose of Grading," Mimeo of speech to Inter-Industry Beef Grading Conference, Kansas City, Missouri, November 14, 1960. (Italics added.)

ordered grade names are useful guides. Some buyers are very anxious to obtain the "best" while others will settle for the "good" if it is a bit cheaper. The market system through a process of sorting and labeling (grading), pricing, and marketing ensures that the best product goes to those buyers who will pay the most for it—and presumably receive the most satisfaction from obtaining it—while the merely good product goes to more price-conscious buyers.

An accurate system of grading in such a situation improves marketing and pricing efficiency over a marketing system lacking such grades. Agricultural economists have traditionally been enthusiastic about such a grading system and quite rightly so. However, if supply can be altered, then consumer satisfaction—and perhaps producer returns—can be improved still further. Cases in which consumer satisfaction cannot be improved by supply alteration must be very rare.

Homogeneous Demand and Alterable Supply

In our previous case, the buyers of "good" quality passed up the "best" quality because of its scarcity and expense. If supply can be altered to make good quality better, are such buyers then better off? Yes, if the quality improvement costs less than it is worth to these buyers. Grading in this situation is a problem of product(s) design. It is no longer a simple problem of sorting what we have because we can control what we have.

Many examples can be cited which seem to fit partially into these assumed conditions. The demands as to purity of fresh milk and the freshness of eggs seem both to be homogeneous demands. Moreover within the production and marketing systems the qualities supplied of these two product characteristics are alterable in an economic context. Considerable alteration in both these products and their grades has occurred in the past few decades.

Heterogeneous Demand and Unalterable Supply

Heterogeneous demand was defined above as the situation in which two or more groups of buyers disagree as to which of two quite different products is the better. "Quality" has a completely different meaning in this case since one group measures it in a different sense than another. To assign rank-ordered grade names is to be arbitrary and to increase confusion. Such grade names would be roughly comparable to telling dedicated Chevrolet owners that Chevies are in a grade second to Fords. In contrast with the cases of homogeneous demand, there can be no meaningful correlation of price and quality because there is no consensus as to "quality."

Grading, however, does have a useful place. Even though there are varying opinions as to quality differences, these quality differences can be sorted into grades. Rank-ordered grade names and descriptions should be studiously avoided. Since the qualities cannot be altered, some demands may not be particularly well satisfied. However, the sorting process aids in matching available qualities with the demanders.

Heterogeneous Demand and Alterable Supply

This situation appears much more realistic than the previous one. Examples might be pink and white grapefruit or dark and light egg yolks.

Perhaps another example of the heterogeneous demand is found in the demands of millers for particular kinds of wheat for different uses such as for bread or macaroni. Filter-tip cigarettes are said to require different tobacco qualities than regular cigarettes. Aside from grade names, the grading principles are very similar to the case of alterable supplies and homogeneous demands. Supplies can be matched quite well with the different demands because of the possibility of altering supplies. In a sense, farmers will now produce what they can sell rather than trying to sell what they have produced. The economics of the give and take necessary to accommodate relative supplies to relative demands will be discussed later.

SUPPORTERS OF GRADING AND THEIR OBJECTIVES

Grading is defined in this chapter as impartial sorting by a disinterested third party. That third party is usually the federal government, although it is sometimes a state government, a municipality, or even a trade association. To organize grades and obtain governmental grading obviously requires a considerable effort. It is worth asking who is willing to exercise such efforts and what are their motives.

The main supporters of grading tend to fall into these groups:

1. Traders, including processors, retailers, and others who buy for resale;
2. Farmers and their friends in government; and
3. Consumers and their friends in government.

Grading Objectives of Traders

The Chicago Board of Trade set up a third-party inspection and grading of grain in 1858. Exchange inspection was superseded by state inspection in most important markets during the next half century.[4] Finally, federal grades for wheat were set up in 1917.[5]

[4] Bruce Price, "Private Exchange and State Grain Inspection," *Marketing Grain* (Chicago: The American Institute of Chicago, 1922), pp. 16–19.

[5] U.S. Department of Agriculture, *Grain Grading Primer,* USDA Miscellaneous Publication No. 325.

Liverpool traders first used cotton grades about 1800.[6] Various industry standards for cotton were attempted in the United States during the 19th century. Congress appropriated funds in 1909 for establishing federal grades of cotton. An international conference at Washington, D.C., in 1923 adopted "universal standards" for cotton.[7]

These thumbnail histories of the evolution of grading of two important commodities indicate:

1. That traders recognized the need for grades almost as soon as large-scale markets developed, and
2. That some industry standards were finally replaced by federal standards and graders.

Whenever trading is in a large market—and particularly in a national network of markets—then meaningful dissemination of market news is naturally demanded by traders. Whenever there is price variation associated with product variation in such a market, then grading is essential to the dissemination of market news. Grades have other uses in such markets. Grade specifications are essential in contracts including those used in futures trading in organized commodity exchanges. Trading may be conducted without time-consuming and expensive inspection by the traders as grades are relied on to indicate quality. Financing is facilitated. Buyers and/or sellers find that their market contacts are broadened whenever grades become acceptable substitutes to personal inspection.

At a later date, retailers found that grades could be of assistance in establishing consumer confidence in their merchandise. The Hotel, Restaurant and Institutional trade became strong supporters of grades. Within the retail and Hotel, Restaurant and Institutional trade, there appears to be a strong need for a government stamp of approval. How better can an employee answer the quality complaints of a customer than to point to the government stamp? How better can chain-store top management ensure that its many employees are maintaining meat quality than to require purchase by government grade? How better can a purchasing agent lessen his responsibility for quality than to purchase by government grade. For example, a leading supplier of meats to ships testified concerning lamb and mutton: "We buy and sell strictly on USDA grade. These vessels, especially tankers, take on meat and meat products for sometimes as long as a year. They require a product that

---

[6] U.S. Department of Agriculture, *The Classification and Grading of Cotton*, USDA Farmers Bulletin No. 591, p. 1.

[7] U.S. Department of Agriculture, *The Commercial Classification of American Cotton*, USDA Department Circular No. 278, pp. 7 and 8.

they can prove has quality in order to answer any complaints which might arise from the crew."[8]

In an employee society, the official stamp of approval on a product may allay many a suspicion and silence many a complaint that employees would otherwise find difficult to handle because they are employees.

Grading Objectives of Farmers and Their Representatives

Farmers shared the interest of traders in grades as an indispensable part of market news. The early efforts in farmers' behalf by the USDA seemed to be mainly concerned with grades as an aid to market news. However, additional objectives developed in the 1920's. The USDA economists saw grading as essential to pricing efficiency and as a means of reducing waste, confusion, and even occasional chicanery in a marketing system which they regarded with some suspicion.

Another quite different objective for grading has been held by various groups of farmers at varying times during the entire history of American agriculture. This objective is the use of government stamp of quality as an aid in promoting sale of an agricultural product. In early American history, governmental inspections for minimum quality were mainly on export goods.[9] These minimum quality standards may be considered to have been the predecessors of the use of conventional grades to promote the sale of higher quality products.

The organization of a Better Beef Association to obtain grade marking of beef is one of the most interesting chapters in the story of farmer support of grading. Agriculture was depressed in the 1920's. The cattle industry and particularly the demand for purebread cattle was especially depressed in the 1924–26 period. Alvin Sanders, editor of the influential *Breeder's Gazette,* led a campaign to solve the situation by promoting the increased sale of beef produced from well-fed and well-bred cattle.

Sanders' primary motivation appears many times in his editorials. He wished to promote an increased demand for well-bred and well-fed beef which would increase the derived demand for purebred beef cattle. Thus, he was able to relate his campaign very directly to the economic and sentimental interests of many of his readers and associates.

Sanders' central argument rarely varied from the following: many consumers—the more well-to-do ones, especially—would buy better quality beef if they knew how to get it. But many eating places and retailers . . . sell very poor quality meat instead. The argument varied over time in the color with which it was enunciated and the remedies suggested.

[8] *Suspension of Federal Grading of Lamb and Mutton* (Hearing, House Committee on Agriculture, 86th Cong., 2d sess., Serial MM, January 11–14, 1960), p. 162.
[9] Elmer R. Kiehl and V. James Rhodes, *Historical Development of Beef Quality and Grading Standards,* Missouri Agricultural Experiment Station Research Bulletin, 728, February, 1960.

By mid-1925, Editor Sanders began to suggest that the government might be able to work out some system of "tagging meat" for what it was. He reported that Dr. Mohler, Chief of the Bureau of Animal Industry, enthusiastically agreed with the tagging idea. Sanders suggested that letters of interested readers would be sympathetically received by Jardine, Secretary of Agriculture. The purposes of the "tags" were to simplify buyer education and—much more important—to discourage the unscrupulous retailer from selling cheap beef as expensive beef.[10]

This campaign of Sanders and other farm leaders eventually resulted in a national organization called the Better Beef Association. The Association worked with packers, retailers, and the USDA and swiftly secured the federal grade marking of the top two grades of carcass beef when such marking was requested by industry. This grading system was the beginning of the present system of federal beef grading.

This entire episode bears special mention for two reasons. First, the promotion of particular qualities of a farm product was a different grading objective than usually supported by producers. Second, this promotional campaign led to the *marking of grades* on the product so that consumers would see and be influenced by the grades. Grades were extended from the central market, in which they were strictly a descriptive device, to the consumer level; this extension was promoted by certain groups of producers in the hopes of benefiting themselves. We have already discussed how grades can influence the *qualities supplied;* these producers conceived of grades influencing the *qualities demanded.*

Grading Objectives of Consumers and Their Representatives

Consumers have not generally been a powerful force in the obtaining of grades, although their support of existing grades sometimes has been important in preserving them. While there has been interest in grades among consumers for a long time, they generally lacked the organized unity essential to successful promotion of grades. Moreover, consumers were faced in many cases with "consumer grades" already established through producer and governmental efforts. These grades were designed to have some relation to consumer acceptability because such a relationship was essential to the aims of the grading supporters. However, consumer representatives have sometimes argued that such grades and brands did not provide sufficient information for informed shopping.

A very considerable effort to obtain compulsory grade labeling of many foods was made by the Consumers Advisory Board of the National Recovery Administration (NRA) in 1933–34 and by the Office of Price Administration in 1943–44, but both attempts failed. While both attempts to obtain compulsory labeling of grades were related to price-fixing

[10] *Ibid.*, pp. 26–28.

programs of governmental agencies, there was support by consumer organizations interested in the benefits to them of grade labels. The National Canners Association led the fight against compulsory grade labels in both instances.[11]

FEDERAL GRADING VERSUS INDUSTRY GRADING VERSUS PRIVATE SORTING

As Alderson points out so clearly, "sorting out" is one of the necessary tasks by which a marketing system efficiently matches supply and demand for various products and qualities (see Chapter 13, Competition among Agricultural Marketing Firms). This sorting function may be performed by employees of the seller or of the buyer or by a disinterested third party. Sorting by a third party is defined in this book as "grading."

Private sorting has some obvious limitations. The man who sorts his own product obviously has a different attitude than he would possess when sorting someone else's product. Some say the situation would be akin to allowing college students to assign their own coursework grades! While private sorting is hardly likely to serve as a satisfactory basis for one-time deals between strangers, it might be adequate for continuing business relationships between regular accounts. An industry in which a few sellers sell the preponderance of industry output to a few buyers has far less need for grading than an industry of thousands of participants selling and buying in widely separated public markets.

If packers A, B, and C sell mainly to retailers X, Y, Z, then their communication problems about quality can be worked out readily. Moreover their prospects of a long continuing relationship is a powerful incentive for good faith and understanding in handling specific disagreements about qualities bought and sold.

For many agricultural products the evolution has been from private sorting to grading under some sort of industry sponsorship to federal grading. Why has grading under public market or industry sponsorship not been more successful? The question appears never to have been carefully studied. One hypothesis is that the sheer size of the American market made it particularly difficult to achieve national standardization. There are other possible causes. Federal grade marking of consumer products may be supposed to be viewed by consumers with more confidence than industry grading. Certainly, those consumer interests who supported compulsory grade labeling also supported federal rather than industry grading. In a number of industries, opinions about the utility of

---

[11] Jessie V. Coles, "Compulsory Grade Labeling," *Marketing, The Yearbook of Agriculture, 1954* (Washington, D.C.: U.S. Government Printing Office), pp. 164–69.

grading have probably been too divided to permit industry-sponsored grading.

Most federal grades are permissive—their use in private trading is not required. However, grains and cotton in interstate commerce and/or traded on the futures exchanges must be graded according to federal standards. States and even occasionally cities may require the use of state or federal grades for certain products. Seattle, for example, has long required the grade labeling of fresh beef by federal standards.

PROBLEMS OF GRADING

Confusion of Ends and Means

Products are graded on the basis of attribute variations which are related to quality as perceived by buyers. Unfortunately, there is sometimes confusion between means and ends which freezes grades in obsolete patterns. Long after research has shown the absence of any relationship of an attribute to buyer-perceived quality, that attribute may remain in the grading standards because it is "right." Grading requires expertise. The experts sometimes come to believe in an expert standard. They argue that a decent standard cannot be based on the average of uninformed opinions of consumers. Standards should be set up "right" whether most people recognize what's "right" or not, these experts say. The economist replies that there must be expert interpretation of market demands rather than personal standards of experts. If market grades are to aid communication, they must deal with market realities rather than with value judgments of experts.

Some experts believe in a Gresham's law of quality deterioration. They argue that competition would deteriorate quality in a free market without grading. Certainly quality as well as price is sometimes varied in competitive battles. But there seems to be no general tendency for quality to deteriorate in the many industries in our economy selling ungraded products.

Obtaining and Maintaining Accuracy

Grading often involves several criteria which are not readily measurable. Subjective judgments and even subjective weightings of several judgments are often required. Such a situation provides some of the most pressing problems faced by a grading service in training and supervising a staff of graders. The grader is somewhat in a position of a first base umpire calling a very close play, except that the grader may call hundreds of such close decisions per week. To escape the problems of subjectivity, measurements are made objectively whenever possible. Chemical or mechanical tests are sometimes possible for measuring some aspect of flavor or texture or tenderness. The arguments for an impartial third party doing the grading are obviously related closely to the amount of subjectivity involved in applying the grade standards.

Another problem is presented by the perishability of many foods. A product that was grade A on Monday may be grade B on Thursday and inedible on Saturday. The problem is less as products move faster through the marketing system, but it still exists and there is no easy answer.

A more fundamental problem of accuracy is that the predictive relationships of grades to buyer-perceived quality may be very poor— either because research has been unable to discover better relationships or because the research findings are not incorporated into the grading standards. Most grades are probably quite accurate, but it is important to note explicitly that any generalizations about the usefulness or effects of grades depends upon the tacit assumption of an accurate relationship between grades and actual qualities. The development of such relationships depends upon a careful interpretation of market demands in terms of grade criteria. The account at the end of this chapter of the lamb grading controversy illustrates the difficulties.

Differing Grade Requirements at Various Market Levels

Grades are useful insofar as they have meaning to buyers and sellers. But buyers at one market level may be interested in somewhat different product qualities than those buyers at the next higher level. For example, packer buyers are quite interested in dressing percentage because it affects considerably the live value of fed cattle. Retail buyers have no interest in dressing percentage, since it isn't relevant to carcasses, but they are interested in the yield of saleable retail cuts. Retail customers have no interest in either retail yield or dressing percentage, but they are very intersted in the eating qualities of the steaks and roasts. Do grade standards change from stage to stage of the market to reflect these changing interests? Or do the standards measure only those qualities that are of common interest at every stage? It is obvious, is it not, that eating qualities *must be* important to retail and packer buyers *because* they are important to the terminal buyer—the consumer in this case. Therefore, those factors important to buyers at any stage should be carried from the producer to that stage.

Presently, there is little or no trading in live cattle on the basis of grades. For a long time, the same grades were used from packer cooler to retail counter and the factor of retail yield of saleable cuts was omitted from grading, although its inclusion had been long debated. There are some very persuasive arguments for including retail yield in grades up to the retailer but not to the consumer level. Grades can be made multidimensional, and a particular dimension such as yield of retail cuts can be used up to retail and dropped at consumer level.

Agricultural economists generally have emphasized the importance of grades running the entire gamut of the marketing sequence. Their emphasis stems from their interest in economic efficiency and in equity. If a farmer produces a more valuable beef he "ought" to be paid for it. Even if this ethical principle does not impress you, the efficiency argument may. Farmers are very likely to produce more of that quality for which they are better paid and less of that quality that is unprofitable. Therefore, if there is to be an efficient matching of relative supplies produced with relative demands, the pricing system must accurately reflect values. Here we arrive at the final phase of the argument. To the extent that grades running through all levels promote such pricing efficiency, they become an essential aid to economic efficiency. It is probably true that the effectiveness with which such grades do promote pricing efficiency is related to the length of the marketing chain, the number of market participants, and the extent of use of private specifications. In those still relatively few markets in which there are only a few buyers and sellers, private specifications may be a very adequate means of communication, and grades may be little used. Thus, the usefulness of grades is related to market structure and also to the degree of vertical integration.

Grade Boundaries and Names and Product Design

Sellers desire the highest possible grade to be assigned to their product. Since not all sellers sell precisely the same qualities, any system of grade names and boundaries will be more acceptable to some sellers than to others. It is likely that sellers overestimate the importance of these grading factors. Economists have often pointed to the uselessness of renaming A grade as AA in the hopes of thereby increasing market returns. But, it is entirely possible that Mr. Brown's net returns are affected by the setting of a grade boundary that determines whether his cauliflower, or eggs, fall in the top of the B grade or the bottom of the A grade. In any case, many producers and traders *believe* that grade boundaries and names can be altered to their relative advantage or disadvantage. Consequently, among the facts of life of many grading services are the industry pressures to change this grade boundary or that grade name. Moreover, such pressures often obtain results. Grading is generally voluntary, and the very existence of the grading services depends upon the maintenance of grades that are acceptable to the industry power structure (or a sufficient part of it). To respond adequately to these opposing pressures and yet to maintain standards which are of service and benefit to the industry and to the economy may take the same high order of statesmanship expected of our elected representatives.

Interference with Merchandising and Product Differentiation

Product differentiation is a widespread fact of life in much of the American industrial economy, as indicated in previous chapters. Sellers lessen price competition and find a "niche" for themselves in the competitive structure by convincing buyers of certain characteristics, or qualities, special to their products. Processors of many agricultural products have attempted a similar type of differentiation—with varying degrees of success.

Larger agricultural processors with established brands (or hopes of establishing them) quite often oppose federal grading. The federal grades may reduce the effectiveness of the brands, reduce product differentiation, and increase price competition. Small processors, without any hopes of establishing effective brands (outside of a tiny local market), may find that grades open up a national market in which they can compete effectively on a price basis with larger processors. Therefore, small firms may support federal grading.

Consequently, federal grading services have sometimes found themselves caught in intraindustry struggles over the effects of grades on relative market power and advantage. Economists, who generally have a strong prejudice toward more competitors and more price competition, have not ordinarily been very sympathetic with the protests of these larger firms. They have argued that some damage to the interests of these firms may not be too great a price to pay for the benefits gained from grades. Williams and associates have stated forcefully their belief as to the effects of federal beef grading upon competition and pricing efficiency:

THE INFLUENCE OF FEDERAL GRADING ON COMPETITION AMONG PACKERS AND EFFECTS ON PRICING EFFICIENCY

It is generally believed that the shift of an industry in the direction of more widespread, free, and intensive competition on a price basis will contribute to an improvement in pricing efficiency. More free and intensive price competition contributes to an increase in the accuracy, ease, freedom, effectiveness, and speed by which prices are established in the market. Competition, in turn, tends to become more free and intensive as (1) the firms in the market increase in number, (2) the largest firms decrease in volume to the point that no one of them exercises any dominant influence on product prices, (3) knowledge throughout the industry increases and equalizes in point of time and space, and (4) prices become clearly identifiable according to homogeneous grade or quality groupings. The impact of changes in any one of these factors may not be sufficiently large to have any observable effect on pricing efficiency. In combination, however, they are likely to produce a marked effect.

It was pointed out that partly as a result of the introduction and increased use of Federal grades for beef (and lamb), independent packers and wholesalers have increased in number; concentration in the meat-packing industry has declined; and knowledge of factors affecting prices has increased and become more nearly equal among buyers and sellers. All these have tended to increase competition in the beef trade and to improve the efficiency of prices in allocating supplies of beef among competing uses.

Another important factor, related closely to factors already mentioned, which has tended to increase the degree of competition among packers has been the elimination of variable quality as a factor in the bargaining process. The Federal grade standards made it possible to clearly identify prices by grade and weight groups. They tend to reduce the extent of either willful or involuntary misrepresentation of beef in order to sell it at prices higher or lower than justified by market conditions and consumer demand. Standardization of the quality variable, it is clear, has contributed to an improvement in pricing efficiency at the packer and wholesaler levels.[12]

On the other side is a Swift and Company economist who asks "whether there exists in principle a justification for the Department of Agriculture to deliberately foster the competitive advantages of one segment of the lamb slaughtering industry against another, by deliberately building a merchandising symbol for those who find it difficult to build one for themselves, under the guise of a grading service."[13]

SOME FURTHER THEORETICAL CONSIDERATIONS

Competitive Relationships among Grades

Grades compete among themselves in the marketplace in much the same fashion as other products. It should be no surprise that certain grades become "empty boxes" over time because of adverse changes in their competitive advantage. Certain generalizations can be made about these competitive relationships and about the economic conditions contributing to more or less stability of the grade-price structure.

Homogeneous Demand.[14]   When demand is homogeneous, relative prices are a very important determinant of the choices among grades made by many consumers. Consumers, by the definition of this demand situation, are agreed on the direction of quality—i.e., on the ordinal relation of the various grades.

Market price must be correlated with quality in the sense illustrated in Figure 17–1. Assume any other type of price-quality relationship and you will see that it cannot long endure in the marketplace. Suppose, for example, that grade C is priced the same as grade B. Since all consumers agree that B is superior to C, there is no longer any reason to buy C, and its plummeting sales remove it from the market. Or suppose that the quality gap widens greatly between grade A and other grades without any corresponding widening of the price gap. Then grade A may capture most of the market and some of the "lower" grades may be dropped for

[12] Willard F. Williams, Earl K. Bowen, and Frank C. Genovese, *Economic Effects of U.S. Grades for Beef,* USDA Marketing Research Report No. 298, 1959.
[13] Roland Welborn, "Discussion: Economic Effects of Recent Changes in Lamb Standards," *Journal of Farm Economics,* December, 1961, p. 1398.
[14] Cf. Abbott's discussion of vertical and horizontal quality competition. Lawrence Abbott, *Quality and Competition* (New York: University Press, 1955).

lack of sales. Suppose that grades A and B are really identical in eating quality but that the A units cost more to produce and are a little different in appearance. Is it possible that the difference in appearance, the higher price, and the higher grade will combine to convince a sufficient number of consumers that grade A is of higher quality than B so that A will long survive? Quality is what buyers think it is. Thus, within reasonable limits, the assignment of a grade to a product can influence preference for it.[15] Many retail chains have spent much money advertising the high U.S. grade of their beef.

FIGURE 17–1

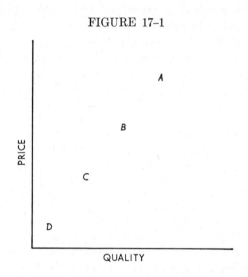

What are the economic forces which would permit the delicate price-quality equilibrium of several grades in the marketplace? One's first thought might be the unalterable supply situation. If several qualities are produced, like so many joint products, then market price will adjust to quality differentials so that all units of all grades clear the market. The only possible exception would be units at the bottom of the quality scale that were so poorly accepted that their market price would not cover their marketing cost (or that were removed by industry action to avoid spoiling the market). Since the supplies of many products are alterable only over a considerable time period, this aspect of the supply function does give considerable stability to price-grade relationships.

Can a multigrade equilibrium also persist in the case of alterable supplies (after sufficient time has elapsed for supplies to alter)? Yes, but it need not. In any economy that is reasonably competitive, relative retail

[15] V. James Rhodes, "Acceptance and Yield of Choice and Good Beef: Research Results and Implications," *Journal of Farm Economics,* May, 1961, pp. 181–96.

prices of grades may be assumed to be closely related to the relative combined costs of production and marketing. Therefore, the equilibrium can persist as long as relative costs (and hence retail prices) stay in line with consumers' relative valuation of the grades. The equilibrium is endangered by any change in cost of production or of marketing or in relative preferences. In a number of agricultural products, new technologies of production and marketing have made the maintenance of first quality little more costly than the maintenance of second or third quality. Consequently, the inferior qualities have largely disappeared from the market. In some other cases, consumer sentiment has moved toward the top grade—e.g., grade A fresh milk—and eliminated the inferior grades. Likewise grade A milk is gradually pushing out grade C in manufactured milk products and someday will eliminate grade C entirely. McCallister observed in 1951 that there was a trend in fruits and vegetable grading toward fewer grades and an increased proportion of output in the higher grades.[16]

The alterable supply–homogeneous demand situation seems to be a rather common one. In an economy such as ours with many changes in technology, rising consumer incomes, and some changes in consumers' preferences, market relationships of grades may be expected to be rather dynamic. The grading service which elects to fight to maintain the same 3 or 4 "working grades" and grade boundaries that were set up 30 or 40 years ago may find itself fighting against overwhelming economic forces.

It may be relevant to note that the modern supermarket is willing to stock thousands of "different" items but rarely is willing to stock two or more grades of an agricultural product. Moreover, it often does not stock two or more qualities of many processed and packaged items, although it may stock several brands of similar price. This attitude of mass merchandisers—stemming from inventory and shelf-space problems and from a desire to promote and merchandise a single top-quality image—exerts pressure toward one wide, working grade at retail. Perhaps, there is still "room" in the economy for one small grade of higher quality for the restaurant trade and one small, bottom-quality grade for especially low-income retail or other outlets.

Heterogeneous Demand.   Grades are poor substitutes for one another when demand is heterogeneous. Relative prices are only a minor determinant of the choices made among certain grades by certain groups. To simplify, assume grades x and y. Group 1 consumers considers x to be distinctly superior to y, and group 2 consumers considers y superior to x.

---

[16] Kenneth McCallister, "Principles and Practices in the Development of Standards for Grades for Agricultural Products," *Proceedings of National Marketing Workshop,* 1951, pp. 61–66.

However, most consumers in each group would buy the "inferior" grade at sufficient discount.

Since each grade has its devoted customers, it will persist in the marketplace at a price somewhat above or below the other grade. Which grade is more expensive depends upon the happenstance of relative supplies and demands (including quality and cost relationships when supplies are alterable). The competitive situation in the case of heterogeneous demand–alterable supplies is likely to be considerably more stable than in the case of homogeneous demand–alterable supplies. However, even grades in the heterogeneous demand case are not totally immune from competition since the "inferior" product will be purchased when the discount is sufficient. For example, many devoted owners of big American automobiles will buy Volkswagens if the price is attractive enough.

There is, of course, no meaningful way that grades x and y may be put on a single dimension of quality such as is in Figure 17–1. This fact is likely to be ignored by those experts who can rank x and y on *their own standard of quality*. Likewise, those economists who want grades to correlate with market prices can find no meaningful relationship, although they may slip into the easy assumption that the higher priced one is the higher quality.

Designing the Grade Standards

The problem of defining market grades in reality is one of determining the considerations which are of economic importance in influencing demand and then to find technical factors which are susceptable of measurement as a means of assigning proper weights to each of them.

No useful purposes is served in attempting to judge the flavor of butter unless flavor affects the demand for butter.[17]

Waugh attempted to assign proper weights to various product characteristics by studying the correlation between a number of physical measures of asparagus and its wholesale selling price.[18] This technique would develop grades that were highly correlated with market price—in the period studied, at least. It would seem to have more utility in a homogeneous demand situation than in a heterogeneous demand. Moreover, any attempt to set up consumer grades, as well as wholesale grades, would need to go beyond data available in the wholesale market because wholesale buyers may have economic reasons for emphasizing certain criteria which are irrelevant to consumers.

The concept of designing grades so that they would correlate with

[17] O. B. Jesness, "The Economic Basis of Market Grades," *Journal of Farm Economics*, October, 1933, pp. 708–9.

[18] Frederick V. Waugh, *Quality as a Determinant of Vegetable Prices* (New York: Columbia University Press, 1929).

price was still prominent at the 1951 Marketing Workshop on product quality. As indicated in the above analysis, such correlations are useful only when demand is homogeneous. Even then, there is much more to designing grades than simply making sure that grade A generally sells for more than grade B.

In contrast, a food technologist proposed that a grade for any food should consist of a weighted mean of:

1. The subjective (sensory) quality.
2. The corresponding objective quality.
3. The biological value (nutritive value, degree of deterioration, bacterial count, etc.).
4. Appearance.

He proposed to weight these factors, in order as above, with the weights 40 or 50 percent, 10 or 20 percent, 30 percent and 10 percent.[19] Most grades will involve a weighting of such qualities. But the weightings of buyers in the marketplace will vary tremendously among products—e.g., fresh eggs versus fresh beef. A weighting scheme set up by experts independent of the marketplace valuations is usually doomed to fail.

Width of Grades. An "optimum" grade standard would divide the products into homogeneous groups so that all units in a given group possess an identical market value to any given buyer. This guide would work as well for heterogeneous as for homogeneous demands. There might be disagreement between consumers as to the relative values of the various grades, but there would be agreement that units within a grade were perfect substitutes in a value sense. However, for various practical reasons, the optimum may only be a guide that indicates direction but is impossible of attainment. A minimum proposal is that value heterogenity within a grade must be less than in the total supply.[20]

The practical, working grades lie somewhere between the optimum and the minimum. If buyers are to accept a grade as a substitute for personal inspection, then there must be a great deal less value difference within the grade than between grades, as far as they are concerned. In fact, if value differences within a grade are very significant, a buyer who buys a grade "blind" can be confident as to which portion of the grade he will receive, providing the seller can sort out the lower valued items. In general, whenever a grade is so wide as to permit multivalues within it, then trading must necessarily depend on descriptions, or additional specifications, or personal inspection.

[19] R. P. Plank, "A Rational Method for Grading Food Quality," *Food Technology,* 1948, pp. 241–51.

[20] Gerald Engelman, "An Economist Looks at Meat Grading and Consumer Studies," *Proceedings of the Conference on Consumer Studies,* University of Missouri, September, 1957.

ATTEMPTING TO MAXIMIZE CONSUMER EXPENDITURES THROUGH DESIGN AND MANIPULATION OF GRADES

Agricultural economists have occasionally studied the possibilities of manipulation of quantities sold in the various grades for the purpose of maximizing total consumer expenditures for the product. Producers generally do not have the unity of purpose and industry organization which would allow them to benefit in the long run from such manipulations, even if they could accomplish them. However, there are real situations which are somewhat related. A number of the fruit and vegetable marketing order committees do more or less culling as dictated by their estimates of market supplies. In order to protect market prices, this lower quality product is diverted from normal trade channels to other uses or is destroyed. As of January 1, 1966, regulations authorizing the control of grades shipped were in effect in 40 of the 48 federal market orders for fruits, vegetables, tree nuts, and special crops.[21] Such regulations reduce total volume shipped and increase average quality and price. One of the problems is that the producer with a high-grade crop is helped more than the one with a lower grade crop.

Possible manipulation might vary from changing grade boundaries in order to redistribute this season's production among grades, to redesigning a grade in such a way as to affect the qualities produced in the next crop or in the next generation of livestock. The designing of grades to enhance the development of demand is much like product design of manufactured products. While biological constraints to such design exist, the biggest obstacle is probably the absence of self-interested, united entrepreneurship in the design of grades. Grades are designed by committees, and they look like it. If supplies are alterable and if demand may be somewhat influenced by grades, then it is extremely difficult to predict the long-run effects of a specific change in grades.[22]

THE POLITICAL ECONOMY OF GRADING LAMBS

Several years ago certain producer and market interests were nearly successful in terminating the grade marking of lamb carcasses. The highlights of this struggle will be reviewed as an example of the economic and noneconomic forces which can operate and the political framework of the struggle. This case is rather typical of the industry

---

[21] U.S. Department of Agriculture, Agricultural Economic Report No. 95, *Agricultural Markets in Change*, 1966, p. 209.

[22] Cf. the discussion in George L. Mehren, "The Function of Grades in an Affluent, Standardized-Quality Economy," *Journal of Farm Economics*, December, 1961, pp. 1377–83.

disagreements about livestock grades but is not typical of fruit, vegetable, grain, and fiber grades which have been much more generally accepted. Disputes appear more common for those products in which the grade label reaches the consumer and is involved in retailer-processor presentation and merchandising.

The opening statement of Clarence Miller, Assistant Secretary of Agriculture, to the House Committee on Agriculture gives a succinct history of the early part of the lamb grading controversy.

MR. MILLER.   We in the Department of Agriculture appreciate this committee's interest in the question of the Federal service for grading lamb and mutton. As you know, this is a voluntary grading program and has been a subject of controversy over the past year.

A request to suspend Federal grading of lamb was brought to the Department's attention by the National Wool Growers Association in a resolution adopted on January 29, 1959, stating that federal grading was detrimental to the efficient merchandising of lamb and urging that the Department suspend Federal lamb grading immediately. The National Lamb Feeders Association had adopted a similar resolution on January 10, 1959.

In response to this request, the Department called a meeting on April 17, 1959, of individuals representing various organizations, from producers to retailers, which were directly concerned with producing, feeding, and merchandising of lamb. From the statements presented at that meeting, it was apparent that there was widespread interest in the subject and that the entire industry as well as others interested should have an opportunity to comment prior to the Department's taking action on the request to suspend lamb grading. Consequently, notice was published in the Federal Register on May 28, 1959, announcing that the Department of Agriculture was considering the suspension of lamb grading on August 1, 1959, and inviting all interested persons to submit comments. . . .

On July 13, 1959, Department officials appeared before the Livestock and Feed Grains Subcommittee of the House Committee on Agriculture to discuss current developments in the lamb grading problem in relation to the consideration being given by the Department to the suspension of the Federal grading service for lamb and mutton on August 1, 1959. The subcommittee was advised that after all comments in response to the Department's formal request were received, the record would be analyzed, carefully reviewed, and thereafter the Department's decision would be announced as promptly as possible.

After considering comments of more than a thousand organizations and individuals, and weighing the subject carefully, the Department issued a press release on July 23, 1959, announcing that Federal lamb grading would be continued, and further stating that the Department would proceed promptly to consider revised grade standards for lamb and mutton to eliminate any deficiencies in the then present standards. At that time it was stated that, "If improved grade standards for lamb and mutton are not developed to meet more adequately the needs of the industry the Department will give further consideration to suspension of Federal grading of lamb and mutton carcasses."

Following the announcement, Department officials met with an industry group at Kansas City on August 26, 1959. Representatives from all segments, from producers to consumers, attended this meeting and advised the Department concerning the objectives to be accomplished in revising the standards. General agreement was reached on the principle of the revision, which was to lower the requirements for the two highest grades, Prime and Choice, with the objective of attaining sufficient volume within each of these grades for effective merchandising.

Subsequent to the meeting of the general group in Kansas City, Department officials met with a technical committee of eight members selected from industry to advise on the techniques of effecting the changes which were to be proposed. This group met again in Omaha on September 16 to review the tentative proposals which the Department had developed. At this meeting the technical committee indicated its general agreement with the objectives of the grade standards and final grades placed on demonstration lambs in accordance with the new standards. However, six of the eight members of the committee strongly objected to the use of interior carcass indications of quality in determining grade.

The Department indicated to the technical committee its belief that the standards should contain all indicators of quality necessary to accomplish the most precise possible evaluation of grade. It also pointed out that without the consideration of internal indications of quality in determining grade, Department graders would not be able to maintain a satisfactory degree of uniformity in grading. Consequently, the Department formally proposed the newly revised standards which were published in the Federal Register on October 21, 1959.

Comments concerning these proposed revised standards were received through November 21, 1959, and clearly indicated a substantial lack of agreement within the lamb industry. Positions taken by responsible groups ranged from complete abolishment of the lamb grading service to demands that no change of any kind be made. Consequently, on December 2, 1959, it was announced by the Department that Federal lamb grading would be suspended for 1 year, effective January 4, 1960, and hope was expressed that representative groups in the industry would make every effort to resolve their differences in order to propose a generally acceptable grading plan for the Department's consideration.

Since issuing this announcement, the Department has received numerous comments. We have met with a large number of representatives in Government and industry interested in this subject to hear further expressions of their views regarding the Department's position.

Pursuant to the request of Chairman Harold D. Cooley, of the House Agriculture Committee, the Department announced on December 30, 1959, that its decision on suspending Federal Grading of lamb and mutton for 1 year is being withheld for a period up to 1 month so as to provide the committee with an opportunity in which to become more fully acquainted with the problem.[23]

---

[23] *Suspension of Federal Grading of Lamb and Mutton* (Hearing, House Committee on Agriculture 86th Cong., 2d sess., Serial MM, January 11–14, 1960).

The Department of Agriculture, like other executive agencies, has considerable flexibility to change "rules of the game" such as grading. The Congress has set up administrative procedures which require the executive agency to give public notice of proposed changes, receive written comments, and even hold public hearings. Whenever these changes are quite controversial, Congress may choose to exercise what amounts to a veto power on the executive agency. The lamb grading controversy had reached the point of intervention by the Congress at the time of Assistant Secretary Miller's testimony, as quoted above.

Industry Conflict about the Fat Problem

Discontent with lamb grades had arisen long before the 1959 termination request of the National Wool Growers. That association had complained as early as 1943 about the narrow width of the Choice grade. The grades were changed twice in the postwar period to reduce fat requirements and to make some other minor adjustments. Yet, in 1959 the feeling was strong among powerful industry groups that the fat requirements for the top grades of Prime and Choice were still excessive.

The catalyst of this 1959–60 controversy was generally regarded as the lamb price break in 1958 following a postwar period of slowly declining per capita consumption and depressed prices. Thus, the lamb producers' focus on grades as a remedy had a striking parallel to the beef producers' actions through the Better Beef Association in 1925.

The conflicts in the industry over the fat problem have been summarized succinctly by a USDA report:

> The levels of lamb quality included in the Choice grade are of primary interest to the industry. The bulk of the demand for federally graded lamb is for U.S. Choice, and it serves as a goal for most producers. Much of the pressure on Federal grades for lamb in 1959 arose out of a disagreement over the quality levels that were included in U.S. Choice. Federal standards for lamb were designed on the basis of meat-type characteristics more prominent in native lambs. A smaller proportion of western than native lambs met conformation standards for U.S. Choice prior to the 1960 revision. In an attempt to qualify for U.S. Choice by improving quality to offset a lack of conformation, many lambs were fed to heavier weights and discounted in price. This in turn led western producers to oppose Federal grades as such, or the grade standards in use at that time. The lower conformation requirements in the new standards increased the proportion of western lambs grading U.S. Choice. More lambs can now be sold directly off grass for slaughter.
>
> Native state lamb producers favored the old Federal grade standards. They produce lambs primarily for meat—lambs which are lighter and younger when marketed. These lambs develop more internal feathering without excessive outside fat; age or weight are not problems. Higher proportions of native than western lambs qualified for Prime and Choice under the old standards; natives usually brought higher prices than fed western lambs.
>
> The West Coast packers who generally favor Federal grading in princi-

ple wanted the standards lowered. The extensive use of federally graded lamb in the western market and, in particular, the pressure to supply the market with more U.S. Choice was largely responsible for their stand. Packers who depend on Federal grades in their selling operations generally prefer lower standards for U.S. Choice to ease their supply problems.

Retailers using Federal grading also want large dependable supplies of lamb stamped U.S. Choice, but they want the quality consistent with maximum consumer satisfaction. Consumers want tender and flavorful lamb, but they object to excessive fat. Consumers need a reliable guide to help them choose consistent levels of quality in successive purchases. One test of consumer satisfaction with the new grades is the change in use of Federal grades by retailers. The assumption is that retailers will limit their use of the Federal grades if sales decline or customers complain about quality.[24]

The position of the National Wool Growers is illustrated by the following excerpt of their president's testimony:

The excess fat problem was emphasized by John A. Logan, president, National Association of Food Chains, in his address before our recent convention. To improve consumer acceptance of lamb meat, he included these recommendations: Give Mrs. Homemaker just about half as much undesirable fat as she now gets—try to market lambs that are not too wasteful—set up a program to deemphasize overfat carcasses—produce a lamb with a minimum of waste fat on the outside.

Are these recommendations consistent with Federal lamb grading specifications? We think not.

Not only are Government grade standards producing lambs that are unattractive to the housewife but these same standards are resulting in conditions which are costing both growers and feeders many thousands of dollars.

The most recent example is the market fiasco this past fall and winter. Many thousands of lambs which broke the market last November and December could have been sold to the packer earlier in the fall if the buyers had not been afraid they would not grade Choice under unrealistic Government grade standards. These lambs, instead of going into consumption, went to the feeder who fed them longer than he should in order to get them fat enough for the Government grader to put them in the Choice category. In so doing, he had to market these lambs $4 to $5 per hundredweight under the price at which they went into his feedlot. The results were costly lambs, overfat lambs, wasty lambs, discounted by the packer and limited in retail outlet.[25]

Industry Disagreement and Congressional Intervention

There was sufficient support for reducing fat so that the USDA Livestock Division proposed a revised set of standards. If those standards

---

[24] Darrell F. Fienup, *et al.*, *Economic Effects of U.S. Grades for Lamb*, U.S. Department of Agriculture Agricultural Economic Report No. 25, February, 1963, pp. 5–6.

[25] *Suspension of Federal Grading of Lamb and Mutton* (Hearing, House Committee on Agriculture 86th Cong., 2d sess., Serial MM, January 11–14, 1960), p. 57.

had proven acceptable, lamb grading might not have been suspended and the dispute might never have reached the Congress. A technical committee from industry, and appointed by the USDA, was critical of the revised standards. The following testimony of one of the committee indicates the problem as he saw it:

In the final meeting at Omaha on September 16, 1959, the six members of the technical committee who represented interests that have dollars and cents invested in the producing, feeding, processing, retailing, and distribution of lamb, were in unanimous agreement that the new standards for the grading of lamb and mutton should be written without the inside factors of feathering in the ribs and streakings in the flank.

They were all of the opinion that the four points they recommended should be adopted: (1) conformation; (2) outside covering of fat; (3) firmness of flesh and fat; (4) the elimination of the present maturity factor, so that lamb is lamb until it breaks a spool joint.

This is the most practical method of grading lamb and the method used to judge the quality of lamb prior to Federal meat grading. It would provide the type of lamb in the Prime and Choice grades which is neither too heavy nor too wasty; particularly in the Choice grade, which is most used by consumers.

The representatives of the Livestock Division refused to simplify the present language and published new standards which they stated would accomplish the same thing with respect to the percentage of lambs to be placed in the Prime and Choice grades. However, the technical committee is still of the unanimous opinion that the new standards should be written in simple language and should not include the inside factors of feathering in the ribs and fat streakings in the flank.

The main reason I called you is that I had been told that the Livestock Division said that without these inside factors a fraud would be perpetrated on the consuming public in the grading of lamb. Nothing is further from the truth than this statement. In fact, I believe the public has been defrauded by the present technical grade standards, because it has forced overweight, overfat lamb on the public, which it does not want.

The Livestock Division has insisted on continuing the same type of technical standards which contain much ambiguous language which is subject to conflicting interpretations by the grader and the seller of lamb.[26]

The Livestock Division of the USDA was charged with "a very adamant attitude toward the revision of lamb grading."[27] The USDA graders apparently desired to "protect quality" by less revision of the standards than requested by the Wool Growers and to obtain two or three working grades in place of one.[28]

[26] *Ibid.*, p. 55. Letter of President of Western States Meat Packers Association to the Secretary of Agriculture.

[27] *Ibid.*, p. 50.

[28] Cf. letter of president of National Wool Growers to Ezra Benson, Secretary of Agriculture, p. 50, of *Hearings on Suspension;* also the testimony of David Pettus, Director of the Livestock Division, p. 37, of *Hearings on Suspension;* also Fienup, *et al., op. cit.,* p. 64.

How Many Working Grades?

The USDA report states: "An objective of the change in standards was to define the grades so there would be at least three 'working' grades, each with an important proportion of the demand and supply. But this has not occurred. To most of the trade the demand for federally graded lamb is more than ever concentrated on U.S. Choice."[29]

This objective was apparently shared by USDA economists and graders but not by industry interests. The economists' belief in grades as a sorting device leads rather easily and naturally to the thesis of two or more "working grades."

A more recent public statement by a USDA grading official indicated his attitude:

"Many of us doubted if this change (the 1960 lamb grade revision) was in the best interest of the industry. In this connection, a recent report from the West Coast indicates that 94 percent of the lambs graded there now fall into either the Prime or Choice grade and sell for the same price. You can question the value of a grading system when this situation exists. . . ."[30]

Apparently, as suggested in this USDA report, retailers have found U.S. Choice grade to be a popular and successful "brand." The qualities supplied are alterable within limits and demand appears to be homogeneous. Following the theoretical reasoning above, it appears that the range of quality marketed—and of "working grades"—will almost inevitably narrow. The conflicting objective of producing wool-type lambs remains an important obstacle to a greater homogenity of supply. The chief opportunity in grading may be to design the optimum single grade for retail rather than to try to preserve several working grades. The reader should ask himself the demand conditions which would make it useful to continue distinguishing between Prime and Choice lambs if their carcasses sell at the same prices (as they did in 1965).

The Second Revision

The House Committee on Agriculture held its public hearings on the lamb grading controversy in January, 1960. The Committee recommended that federal grading of lamb and mutton be continued; it was. The Committee recommended that another attempt be made at obtaining satisfactory standards. Revised standards became effective March 1, 1960. The minimum requirements for Prime and Choice grades were reduced by one-half grade or more, so that the distribution of lamb

[29] Fienup, *et al., op. cit.,* p. 64.
[30] W. E. Tyler, "The Federal Viewpoint," *Proceedings* of 1963 National Marketing Service Workshop, Kansas City, Kansas, November 19–21, 1963.

among federal grades was changed greatly. About one half of the 1959 slaughter was of U.S. Choice quality but about two thirds would have been Choice under the revised standards. The percentage of federally graded and rolled Prime rose from 1 percent in 1959 to 16 percent in 1960. Retailers were generally pleased with the new leaner grades.[31]

The reader should be aware that he has not been given the "whole story." The details are much too voluminous for this book. Moreover, published material is rarely complete as to the motives and positions of the various parties to a controversy. The effects of the grade change and of lamb grading, itself, cannot be perceived with clarity because they are only part of the economic forces at work. For example, other forces than grades are affecting competitive advantage and market structure of packers and retailers. Changes in supplies of beef have big impacts upon retail lamb prices. Other forces than grading standards affect the number of lambs that are fed and the weights at which they are marketed.

SUMMARY

Grading is defined as the sorting of a product into quality classifications by a disinterested third party. Quality is defined as the sum of the attributes of a product which influence its acceptability to many buyers. There are many economic, technological, political, and practical problems in translating consumer demands into specifications of grades. Many of these problems are illustrated in the short case history of the recent controversy about lamb grades.

Despite the costs and occasional controversies associated with grading, it is generally agreed to be of social benefit. Its varying costs and advantages to farmers, traders, and consumers are discussed. Grading is often a very useful part of the sorting process by which supplies and demands are matched. If the grading obtains reasonably homogeneous value within each grade, then grading contributes to pricing efficiency and to the satisfaction of varying consumer demands. Such grades increase efficiency in the exchanging of goods and titles by making possible transactions and financing without personal inspection. However, grading like most of our inventions does not necessarily improve everyone's welfare. Grading is regarded much differently by atomistic than oligopolistic sellers.

Separate grades of a product compete with one another. If one grade "wins" the competition, then there may be only one "working grade" in the marketplace. The economics of this dynamic competition among grades, which is seldom understood by those most involved in grading, revolves around the degree of homogeneity of consumer de-

[31] Fienup, *et al., op. cit.,* pp. 41–43 and 64.

mand and the degree of alterability of qualities supplied. Whether grades should be rank-ordered and whether those grades should correlate with market price also depend upon the homogeneity of consumer demand. We cannot predict accurately all the short- and long-run economic effects of the institution of grading or even of a change in its specifications. However this chapter attempts to present a theoretical framework for analyzing these effects and understanding the kinds of controversies which occasionally arise.

PART IV

Agricultural Policy

Chapter 18

GOVERNMENT AND THE
AGRICULTURAL ECONOMY

The functions of an economic system are many and are quite complex. However, a society need not accept the dictates of the economic system as final. Even in a free enterprise society such as ours a role has been found for government in attempting to produce results more in line with the values and goals of society.

Involvement of government in the agricultural economy has increased considerably during this century. Initially, effort was directed toward increasing the efficiency of production and marketing and included legislation directed toward establishing and strengthening cooperative marketing, educational and information services for farmers, grading and inspection programs, and regulatory services.

Periods of crisis such as the great depression of the late 1920's and the early 1930's often provide the setting for major changes in government activity. This was certainly true with respect to agriculture. Programs facilitating extensive changes in the credit structure for agriculture were initiated, and direct price and income support programs such as those common today were formulated and put into effect for the first time.

Government activity involving the agricultural sector of the economy did not just develop suddenly nor did it evolve under its own power. Situations in the agricultural economy were such and the free enterprise system was functioning in such a way as to produce "unsatisfactory" results. The results were unsatisfactory in the sense that they fell short of what society felt "ought to be." The values which society holds with respect to agriculture are many and varied.[1] Rather than attempt to catalog the important values and indicate the areas where the economic system fails to some extent, an effort will be made here to indicate some characteristics of the agricultural economy which have led to society becoming concerned and involved through government programs.

---

[1] For an example, see *Goals and Values in Agricultural Policy*, Iowa State University Center for Agricultural and Economic Adjustment (Ames: Iowa State University Press, 1961).

THE BASIS FOR GOVERNMENT PRICE SUPPORT PROGRAMS

The Structure of Agriculture

The structure or organization of the agricultural economy has already been discussed in Chapters 11 through 15. As pointed out in Chapter 15, the nature of the market structure is such that there are great pressures to adopt new technology and no incentive for the individual farmer to restrict output. The result is that each individual farmer attempts to become more efficient by adopting the latest technology, which usually turns out to be output increasing. At the same time the individual farmer can sell as much as he can produce at the same price so there is no reason for him to consider production at less than the maximum rate dictated by his cost in relation to the horizontal demand curve. It is this seeming helplessness of the individual farmer which has in part suggested to society a need for government action.

The Nature of Demand

The nature of the demand for agricultural products also poses problems. The price elasticity of demand for agricultural products in the aggregate is low. People in the United States are relatively well fed. Food expenditures are less than 20 percent of total expenditures, and therefore even sizable reductions in price cause only small increases in per capita food consumption. Expressed another way, the demand is such that a small change in output leads to a large change in price. Much of any increase in total agricultural production is sold on the export market and hence is forced to compete at world prices.

Although the price elasticity of demand for most individual products is higher than for agricultural products in the aggregate, estimates for many products indicate an inelastic demand. Numerous empirical studies have been made for individual products and major product groups. Estimates vary to some extent depending on methodology, time period, level of demand, i.e., retail or farm, and whether export and industrial use were considered along with demand for domestic consumption. A rather complete study of the interrelations among demands for farm products conducted by George Brandow at Pennsylvania State University is indicative of the results commonly found in these demand studies (Table 18–1).[2] It should be emphasized that these are elasticity estimates for demand at the farm level. The reader may want to refer to Chapter 16 for information on the difference between the farm and retail estimates.

[2] G. E. Brandow, *Interrelations among Demands for Farm Products and Implications for Control of Market Supply,* Bulletin 680 (University Park, Pa., Pennsylvania State University Agricultural Experiment Station), p. 59.

TABLE 18–1

FARM-LEVEL PRICE ELASTICITIES OF TOTAL DEMAND FOR
FOOD PRODUCTS, 1955–57

Farm Product	Price Elasticity
Cattle	−0.68
Calves	−1.08
Hogs	−0.46
Sheep and lambs	−1.78
Turkeys	−0.92
Eggs	−0.23
Milk used for—	
Fluid milk and cream	−0.14
Evaporated and condensed	−0.26
Cheese	−0.54
Ice Cream	−0.11
Butter	−0.66
Other Use	−0.36
Soybean oil*	−3.99
Cottonseed oil*	−6.92
Other food oils*	−7.04
Lard, total use*	−0.54
Beverages†	−0.36
Fruit and tree nuts	−0.36
Vegetables	−0.10
Sugar*	−0.18
Potatoes, sweet potatoes	−0.11
Dry beans, peas, peanuts	−0.23
Wheat‡	−0.02
Rice (rough)‡	−0.04
Rye‡	−0.04
Corn‡	−0.03
Oats‡	−0.01
Barley	−0.07

* Wholesale prices and quantities.
† Retail prices and quantities.
‡ Does not include quantity demanded for export or for feed.
SOURCE: G. E. Brandow, *Interrelations among Demands for Farm Products and Implications for Control of Market Supply*, Bulletin 680 (University Park, Pa., Pennsylvania State University Agricultural Experiment Station), p. 59.

The estimates for food grains and feed grains are not representative since they did not include the demand for export and for feed. The possibility of substituting one feed grain for another is so important that it is virtually impossible to estimate the demand relations for an individual feed grain. Addition of the feeding and export equations in the Brandow study indicated a price elasticity of −0.36 for the low-protein feeds as a group. The demand for an individual feed grain would depend on its relative importance, with the estimate for corn being lower than the other less important low-protein concentrates. As indicated in Table 18–1, the demand for wheat is nearly perfectly inelastic for domestic food use. The demand for wheat for feed and export use is very small at relatively high price levels comparable to those which existed during the 1950's. Wheat was simply not priced at a level competitive with feed grains nor was it priced low enough to move into world markets without subsidy. At lower price levels the demand would be much more elastic but probably would still be less than −1.0.

FIGURE 18–1

Effects of Changes in Supply Available on Prices and Total Revenue Received for Agricultural Products

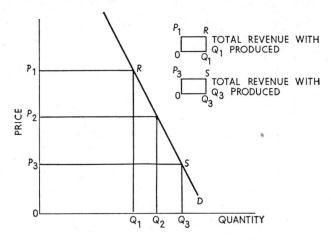

The relatively low price elasticity of demand for most agricultural products means that fluctuations in supply will lead to large price changes (Figure 18–1). Farm income will likewise be subject to considerable fluctuation as a result. Increases in the quantity produced will result in lower total revenue for farmers faced with the inelastic demand.

Rates of Change in Supply and Demand

The supply of and demand for agricultural products are constantly changing. Price changes and subsequent changes in farm income are quite often determined by the direction and magnitude of change in supply and demand. During most of the 20th century both demand and supply have been increasing but the rate of increase has varied considerably. Not only has the rate of change varied but the individual farmer has been able to do very little about either the direction or the rate of change.

The changes in demand have largely been due to changes in population, disposable income, and export demand in those instances where exports are important. Population has increased each year, but the other two factors have not been so consistent (Table 18–2). Income has

TABLE 18–2

Population, Per Capita Income, and Value of Exports for the Period, 1925–65

Year	Population (Million)	Per Capita Disposable Income (Dollars)	Value of Exports* (Billion Dollars)
1925	115.8	636	2.9
1930	123.1	604	2.3
1935	127.2	459	1.6
1940	132.1	576	1.2
1945	139.9	1,075	2.1
1950	151.7	1,369	2.8
1955	165.1	1,660	3.0
1960	179.3	1,935	5.1
1965	193.3	2,409	6.1

* Constant prices based on calendar years 1957–59 average prices.
Source: *Supplement for 1961 to Consumption of Food in the United States, 1909–52,* Supplement for 1961 to Agricultural Handbook No. 62 (Washington, D.C.: USDA, September, 1962); and *Handbook of Agricultural Charts,* Agriculture Handbook No. 325 (Washington, D.C.: USDA, October, 1966).

trended upward, especially since 1940, but it did show a sizable decline during the 1930's. Exports declined after World War I, and there was a definite downward trend until the early 1940's and the beginning of World War II (Figure 18–2). There was a modest decline in the late 1940's from the high levels achieved during the war. There was another increase in exports during the Korean conflict and a decline afterward. Exports have trended upward since 1953 due in part to export subsidies. Much of the uncertainty about demand in the near future is related to exports, and particularly those under the Food for Peace Program or similar efforts to expand food supplies in underdeveloped countries.

The supply of agricultural products has also varied over time. One must be careful to distinguish between supply and actual output. As

FIGURE 18–2

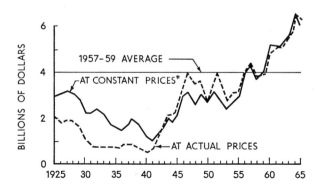

indicated in Chapter 15, the competition among farmers is such as to encourage adoption of new technology and other cost-reducing techniques. This would tend to increase supply over time in terms of the quantities farmers are willing to produce at various prices. But output during a specific year or output period may decline because of adverse weather or other phenomena beyond the control of the farmer. Furthermore, the rate of change in supply may vary from one period to another. For example, there was a slight increase during the period 1920–30, an actual decline during the mid 1930's, and a steady increase since 1938. Changes in supply as reflected by indexes of output are apparent in Table 18–3.

TABLE 18–3

FARM PRODUCTION: INDEX NUMBERS OF TOTAL
OUTPUT, TOTAL LIVESTOCK AND LIVESTOCK
PRODUCTS, AND ALL CROPS, UNITED STATES,
1920–65 (1957–59 = 100)

Year	Total Output	Livestock	Crops
1920............	59	52	76
1925............	59	58	72
1930............	61	64	69
1935............	61	59	70
1940............	70	71	78
1945............	81	86	85
1950............	86	88	89
1955............	96	99	96
1960............	106	102	108
1965............	115	111	117

SOURCE: *Changes in Farm Production and Efficiency, 1965*, Statistical Bulletin 233 (Washington, D.C.: USDA, June, 1966).

Overall movements in the level of agricultural prices are associated to a large extent with these differential rates of change in supply and demand. During those periods when demand has expanded faster than supply, there have been upward movements in prices; and when supply has changed more, there have been declines.

Instability of Prices and Incomes

Agricultural prices are characterized by much greater variation than products of most other industries. This characteristic, along with the level of farm income, has been an important concern of farm leaders and policy makers for several decades. In fact many who would hesitate to suggest programs to support or raise farm income are not hesitant to argue for measures to reduce or minimize the extent of price variability. This variability is primarily a result of the competitive structure of agriculture and the inelastic demand for agricultural products combined with uncontrolled factors such as weather which cause output to vary from one period to another.

Price Uncertainty. The individual farmer, subject as he is to several types of uncertainty, bases many of his decisions on the situation during the recent past. If prices were high, he is encouraged to expand production along with thousands of other farmers. In the case of crops this results in changes from year to year or annual variation in prices, while for livestock products the result is a cyclical pattern with the length of cycle depending on how long it takes farmers to react and the length of the production process. So the farmer and the biological nature of agricultural production are responsible for part of the price variation because of the lag between changes in prices and changes in production.

Weather Uncertainty. But the farmer is not the only cause of variability. The importance of weather uncertainty was discussed in Chapter 8. A number of studies have been carried out recently in an attempt to measure the extent to which weather has been responsible for changes in the output of agricultural products.[3] The fact that weather affects output is unquestioned, but the extent of effect is much more open to debate. Two major difficulties are involved in measuring the effect of weather. First, there is the problem of measuring the complex variable weather. Difficulties arise in combining rainfall, temperature, humidity, wind velocity, and the other aspects of weather into one numerical measure. Secondly, it is impossible to control or account for all the other variables while weather is allowed to vary as in a controlled experiment. Therefore, there are some real problems involved in isolating the effect of weather on agricultural output, but the fact that it causes variation in output is not questioned.

Varying Degrees of Price Instability. The degree of price fluctuation varies considerably among different agricultural products. The price of a few products such as milk are relatively stable, while others are characterized by a high degree of instability. Among the latter are products such as potatoes, onions, apples, citrus fruit, and to a lesser extent soybeans, hogs, and eggs. The degree of variability is influenced by the extent to which weather affects output, the length of time required for farmers to change production, the magnitude of fixed assets required in the production of the product, and the level of world supplies in those instances where the export market is important.

---

[3] For example, see James L. Stallings, "Weather Indexes," *Journal of Farm Economics,* Vol. XLII (February, 1960); and L. M. Thompson, "How Weather Has Affected Our Feed Grain Surplus," *Better Farming Methods,* September, 1962.

Effects of Instability. Instability of prices has two types of undesirable effects. First, as already suggested, the variation in prices usually means a variation in income received by farmers (Table 18–4). Changes in yields may offset price changes if total domestic production moves in the same direction as that for a given area, but in many instances a particular region may be faced with declining prices accompanied by lower yields which accentuates the instability. Cotton farms in the Mississippi Delta were an example of a price decline and lower yields during 1965 (Table 18–4).

TABLE 18–4

NET FARM INCOME, PRICES RECEIVED FOR PRODUCTS SOLD, AND CROP YIELD PER ACRE ON SPECIFIED TYPES OF COMMERCIAL FARMS, 1964 AND 1965*

Type of Farm	1964	1965
Hog-beef fattening (Corn Belt):		
Net farm income	$ 9,349	$16,488
Prices received	92	106
Crop yield per acre	114	122
Cotton farms (Mississippi Delta Large Scale):		
Net farm income	35,811	29,563
Prices received	99	97
Crop yield per acre	123	117
Tobacco (North Carolina Coastal Plain):		
Net farm income	6,425	5,296
Prices received	101	110
Crop yield per acre	143	124
Winter wheat-grain sorghum farms (Southern Plains):		
Net farm income	7,925	12,138
Prices received	85	84
Crop yield per acre	80	115
Cattle ranches (Southwest):		
Net farm income	3,752	9,312
Prices received	78	94
Range condition	89	98

* Data from *Farm Costs and Returns*, Agriculture Information Bulletin 230, ERS, USDA. Prices received, crop yield per acre, and range condition are expressed as index numbers with 1957 − 59 = 100

Since the degree of price instability for individual commodities varies, the different segments of agriculture, both geographic areas and types of farming, are characterized by varying degrees of income instability. Areas specializing in a commodity with considerable price instability are particularly subject to fluctuations in gross income. Some of these areas such as those producing horticultural crops or those with intensive beef or hog fattening enterprises also have high cash outlays relative to total production costs. These areas and types of farming are subject to extreme variations in net farm income when prices change. The changes in net farm income experienced by hog-beef fattening farms and cattle ranches, as shown in Table 18–4, typify the effects of price instability.

In addition to the income effect of price instability, there is the effect on efficiency of resource allocation. Faced with considerable price uncertainty, farmers are not likely to arrive at the optimum allocation of resources. This problem is exemplified by the ups and downs of the hog and beef cycles. Periods of high prices encourage farmers to commit excess resources to a specific enterprise, and then when production increases, prices fall, and too many resources are withdrawn from production. This hinders the construction of facilities and establishment of enterprises of optimum size or scale of operation.

Immobility of Resources

The other characteristics of agriculture already discussed would not be nearly so serious if resources were quick to adjust to new supply and demand situations. But such is not the case. Labor has moved out of agriculture at a rapid pace, and the amount of capital used has been increasing so that total inputs used has remained at about the same level as in 1940.

Even though labor decreased by more than one half between 1940 and 1965, a problem of excess labor in agriculture continued to exist. The problem was not so much one of unemployment as underemployment. This is evidenced by the fact that approximately one third of the farms produced over 75 percent of the total output. On many farms, the capital and land resources were not adequate to keep the labor fully employed.

Several reasons for the immobility of resources in agriculture are fairly evident. Land does not return much for other uses unless it happens to be in an area of urban expansion or highway construction. Much of the labor in agriculture is not trained for other types of employment and is too old to consider retraining. Even capital becomes rather fixed when invested in specialized types of machinery or facilities. The situation is such that the marginal value product of major inputs may decline when prices received decline but remain above the return in alternative uses (Figure 18–3). In such instances the quantity of an input used would remain at Q_x even though the price of the product declined.

The tendency for resources to become fixed in agriculture, particularly labor, means that even though returns decline considerably, the resources do not shift to other uses. The farm operator and his family accept a lower income and exist with a lower level of living rather than seek employment elsewhere. The problem becomes even more serious when unemployment in the economy increases and when the level of skill required for nonfarm employment increases.

In summary, the characteristics of agriculture are such that the individual farmer is encouraged to become more and more efficient and

FIGURE 18-3

Optimum Use of an Input with a Decline in the
Price Received for the Commodity Being Produced

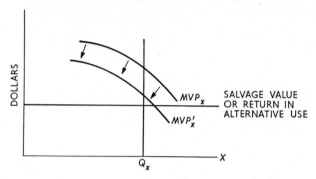

to produce at full capacity. This encouragement often pushes the supply curve to the right, or, expressed another way, it causes supply to increase faster than demand. This tendency, combined with an inelastic demand for agricultural products, results in lower prices and even lower total returns in many instances. Agricultural resources, immobile as they are, accept lower returns as a result. These characteristics, singly or more often in combination, lead to results which society has deemed "unsatisfactory." Efforts have been made to assist agriculture with respect to these characteristics, and in some instances government has become directly involved through price and income programs for agriculture.

FARM PROBLEMS AND PROGRAMS OF THE RECENT PAST

It is often helpful to back away from current problems and proposed solutions and examine the history of developments in a particular area. Such an examination is helpful because it broadens our thinking by forcing us to examine the types of problems important in the past, and secondly, it provides information about the results of various types of attempts to deal with these problems.

Throughout the present century Congress has made frequent attempts to solve one or more of the problems facing agriculture. This task has been a continuous one because of constantly changing conditions. Each succeeding Congress has studied and sought to satisfy the demand for farm legislation.

This review of the economic problems facing agriculture and the programs proposed to deal with these problems will be divided into four periods, corresponding to the last four decades. This is not to imply that agricultural programs have been restricted to these periods or that they fit neatly into this sort of a division, but the review must be limited, and this type of examination should serve our purposes.[4]

The 1920's

The Effects of World War I.   The decade beginning in 1920 might also be called the aftermath of World War I. During the war, increased exports led to an increase in demand and relatively high prices for agricultural products, especially wheat, tobacco, and hogs. These higher prices also led to greatly expanded output.

United States donations to its allies terminated in 1920. Export demand declined considerably. Farm prices fell from an index of 228 in 1919 to 128 in 1921. The output of agriculture faced a smaller, inelastic market, and it did not adjust immediately. The sharp drop in prices and the lower incomes which resulted brought pressure from farm groups for legislation and led to the formation of the "farm bloc" in Congress. Most of the proposals and programs which were actually adopted during this period were attempts to make the marketing system more efficient in hopes of increasing the derived demand for agricultural products. Many of the attempts were regulatory in nature, while others took the form of trying to strengthen farmer cooperatives. No programs were passed to support farm prices directly.

McNary–Haugen Bills.   Since prices declined the most for those commodities formerly exported in large quantities, pressure eventually developed for a two-price plan known as the McNary-Haugen Bill. The plan took various forms but essentially involved subsidizing exports of such commodities as wheat and cotton. Five McNary-Haugen bills were introduced during the period 1924–28, one during each session of Congress. The fourth and fifth McNary-Haugen bills passed Congress but were vetoed both times by President Coolidge.

The Federal Farm Board.   The first actual program passed to support farm prices directly was the Agricultural Marketing Act of 1929. This act established the Federal Farm Board which had as its main objective the financing of orderly marketing of agricultural products. The problem was seen as one of dealing with seasonal or unusual gluts. Therefore, Congress appropriated $500 million which was to be used to buy and sell commodities for the purpose of stabilizing prices. The money was to be loaned to cooperative marketing agencies which were to do the actual buying and selling of commodities with losses to be covered by the Federal Farm Board. Continuation of the decline in demand for farm products with the onset of the great depression, along

[4] For a more detailed account and description of developments in agricultural policy, see Murray R. Benedict, *Farm Policies of the United States, 1790–1950* (New York: Twentieth Century Fund, 1953).

with good crop years, caused the Farm Board to run out of money before the stabilizing effect was achieved.

The situation during the decade of the 1920's may be summarized as one of declining exports following the end of World War I, slight increases in production resulting from the farming of more land, and some increase in feed efficiency. A decline in domestic demand began in 1929 which was to become an even more serious problem during the decade to follow.

The 1930's

The Great Depression. Even though farm prices were relatively low during the 1920's, they continued to fall during the period 1929 to 1933. The average level of farm prices fell 64 percent. The 1931 and 1932 corn crops sold for prices averaging 32 cents a bushel while wheat averaged 38 to 39 cents per bushel. The average price of eggs was 13 to 14 cents a dozen, and turkeys averaged 11 to 12 cents per pound. Farm prices fell more than nonfarm prices between 1929 and 1933 just as they had following World War I. In discussing the situation Arthur Schlesinger wrote:[5]

No group in the population, except perhaps the Negro workers, was more badly hit by depression. The realized net income of farm operators in 1932 was less than one-third what it had been in 1929—a dizzying collapse in three years. Farm prices had fallen more than 50 percent; and the parity ratio—the ratio of prices received by farmers to the prices they paid—had plummeted from 89 in 1929 down to 55 in 1932 (in terms of 1910–14 as 100). The seething violence in the farm belt over the winter—the grim mobs gathered to stop foreclosures, the pickets along the highways to prevent produce from being moved to town—made it clear that patience was running out. In January 1933, Edward A. O'Neal, the head of the Farm Bureau Federation, warned a Senate committee: "Unless something is done for the American farmer we will have revolution in the countryside within less than twelve months."

The problems of this period were similar to those of the preceding decade plus the added and more important unemployment problem in the nonfarm economy. Unemployment as a percent of the civilian labor force increased from 3.2 percent in 1929 to 24.9 percent in 1933. Instead of resources leaving agriculture as a result of the declining farm prices, the lack of employment opportunities in the nonfarm sector led to migration back to the farm.

The New Deal. The first real attempt to raise farm prices was the Agricultural Adjustment Act of 1933. The act was aimed at adjusting output of certain farm products, namely corn, wheat, cotton, and to-

---

[5] Arthur M. Schlesinger, *The Age of Roosevelt—The Coming of the New Deal* (Boston: Houghton Mifflin Co., 1959), p. 27.

bacco. Cash payments, financed by processing taxes on the handlers of a commodity, were made to producers who took land out of production. The act also established the Commodity Credit Corporation which was to hold products off the market when needed as a temporary measure. In January, 1936, the Supreme Court ruled the Agricultural Adjustment Act of 1933 unconstitutional. The Court gave as the basis for its ruling the argument that state governments and not the federal government had the right to control production. Since the processing taxes were tied to the effort to control production, they were also declared illegal.

The Agricultural Act of 1936 was entitled the Soil Conservation and Domestic Allotment Act. It sought to accomplish most of the same objectives, but the act made payments available to farmers from federal funds rather then processing tax funds. Farmers received payments for reducing their acreage of "soil depleting" crops and increasing their acreage of "soil conserving" crops such as legumes. The "soil depleting" crops happened to be essentially the same as those involved in the act of 1933. Large crops in 1937 and the subsequent declining prices soon brought pressure for a more extensive farm program.

The Agricultural Adjustment Act of 1938 reinstated many of the features of the original act of 1933. Whereas the earlier efforts had been promoted as emergency measures, the act of 1938 indicated a more permanent need for agricultural price supports. The act provided for (1) mandatory price support loans at 52–75 percent of parity on corn, wheat, and cotton; (2) when necessary, marketing quotas keyed to acreage allotments on tobacco, corn, wheat, cotton, and rice; and (3) permissive supports for other commodities. In its amended form, this act has provided the basic framework for the major farm programs since that time. The Commodity Credit Corporation, with its authority to support prices, continued under this act as did the payments to encourage soil conservation.

Efforts directed toward more efficient marketing of agricultural products continued during the decade of the 1930's. Perhaps the most important of the efforts during this period was the Agricultural Marketing Agreement Act of 1937. This act provides the enabling legislation for marketing agreements and orders. These programs will be discussed in greater detail in a later chapter. In addition, efforts to increase demand or widen market outlets for surplus agricultural commodities also were continued. Among the more important results along this line was Section 32 legislation which authorized the Secretary of Agriculture to use an amount equal to 30 percent of customs receipts to encourage domestic consumption, divert products from normal channels of trade, or export surplus agricultural commodities.[6]

The decade of the 1930's witnessed the beginning of direct govern-

---

[6] Section 32 of Public Law 320, 74th Congress.

ment involvement in the agricultural economy. A continued low level of exports combined with a severe drop in domestic demand, as a result of the depression in the general economy, resulted in an agricultural situation which was deemed critical. Legislative attempts were made to increase demand, reduce production, and support directly the prices of agricultural products. The situation did improve but was still far from prosperity prior to the beginning of World War II.

The 1940's

Conditions in the agricultural economy changed abruptly in the early 1940's. The index of prices received by farmers increased from 100 in 1940 to 193 in 1943. Farm output also increased but not nearly so fast, going from an index number of 70 in 1940 to 80 in 1943. The objective of agricultural legislation became that of getting farmers to produce more to help in the war effort while holding food prices at a reasonable level. The government programs did not change during this period in terms of the basic provisions in effect, but there were no restrictions on production and price supports were increased.

Early in 1941, support prices on the basic commodities (wheat, corn, cotton, tobacco, rice, and peanuts) were raised to 85 percent of parity. Later that year the Steagall amendment was passed making it necessary for the Secretary of Agriculture to support the price of any commodity for which an increase in production was requested at a level of not less than 85 percent of parity. The mandatory level was raised to 90 percent of parity in 1942, and the amendment required that support continue at this level for two years after the end of the war. The Steagall amendment was in effect up to December 31, 1948, and subsequent legislation continued this level of support on most commodities through 1949 and 1950.

The decade was one of tremendous increase in both export and domestic demand. Supply also increased but not nearly so fast as demand, so that by the end of the decade prices were nearly triple what they were at the beginning.

The 1950's

The outbreak of hostilities in Korea during the summer of 1950 stimulated both domestic and foreign demand for agricultural commodities. As a result, the general level of prices received by farmers, which had dropped in 1949, resumed its upward movement. The small surpluses which had begun to appear also moved into domestic or export use.

At the end of the Korean war, surpluses became important again. Commodity Credit Corporation inventories which were valued at $1.3 billion at the end of the fiscal year 1952 rose to $5.8 billion at the end of fiscal year 1954. Unlike the 1920's and 1930's, the decade of the 1950's did not involve a decrease in export and domestic demand but rather a tremendous increase in the supply of agricultural products. Farm output increased 20 percent during the years 1950 to 1959. Despite substantial efforts to support agricultural prices, buildups in surplus stocks, and sizable price support expenditures, the prices of agricultural products declined during the decade from an index of 302 in 1951 to 240 in 1959.

Mounting surpluses and increased costs of government programs led to the enactment of a flexible price support program in 1954. The objective was to decrease price support levels when surpluses were in large volume and thereby reduce the production of surplus commodities. The impact of new technology was so great though that even with lower price supports production increased and the surpluses continued to mount. It took policy makers several years to recognize the *sustained impact* of new technology on output as a new force in the supply and demand picture requiring new policies. Meanwhile a series of makeshift quasi emergency programs were initiated to deal with specific commodities.

Two other very important programs were adopted during the 1950's in an effort to improve the agricultural situation. The Agricultural Trade Development and Assistance Act of 1954, popularly known as Public Law 480, was passed as a vehicle for helping dispose of surplus agricultural commodities overseas. Large quantities of agricultural products were moved overseas under this program, particularly of the basic commodities. The other important program passed during this period was the Agricultural Act of 1956 or the Soil Bank Act. This was an attempt to help restrict the production of agricultural products and grew out of a conclusion on the part of many that total agricultural production was in excess of the demand for food and fiber at prices considered "satisfactory" to farmers and those concerned with the development of agricultural policy.

Each of these three programs represented a slightly different approach to affecting the level of prices and incomes in agriculture. Each was directed not only at the current price-income problem but also at the mounting surpluses—a prime source of fiscal and political concern. The flexible price support approach was an attempt to influence production through varying the price support level. The other two were more indirect in nature with Public Law 480 attempting to increase the demand or consumption of agricultural products, while the Soil Bank Act was an attempt to reduce the supply of agricultural products through a reduction in one of the major inputs.

The developments during the four decades indicate the importance of various factors in the determination of agricultural prices and income. The policy problem has always been an imbalance of supply and demand. The size of the imbalance has been an important variable. The size of accumulated surpluses, inadequate reserves, and expectations about future imbalances have also been important factors. Likewise the legislative attempts to change the results forthcoming as a result of the economic forces in operation have been many and varied. Some have sought to expand the demand for agricultural products, others have restricted one of the inputs used in agricultural production, namely land, while others have supported prices directly.

EFFECTS OF PAST GOVERNMENT PROGRAMS

The importance of government involvement in the agricultural economy during recent decades is obvious. However, the desirability of some of the effects of government activity is much more controversial. The effects are so many and varied that both the ardent opponent of government involvement in agriculture and the advocate of government farm programs can find support for his attitude toward government programs. Changes in our society and in the agricultural economy have been so fast and so complex during recent decades that it is almost impossible to isolate and measure exactly the effects of government programs. However, some of the more important effects will be considered along with empirical analyses of individual programs or all programs in combination.

Price and Income Effects

During recent years a number of research studies have been conducted to determine the effect of government price support programs on prices received by farmers. The problem becomes one of determining what the level of prices and incomes would have been without the various programs.

Estimating Effects. One approach to this problem is that of taking government purchases and increases in Commodity Credit Corporation loans and inventories and multiplying the sum of these two by an estimate of price flexibility.[7] For example, if the price elasticity of demand for the products involved is 0.4, then the price flexibility would be 2.5 and would suggest that farm income is increased $2.50 for each $1 reduction in farm products moving through commercial marketing channels. This figure when added to direct government payments gives a rough estimate of the contribution of price support activities. This approach was used in a study by Wilcox reported in the *Journal of Farm*

---

[7] This approach assumes that agricultural products purchased by the government or added to loans and inventories are removed from the market and reduce the quantity available by that amount. A value for the price flexibility, which is approximately equal to the reciprocal of the price elasticity of demand, must be assumed.

Economics in 1958.[8] The results indicated that for the period 1952 to 1956 net farm income would have been 28 percent or more lower without price support activities.

Three rather detailed and complex research studies were conducted during the late 1950's in an attempt to answer this same question.[9] Though the studies differed somewhat in the data used, in procedures and analytical techniques, and in some of the assumptions required, the results were strikingly similar. One study was instigated at the request of Senator Ellender, Chairman of the Senate Committee on Agriculture and Forestry. This study was conducted by the USDA in consultation with an advisory committee composed of six members of the Land Grant College interregional research committee on agricultural policy (IRM-1). Another study was conducted by the Center for Agricultural and Economic Adjustment at Iowa State University, while the third was carried out by W. A. Cromarty at Michigan State University. The USDA and Iowa studies were similar in that they involved the aggregation of analyses for individual products or product groups while the Cromarty study was an econometric model of the agricultural economy with the major interrelations in an integrated system.

A comparison of the USDA and Iowa studies indicates that the primary assumptions in each study were that there would be no production controls and no price supports on the major agricultural commodities except in the case of tobacco. Both groups assumed population, total disposable income, and disposable income per capita would increase yearly while prices paid by farmers would remain constant at the 1959 rate. The projections of planted acreage, yield per acre, and production of crops were very similar. The livestock output projections differed more with the USDA study projecting a greater increase in hog production and the Iowa State study projecting a greater increase in beef cattle and milk production. These differences in output projections for livestock and livestock products show up to some extent in the estimated prices. Table 18–5 provides some examples of the results obtained and a comparison with actual prices.

As indicated earlier, the estimates of the impact of elimination of production restrictions and price supports were very similar. Each of the

[8] Walter W. Wilcox, "The Farm Policy Dilemma," *Journal of Farm Economics*, Vol. XL (August, 1958), pp. 563–71.

[9] Arnold Paulsen and Don Kaldor, "Methods, Assumptions and Results of Free Market Projections for the Livestock and Feed Economy," *Journal of Farm Economics*, Vol. XLIII (May, 1961), p. 361; *Report from the United States Department of Agriculture and a Statement from the Land Grant Colleges IRM–1 Advisory Committee on Farm Price and Income Projections 1960–65* (Senate Document No. 77, 86th Cong., 2d sess. [January 20, 1960]), p. 23; W. A. Cromarty "Free Market Price Projections Based on a Formal Econometric Model," *Journal of Farm Economics*, Vol. XLIII (May, 1961), pp. 365–78.

TABLE 18–5

PROJECTED PRICES FOR WHEAT, CORN, AND HOGS WITH NO
PRICE SUPPORTS OR PRODUCTION RESTRICTIONS, COMPARED
WITH ACTUAL PRICES, UNITED STATES, 1962

Study	Projected Farm Prices		
	Wheat (Dollars per Bushel)	Corn (Dollars per Bushel)	Hogs (Dollars per 100 Pounds)
Iowa State*..............0.74		0.66	11.00
USDA†.................0.90		0.80	11.20
Actual prices............1.96		1.00	16.40

* Arnold Paulsen and Don Kaldor, "Methods, Assumptions and Results of Free Market Projections for the Livestock and Feed Economy," *Journal of Farm Economics*, Vol. XVIII (May, 1961), p. 361.

† Report from the United States Department of Agriculture and a Statement from the Land Grant Colleges IRM-1 Advisory Committee on Farm Price and Income Projections 1960–65 (Senate Document No. 77, 86th Cong., 2d sess. [January 20, 1960], p. 23.

studies indicated an estimated decline in net farm income of from 25 to 40 percent. Similar results have since been obtained in another study by Brandow at Pennsylvania State University.[10]

Impact on Thinking. The results from these studies had an impact on the thinking of policy makers during the early 1960's. More people believed that prices and incomes would drop sharply with an elimination of price support programs. However, a more difficult question arises with respect to what the outcome would be in terms of subsequent long-range adjustments. In a free market would the supply of agricultural products eventually decline to the point where prices would increase? Or as an alternative, would the more efficient farms which were able to continue production with lower prices be able to continue to exist profitably with the lower prices? These questions are considerably more difficult and are the basis for much disagreement on agricultural policy. The answers depend largely on the nature of the supply relationship, and empirical analyses of supply have not been adequate to provide satisfactory answers.

In addition to the studies of the impact of all government price support programs on farm prices and incomes, there have been studies of individual commodity programs. For example, there have been studies of programs for wheat, corn, cotton, dairy products, potatoes, burley tobacco, and dry beans. In addition a number of researchers have attempted to determine the indirect effects of commodity price supports on prices and incomes of farmers producing various commodities. It is

[10] Brandow, *op. cit.*

impossible to summarize the results of all these individual commodity studies. However, practically all the studies suggest that prices of the products involved would have been considerably lower without the price support programs. Also, as in the case of the more aggregative type studies, researchers found it difficult to estimate or determine what types of adjustments might have taken place in the absence of price support programs.

Impact of Specific Programs. In addition to the effect of individual commodity price support programs on the level of prices and incomes, practically all of the research studies indicate that year-to-year variation in price was reduced as a result of the programs. This was particularly true for those commodities which were formerly subject to a high degree of price instability. Typical of the findings is a comment by Hathaway in his report on a study of the dry bean industry: "The big difference was that with supports, the price varied little from the average; without supports, the large crops would have sold for a very low price and the small crops, a high price."[11] This finding is rather important because, as suggested earlier, agricultural prices are quite often subject to extreme variability. Not only is that important from the standpoint of its effect on income variability but it also affects the efficiency with which resources are allocated.

Efficiency of Resource Use

Farmers are subject to a number of different types of uncertainty. As pointed out in Chapter 8, price uncertainty is one type of uncertainty facing farm managers. Government price support programs have made a positive contribution to the extent that they have removed or reduced price uncertainty. Price support programs, by reducing price variability, have reduced uncertainty and in so doing have contributed to greater efficiency of resource use.

As price supports have reduced price uncertainty, another type of uncertainty has entered the picture with the increasing importance of price support programs. This is uncertainty with respect to the type of price support program and the level of price support. Uncertainty about the 1964 wheat program is an excellent example of this type of uncertainty. Wheat farmers were forced to plant the crop, not knowing whether a new wheat program would be passed nor the level of support. Some farmers overplanted their allotment thinking that the May, 1963, referendum had for all practical purposes ended wheat price support programs. Other farmers stayed within their allotments expecting a new

[11] Dale E. Hathaway, *How Price Supports Affected the Dry Bean Industry in Michigan,* Special Bulletin, 399 (East Lansing, Mich.: Michigan Agricultural Experiment Station, September, 1955), p. 7.

1964 wheat program or fearing that overplanting of allotments would result in loss of acreage history which would be costly with the passage of new wheat legislation in later years. Whereas price supports contribute to greater efficiency when they reduce price variability, the uncertainty caused by changes in programs reduces efficiency and emphasizes the importance of a charted direction for agricultural policy.

The level of price supports is also a factor in the efficiency of resource use. Price supports maintained at consistently higher levels than the normal equilibrium price encourage allocation of resources to the production of that commodity above and beyond what might be considered desirable. This is a more serious problem if there are shortages of some commodities while other products are in surplus. There is evidence to suggest that this was not the case during the 1950's and early 1960's in the United States. Total agricultural production was estimated to be 6 to 8 percent above that needed to supply the markets at prices then existing.[12] Further evidence of an overall surplus condition in agriculture is the fact that index numbers of prices received by farmers by commodity groups practically all show a decline during the 1950's (Table 18–6).

TABLE 18–6

INDEX NUMBERS OF PRICES RECEIVED BY FARMERS, BY COMMODITY GROUPS, UNITED STATES ANNUAL AVERAGES, 1950–65

Year	Food Grains	Feed Grains and Hay	Cotton	Oil Bearing Crops	Fruit	Commercial Vegetables	Dairy Products	Poultry and Eggs	Meat Animals
1950....224	193	282	276	194	211	249	186	340
1951....243	226	336	339	181	269	286	228	409
1952....244	234	310	296	188	271	303	206	353
1953....234	206	268	279	196	230	267	221	288
1954....232	203	274	304	209	216	246	178	283
1955....228	183	272	249	202	223	247	191	246
1956....224	182	268	255	215	232	255	176	235
1957....225	166	263	244	203	227	259	162	275
1958....208	154	253	225	248	238	254	170	335
1959....202	156	267	219	212	235	257	143	313
1960....203	151	254	214	242	223	259	160	296
1961....209	151	261	257	247	219	260	146	299
1962....226	153	270	248	220	244	253	145	310
1963....224	164	271	258	279	231	253	146	290
1964....190	166	262	256	298	246	256	142	270
1965....164	173	245	265	243	260	260	145	320

SOURCE: *Agricultural Prices*, Statistical Reporting Service, USDA (Washington, D.C., 1960–66).

[12] B. F. Jones and Dale E. Hathaway, "The Volume of Commodities Involved in Price Support Programs Related to the Indexes of Farm Output, 1948–1960," *Journal of Farm Economics*, Vol. XLIV (August, 1962), pp. 850–66.

Price support programs may also affect the efficiency of resource use through their effect on location of production. One way this may be done is through the setting of price support loan rates different from the normal geographical price pattern. A second important problem area is in the distribution of acreage allotments. Acreage allotments distributed differently from location of production under normal competitive conditions may reduce the efficiency of resource use.

Government Costs

The realized cost of programs primarily for stabilization of farm prices and income must be considered an important effect. This has been particularly true in recent years with the general increase in cost of price support programs. The cost of programs for a few commodities has been particularly high. For example during the period 1932 to 1959 the realized cost of programs for wheat, cotton, corn, and dairy products amounted to two thirds of the total cost of all such programs.

One mistake commonly made is to regard total United States Department of Agriculture appropriations as an indication of price support program costs. This is grossly unfair to price support programs because USDA appropriations include many activities other than those associated with price support programs. Such activities include soil and water conservation, school lunch and school milk programs, research, forest service funds, and efforts to maintain or improve the quality of food and increase its availability. In 1960, those items in the USDA budget predominantly for the benefit of the farmer were estimated to account for something less than one half of the total USDA budget.[13] However, this is not to imply that such costs are unimportant or that they should be emphasized less because they have come to be of increasing concern and must be considered when evaluating the various price support programs.

The cost incurred in carrying out price support loan and storage programs such as the programs used during the 1950's depends mainly on the level of price support relative to the normal long-run equilibrium price and the cost of storage. The relationships may be stated as the cost of storage; then

$$\text{Costs} = SP(Q) + SC(Q) - SV$$

where

SP = Support price
Q = Quantity acquired by the government
SC = Storage cost per unit
SV = Salvage value or returns realized from disposal programs

[13] *Price Support and Production Adjustment Activities* (Twenty-Sixth Report by the Committee on Government Operations, House Report No. 2219, 86th Cong., 2d sess. [Washington, D.C., August 31, 1960]).

depends on the relative price elasticities of demand and supply and the cost of holding the product in storage. The more elastic the demand and supply for the product, the greater the quantity will be moving under the price support loan and storage program and hence the greater the total cost of storage. The relative price elasticity of supply is important in that the greater the elasticity the more responsive production will be to the higher price levels involved with supports. In the same way, the price elasticity of demand is important in the sense that if the demand is relatively more elastic, the greater the reduction will be in the quantity demanded as a result of supporting price at higher than the equilibrium level. There are of course a number of factors which influence cost, of which the actual cost of storage per unit is one, which are related to the physical characteristics of the commodity rather than the economic characteristics of the market for the commodity.

The wheat and cotton programs have been two of the more costly programs. In the case of wheat, the support level was considerably above the equilibrium price during the period 1955–63, and wheat continued to move into storage with very little moving out other than that disposed of through foreign disposal programs.[14] The cotton program has also been relatively costly because the support price was above the equilibrium price and the elasticity of demand was apparently much greater than earlier believed. As a result domestic mill consumption of cotton was actually lower in the early 1960's than 10 years earlier.

Freedom of Decision Making

Changes in society and its institutions often result in changes in the focal points at which various types of decisions are made. In the case of agriculture, this is true with respect to cooperative arrangements, contractual agreements, marketing agreements and orders, and various types of government price support programs. Decisions once made by individual farmers may be made by groups of farmers as a result of changes in some of the basic relationships. In many instances the individual farmer may be willing or may be forced to relinquish his freedom to make certain types of decisions in order to obtain other types of benefits. In other instances farmers may be willing to give up certain types of advantages or benefits in order to be able to make certain types of decisions. Both types of situations have been prevalent during the history of government price support programs, and the effect that these programs have on freedom of individual decision making is considered quite important in many instances.

Decisions with respect to the use of the land input have been

[14] John A. Schnittker, *Wheat Problems and Programs in the United States,* North Central Publication 118 (September, 1960).

affected and in many instances almost given up by farmers as a part of government price support programs for specific commodities. This has taken place as a part of acreage allotment programs to control or at least limit the production of specific commodities. This is perhaps the most important single way in which freedom of decision making has been affected by government price support programs. Freedom of decision making has also been influenced by other developments in the agricultural economy. For example, contractual arrangements such as those prevalent in the broiler industry have shifted many of the decisions with respect to output, type of feed used, management practices, and methods of marketing from the farmer to the other parties involved in the contractual arrangements. Of course the farmer was initially free to decide about signing the contractual arrangement, but once committed, much of the freedom of decision making was no longer present.

Developments such as those taking place in government price support programs and also in other production and marketing arrangements have had some effect on the level at which decisions are made. This is another important type of effect which farmers as well as others in society must consider in evaluating changes in the institutions of society.

This discussion of some of the effects of government price support programs and government involvement in the agricultural economy was not meant to be complete. Other changes resulting from these programs are perhaps of equal or even greater importance. Consumers and marketing firms have been affected by these price support programs just as have farmers. The programs have affected the production practices used on farms, the quality of products as well as the quantity produced, the marketing patterns, and distribution practices. Rather than attempt an exhaustive listing or discussion of the effects of price programs, this discussion was meant more to show how the economic characteristics of the market have given rise to price support programs and in turn how these programs have affected the agricultural economy.

GOVERNMENT AND THE DEMAND FOR AGRICULTURAL PRODUCTS

Chapter
19

The degree of government involvement in the agricultural economy will never be satisfactory to everyone. There will always be those who argue that with the problems that exist, government must become more active and play an increasing role. At the same time there will be others who argue that the situation would be much better if government left more of the decisions and actions to individuals or other groups or institutions. Such diversity of opinion is to be expected with the different values held by individuals in our society. However, there are some types of programs which have more general appeal to members of our society than others. Programs to expand the demand for agricultural products are such programs.[1]

Government activities to expand the demand for agricultural products, to shift the demand curve to the right, are generally acceptable to all farm organizations. This is one approach upon which the small farmer and the large farmer, the producer of crops and the producer of livestock, the farmer and the agribusinessman, the wheat farmer of the Great Plains and the cotton grower of the Mississippi Delta can all agree. Perhaps of even greater importance is the fact that such programs do not ordinarily involve giving up any power of decision making and therefore are more acceptable to those who would ordinarily oppose government activity. Since this type of approach is so much more acceptable to members of society, it deserves attention and an analysis of the theory behind such an approach, the mechanics involved, and some of the consequences and potentials of demand expansion.

FACTORS AFFECTING DEMAND

The nature of demand for farm products was discussed in Chapter 18. It was pointed out that the quantity demanded of a product is largely a function of price, income, population, prices of substitutes, and changes

---

[1] Frederick V. Waugh, *Managing Farm Surpluses*, an Agriculture Committee Report, National Planning Association Pamphlet No. 117, (Washington, D.C., 1962), pp. 30–44.

in taste. In addition to these, there are some additional factors which must be considered for those products which are exported in large quantities. For example, supplies in other major exporting countries and general economic conditions in importing countries would also be important. A description of the magnitude and the rate of change in demand during recent decades was also presented in Chapter 18. In this chapter our concern will be with the possibility of expanding the demand for farm products through purposeful action on the part of the government.

Demand Shifters

The demand curve shifts to the right when population increases, per capita incomes increase, prices of substitute products increase, or when preferences for a particular product increase. To what extent can government through its activities increase demand through one of these factors? The possibilities appear negligible with the possible exception of activities which would increase per capita income. Government can and does take action to increase the level of per capita incomes and in so doing does increase the demand for agricultural products to some extent. However, this is more of a general economic goal and is not considered as a specific action taken to increase the demand for food or other farm products.

Government can hardly afford to take action to increase population, increase the prices of products which are substitutes, or attempt to change tastes and preferences except when such action leads to improved diets. So, with the exception of action to increase the level of general economic activity, very little can be accomplished by working with the factors which are normally considered demand shifters.

Purposeful Action to Expand Demand

Efforts to expand the demand for farm products have been of two distinct types. One type has included efforts to shift the demand curve for farm products by programs of education, information, new product development, and activities of this type. This approach has been used by commodity groups, cooperative organizations, marketing firms, and by the government. Such activities have also commonly been a part of efforts to increase the use of our farm products in overseas markets.

The other type of effort to expand demand has involved some type of price subsidy. The price subsidies have been used to reduce the price of farm products which in turn results in an increase in the quantity demanded.[2] These programs of course do not shift the demand curve but

---

[2] It will be demonstrated later in this chapter that the effect of such programs on farm prices is more nearly one of reducing the quantity available in the normal marketing channels and therefore might be considered a reduction in supply.

rather result in a movement along the demand curve. This approach has normally been used to encourage consumption by particular groups who would not ordinarily purchase the commodity and has been used in both the domestic and export markets.

The programs actually used to expand the demand for farm products have in many instances been variations of these two distinct types of effort and in some instances a combination of the two types. For example, in the school milk program the price paid for the milk is reduced and the program is also thought of as a means of encouraging greater use of milk in later years.

Some efforts, particularly those of commodity groups and individual firms, are directed towards an increase in consumption of a particular product even though the consumption of another agricultural product may be reduced as a result. These types of efforts will not ordinarily result in any increase in total food consumption. However, they may result in increased use of farm resources if more resources are required to produce the commodity for which the demand is increased. Even though demand expansion efforts all have the objective of increasing the consumption of food, the techniques and approaches used have been so different that each must be examined before conclusions can be drawn with respect to the potential of such programs.

APPROACHES TO DEMAND EXPANSION

The actual approach to demand expansion has varied considerably depending upon the conditions existing at the time the program was initiated. Political and social as well as economic issues have often been involved. As a first step in examining the approaches used to demand expansion, it is necessary to consider some of the reasons used to justify such programs.

Reasons for Demand Expansion

The importance of different objectives involved in demand expansion programs have varied from time to time. Likewise, those individuals or groups attempting to obtain the necessary legislation have often wanted the programs for quite different reasons. However, two major objectives stand out as being of primary importance as a rationale for demand expansion programs. First, there have been those who were concerned about farm prices and were interested in programs to increase the demand for farm products. They hoped to increase farm prices or at least prevent further price declines. Secondly there have been those who were concerned with the nutritional adequacy of diets among certain segments of the consuming population. The programs adopted during recent years have usually had both of these objectives in mind, but such has not always been the case.

Concern with the adequacy of diets from a nutritional standpoint was first evidenced during the 1930's. The increase of several million unemployed heads of families accompanying the great depression led to concern over the diets of many of the unemployed, and those with extremely low incomes. The number of people on relief increased, and the number of people who were actually going hungry became of great concern to policy makers. The existence of surpluses of specific farm products at the same time caused many individuals to become interested in the possibility of using some of these farm products to improve the adequacy of diets. Thus the idea of demand expansion became more generally accepted.

Domestic Demand Expansion Programs

Domestic demand expansion activities began in the early 1930's, and a number of programs have been developed since that time. The groups of programs which are designed to improve national dietary levels and to expand current and future markets for food along with information on dates of operation, activities involved, and groups affected are indicated in Table 19–1.

Direct Distribution. The direct distribution program was placed on a permanent basis with the passage of Section 32 of the Act of 1935. Since that time, Section 32 funds, derived from customs receipts and supplemental appropriations, have been used to purchase surplus agricultural commodities. Although Section 32 commodities can be exported, they have been used primarily in the direct distribution program.[3] The products distributed under this program have varied from time to time depending on what products happened to be in surplus at a particular time. Practically all major agricultural commodities in some form have been involved in the direct distribution program since its beginning in 1935.

The magnitude and scope of the program has varied with the number of needy people on relief, the number of needy people in charitable institutions, the emphasis being placed upon the program by the administration, as well as the quantity of surplus food being purchased. For example the number of people in needy family units receiving donated foods increased from 3.7 million in December of 1960 to 6 million in November of 1961 as a result of an executive order from President Kennedy. At the same time the retail value of these donations increased from $3 per person a month to $6 per person per month.[4] Usually the emphasis in this program was on the disposal of surpluses

---

[3] During the period 1936–61 only 12.4 percent of Section 32 expenditures were payments for agricultural exports.

[4] Isabelle M. Kelley, paper given at the 39th Annual Agricultural Outlook Conference in Washington, November, 1961.

TABLE 19–1

DOMESTIC DEMAND EXPANSION PROGRAMS, 1930–66

	Direct Distribution	School Lunch	Food Stamp	Special Milk	Plentiful Foods
Dates of operation	1930 to present	1933 to present	1939–43 1961 to present	1940 1954 to present	World War II to present
Major activity	Distribution of surplus foods	Contribution of foods and financial assistance	Food price subsidy	Subsidy paid on milk sales to school children	Merchandising and informational program
Program clientele	Needy families, school lunches, charitable institutions	Elementary and secondary school children	Needy families	Elementary and secondary school children	All consumers
Advantages	Is selective in that surplus products are involved	Achieves nutrition objectives while at the same time increasing food consumption	Increases food consumption and nutritional level	Increases milk consumption and nutritious	Enhances level of knowledge about surplus food products
Weaknesses	May not include food needed to improve diets; does not use normal market channels	Failure of some to participate and is limited to school children	Costly to the government and difficult to administer	Limited to the single food product	Is strictly educational and many do not receive and use the information

rather than adequate and suitable diets for the recipients. However, in recent years more effort has been made to provide a variety of foods to needy families through the direct distribution program and thereby improve the nutritional content of the diet.

School Lunch. Government assistance to the school lunch program was initially limited to the donation of surplus foods. Section 32 increased the magnitude of food donations since it provided a permanent source of funds for this purpose. The program was broadened and placed on a more permanent basis with the National School Lunch Act of 1946. This program has expanded steadily, and in 1966 over 16 million school children took part in the program.

Food Stamps. One disadvantage of the direct distribution program is the fact that the food must be handled through channels other than the normal marketing channels. The Food Stamp Plan was an approach designed to overcome this shortcoming with respect to needy families. A food stamp program operated during the period 1939 to 1943, and a variation of this program was initiated on a pilot basis in 1961. Under this program persons meeting stipulated eligibility requirements have their food purchasing power increased through allotments of food coupons which can be used to purchase foods in regular commercial outlets. The eligible families pay an amount for food coupons that they would normally be expected to spend for foods included in the program. The value of the coupons obtained is normally considerably above the amount paid for the coupons. For example, during the 1964 fiscal year the families involved in the food stamp program received coupons valued at $73 million for which they paid $44.4 million. The program was placed on a more permanent basis as a result of legislative action in 1964 and has replaced the direct distribution program in many areas as the vehicle for expanding the consumption of food by needy families.

School Milk. The special milk program was instituted as a part of the Agricultural Act of 1954 and placed on a more permanent basis in 1961. Schools and institutions participating in the program purchase fluid milk from local marketing firms and the federal government pays part of the cost of the milk. Approximately 2 percent of the fluid milk consumed by the nonfarm population is moved through this program. It is also estimated that the program is available to at least three out of every four children in school.[5]

Plentiful Foods. The plentiful foods program is quite different from the others discussed above because it is primarily information in nature. A number of agencies within the Department of Agriculture as well as some outside groups are involved in selecting foods to be included on the plentiful foods list. An effort is made to obtain the coopera-

[5] *Ibid.*

tion of food marketing firms and the institutional trade in publicizing the products which have been categorized as plentiful. This program does not attempt to bring about a permanent change in the demand for products involved but rather to temporarily shift the demand for a particular product in line with its availability.

The first actions of President Roosevelt and his administration in 1933 were designed to reduce the output of surplus agricultural commodities. However, at the same time there was concern with the inadequate diets of needy families. A search began for some way to raise farm income without reducing the availability of food to those suffering from malnutrition. As a result the programs discussed above were developed during the decade to follow with the dual objectives of increasing the consumption of farm products and at the same time providing for better nutrition among needy families. More emphasis has generally been given to the objective of reducing unwanted surpluses, but in recent years increased concern has been evidenced with the dietary needs of those individuals receiving products as a part of these programs.

Export Demand Expansion Programs

Export demand expansion was the central idea in the McNary-Haugen bills of the 1920's. There were also attempts to obtain legislation which would establish additional institutions to finance the export of agricultural commodities. During this period the primary concern was with increasing exports. This was seen as a vehicle for reducing the quantity in the domestic market, and there was very little evidence that people were concerned with food shortages in other countries. The first actual program to increase exports was during 1931 and 1932 when the Grain Stabilization Board undertook a program to stimulate exports. Some gifts were made to foreign governments, and there were also price concessions to increase sales. Although activity during this period was relatively small, some of the ideas were adopted in later programs.

Early Efforts. Many of the programs which were proposed during the 1920's became a reality during the following decade. The Agricultural Adjustment Act of 1933 contained a provision whereby the tax which had been imposed upon processors of agricultural commodities would be refunded to exporters of those commodities involved. To a limited extent this established a two-price plan for those commodities subject to the processing tax. In 1934 the Export-Import Bank was established with the purpose of extending emergency credit to finance exports. One of the three major clauses of Section 32 of the Agricultural Act of 1935 involved export subsidies. This legislation authorized the use of customs receipts to make cash payments to commercial exporters following the export of agricultural commodities. The final type of export program authorized prior to the beginning of World War II was the authorization in 1939 of exchange of surplus agricultural commodities for strategic and critical materials produced abroad. Thus, during the 10 years preceding World War II, programs were initiated to establish a two-price system for export products, provide direct subsidy payments to exporters, and authorize barter programs.

A different set of problems was prominent during and immediately following World War II, namely that of encouraging production, helping to feed the allies, and assisting in relief and rehabilitation following World War II. The Lend Lease Act passed in March, 1941, the Marshall Plan passed in 1948, and Section 32 programs were the main vehicles for encouraging and assisting exportation of agricultural commodities during this period.

Just prior to the outbreak of hostilities in Korea a number of congressional acts were passed to alleviate the surplus problem which was beginning to develop.[6] Among these were reiteration of the exemption of export sales from restrictions on resale price of CCC owned commodities and an amendment to the CCC charter authorizing barter of surplus agricultural products for strategic and critical materials.

Commodity Credit Corporation loans and inventories mounted rapidly as the Korean war came to an end. There was also increasing concern with malnutrition and insufficient food supplies in a number of underdeveloped countries. Just as in the case of domestic demand expansion, the surplus disposal objective was coupled with one of improving diets of recipients overseas. Many of the countries in need of additional food were attempting to limit imports as they were lacking in purchasing power, especially in the form of dollars. These conditions led to the most significant development in the history of export demand expansion, the passage of Public Law 480.

Recent Efforts.   Export demand expansion activities in recent years have been of three major types. They include commercial exports with government assistance, concessional sales, and grants or donations. The first of these, commercial exports with government assistance, is carried out under the regular price support programs, and the Commodity Credit Corporation charter authorizes exports for which payment is made in dollars but at prices less than domestic levels. These involve payment of export subsidies to private firms engaged in international trade or the acceptance of losses on commodities held in Commodity Credit Corporation inventories. Since these exports normally go to countries which are more highly developed, the subsidies may be considered merely as payments necessary to reduce the difference between world prices and

[6] Elmer L. Menzie, Lawrence W. Witt, Carl K. Eicher, and Jimmye S. Hillman, *Policy for United States Agricultural Export Surplus Disposal,* Technical Bulletin 150 (Tucson: Arizona Agricultural Experiment Station, 1962), p. 28.

domestic price support levels. The objective is primarily one of reducing surplus commodity stocks, and very little thought is given to the nutritional level of diets in the recipient country. Slightly over one fifth of all agricultural exports during the period 1953–63 were commercial exports with some government assistance.[7]

Public Law 480. The other two types of export demand expansion activities were authorized by the Agricultural Trade Development and Assistance Act of 1954 (Public Law 480) and the Mutual Security Act of 1953. Both of these acts provide authority for exports in exchange for currency of the recipient country, and Public Law 480 also provides authority for barter, grants, credit sales, and donations. Title I of Public Law 480, sale of farm commodities for foreign currency, has been by far the most important of the special export programs. Title II provides for grants of food for disaster relief and other assistance, while Title III provides for domestic and foreign donations of foods for distribution by nonprofit volunteer relief agencies of the United States and international organizations as well as barter of surplus food and fiber in exchange for strategic and other materials needed by the U.S. government. Title IV of Public Law 480 is directed toward those countries which have progressed more in their economic development and authorizes long-term dollar credit sales of surplus agricultural commodities. The relative importance of the programs authorized by Public Law 480 is indicated in Figure 19–1. As of June 30, 1966, $9,755 million worth of commodities had been shipped under Title I.[8] Titles II and III were responsible for $1,328 million and $3,991 million respectively during the same period. Title IV has increased in importance recently with the total value of agricultural commodities shipped under this section amounting to 10 percent of total Public Law 480 shipments during the fiscal year ending June, 1966.

Wheat, cotton, fats and oils, feed grains, and rice represented over 90 percent of the market value of commodities sold under Title I of Public Law 480 during the period 1955–66. In fact, wheat and cotton ranged between 58 and 75 percent of the total value of shipments under Title I of Public Law 480 up to the end of 1961.[9] It would appear that surplus commodities dominated the export demand expansion program during the late 1950's and early 1960's. Therefore, surplus disposal was apparently the major objective with meeting the food needs of recipient countries a secondary objective during this period.

Disappearance of surpluses during the mid 1960's resulted in a shift in philosophy regarding export programs. As Secretary Freeman stated in

---

[7] *Ibid.,* p. 36.

[8] *Foreign Agricultural Trade of the United States,* Trade Statistics and Analysis Branch, Foreign Development and Trade Division, ERS (Washington, D.C.: USDA November, 1966), p. 23.

[9] Menzie, *et al., op. cit.,* p. 40.

FIGURE 19-1

Value of U.S. Agricultural Exports under Public Law 480

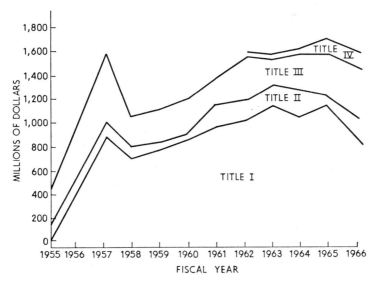

Source: *Foreign Agricultural Trade of the United States*, November, 1966.

March, 1966:[10] "Commodities available to food recipient countries will no longer be limited as they have in the past. The commodity 'mix' sent abroad under concessional programs will be geared to the kind needed rather than circumscribed by the kinds held in stocks. We can expect the trend to be in the direction of commodities with special nutritional values."

The situation was changing so that needs were being considered rather than surpluses; efforts were being made to help countries develop their own agriculture; and an attempt was being made to emphasize long-term dollar credit sales rather than sales for foreign currency.

CONSEQUENCES OF DEMAND EXPANSION EFFORTS

How much can the demand for food be expanded? What methods are likely to be most effective? To answer these questions it is necessary to know something about the effects of alternative approaches to demand expansion. Information is needed on the extent to which food consumption is increased with the alternative approaches, the agricultural resources required to produce the additional quantity of food consumed,

[10] Hearings before the Committee on Agriculture and Forestry (United States Senate, 89th Cong., 2d sess., March, 1966).

nutritional effects, and the cost of operating programs at various levels.

The effects of demand expansion programs differ considerably with the many alternative types of approaches which have been used. The effects differ depending on the mechanics of the program, the magnitude of the program, and the economic parameters which are involved. Alternative types of programs will be examined here to indicate their effect upon prices and incomes of farmers, nutritional levels, resources required in agriculture, and cost to the government. Primary attention will be given to the short-run impact of alternative type programs. The longer run impacts are much more difficult to assess and require information which is in many instances presently not available. Three alternative types of programs will be examined to provide examples of procedures used in an analysis of impact and to indicate some of the effects to be expected.

The Direct Distribution Type

The direct distribution type program involves purchase of commodities by the United States Department of Agriculture, the Commodity Credit Corporation, or some similar government agency. The commodities are then given away to a variety of recipients such as school lunches, people on relief, or charitable institutions. An important assumption is that the commodities which are purchased are removed from the normal marketing channels and are donated to individuals or groups who would not otherwise purchase the commodity. Many of the consequences of this approach depend on the degree to which this assumption is true.

Impact on Price. The short-run impact of a direct distribution type program may be analyzed by assuming a fixed quantity of the product available during the short-run period as in Figure 19–2A. The total quantity available is represented by Q_1, and the difference between Q_1 and Q_2 is the amount of the product which is purchased. The new price resulting in the normal marketing channels is equal to P_2 and exceeds the old price by an amount depending upon the magnitude of the purchase and the slope of the demand curve. The more inelastic the demand curve at the level of output involved, the greater will be the increase in prices and incomes received by farmers as a result of the purchase program. If the price flexibility for the product involved is high, meaning a low price elasticity, the effect of the program on incomes of producers will be large. For example if the price elasticity is equal to 0.25, the price flexibility would be equal to four and a purchase of 5 percent of the total quantity available would result in a 20 percent increase in price of the product. Under such conditions the increase in total receipts of farmers would be considerably greater than the expenditure of the government for the product.

A more complicated situation is involved if the product donated to

FIGURE 19–2

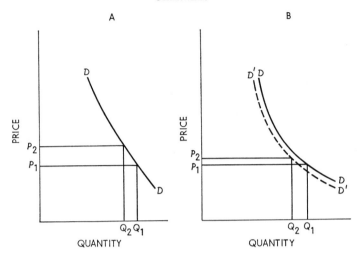

eligible recipients replaces to some extent what would have otherwise been purchased. For example, a school receiving dried eggs through the direct distribution program may not purchase as many eggs through normal market channels. This results in a decrease in the demand for the product in the normal market channels and reduces the price and income effect of a purchase program of a given size. Such a situation is illustrated in Figure 19–2B. In this example the quantity purchased was the same as in Figure 19–2A, but since the product donated through the direct distribution program replaced some of the normal purchases, the market demand curve shifted to the left and the increase in price from P_1 to P_2 was considerably less.

Impact on Diets.   The extent to which direct distribution type programs improve diets depends on the food products included. Products high in protein might make a big contribution to better nutrition while a program including only foods high in starch content would do very little. If the improvement of diets, through the distribution of foods which are often not a part of the eligible recipient's diet, is a major objective, then the selection and inclusion of products which will remedy the nutritional deficiency is important. This requires conscious effort on the part of program administrators to see that such products are purchased and distributed.

Impact on Resource Use.   Agricultural products require varying amounts of resources in the production process. In general, production of calories in the form of livestock products requires more agricultural resources than does the production of an equivalent number of calories in the form of crops. If there are excess resources in agriculture, then the quantity of resources used in the production of products involved in the direct distribution program becomes an important issue. The purchase and distribution of high-resource-using food products encourage the production of such products and thereby helps reduce the excess quantity of resources in agriculture.

Costs of Program. The total government cost of direct distribution programs is easy to control. It can be increased or decreased by varying the quantity of products purchased. However, the level of purchases and distribution required to achieve specific price or nutritional objectives depends on a number of other economic parameters besides the quantity purchased. The cost of a direct distribution program will be greater in relation to the increase in price achieved when the total value of production of a commodity is large, when the price elasticity is high, and when products distributed are substituted in sizable quantities for normal market purchases. If the product requires additional processing or movement over greater distances in order to be used in the direct distribution program, then this will also increase the cost to the government. These same factors will determine whether a direct distribution program is less costly or more costly than other alternative types of demand expansion efforts.

The Food Stamp Program

The food stamp program is essentially a multiple pricing scheme in which one price exists in the marketplace and eligible families are able to buy food at a lower price. The difference between the price in the market and the price paid by recipients for food stamp coupons is made up by the government. It might also be thought of as an income subsidy program in the sense that food purchasing power is increased, but in this program the increased purchasing power must be used to purchase food. Such a program is usually restricted to low-income families similar to those who would participate in a direct distribution program; therefore, the program has the dual objectives of reducing surplus agricultural production by increasing food consumption and improving nutritional levels among low-income families.

Impact on Prices. Certain assumptions are necessary in order to illustrate graphically the effects of a food stamp type program. Figure 19–3 assumes no price supports and that the total quantity produced is clearing the market. It is also assumed that the total demand for food (D_T) can be divided into the demand by participating families (D_P) and the demand by nonparticipating families (D_{np}). The division of the total quantity of food available during a particular period between

FIGURE 19-3

THE EFFECTS OF AN INCOME SUBSIDY TO LOW-INCOME FAMILIES ON DEMAND FOR FOOD, ASSUMING A FIXED QUANTITY AVAILABLE

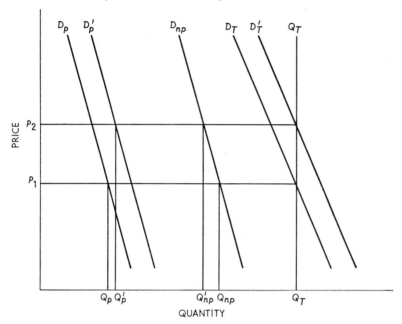

participating and nonparticipating families would be dependent on the shape and location of the demand curves representing the two groups. An increase in food purchasing power may be illustrated by shifting the demand curve for participating families to the right (from D_p to D_p') which also results in a similar shift in the total demand for food (D_T to D_T'). In the short run, the expanded demand for food due to the food stamp program will result in higher food prices (P_2 instead of P_1). With these assumptions the quantity of food consumed by high-income families or the nonparticipants will decline (from Q_{np} to Q_{np}') while the food consumption of participating families will increase (Q_p to Q_p').

The situation during the early 1960's did not fit the assumptions used above. Rather, the situation was one in which prize supports for many food products were in existence and surpluses were accumulating. This situation is illustrated in Figure 19–4 with food products supported at price P_o. The total quantity demanded was not as large as the quantity available during a particular period so the quantity $Q_o - Q_T$ was added to surplus stocks. The additional food purchasing power provided to participating families would increase their food consumption by a greater amount than when total quantity is fixed but would not affect

FIGURE 19–4

THE EFFECTS OF AN INCOME SUBSIDY TO LOW-INCOME FAMILIES ON DEMAND FOR
FOOD ASSUMING THERE IS A PRICE SUPPORT PROGRAM WITH SURPLUSES MOVING
INTO STORAGE

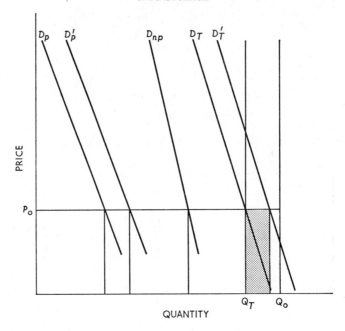

consumption by nonparticipating families since food prices would not be
affected. Under these assumptions the increase in demand would not
result in higher prices but rather the quantity added to surplus stocks
would be reduced. The reduction is represented by the shaded portion of
Figure 19–4.

Effect on Food Consumption. A food stamp type of program is
operated in such a way as to provide adequate purchasing power for a
nutritionally balanced diet. However, there is no assurance that food
purchases with the food stamps will be such as to actually provide a
nutritionally adequate diet. Recipient families are given food stamps
equal in value to an amount sufficient to provide the nutrients needed,
but the actual expenditure of these food stamps is at the discretion of the
family. Strict administration of such a program insures that the stamps
are used to purchase food, but the choice of food items may be such as to
allow deficiencies in certain food nutrients. Although no generalizations
can be drawn with respect to the effect of such a program on the
nutritional level, it is true that families with higher food expenditures
ordinarily purchase a greater variety of food and nutrients.

The pilot food stamp program initiated in 1961 was an attempt to obtain information on the effects of such a program. Those concerned with the program were particularly interested in reaction to the program, administrative problems, and effects on expenditures for the various groups of food products. Although the results from analyses of the program are somewhat limited, the initial reports indicated that increases in expenditures were concentrated mainly in meats, dairy products, poultry products, fruits, and vegetables.[11] Total food consumption did increase with the value of foods purchased increasing approximately 85 to 95 cents for each dollar spent by the government. As of June, 1965, participants were receiving a monthly subsidy equal to $6.38 per person. The average participant was receiving coupons worth $16.77 in exchange for $10.39. This level of subsidy was fairly typical of the program during its first six years of operation.

Government Cost. The cost incurred by the government in operating a food stamp type program is largely dependent upon the participation in the program. Participation is affected by the scope of the program, the value of coupons received relative to their cost, the eligibility requirements, and economic conditions in the United States. A program of this type tends to be more costly than a direct distribution type program because it involves a larger number and greater variety of products. The fact that it would involve a greater number and variety of products is an advantage to the extent that the program leads to an improvement of diets but is a disadvantage from the standpoint that it would not necessarily involve those products which are in surplus in the form of government stocks or depressed prices in the market. Such a program would lead to greater consumption of food and thus reduce the effects of excess resources in agriculture but might not remedy the problems of malallocation in terms of temporary excess production of particular commodities.

Export Demand Expansion Programs

Considerable effort is directed toward increasing the demand for United States agricultural products in other developed countries. Much of the effort is educational in nature or is directed toward the reduction of trade barriers. These are exemplified by the numerous trade missions, agricultural exhibits, and trade negotiations under the Trade Expansion Act of 1962. When these efforts are successful, the demand curve is shifted to the right and there is a positive effect on prices and incomes received by farmers. The nutritional objective of demand expansion programs is not involved to any large extent since most of the countries involved are relatively well fed. To the extent that demand is increased, markets are provided for the products of some of the excess resources in

---

[11] *The Food Stamp Program, an Initial Evaluation of the Pilot Projects*, AMS-472 (Washington, D.C.: USDA, 1962), p. 31.

agriculture. Increased shipments of soybeans and wheat to Japan and of soybeans, feed grains, and poultry products to Europe are good examples. Commercial exports of soybeans to Japan and Europe increased from approximately 65 million bushels in 1956 to 200 million bushels in 1965. During the same period exports of feed grains to Europe more than tripled which aided considerably in the reduction of feed grains stocks during the early 1960's.

Multiple Pricing Schemes. The export demand expansion programs of greatest magnitude in recent years have not involved countries which are large commercial importers. Rather the countries were those deficient in food production and lacking in purchasing power. Large quantities of agricultural products have moved abroad with some form of subsidy. In some instances the United States government has paid an outright cash subsidy to commercial exporters while in other instances foreign currency has been accepted in payment for government exports. In either case the value of what was received in return for the exports was lower than the domestic price so the programs have essentially been one of multiple pricing. For example wheat is sold for one price in the domestic market, is exported in the commercial market at a second price which is somewhat lower, and is moved under the Public Law 480 program at a value equivalent to an even lower price.

It is difficult to generalize about the various types of effects of the multiple pricing schemes used to increase exports of agricultural commodities. However, without such programs more of the products would have been forced on to the domestic market, depressing prices, or there would have been sizable increases in government stocks. If prices of agricultural products are supported and if the output at that level of price exceeds the quantity that will be consumed in the domestic market, then the decision must be made to either restrict production of the product or devise some method of surplus disposal. Strict production controls will reduce the cost of surplus disposal while more lenient policies toward production result in greater subsidy costs to dispose of the excess production. It has been suggested that the administrators would presumably try to optimize their position by equating net marginal production control costs with net marginal subsidy cost.[12] However, measurement of the two cost functions is not an easy matter.

It is probably more realistic to say that with the buildup of stocks during the 1955–65 era we were forced to do something. Subsidizing exports was feasible because of this situation. During the late 1960's the need for food in many of the underdeveloped nations forced us to do something for foreign policy reasons. Although the motivating factor was different, export subsidies were still feasible. In an uncertain world and

---

[12] Menzie, *et al., op. cit.,* p. 88.

in the United States where only a small difference exists between too much and too little we plan on using reserves or surpluses and subsidized exports as cushions against the uncertainities of weather, war, and technological change.

Costs of Export Demand Expansion. The costs of export demand expansion programs as a means of surplus disposal are difficult to measure because of the foreign aid aspects of such programs. The cost which should be attributed to these efforts to increase exports is no doubt less than the total cost of the commodities to the Commodity Credit Corporation plus handling and shipping charges. Any attempt to determine an exact cost figure attributable to surplus disposal involves some judgment as to the foreign aid benefits derived from the program, some of which are not measurable. These export programs also provide a sizable market for the resources used in agriculture, but here again the problem of determining the exact effect on resources hinges on whether or not production of the product would have been restricted had there been no export programs.

Effect on Diets. Export demand expansion programs such as Public Law 480 do improve diets in the recipient country. Many of the countries receiving Public Law 480 products have a relatively low average level of calorie intake. Even though the products provided under Public Law 480 are not necessarily the ones most severely needed, they do add to total food supplies and to this extent do help remedy some of the nutritional deficiencies which would otherwise be present. Just as in the case of the direct distribution type program, the selection of commodities to include is the important factor in determining the extent of the contribution to better diets. However, the need for food in many of the recipient countries is so great that this factor is of lesser importance in the export demand expansion programs.

The Magnitude of Past Efforts

The magnitude of past demand expansion efforts may be measured in terms of participation, quantities of food involved, or cost to the government. Of the domestic demand expansion programs, the direct distribution program has been in existence the longest and has involved the largest number of people, with the school lunch, school milk, and food stamp program following in order of magnitude. Data on quantities of agricultural products involved are not readily available so information on participation and cost of the programs will be used to provide some indication of their relative importance. There is some problem of double counting in the sense that the direct distribution program includes food donated for school lunches in addition to that distributed to other groups.

Participation. The direct distribution program is by far the largest in terms of participation since in addition to those eating school lunches it includes families on relief and individuals in charitable institutions. During 1961 approximately 24 million people in this country were receiving donated food under the direct distribution program. This included 16 million school children, 1.5 million needy people in charitable institutions, and over 6 million people who were members of needy families receiving foods distributed through the program. The number participating in the special school milk program varies from day to day, and exact figures on participation are not available. However, it is estimated that the program is now available to at least three out of every four children in school. The food stamp program was on a pilot basis until 1964 so data on participation underestimate the relative importance of the program in succeeding years.

Cost of Programs. The cost of domestic demand expansion programs increased rather steadily during the early 1960's with the total cost climbing from slightly less than $500 million in 1961 to near $800 million in 1966. Approximately one half the cost of these programs is attributable to the direct distribution program. The school lunch program is the second most costly of the programs with cost in recent years of nearly $200 million.[13] The cost of the direct distribution is more variable than the cost of other programs because the level of activity is dependent on emphasis being given to the program and the number of perishable agricultural commodities in surplus. On the other hand, the cost of the school lunch program has been much more stable and has increased steadily each year as the number of school children participating increased.

The cost of the special school milk program has also increased since its beginning, and its cost is now equal to approximately one half that of the school lunch program. As the food stamp operations have increased and the program extended to additional areas, the cost of the program has also climbed to over $100 million and estimates indicate a full-scale program might cost between $300 and $400 million.[14] However, many of the families receiving food stamps would no longer be involved in the direct distribution program so the cost of the latter program would be expected to decline.

Size of Export Programs. Export demand expansion programs have been much larger than domestic demand expansion programs regardless of the criteria selected for comparison. For example, while the total cost of domestic demand expansion programs was just slightly more than

---

[13] It should be noted that the cost of the school lunch program is exclusive of the value of products received through the direct distribution program.

[14] *The Food Stamp Program, an Initial Evaluation of the Pilot Projects*, AMS-472 (Washington, D.C.: USDA, 1962), p. 6.

one-half billion dollars during the early 1960's, Title I of Public Law 480 alone was costing more than a billion dollars. If all export demand expansion efforts were grouped together, the total cost would approximate $2 billion dollars during recent years. As indicated earlier, relatively large quantities of specific commodities have been involved in the export program. In fact, approximately one half of all U.S. agricultural exports have moved under some type of government assisted or special export program.

LIMITS TO DEMAND EXPANSION

Government costs are probably the most important factor limiting the magnitude and potential of demand expansion programs. Present efforts to increase domestic food consumption cost approximately $750 million. It is doubtful if an expenditure exceeding one billion dollars would be acceptable to the Congress. This would allow some expansion of the school lunch and school milk program and the operation of a food stamp program on a low level of operation, in addition to the present direct distribution program.

During recent years Congress has demonstrated a reluctance to either reduce or increase the magnitude of domestic demand expansion programs. President Johnson suggested a reduction in federal appropriations for the school lunch and school milk programs as a part of his budget recommendations for the 1967 fiscal year. The recommended reductions were based on the idea that most families could well afford to pay the full cost of the lunches and milk received through the program and that federal subsidies should be limited to subsidizing the total cost of the program for those students who could not afford to pay. However, Congress did not go along with the recommended reductions but rather continued the programs at about the same level in terms of appropriations. On the other hand, expansion of the food stamp program has been restricted somewhat because of lack of funds. Other factors which limit demand expansion efforts to some extent are the difficulties of administration and the reaction of the food trade to specific types of programs.

In general, the people of the United States are well fed. This also serves as a major limitation to domestic demand expansion programs. However, this is not true with respect to export demand expansion programs. The United States has been spending nearly $2 billion a year to expand agricultural exports and has proposed to spend additional billions over future years. However, it is doubtful if any sizable increase in export demand expansion activities could take place without reaching a limitation of cost, resistance from other exporting countries, or resistance from agricultural interests in recipient countries.

DEMAND EXPANSION AND AGRICULTURAL SURPLUSES

Examination and evaluation of alternative approaches to the problems of agriculture are eventually faced with the question of their potential relative to the excess capacity in agriculture at any particular point in time. Could domestic consumption of food have been expanded to the point of using up a quantity equivalent to that which was added to surpluses during the 1950's and early 1960's? Although an unequivocal answer cannot be given, the answer appears to be no. A University of Minnesota study published in 1961 concluded that reasonable levels of expenditures on demand expansion could have reduced the agricultural surplus prevailing at that time by only one fourth to one third.[15] The approach has considerable appeal because of the additional objective of improving diets and removing nutritional deficiencies, but it is limited and cannot be looked at as a panacea for agriculture. Rather it seems that these programs are now built into the system and hence provide very little flexibility for dealing with surpluses.

What about the potential of export demand expansion? Here the answer is much less apparent. Events of the mid 1960's suggest that the food deficit in many parts of the world could easily wipe out surpluses in the United States if these food needs could be translated into effective demand. Is there a willingness on the part of the people of the United States to finance such programs? Will food production potential in underdeveloped countries continue to lag behind population growth? The answers to such questions will be of crucial significance to the agricultural economy of the United States.

[15] Martin E. Abel and W. W. Cochrane, *Policies for Expanding the Demand for Farm Products in the United States, Part II, Programs and Results,* University of Minnesota Agricultural Experiment Station Technical Bulletin 238 (April, 1961), p. 76.

THE GOVERNMENT AND THE SUPPLY OF AGRICULTURAL PRODUCTS

Chapter
20

The Federal Farm Board was not equal to the task confronting it at the beginning of the great depression. It was supposed to achieve price stabilization by maintaining price at a particular level with the surpluses accumulated during good crop years being returned to the market during years when crop production was low. A declining demand for agricultural products did not permit the returning of accumulated surpluses to the market. Concern with farm output as well as domestic and export demand became an area of discussion with respect to the economic problems of agriculture. Restriction of farm output does not have the automatic appeal that certain other approaches to agricultural problems have, so the theoretical basis for such an approach as well as the other considerations involved are topics suitable for discussion. Although terms such as output controls, production controls, and supply management have been used as the popular phraseology at different times, they are used synonymously here.

THEORETICAL BASIS FOR CONTROLLING SUPPLY

Some argue that efforts to control farm output are merely pieces of evidence pointing toward an overly ambitious government. On the other hand some would suggest that there are economic principles readily available to support such an approach. Several different ideas must be examined in the process of determining the theoretical basis for efforts to control supply. An acquaintance with the nature of the supply relationship in agriculture is helpful in understanding changes in farm output. The nature of competition, the irreversibility of supply, and the price elasticity of demand are also important to an understanding of government activity as it relates to restriction of the supply of agricultural products.

The Competitive Structure

What is good for the individual farm is not necessarily also good for agriculture. This might not be the initial reaction, but the discussion of various degrees of competition have already shown this to be true (see

Chapter 11). The individual farm, operating as one among many, faces a horizontal demand curve. This is true because its output is such a small part of the total output and its product is so similar to that of many other farms that regardless of the amount produced the price received is normally the same. The farmer's optimum output then depends largely on the nature of his cost relationships. Further, almost any reduction in cost will encourage him to increase output. This situation has great significance when all the individual actions are added together. Individual farmers strive to become more efficient, adopt new technology as it becomes available, and take various forms of actions to increase output. The effect on total farm output is obvious.

As the total output of a particular farm product increases, prices received by producers decline. What started out as individual decisions to increase output on individual units has consequences for the group. An important aspect of the situation is that the decision with respect to the level of production is made prior to the time the product is ready to sell. In many instances this may be several months or even in a few cases many years prior to the time the product is sold. Research related to individual decision making with respect to level of output has shown that decisions are based on current price or the price which has existed in some recent past period. The level of individual farm output may or may not be the optimum one if price changes during the production period. However, assume for the moment that the individual farmer is well aware of the fact that if he and other individual farmers increase output prices will decline. Will he as an individual find it desirable to restrain his increase in output? Only if he can be assured that others will act in a similar way—an assurance he does not have! The overall outcome may or may not be desirable depending upon the relative changes in output and price. The magnitude of the relative price and output change in turn depends on the price elasticity of demand for the product.

Price Elasticity and Total Revenue

Farmers produced 1.7 percent more eggs in 1962 than in 1961. Even though production increased, cash receipts from the sale of eggs declined 2.9 percent during the same period. This is a phenomena that is not easy for people to understand, particularly the producers of the product involved. However, far from being a rare occurrence, this is quite common in agriculture. As indicated earlier, this type of an occurrence is related to the price elasticity of demand. Although the concept is theoretical, the results have some very practical implications as far as agriculture is concerned.

If the quantity of a commodity available increases during a particular period, price must decline in order to move the additional quantity into consumption. The percent decline in price is sometimes greater than the percentage increase in the quantity available. Such is the case for many agricultural commodities. And the demand is said to be inelastic. The reverse is also true in the sense that when the quantity available declines, the price increases, and the increase in price is proportionately greater than the decline in output. So, if the variation in output is within that segment of the demand curve that is inelastic, an increase in output will result in lower total receipts while a decrease in output will result in greater total receipts. On the other hand the demand for some products is elastic. This means that quantity will respond proportionately much more to changes in price, and hence if the quantity increases, price will not have to decline as much and therefore total revenue will not decline with increases in quantity. In the same way, when the quantity produced decreases, price will not increase as much and therefore total receipts will not increase with a decline in the quantity available. This relationship between price elasticity of demand and total revenue becomes quite important when decisions are being made with respect to the level of output. This is true regardless of whether it is the individual firm or some governmental agency making decisions which influence the final result.

The theoretical justification for supply control begins to take form. The conclusion is reached that individual farmers acting in such a way as to maximize their profits will not be able to restrict output. In fact, there is evidence to suggest that with increased efforts to become more efficient, with the availability of new technology, and with improved managerial skills, output will probably increase markedly. This, in combination with an inelastic and slowly increasing demand will result in lower total revenue or cash receipts. The reactions of individuals in society to this situation will vary depending upon their value systems or their concepts of "what ought to be." Some will conclude that since the individual farmer cannot resolve the situation, there is a role for government to play in helping him to restrict his output.

The reasoning above is not the sole argument for the restriction of agricultural output. Another one which is quite important arrives at somewhat similar conclusions via another route. It starts with a concern over the level of farm prices and farm income. Advocacy of price supports above the long-run equilibrium level develops. However, the higher level of prices stimulates increased output which tends to drive the market price even lower. If the price support program is one involving loans and storage programs, then storage stocks increase in magnitude. Eventually a point is reached where it is decided that in order to maintain the price at the higher level and yet not incur excessive storage costs, output must be restricted. This argument is not unrelated to the characteristics of agriculture discussed above. Often involved in the argument for higher level price supports is the inability of individual producers to adjust output to the desired level. With the inelastic demand for many agricultural products and for total food, the result is continued low returns.

Falling Prices and Increasing Output

Although not necessarily related to the arguments in favor of restricting agricultural output, there is another aspect of the supply relationship which becomes involved in justification of price and income supports for agriculture. Favorable prices lead to the commitment of additional resources to the production of a particular commodity. Additional land is devoted to the output of the product; new buildings or facilities are constructed; new machines are purchased; or any number of similar type actions are taken to increase the output of the product. Numerous periods during the past provide evidence of the responsiveness of output to increasing prices. The increased output which results causes price to decline if demand has not also increased simultaneously. The problem occurs when prices decline, because output is not as responsive to declining prices as it is to increasing prices. The resources which were committed when prices were favorable do not move out of agriculture readily. The picture is one of an irreversible supply curve in the sense that output increases when prices rise but does not contract as fast when prices decline. Numerous explanations exist for this type of response, but in general many of them are related to the relatively high fixed cost in agriculture or the fixity of many of the resources which are used in the production process. That is, since a high proportion of their costs are incurred regardless of the level of production or since they have assets which will provide a greater return in production than if disposed of, or used to produce something else, it will pay the farmers to continue producing at the same level even though prices have declined.

This peculiar nature of the supply response in agriculture has implications in terms of returns to farmers over time. Increased output and the lower prices which would result would in turn lead to lower output if the supply curve did not take this particular form. If the quantity produced evidenced as much response with declining prices, then the impact of an inelastic demand would tend to average out over time. However, the situation is such that prices may decline and returns may continue to be depressed over a considerable length of time without bringing about a reduction in output. This lack of response to declining prices also becomes an argument which is used to suggest that adjustment problems in agricultural output are serious and assistance may be needed.

ALTERNATIVE METHODS OF CONTROLLING PRODUCTION

Some of the theoretical groundwork for restricting agricultural production has been laid. From a profit maximization standpoint for the industry there appears to be adequate support for considering this type of program in some instances. The argument may be one of simply reducing production to take advantage of an inelastic demand or may be one of reducing production to hold surplus accumulation down to a reasonable level. Assuming the validity of one of these arguments, what are the alternative approaches to accomplish the task? Several alternatives would appear feasible from a theoretical standpoint. A number of these will be examined to see the economic principles involved and to explore some of the potential effects of such action. Most of these are not just ideas tossed around in ivory towers but rather have actually been used, or at least debated, in the halls of Congress during periods when surpluses were in existence.

Input Controls

Everyone knows it takes inputs to produce output. Policy makers jumped on this idea early in the history of price and income support programs. Problems with the Federal Farm Board made the next administration quite conscious of the need to ease the price support task by reducing the amount of production. Placing a limitation on one of the inputs used in the production of agricultural products appeared to be a ready-made solution. Needless to say, the ones who first instituted this type of program had not read Chapter 5 of this book, and they were not aware of the pitfalls which lay ahead because of input substitution.

Controls on the Land Input. Consideration of the other input categories make it more obvious why land was selected as the input to control. Capital was already short in agriculture at this stage of the development of the agricultural economy. Its marginal value product was high, thus it did not appear to make sense to restrict what was already limited. Labor on the other hand was quite difficult to limit. A farmer could not be told how many hours he was to work or how hard he was to work on his farm. Even control of the use of hired labor would have been almost impossible. At the same time land was obviously an important input and one which could be measured. Rules could also be laid down as to its use. And so began in the 1930's the history of programs to restrict the land input in hopes of reducing the output of one or more farm commodities. Land is the only input which has been controlled, but the types of programs designed to limit the land input have varied considerably. Some have been voluntary, others have been mandatory, and the actual mechanics have varied over time.

Voluntary and Mandatory Controls. Perhaps the words voluntary and mandatory should be used with caution. In most instances it has been merely a matter of degree. The word voluntary has been used in most instances where compliance or noncompliance with the program was left for the farmer to decide. This meant that he could continue to produce the product involved, even though he did not choose to comply with the program limiting the land input. The noncomplier might sacrifice certain advantages as compared with the farmer who complied. For example, he might not be eligible for price support at as high a level, he might not be eligible for certain payments, or he might not even be eligible for price supports. The incentives for participation or compliance with programs to restrict the use of land have varied from practically nothing to the point where compliance might be said to be mandatory. For example, in some instances the penalty for failure to restrict the use of land was so large that noncompliance was definitely unprofitable.

Acreage Allotments. The first actual attempt to limit the use of land was essentially an acreage allotment program. Producers of some of the major crops such as cotton, tobacco, and wheat were encouraged to enter into agreements to restrict or reduce the acreage of the specified commodity. In return, the farmer was exempted from a tax imposed upon the nonparticipant. Acreage allotment programs similar to those first used in 1933 have continued in some form since that time with various types of incentives to the complier.

Land Diversion. A close relative to the acreage allotment is the land diversion program. After the Agricultural Adjustment Act of 1933 was declared unconstitutional in 1935, a new program was developed in which farmers were paid to shift specified percentages of their acreages of soil depleting crops into soil conserving crops. In return for this land diversion, payments were to be made. Generally speaking, the soil depleting crops were also the same crops which earlier had been subject to acreage allotments. This approach has also continued in use during various periods up until the present. In some instances the land diversion programs have been combined with acreage allotments in the sense that farmers were required to restrict the production of a particular commodity to a specified acreage and were also required to divert a certain percentage of their acreage to a soil conserving or otherwise specified use.

The Soil Bank. A third and more recent arrival on the scene was the soil bank program of the mid 1950's. The acreage reserve aspect of the program differed only slightly from other land diversion schemes which had been used earlier and which were to reappear later. But the conservation reserve aspect was different in the sense that land was to be retired for 3, 5, or 10 years to a specified type of use, primarily grass which could not ordinarily be grazed. During the time the conservation reserve was in existence, both part and whole farms were retired. This program was not tied to any specific commodity but rather was a general effort to reduce the amount of land used in crop production.

Programs of the 1960's. The emergency feed grain program passed in 1961 and the feed grains, wheat, and cotton programs in effect during most of the 1960's were also land diversion programs. However, they were somewhat more effective than acreage allotments in restricting output in that farmers could not divert the acreage to some other crop. Instead, the land was to be diverted to some soil conserving use and had to be in addition to the normal acreage in soil conserving uses. Again in this instance there were incentives to encourage compliance including diversion payments and eligibility for price support loans and payments.

Effectiveness of Past Efforts. Practically all of the efforts to limit the use of the land inputs have had some effect. However, it would probably be safe to say that few of the programs have had as much impact as the designers might have desired. Several problems have been involved. Chief of these has been the ability of farmers to find ways of increasing output even though land was limited. More intensive cultivation, hybrid seeds, fertilizers, and other output increasing techniques have been used to overcome the limitation of the land input. As indicated earlier, the substitution of other inputs, particularly capital, for land has been quite successful. Minimum national acreage allotments below which allotments could not be reduced and exemptions granted to small growers also reduced the effectiveness of acreage allotments. Farmers also chose to retire or to divert the poorer quality land which meant the acres remaining in production were the most productive. In fact, the argument has been made that one reason the restriction of the land input has been as acceptable as it has been is the fact that it does not really control or limit production—at least not to the extent intended.

Restricting Other Inputs. The possibility of reducing the use of other inputs has been suggested from time to time, but it has never really seriously been considered. Of course one very important reason was the political power of firms selling these inputs to farmers. They would certainly have opposed vigorously any attempt to limit the market for their products. Another very important reason why other inputs have not been restricted is the high marginal value product of these inputs. For example, it might be possible to limit the use of fertilizer in the production of crops, but such has never been really seriously proposed. The same might be said of research activities which lead to the development of new technology. Although policy makers have been willing to sacrifice some efficiency in production in order to achieve certain other objectives, the efficiency objective is still important enough that inputs with high marginal productivity are not likely to be limited by legislation.

An exception might be the subsidy provided farmers in the form of low-priced irrigation water. This input is actually provided to farmers at a price much below its cost. The pricing of irrigation water, an input, at a price considerably below the cost to the government does not appear rational while making other efforts to reduce output.

Controls on Marketings

Since input controls have not been terribly effective, the argument is often made that controls on quantities marketed are a more logical approach. Essentially the idea is that each individual farmer would be allocated a specific quantity which he would be allowed to sell. Any amount in excess of the quantity allocated would have to be destroyed, sold at a price much lower than the normal price, sold with a penalty assessed, or held over until the next production period. Although direct controls on output have been debated since the 1920's, the approach has seldom been used in an actual program, except in the case of sugar. The idea did receive increased attention however during the early 1960's as one of its chief proponents, Willard W. Cochrane, became Director of Agricultural Economics in the USDA and a close advisor to the Secretary of Agriculture. The nearest the idea came to becoming a reality was during this period. A National Turkey Marketing Order considered during 1961–62 had quantity controls on output as one of its major features, and the Wheat Referendum defeated in May of 1963 also contained quantity controls on the amount marketed for food use. Both programs were defeated by farmer vote, and the rejection of the wheat program was considered by many as a farmer vote for greater freedom and less government control. It is not difficult to see why direct controls were quite unattractive to farmers when compared with the system of price support loans and payments, storage programs, and loose input controls in effect at that time.

Although quantity control programs are often thought of as efforts to control total production, such is not always the case. Many of the proposals would merely control the quantity marketed for a particular use. In reality the Turkey Marketing Order and the wheat program considered in 1963 were also of this type. Several industry programs are actually of this type with the quantity going into the primary market limited and the remainder diverted to lower valued uses. The distinction is quite important because a program to control total output would be much more difficult to carry out than one merely controlling the quantity going into a specified use.

Increasing Mobility of Resources

Although not often thought of as a method of controlling production, efforts to increase mobility of resources will essentially achieve the same results. Resources which are mobile will move into another use when earnings in one type of enterprise decline relative to another. As indicated earlier, one of the characteristics of agriculture is the fact that resources once committed become quite fixed. Therefore, activities which increase the mobility of resources will help reduce production even though such activities are not production control in the strictest sense.

Efforts to make the labor resource more mobile have been quite common. These have included activities to increase the general level of education as well as programs to provide specific types of training. Programs to increase the information available about job opportunities have also been involved. There have likewise been some attempts to increase the number of uses which can be made of the land resource. An example of this is the encouragement given to the use of agricultural land for recreational purposes. Most of these efforts to make resources more mobile do not result in immediate improvement but may have considerable impact over time.

PROBLEMS IN EFFECTIVE SUPPLY CONTROL

Differences between the approaches to supply control are not really fundamental. Regardless of whether inputs or marketings are controlled, the objective is the same. The degree to which production is actually controlled by any of the measures is really the crucial question, and is the central core of many of the problems with respect to production control. Regardless of whether production controls are used as the only method of supporting prices or whether they are used in conjunction with other measures, a number of problems will arise. Among these are conflicts in values, lack of cross-compliance, input substitution, and numerous administrative difficulties.

Conflicts in Values and Group Interests

Agricultural policy concerns itself with problems which are of concern to a sizable segment of our society and has as one of its alternative approaches the use of some form of public action. The problems ordinarily cannot be solved to everyone's satisfaction by the action of one individual or a single firm. The fact that a plurality is involved gives rise immediately to the possibility for conflict. Disagreements may develop as the result of differences in information available, differences in values or peoples' concepts of "what ought to be," or differences in the way in which an individual, group, or society expects to be affected by the problem or proposed solutions. It is possible to reduce the differences caused by lack of information by determining the facts and by making them more readily available. The differences caused by conflicts in interests and values are more difficult to resolve.

Production control as an approach to agricultural policy is confronted with difficulties of all three types discussed above. For example there are differences in the information relied upon by different individuals in the sense that some might argue that a particular product has an inelastic demand while others would argue the demand to be more elastic. Actually very little is known about long-run price elasticities. The lack of empirical price and quantity data over wide ranges may make this seemingly simple question rather difficult to resolve. The estimation process for price elasticities of demand may bring forth differences in assumptions, differences in the data used, and differences in estimating procedures, which in total leave considerable basis for disagreement.

The idea of production control also provides ample basis for conflicts in values. Even if everyone agreed that farm income ought to be higher and that supply management would result in higher incomes, there would still be disagreement as to how the increased income ought to be distributed. Should it be distributed according to the effort made to reduce production, equally among all farmers, primarily to landowners as opposed to farm operators or vice versa, or according to the historical record of past production? Values with respect to efficiency may conflict with the general idea of production control or at least with specific techniques. The conflict may be in terms of its effect on resource combination, production pattern in relationship to comparative advantage, and possibilities of achieving economies of scale. Perhaps the most widely discussed conflict is that of production control and freedom. There is much debate about the impact of production control efforts on freedom of individual decision making. Although freedom to expand output may be limited only by the cost of purchasing additional marketing certificates or land with acreage allotments, the imposition of this additional limitation or cost variable becomes quite important to those involved.

Opposition to efforts to control farm ouput caused by value conflicts is often difficult to distinguish from that caused by realization that such an approach would place at a disadvantage specific individuals or groups. Some farmers would object to supply management because their output would be curtailed while others would disagree strictly on a value basis. Operators of farm supply or marketing firms might argue against production control on the basis of its interference with freedom of individual decision making while at the same time others might object because their volume of business would be lower with the use of supply management. These differences are often related, difficult to detect, and in some cases impossible for the individual to distinguish. Needless to say, objection to supply management does result both from conflicts in values and conflicts with interests of individuals. Both types of conflicts are difficult to resolve.

Participation in various types of government programs and specifically those to reduce agricultural production does not necessarily indicate absence of value conflicts. Participation often involves reconciliation of values with certain other objectives involved in operating a farm, including that of making more money. Farmers may evidence considerable opposition to government intervention in agriculture and argue that the government ought to be less involved while at the same time participating in specific programs. Voting in referendums and participation in a specific program also seem to indicate differences between values and participation. This has some significance in the sense that if in a referendum which is not loaded in one direction, farmers are allowed to indicate their preference, they are likely to defeat the program even though they might participate in the program if it were put into effect. Once a decision is forced with respect to an individual's own farm operations, his decision may be quite different from what he considers ought to be the case with respect to the industry.

Cross-Compliance

The seriousness of the problem of cross-compliance was not fully realized during the early history of efforts to control production. Farmers decreased the acreage used for some crops while increasing the acreage devoted to others. In some cases it was possible to participate in a production control program for one crop while in another case choosing not to comply, even though efforts were being made to control the production of the second crop. An indication of this is provided by changes in land use for major crops which during the period 1952 to 1959 were as follows:[1]

	1,000 Acres
Wheat	−16,272
Cotton	−11,661
Feed grains	+ 8,004
Soybeans for beans	+ 8,533

Participation in the benefits from one program were not contingent upon participation in another. Although some effort was being made to restrain the production of feed grains, it is estimated that one third of the increase in production during the period from 1952 to 1959 resulted from transfer of cropland from wheat and cotton to feed grains.[2]

By the mid 1950's there developed a more general acceptance of the idea of overall excess capacity in agriculture. Up until that time the feeling was more nearly one of malallocation of resources within agriculture in the form of surpluses of some crops but shortages of others. The simultaneous buildup of stocks in a number of important commodities with no apparent shortages of others led to the adoption of the soil bank program in 1956. It was based upon the idea that total overall capacity needed to be reduced. Concern was expressed with acreage allotment programs in which lack of cross-compliance tended to negate efforts to

---

[1] *Farm Production—Trends, Prospects and Programs,* Agriculture Information Bulletin No. 239, Agricultural Research Service (Washington, D.C.: USDA, May, 1961), p. 32.

[2] *Ibid.,* p. 32.

restrict production. However, expression of concern and accomplishing cross-compliance in acreage allotment programs are two different things, and very little was done immediately to resolve the problem.

The 1961 feed grains program did move in the direction of cross-compliance by requiring that land diverted from feed grain production be devoted to a soil conserving use and that this be in addition to the acreage normally in a soil conserving use. The 1962 wheat program also contained a similar feature. Requiring cross-compliance is a movement toward stricter production control and therefore faces opposition similar to that faced by any movement toward stricter control.

Disappearance of wheat and feed grain surpluses during the 1960's resulted in a return of much of the diverted land back into production and much less concern with cross-compliance. However, it may well be argued that much of the success of the techniques used to get rid of the surpluses during the early part of the decade was associated with the features requiring cross-compliance.

Input Substitution

The change in the inputs used in agriculture during the last 35 years has been quite dramatic. Most of this change was due to the adoption of new technology. Farmers now spend over $30 billion a year for goods and services to produce crops and livestock. This is indicative of the tremendous increase in the use of purchased inputs. The use of purchased inputs has nearly doubled since the 1930's and has increased over 25 percent just since 1950. During the same periods the use of nonpurchased inputs has declined rather rapidly and has actually declined nearly 25 percent since 1950. Substitution of capital inputs for labor and even for land have been quite common. This is indicated in Figure 20–1. Most notable has been the tremendous increase in the use of fertilizer and lime, and the steady decline in the use of farm labor. Although the amount of land used for crops has moved up and down during this century, it has declined rather steadily since 1955, and 10 to 13 percent less land was used for crops during the early 1960's as compared with 1955. During the same period farm output increased approximately 12 percent so the substitution of other inputs for land and labor is quite evident.

One might want to think for a moment about the profitability of adding more capital inputs on a smaller quantity of land. A review of the principles of input substitution in Chapter 5 would suggest that such action would not be profitable if the farm were using the optimum quantities of inputs prior to restriction of the land input. However, the "if" here is an important one. Comparisons of research results on the optimum rates of input use with actual use on farms suggest that some inputs are not used at optimum rates but rather at much lower levels.

FIGURE 20-1

Use of Selected Inputs in United States Agriculture, 1950–65

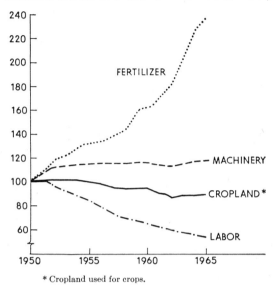

* Cropland used for crops.

Restriction of the land input forces many farmers to become much more conscious of alternative means of maintaining or increasing output. Application of more fertilizer is a classic example of the results. Moreover, over time new technology is continually changing capital-labor ratios of substitution so as to make profitable the use of more capital.

Substitution of other inputs for land makes it difficult to control farm output by restricting the land input. This is true regardless of whether the program is one involving acreage allotments, land retirement, or cropland diversion. Whole farm land retirement is an exception since it also results in some reduction in the use of other inputs. When using the land input control approach, the reduction in the land input must be great enough to compensate for substitution of other inputs. This can easily result in some loss in efficiency as there is not likely to be an optimum combination of inputs in the production of the commodity involved.

Administrative Difficulties

The difficulties involved in administering production control programs are no doubt one of the more important problems in effective production control. Administration of mandatory programs in such a way as to insure compliance is necessary in order to actually control production and to assure that those choosing not to comply with the program do not benefit at the expense of those in compliance. This is a problem in agriculture because even though the program might be desirable from the standpoint of the industry, each individual farmer has an incentive to produce as much as possible. Even though the control of the land input is subject to the problems associated with cross-compliance and input substitution, such a program is easier to administer than one involving controls on quantities marketed. This is no doubt one reason why this approach to supply management has been used more widely.

It is also important that supply control programs be administered in such a way as to avoid freezing production patterns. Unless care is taken, allocation of the production privilege will tend to result in continuation of obsolete production methods as well as fixing the geographic location of production. Such results may not be in the best interest of efficiency. To avoid this it is necessary to provide methods of transferring the production privilege. In his book advocating the use of controls on quantities marketed, Cochrane suggested that marketing certificates would need to be negotiable.[3]

However, this does not resolve the difficulty because once the production privilege is made negotiable the benefits from the program tend to be capitalized into the instrument used to allocate the privilege to produce and market the product. This is true for either input controls or controls on quantities marketed. For example in the flue-cured tobacco-producing area it has been estimated that an acre of tobacco allotment is worth over $2,000.[4] A committee appointed by the National Milk Producers Federation suggested a plan in which each producer would have been issued a permanent base or quota and would have received annual marketing certificates equal to some uniform percentage of the base. A study was made of the certificate aspect of this proposal, and estimates were derived of the prices of the negotiable marketing certificates.[5] Results indicated that the equilibrium prices of certificates in most years would fall between 50 cents and $1 per hundredweight.

Therefore, even though it appears that mechanics must be provided to permit transfer of the production privilege, many of the benefits from the program will be capitalized into the price of the control instrument, and the initial recipient—and his heirs—will be the primary beneficiary. The price of the production privilege would then become a cost of doing business for new entrants into the production of the controlled commod-

[3] Willard W. Cochrane, *Farm Prices—Myth and Reality* (Minneapolis: University of Minnesota Press, 1958). p. 173.

[4] Frank H. Maier, J. L. Hedrick, and W. L. Gibson, Jr., *The Sale Value of Flue-Cured Tobacco Allotments*, Virginia Polytechnic Institute Agricultural Experiment Station Technical Bulletin No. 148 (Blacksburg, April, 1960).

[5] K. L. Robinson and M. H. MacDonald, "Prices of Negotiable Marketing Certificates for Milk," *Journal of Farm Economics*, Vol. XLIV (August, 1962), pp. 781–95.

ity. The absence of administrative devices for controlling production without either freezing production patterns or permitting the capitalization of benefits into the price of the production privilege has been a big factor retarding the acceptance of production control programs.

There are some unique difficulties associated with the administration of programs to control quantities marketed. One of the more important of these is the numerous ways in which a particular commodity can be marketed. Some commodities can be used on farms in the production of another agricultural commodity, assembled for movement through the regular wholesale and retail channels for sale fresh, sold directly to processors, or sold directly to consumers. The nature of demand in the different markets varies, and allocation among markets as well as certification of quantity sold becomes quite difficult.

Inability of farmers to determine exactly the quantity of final output poses a second type of difficulty in administering effective quantity controls. Farmers faced with a quantity allocation must either reduce production enough so that it will definitely be below the quantity allocated or stand the chance of producing more than can be marketed. This is particularly true for crops subject to considerable variation in production as a result of weather. Damage from disease and insects introduces additional uncertainty. In the case of livestock, variation in rate of gain and death loss make it quite difficult to produce to exact quantity allocations. Disparity between plans and final outcome in terms of output makes it almost imperative that programs have some flexibility within the mechanics. However, providing flexibility without weakening the control features is not easy. These difficulties inherent in programs to control the quantity marketed have no doubt been an important reason for their limited use.

EFFECTS OF PROGRAMS TO CONTROL PRODUCTION

A number of research projects have been conducted in recent years in which at least part of the study was devoted to an analysis of programs to restrict agricultural production. A variety of techniques have been considered ranging from voluntary land retirement to strict controls on quantities marketed. Some of the projects were directed toward the analysis of a single approach while others were concerned with a comparison of alternative approaches. Among the approaches considered have been those actually in existence at some time in the past, those seriously considered by Congress at some time in the past, and those proposed but never seriously considered. The various studies have used different assumptions, have appraised alternative approaches, and have considered different types of effects.

Research findings indicate the diverse impacts to be expected from production control programs. The results from specific programs will be desirable from the viewpoint of some and undesirable from the viewpoint of others. Since the relevant criteria to use in an evaluation of supply control programs differs between individuals and groups, the research results make it obvious that reaction will vary, and disagreement is to be expected.

Effects on Farmers

The aggregate effects of production control programs are much easier to evaluate than the effects on individual farms. The aggregate effect might appear to be desirable and yet have quite an opposite effect on individual farm operations. Much of the aggregate effect depends upon the price elasticity of demand for the product involved. Given the price elasticity, conclusions can be drawn about receipts, gross income, and prices of the product involved. Total cost of production is normally expected to be lower, but the actual magnitude of decrease is dependent upon a number of factors including the distribution of production rights as well as the resulting difficulties in achieving economies of scale and proper allocation of resources.

For example, are all wheat farmers to be permitted to produce up to a certain minimum with the restrictions imposed primarily on the larger producers who normally have lower costs of production? Or, do the limitations imposed prevent the cotton producer from having an acreage adequate to justify the kinds of machinery necessary for efficient production?

The effect on net farm income can usually be determined at least in a directional sense, even though specific levels are difficult to derive. Aggregate freedom to expand output is obviously restricted as this is the object of a supply management approach. The effect on individual managerial freedom depends largely on the mechanics used in the program and the nature of the individual farm operation.

The impact of almost any approach to agricultural policy will differ on individual farms because of the heterogeneity which is characteristic of farms in the United States. Differences in size of enterprises, relative profitability of alternative enterprises, and production efficiency are such that a supply management program might be advantageous for some farms while being detrimental to others. Some farms have achieved such economies of scale or have combined resources so as to achieve levels of efficiency and cost of production such that they can compete quite profitably at low price levels. For example farms with cost conditions similar to that in Figure 20–2 could cover all costs at the relatively low price represented by P_1 while if production were restricted, cost of production would increase considerably. Efficiency on these farms might be impaired by restriction of production.

FIGURE 20–2

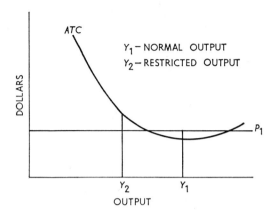

Other farms are organized in such a way as to have a high degree of flexibility in terms of size of enterprise and might benefit considerably by a lower level of production and higher prices. Such a farm might have an *ATC* curve similar to the one in Figure 20–3. In this instance, although cost of production was higher initially, a reduction in production would increase cost of production very little. This latter situation is much more likely to be the case for the farm with the ability to produce multiple enterprises or shift resources from one enterprise to another fairly readily.

Even the extent to which managerial freedom is restricted would be dependent upon the characteristics of the individual farm. Relatively few, if any, supply management proposals contain absolute restrictions on the production of individual farms. Some mechanism is usually included whereby individual farmers can increase production by obtaining

FIGURE 20–3

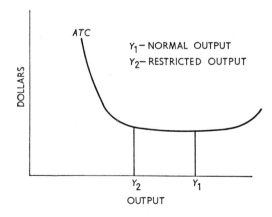

control of additional land or purchasing marketing certificates or other instruments used for control. Restriction of individual managerial freedom then becomes dependent upon the ability to obtain additional rights to produce the commodity involved.

Effects on Marketing Firms

Firms which sell supplies to farmers, as well as those which buy products from farmers and move these commodities through marketing channels, are all likely to be affected by a program to restrict agricultural output. The relationship between level of farm output and margins or incomes of firms handling agricultural products was discussed in Chapter 16. The relationship between incomes of firms which sell supplies to farmers and the level of farm output is similar, but in this instance the effect varies with the type of farm supplies involved and the approach used to restrict production.

Firms involved in marketing farm products generally evidence a relatively stable margin per unit handled. Total revenue and net profits tend to be higher when farm output of the products involved is high. This is true almost regardless of the function performed by the marketing firm. Under these conditions the effect of programs to restrict farm output becomes rather obvious to the extent that the programs actually do reduce output. Profits of firms handling agricultural products will likewise be reduced. However, once again caution must be exercised in accepting this conclusion as the final word. If a program to control production resulted in a particular area continuing to produce the product whereas otherwise it might have been forced out of production, the marketing firms in that area will benefit from the program and with an expanding population it may only be necessary to slow the rate of growth in output rather than actually reduce output. Also programs which stabilize farm output over time would assist marketing firms in planning and organizing units of a more efficient size due to the increased certainty about the volume of product to be handled. Generally speaking, though, for maintenance of profit and other reasons, these firms oppose programs to restrict output.

Programs which restrict farm output reduce the need for inputs used in production. But for specific inputs, the effect differs with the approach used to limit production and the type of input involved. Most of the past efforts have involved restriction of the land input, and in many instances the use of other inputs has increased where it was possible to substitute the input for land. Analyses of the conservation reserve program indicate that whole farm land retirement results in a greater decrease in the use of other inputs than does land retirement on a part-farm basis.

A program to restrict the *quantity* of products marketed would be expected to reduce the farm supplies needed in production of the product unless other programs were also in existence. Output would decrease, most of the agricultural land and labor would continue in production, and therefore the need for purchased inputs would be less. As in the case of firms handling agricultural products, the effect will vary some among areas and individual firms, but the general effect of programs to restrict output is to reduce demand for farm supplies.

Effect on Consumers

Consumers are concerned with the effects of production control programs to the extent that they affect the quantity, quality, or price of products consumed and the cost of agricultural programs to them as taxpayers. Farmers facing limitation on quantities which could be marketed might be expected to strive for higher quality in order to increase total receipts. On the other hand, two of the products subject to control in recent years, cotton and to some extent wheat, both had quality problems. This was especially true of cotton. In fact, much of the surplus was in short fiber cotton that was considered undesirable by the trade. It is probably true that the surplus problem would have been much less serious had all of the product been of higher quality. Otherwise no direct connection between production control programs and the quality of products is obvious.

The quantity of agricultural products and their prices at the retail level would be affected by efforts to restrict production. In order to increase farm prices and incomes with a production control program, it would be necessary to reduce the quantity marketed and thereby increase the price of the product. Assuming no change in marketing margins, consumers would be faced with a smaller quantity of the product available and higher prices at the retail level.

Equal absolute price changes at the farm and retail level do not result in equal percentage changes (see Chapter 16). The relative changes at the two levels depend upon the size of the marketing margin. The demand model developed by Brandow was used to estimate what the effect would have been had all of the output from agriculture during the period 1955 to 1957 cleared the market. Results from the analysis indicated that farm product prices would have declined 15 percent while retail food prices would have declined only 4.67 percent.[6] For individual commodities the decline in farm price would have been greatest for those with the most inelastic demand and the largest marketing margin. Likewise a production control program which resulted in higher farm prices would also result in increased retail prices, but the increase at the retail level would be much less in percentage terms. This is particularly true for some of the commodities in greatest surplus during the decade of the 1950's such as wheat and cotton. In these cases the farm price is such a

[6] Brandow, *op. cit.*, p. 9.

small proportion of the retail price for the finished product that efforts to enhance the farm price through supply management would result in relatively small percentage changes in retail prices.

In the absence of price and income supports, the prices of many farm products are characterized by a high degree of variation. Although a lag of several months or years may be involved, production also eventually varies. Cyclical variation in livestock prices and production is indicative of the result. During some periods consumers are faced with relative scarcities of particular products and extremely high prices while at other times products are in surplus and prices are fairly low. Supply management would tend to even out the level of production, and prices and quantities would tend to be more stable over time. To the extent that variations in prices and quantities is undesirable to consumers, the increased stability might offset some of the disadvantages associated with higher retail prices.

A General Comparison

The extent to which supply control programs are desirable or undesirable actually makes sense only when compared with other approaches to agricultural policy. Most of the empirical analyses which have been conducted in recent years have compared this approach with either conditions approaching the free market or the existing system of price support. As suggested earlier, the results vary depending upon the assumptions regarding economic activity, the mechanics of the program involved, and the objectives toward which the program is directed.

One reason programs to control quantities marketed were considered during the early 1960's was the tendency of existing programs to result in higher food prices, smaller quantities available in the domestic market, and fairly high government cost. While a program to control marketings would also result in increased prices and smaller quantities, it was argued that such a program would at least reduce government cost.

In addition to the other effects considered, a production control program imposes certain restrictions on output and thereby affects managerial freedom. This in a sense is the objective of the program; it substitutes discipline of the industry for individual discipline in control of output. Since there is a lack of individual incentive to restrict output, as contrasted with other industries, another type of mechanism is suggested. Some of the early activities by government in the agricultural economy such as market news, statistical reporting, grading, inspection, and other services were designed to do for agriculture what it was not possible for individual farmers to do for themselves. Supply control is suggested by some as a similar type activity, but it is one which is much more controversial.

Chapter 21

THE GOVERNMENT AND SELF-HELP PROGRAMS

Efforts by the government to alter competitive conditions are quite common throughout the economy. During the past few decades the government has taken many positive steps to increase or at least maintain competition within the agricultural economy. On the one hand steps have been taken to check the growth of private or corporate concentration of control and on the other it refrained from governmental regulation or restriction of farmer owned and operated businesses. Whenever it has appeared that traders, processors, or transportation agencies that handle farm commodities were operating to the disadvantage of the farmer, various protective steps were taken. Prominent among these have been efforts to assist farmers gain what some have termed countervailing power. This chapter is concerned with this type of program and particularly those which might be classified as self-help programs.

TYPES OF PROGRAMS

Cooperatives

Programs designed to promote the establishment and growth of cooperatives are good examples of efforts to increase competition. Down through the years there has been an attempt to assist small-scale firms in gaining advantages that come in other industries through large-scale operation. The actions taken have enabled individual farm operators to join together for the performance of commercial, credit, and even operative functions which could not be performed effectively, economically, or at all within the limits of the individual farm. The licensing of cooperatives, provision of credit, and exemption from antitrust are evidences of the efforts in this area.

Cooperatives now play an important role in the marketing of inputs used in agricultural production, provision of electrical and telephone services, credit, and the marketing of agricultural products. Cooperatives such as Agway in the Northeast, Farmland Industries in the Midwest, and Cotton Producers Association in the South have become large-scale business operations. The estimated volume of business handled through marketing, farm supply, and related service cooperatives had a gross value of $17.2 billion in the 1961–62 fiscal year.[1]

Marketing cooperatives handled at some stage of the marketing process approximately 25 to 30 percent of the total output of agricultural products in 1964. They market 60 percent of our dairy products, 40 percent of our grain, and as high as 90 percent of some fruits. Cooperative brand names such as Land O'Lakes butter, Ocean Spray cranberries, Welch grapejuice, and Sunkist oranges and lemons are widely recognized at the consumer level. Cooperatives are also important in the farm supply business, handling about one seventh of all production supplies and equipment and accounting for approximately one fifth of the money spent for feed, seed, fertilizer, petroleum, and pesticides.[2]

The objectives of cooperatives are multiple and complex in nature. Among the more important ones are the achievement of greater efficiency in marketing inputs and agricultural products, increasing competition in the markets involved, obtaining increased bargaining power for farmers, and the provision of services which would otherwise be very costly or unavailable. Cooperatives are also central to the success of the other self-help type programs discussed in this chapter.

Marketing Agreements and Orders

Enabling legislation for marketing orders and agreements is a good example of self-help programs designed to provide countervailing power to farmers. The marketing order idea received its impetus from at least three different sources. These were the general concern with cooperative marketing and efforts to facilitate the growth of cooperatives; experiences of grower groups in California; and the thinking of Mr. George N. Peak who was the first administrator of the Agricultural Adjustment Act of 1933.

Sapiro Movement. Farmer cooperatives experienced rather rapid growth during the 1920's. Having observed the experiences of some small localized cooperatives in California, a young lawyer named Aaron Sapiro believed that similar techniques would be useful for major crops. The scheme developed by Mr. Sapiro included binding contracts with producers; integration forward in the marketing channels to include selling, warehousing, pricing, and exporting; and holding surpluses off the market or diverting surpluses to exports so that the cooperatives would have stronger bargaining power.[3] The idea moved too fast, and the cooperatives were not strong enough to carry through with the ambitious plans. However, some of the problems did become obvious, and one of these

---

[1] *Farmer Cooperatives in the United States,* Farmer Cooperative Service Bulletin 1 (Washington, D.C.: USDA, 1965), p. 73.

[2] *Ibid.,* p. 248.

[3] Murray R. Benedict, *Farm Policies of the United States, 1790–1950* (New York: Twentieth Century Fund, 1953), pp. 194–98.

problems involved the producers who were not members of the cooperatives.

Tokay Grape Growers Agreement.   A few years later a group of Tokay grape growers in California were struggling with the problem of large production and low prices in some years and smaller crops and higher prices in other years.[4] The problem of low reservation prices discussed in Chapter 15 was apparent. In 1932 a group of the growers decided to prorate shipments during the season. The idea worked fairly well for three weeks, but it was discontinued after that time because the noncooperating shippers who only represented 15 percent of the production were selling 50 percent of the grapes. In this instance it was obvious that the small percentage of noncooperating producers were destroying the plan for increased industry returns.

Ideas of George Peak.   At about the same time Mr. Peak, who was later to become the first administrator of the Agricultural Adjustment Act of 1933, was attempting to transfer experience in industry to the agricultural economy. Mr. Peak believed that agreements could be reached between government agencies, processors, handlers, and producers which would result in more satisfactory prices for farmers.[5] In fact Mr. Peak believed that marketing agreements were preferable to the types of production adjustment activities being suggested for basic crops at that time. Mr. Peak's influence, plus the support of cooperative leaders, especially those representing specialty crops in California, was largely responsible for the marketing agreement provision in the Act of 1933. Only brief attention was given to marketing agreements in the 1933 Act. The Act authorized the Secretary to enter into marketing agreements with processors and handlers and to issue licenses. The primary purpose of the license was to eliminate unfair trade practices. These licenses were later used to force would be noncooperators to comply with the agreements. This license feature was the forerunner of the present marketing order, and it was changed to that term in the 1935 amendments to the original act.

Act of 1937.   The concepts of marketing agreements and marketing orders matured over time, and more or less permanent legislation was passed in 1937. The act was known as the Agricultural Marketing Agreement Act of 1937, and in amended form it furnishes the basis for marketing agreements and orders today.[6] As contrasted with Peak's view that marketing agreements should be limited to basic commodities, the ena-

---

[4] H. E. Erdman, "The California Agricultural Prorate Act," *Journal of Farm Economics,* Vol. XVI (October, 1934), pp. 624–36.

[5] George N. Peak, *Why Quit Our Own* (New York: D. Van Nostrand Company Inc., 1936), p. 76.

[6] *Compilation of Agricultural Marketing Agreement Act of 1937, Reinacting, Amending, and Supplementing the Agricultural Adjustment Act, as Amended, as of January 1, 1963,* Agriculture Handbook No. 243 (Washington, D.C.: USDA, April, 1963).

bling legislation came to be looked upon more and more as a means of assistance to growers of specialty crops and perishables. The 1937 Act authorized both marketing agreements and marketing orders with the two differing mainly in terms of their regulatory coverage.[7]

A marketing agreement is a voluntary contract entered into by the Secretary of Agriculture and handlers of a commodity and regulates only the signers (see also Chapter 15). On the other hand a marketing order is an order issued by the Secretary of Agriculture which makes the terms of the marketing agreement program effective on all handlers in the industry, irrespective of whether or not they sign the agreement. Thus, the development of marketing orders faced up to the problem of the minority who might choose not to comply and resolved this issue by making compliance mandatory.

Commodities Eligible for Orders. The latest amendment to the original act was in 1961 and increased somewhat the number of commodities which can be included under marketing agreements and orders. Marketing orders can now be issued for any agricultural commodity except fruits and vegetables for processing, honey, cotton, rice, wheat, corn, grain sorghums, oats, barley, rye, sugar cane, sugar beets, wool, mohair, livestock, soybeans, cotton seed, flax seed, poultry, and eggs. Turkeys and turkey hatching eggs however are not among the exceptions which means they can be included. All fruits and vegetables for canning and freezing are excluded except apples in certain states, cherries, cranberries, grapefruit, olives, and asparagus. As of the later part of 1961 there were approximately 45 marketing orders in effect for fruits, vegetables, and nuts and approximately 82 milk marketing orders.[8] There were no marketing agreements in effect unless also accompanied by a marketing order.

Bargaining Associations

Another development which has been of increasing significance during recent years is the bargaining association (see also Chapter 15). Evidence of this is seen in the organization and growth of the National Farmers Organization, the development of numerous commodity bargaining associations, and the increased attention given to the subject of bargaining power by farmers, political leaders, and academicians. These bargaining associations have been of several different types. Some of the bargaining associations have been typical marketing cooperatives in the sense that they take title to and handle physically the products produced by their members while others have not assumed this responsibility but

---

[7] *Self-Help Stabilization Programs with use of Marketing Agreements and Orders,* PA-479 (Washington, D.C.: USDA, November, 1961), p. 2.

[8] *Ibid.,* p. 7.

rather have restricted their activities to that of bargaining. Some have been in connection with marketing orders while others were not.

Bargaining associations now exist for fruits, vegetables, sugar beets, milk, livestock, and other important agricultural commodities. It was estimated that in 1961 there were approximately 40 fruit and vegetable bargaining cooperatives.[9] The recent growth in this idea is emphasized by the fact that two thirds of these fruit and vegetable associations were organized during the 1950's. Further evidence of support for such efforts is contained in the conclusions of the report by the National Commission on Food Marketing issued in June, 1966.[10] With respect to the marketing and pricing problems of agriculture, the Commission concluded: "We believe, therefore that there is frequent need for group action by farmers to adjust sales more uniformly to market demands at reasonable prices, to improve product quality and uniformity, to negotiate with buyers, and to protect themselves against trade practices and abuses of market power to which they are otherwise vulnerable."[11] The approaches recommended by the Commission for consideration included cooperatives and bargaining associations, marketing agreements and orders, and agricultural marketing boards similar to those used in Canada and some of the Scandinavian countries.

A producer bargaining association is typically a voluntary organization. Efforts are made to obtain a high degree of participation among producers in a given area so that the organization has bargaining control over a large proportion of production in the area. Contractual arrangements are often used whereby the producer grants to the association the authority to bargain about price, volume, time of shipment, and other terms of sale.

Activities of the National Farmers Organization have received considerable attention in recent years. As contrasted with most other efforts to increase farmer bargaining power, the NFO has concerned itself with some of the major farm commodities such as beef, pork, soybeans, and dairy products. The organization had its beginning during the mid 1950's in Iowa and Missouri and has since spread throughout the Midwest and now has members in most of the important agricultural areas of the United States. Utilizing contracts which designate the NFO as the bargaining agent for its members, the organization has used withholding actions to demonstrate its bargaining power in attempts to obtain contracts with processors.

The growth in bargaining associations may be traced to at least two

---

[9] G. Alvin Carpenter, "Role of Bargaining Associations," *Farm Policy Forum,* 14 (Ames: Iowa State University Press, No. 1, 1963–64), p. 34.

[10] *Food from Farmer to Consumer,* Report of the National Commission on Food Marketing (Washington, D.C.: U.S. Government Printing Office, June, 1966).

[11] *Ibid.,* p. 110.

reasons. First, the general dissatisfaction with low prices in agriculture and the awareness of what collective bargaining has been able to achieve for labor. Secondly, many of the cooperative marketing organizations involved in specialty crops and perishable products have matured in terms of organization to the point where bargaining appears to be an obvious extension of their responsibilities.

The large number of self-help programs in existence makes it impossible to treat adequately all of these efforts. Since marketing orders ordinarily involve a greater variety of activities, are somewhat more complex, are often operated in conjunction with a bargaining association, and have the longest history, emphasis will be given to the marketing order type program. In so doing, attention will be directed toward the types of activities involved, some of the typical effects, and the implication of such programs to farmers and marketing firms.

Activities Involved

The activities involved in self-help programs vary greatly. Even in the case of marketing orders there are differences in the objectives and the approaches used. Some marketing orders are established and operated under federal legislation while others operate under state enabling legislation. State enabling legislation differs from state to state and generally follows the pattern of federal legislation, but there are some exceptions. The activities involved in federal orders will be discussed here as they are more generally applicable and also provide some indication of the types of activities which are authorized by marketing orders. The Agricultural Marketing Agreement Act as amended specifies that one or more of a number of authorized programs may be included in an order. As long as an industry group designing an order restricts the provisions to those authorized in the enabling legislation, there is no fixed pattern for formulating or operating the order. The industry group developing the order attempts to include those provisions which are desirable in terms of the particular situation and problems of concern to the industry. With the exception of milk marketing orders, which are slightly different, commodity marketing orders must provide for one or more of the following activities:[12]

(1) specifying grades, size, quality, or maturity of the commodity that handlers may ship to market;
(2) alloting the amount which each handler may purchase or handle on behalf of any and all producers;
(3) establishing the quantity of the commodity that may be shipped to market during any specified period, the total quantity being allocated among all

---

[12] *Self-Help Stabilization Programs with use of Marketing Agreements and Orders,* PA-479 (Washington, D.C.: USDA, November, 1961), pp. 4–5.

handlers under a uniform rule on the basis of past performance, or the proportionate amount of the commodity the handler has available for current shipment;

(4) establishing methods for determining the extent of any surplus, for control and disposition of the surplus, and for equalizing the burden of surplus elimination among producers and handlers;

(5) establishing a reserve pool of the product, and equitable distribution to all financially interested parties for returns derived from the sale of the pool;

(6) inspecting the commodity;

(7) fixing of the size, capacity, weight, dimensions or pack of the container used in handling of the commodity.

Marketing orders also must contain provisions to achieve one or more of the following:

(1) to prohibit unfair methods of competition and unfair trade practices in the handling of the commodity;

(2) to require handlers to file their selling prices, and to sell at prices no lower than those filed—(handlers may change their prices at any time, but adequate notice must be given);

(3) to provide for the selection by the Secretary of Agriculture of an agency to administer the order. (Marketing orders for milk have provided for a Federal Milk Market Administrator, who is appointed by the Secretary).

In addition, a marketing order for crops may contain provisions to establish marketing research and development projects to assist, improve or promote the marketing, distribution and consumption of the commodity or product.

As is suggested by the kind of provisions authorized, marketing orders have as a major objective that of establishing and maintaining orderly marketing conditions. However, orderly marketing and particularly the provisions for quantity and quality controls are only means to an end, that of improved prices and incomes for producers.

As indicated earlier, a marketing order is initiated, designed, and administered by the industry. The U.S. Department of Agriculture serves as a partner in the process. Each marketing order has its administrative committee which is composed according to the provisions of the order. In addition to the industry deciding what provisions are to be included in the order, the administrative committee also has the responsibility for deciding which regulations will be put into effect during a particular period. The one exception to this committee's general authority is that when prices for the product involved exceed parity, only certain shipment regulations are permitted and most of the provisions of the order are no longer in effect.

One notable difference between federal marketing orders and those established under state enabling legislation is a provision for advertising and promotion. Whereas such activities are not possible under federal legislation, many state marketing orders do contain such provisions. In fact, in some states the enabling legislation for marketing orders is limited to the assessment of fees in order to carry out this provision. In other instances advertising and promotion is carried out by industry groups or individual marketing firms.

Bargaining activities are not authorized as a part of federal marketing orders except in the case of milk. This does not mean to imply that provisions of federal marketing orders do not impinge upon the bargaining process (see Chapter 15). Decisions are made with respect to quantities and qualities to be marketed, and information is generated which definitely affects the bargaining between producers and handlers. In many self-help programs other than marketing agreements and orders, the bargaining activity is the primary function. In these programs other activities are merely subsidiary to the bargaining activity.

Participation and Financing

Participation in self-help programs is quite often the key to success or failure. Even Sunkist Lemon Growers Cooperative, with a signed-up membership representing over 90 percent of the California lemon crop, had trouble with nonparticipants.[13] While the Sunkist growers were diverting part of their lemon crop to the processing market in order to improve the price for lemons on the fresh market, outsiders were shipping all their product to the fresh market. This problem continues to plague bargaining associations and has even been given as one reason for the failure of marketing orders in some instances. North Florida vegetable growers gave this as one reason for discontinuing marketing orders for tomatoes and cucumbers.[14] Growers in other areas to the North were not regulating shipments so the Florida growers felt their efforts to stabilize the market were in vain. Marketing orders do insure participation within the area covered by the order and tend to be more successful where most of the production is concentrated in a rather small area.

Financing of self-help programs is ordinarily accomplished by assessment of fees on products marketed by the producers involved. This is true of promotional groups, bargaining associations, and federal and state marketing agreements and orders. In the case of marketing orders the details of the financing procedure are spelled out in the order. Each year the administrative committee prepares and submits a proposed budget and recommended rate of assessment to the Secretary of Agriculture for his approval. The Secretary reviews and approves the budget and fixes the assessment rate.

[13] Floyd F. Hedlund, *The ABC's of Federal Marketing Orders and Agreements for Fruits and Vegetables*, PA-506 (Washington, D.C.: USDA, June, 1962), p. 6.
[14] W. E. Black, "Appraisal of Marketing Order Programs for Florida Vegetables," paper presented before the Conference on Marketing Policy, sponsored by the Agricultural Policy Institute, Raleigh, North Carolina, February 22, 1961.

THE EFFECTS OF SELF-HELP PROGRAMS

Most of the self-help programs which have been developed in the agricultural economy are attempts to overcome some of the economic weaknesses associated with atomistic competition. Earlier chapters such as the one on competition among the many and particularly the one on competition among farmers described some of the problems of atomistic competitors. Marketing orders and other types of self-help programs are responses to the needs which become obvious. Government policy has been favorable toward and has facilitated efforts by farmers to help themselves through group action.

One of the more important government actions along these lines was passage of the Capper-Volstead Act in 1922.[15] This act clarified the status of farmer cooperative associations with respect to antitrust action. Jurisdiction and control over cooperatives in their efforts to improve prices was delegated to the Secretary of Agriculture rather than the Federal Trade Commission. Government policy favorable toward mergers, acquisitions, and joint action by farmer cooperatives has also been present during most of the history of the cooperative movement.

The effects of self-help programs have been many and varied. There have been cooperatives which have failed and there have been those which have been highly successful. Some of these have helped farmers obtain higher prices for the products which they sell, and to obtain farm supplies at lower prices, while others were inadequately planned, poorly organized, and unsuccessful. Bargaining associations have likewise enjoyed varied degrees of success. A few marketing orders have been in effect since the mid 1930's while others were considered but never adopted or were organized and dropped after one or two years. Although it is difficult to generalize about the effects of such efforts, something can be said about the ways in which such programs affect market structure, ways in which such programs can be used to affect supply and demand, and the extent to which such programs provide the mechanics for taking advantage of demand conditions.

Structural Effects

To what extent do self-help programs, and specifically marketing orders, affect the structure of the market? If a marketing order contains a provision for regulating the quality of the product marketed, then the degree of product differentiation will normally be affected. The effect of

---

[15] E. A. Stokdyk, "Cooperative Marketing by Farmers," *Farmers in a Changing World*, 1940 Yearbook of Agriculture (Washington, D.C.: USDA, 1940), pp. 693–94.

a marketing order on the other characteristics of market structure is not so obvious. However, there are instances in which analyses of specific marketing orders indicate that the other characteristics have likewise been affected by the adoption and operation of a marketing order. Since the objective of marketing orders is to improve price and income conditions in the industry involved by establishing and maintaining more orderly marketing conditions, it is obvious that some effect on the conduct and performance of the marketing system is expected. The provisions of the marketing order impose certain rules under which the marketing game must be played. Some of the changes anticipated can be determined through an examination of the rules which have been imposed. Although improved performance of the marketing system is expected with the adoption of the order, it is usually necessary to observe the operation of the order over time before conclusions can be drawn with respect to performance in terms of specific criteria. The fact that some marketing orders have terminated after short periods suggest that performance was not according to the expectations at the time the order was adopted. In some instances individuals or firms found that they could not profitably play the game under the new rules and departed from the scene. Therefore, a change in market structure resulted giving evidence of some circular effect of the order with conduct and performance in many instances eventually leading to changes in the number of firms and hence change in the market structure.

Initiating a Marketing Order. A number of generalizations may be stated with respect to structure, conduct, and performance when a marketing order becomes effective for an industry. First, an industry must go through a number of rather formal steps before an order may be issued. Compliance with the required procedure results in some change in the environment within the industry during the period involved. The steps involved in issuance of an order are as follows:

1. An industry group decides that an order would be desirable and proposes an order to the Secretary of Agriculture. Interested segments of the industry in cooperation with the Department of Agriculture develop the proposed order, and it is submitted to the Secretary of Agriculture with a request for a public hearing.
2. If the Secretary determines that the proposed order would be helpful in promoting orderly marketing, a public hearing is held in the area to be covered by the program. At the hearing any interested person either for or against the order may testify concerning conditions in the industry, the need for the regulations proposed in the order, and the purposes of various provisions. All of the testimony is taken under oath and is subject to cross-examination.
3. A transcript of the hearing along with any written briefs or arguments which have been filed is studied by the Department of Agriculture; a

recommended decision is published in the Federal Register; and all interested persons are given time to file exceptions to the decision.

4. The Secretary of Agriculture issues his decision after the exceptions have been studied. This decision rules on all exceptions, presents findings and conclusions, and either a denial of the order proposed or a revised marketing agreement and order is submitted for approval of growers and handlers.

5. The marketing agreement is sent to handlers for their signatures, and a referendum is held to determine response of producers to the proposal.

6. If the required number of handlers sign the agreement and two thirds of the producers by number and/or volume approve the order, the Secretary may then issue the order making the terms of the marketing agreement effective upon the entire industry.

Changes in the Industry Environment. The environment in an industry is changed considerably as it goes through the process of establishing an order. Producers and handlers become more cognizant of the interrelationships which exist, and producers are made particularly aware of the effect individual decisions have upon aggregate conditions within the industry. For example, during the period when turkey growers were considering a proposed turkey marketing order, even though growers were not convinced the order was desirable they were made aware of some need to restrict turkey production.[16] The hearings and discussion of an order by various segments of the industry contribute to a better understanding on the part of both producers and handlers of the situation and conditions in the industry. The participation by the government in the development, issuance, and operation of the order also contributes to a changed environment.

A New Decision-Making Unit. Perhaps the most important consequence from the issuance of an order is the creation of a new decision-making unit. This new decision-making unit does not replace other firms nor can it be considered as a new firm, but it does assume responsibility for many of the decisions formerly made by either producers or handlers in the marketing system. These decisions are made within a highly regulated framework which is defined in the provisions of the order. Once these decisions are made, the producers and handlers are forced to operate within these constraints. Therefore, the behavior or conduct of firms is almost certain to be different from what it would have been in the absence of the order. Since a majority of the administrative committee are usually producers, consideration will be given to their interests

---

[16] Rudie Slaughter and J. G. West, *Some Factors Affecting Turkey Growers' Attitudes toward the Proposed Turkey Marketing Order,* University of Missouri Agricultural Experiment Station Research Bulletin 845 (Columbia, October, 1963), pp. 12–16.

and considerable priority placed on measures of benefit to producers.

Market Conduct. Perhaps of even greater significance than the changes in characteristics of market structure are the changes in conduct resulting from the initiation of a marketing order. Provisions of the order and decisions made by the administrative committee impose restraints upon the producers and handlers which in turn affect the way in which they conduct themselves. The order increases communication between the participants in the marketing process, and many of the decisions with respect to quantity, quality, and firm practices are made within the administrative committee. Firms are forced to consider their actions in the light of others involved in the bargaining process within the administrative committee (see Chapter 15 for effect on individual bargaining behavior). The order also makes possible certain types of action such as discriminatory pricing which would otherwise not be possible for individual firms to accomplish. In general, industries operating with marketing orders tend to make greater efforts to standardize their products, eliminate lower quality products from shipment when prices are low, develop better communication networks within the industry, obtain data and analyze market conditions, and increase revenue by regulating the distribution of products among markets.

Market Performance. How does performance with marketing orders compare with performance in the absence of orders? Most orders have not been operated in such a way as to increase price significantly but rather to stabilize prices over time. As is true with changes in any conditions under which firms operate, the imposition of the regulations contained in marketing orders do not affect all firms or participants in the marketing process equally. Some firms are benefited while others are placed at some disadvantage. This means that the distribution of income among firms will likely be changed to some extent with an order. The movement toward more orderly marketing and the reduction in price variation permits firms to operate with greater production efficiency as a result of the reduction in uncertainty. The improved coordination also tends to facilitate development of products which are more suitable and more compatible with the desires of the consuming public. Profit rates are determined by prices and the level of output. These are worthy of more detailed consideration.

Supply Effects

Marketing orders have been defined as "economic institutional devices, formulated so as to include specific provisions which affect the supply, demand, and/or price of a specified commodity."[17] Provisions for

---

[17] Sidney Hoos, "The Contributions of Marketing Agreements and Orders to the Stability and Level of Farm Income," *Policy for Commercial Agriculture, Its Relation to Economic Growth and Stability* (Joint Economic Committee Print, 85th Cong., 1st sess. [Washington, D.C., November 22, 1957]), p. 319.

quantity control or measures designed to affect supply are of two general types. One type includes those steps taken to stabilize the volume marketed between time periods. Secondly, some orders are operated in such a way as to distribute the total quantity among different outlets in such a way as to maximize total revenue. An order may be operated in such a way as to achieve one or both of these objectives. The quantity going into one or more markets may be limited with the excess diverted to a surplus pool to be released onto the market later. This permits controlled distribution between markets as well as over time.

It appears that marketing orders can be quite effective in dealing with temporary or seasonal excess supply problems. In such instances the surplus may be diverted to secondary uses or to a surplus pool and thereby even-out supplies over time. On the other hand the provisions which are permissible in marketing orders do not appear adequate to deal with chronic surplus problems.

There appears to be some disagreement as to the extent to which marketing orders can be used for control of production. Some argue "marketing orders do not provide for control of production." This statement is generally true with respect to those orders presently in existence. However, the turkey marketing order which was considered in 1961 and 1962 did contain provisions for control of production. Two orders were initially proposed for the turkey industry. One was for hatching eggs and a second was for turkey meat. The hatching egg order would have controlled the production of poults, and thereby controlled the production of turkeys. As the hearings proceeded, the hatching egg order was dropped and the quantity controls were included in the turkey meat order with the quantity each producer could market limited to a certain quantity, based on historical production. Since the order was not approved by producers in the referendum, the legality of the production control provision was never tested.

Marketing order programs have not proved very successful in increasing returns to producers above what they might earn in producing other agricultural commodities since none of the existing marketing orders contain provisions for control of production. In those instances where prices have been increased through control of the quantity going into the primary market, the production of the commodity has usually increased substantially over time. As production increases, the amount of the commodity diverted to lower valued uses must increase, and the point is eventually reached where total revenue actually declines with increased diversions. An analysis of the lemon order showed a steady increase in the quantity diverted to secondary markets and a consequent decline in the total revenue from the sale of lemons.[18] As a result of this

---

[18] Roy J. Smith, "The Lemon Prorate in the Long Run," *Journal of Political Economy*, Vol. LIX (December, 1961).

tendency it has been suggested that marketing orders are not designed to deal with the problem of excess production over the long run and that other methods should be used to facilitate the necessary production adjustments.

Demand Effects

Advertising and promotion are not possible within the provisions of federal marketing orders. However, this is not true for other types of self-help programs and for marketing orders functioning under state enabling legislation. In fact, promotional type activity is very common under state marketing orders and is often the major activity under these orders.

Advertising and Promotion Programs. During a recent period when 15 states had special enabling legislation for marketing programs, 14 of these states had permissive provisions for advertising and sales promotion type activities. In 1956 the state of California had 28 active marketing programs, and 23 of these had provisions for sales promotion and advertising.[19] The California marketing programs are financed by assessments of participating producers, handlers, or processors. Total assessments during recent years have amounted to several million dollars each year. Expenditures for market promotion amounted to approximately 65 percent of total expenditures. These data provide some indication of the relative importance of promotional type activities in state marketing programs.

Several commodity oriented organizations are also involved in sales and promotional activities. The program of the American Dairy Association is a good example. It is estimated that during 1964 approximately $100 million was spent to promote agricultural products. Much of this was done by groups of farmers organized into a cooperative, producer groups operating under state enabling legislation for marketing orders, or national commodity organizations. These activities represent the major effort involved in attempting to increase the demand for agricultural products so that a greater quantity can be sold at the same price or a higher price received for the same level of production.

The prevalence of attempts to increase demand is obvious, but the effects of these attempts is much more difficult to assess. The effect of promotion programs is difficult to separate from the effect of other demand factors which are also changing. Multiple regression analysis, a statistical technique which attempts to estimate the effect of different variables, has been used successfully in a few instances and in most of these studies indicates some positive effect of promotion programs.

It appears that promotion programs can be used to increase con-

[19] Hoos, *op. cit.*, pp. 812–14.

sumption in the short run. However, the long-run impact is much more difficult to determine, as is the relative effectiveness of promotion compared with other approaches to increasing demand. For example a study of promotion activities by cooperating orange juice processors in Florida indicated an increase in sales of 13 percent over what they could have expected without the advertising campaign.[20] This effort produced $18 million more in sales revenue than what would have been produced by cutting prices by an amount adequate to sell a comparable volume. But would consumers continue to purchase an additional 13 percent over a long period if the promotion program were continued? There is also the question of the effect of increased consumption of orange juice on the demand for other citrus products and other substitute products which provide large quantities of vitamin C. Total food consumption is difficult to expand in the United States, and it is reasonable to believe that increased consumption of one product will largely result in decreased consumption of another. So, a successful promotion campaign for one product may also be successful in decreasing consumption of a substitute product. There is also the question as to how successful producers in a single state can be in increasing demand for their product if the market is a national one and several states produce a comparable product. Questions pertaining to many of these issues remain unanswered with the data and research results presently available.

Changes in Quality. Changes in product quality achieved by cooperative efforts of producers or regulation under marketing orders no doubt have some effect upon the demand for the product involved. In some instances a particular quality may no longer be available, while the supply of other qualities may be much more dependable. The likelihood that extremely low-quality products will be eliminated from the market is great under marketing orders. The demand of those consumers preferring the lower quality product which was also probably lower priced may decline with the change in quality available. On the other hand the general improvement in quality of the product available and efforts to insure a more dependable supply may increase the demand of other consumers. The net effects would depend upon the individual commodity and its peculiar market situation.

Price Discrimination. Demand for a product may also be important from another standpoint. The nature of demand for a product in different markets or in different uses may dictate the type of self-help program which is developed. In this case the program is designed to take advantage of demand conditions rather than to change demand. The raisin order mentioned earlier is a good example. The demand for raisins

---

[20] "Study of Consumer Reaction Can Stretch Ad Dollars," *The Farm Index,* Economic Research Service (Washington, D.C.: USDA, October, 1963), p. 16.

in the export market is more elastic than the demand in the domestic market, and in the operation of the order, raisin grapes were limited in the domestic market with the excess being diverted to the export market. When demand in one market is more elastic than the demand in another market, it will ordinarily be profitable to control the quantities going into the two markets in order to increase total revenue. Such activities are possible and widely practiced in market order programs with volume control provisions. The general principle is illustrated in Figure 21–1. It

FIGURE 21–1

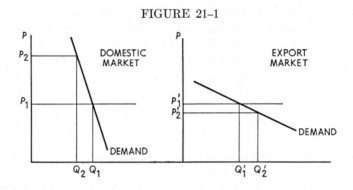

can be seen from the graphic representation of the two markets that when price is equalized in the two markets, the revenue is much lower than when a higher price is charged in the domestic market and a lower price in the market with the more elastic demand.[21] the difference in the elasticity of demand between the two markets is exaggerated in the diagram in order to demonstrate the principle involved, but as long as there is a difference in elasticity, regardless of size, there is a basis for considering controlled distribution of the product. In order to do this it is necessary to be able to control marketings and to assure that the two markets remain separate so that products moved into the market with the more elastic demand are not later diverted to the higher priced market.

IMPLICATIONS FOR MARKETING FIRMS

To what extent will marketing firms be affected by adoption of a self-help program, and particularly one taking the form of a federal marketing order? Here again the answer depends upon the type of program and the activities involved. Some of the answers have already been indicated under the heading of structural effects, but there are also

---

[21] The pricing guide is to equalize marginal revenue in the two markets. When this is done, total returns cannot be increased any further by shifting some product from one market to the other.

other generalizations which can be stated when the results are examined from the viewpoint of marketing firms.

Effect on Bargaining

To the extent that self-help programs are successful they do affect the degree of competition or at least the conduct of firms. In the latter case the degree of competition among marketing firms and between marketing firms and farmers may remain unchanged in the sense that there are no structural changes in the market. However, as suggested earlier, the marketing firms are faced with a different environment if a new bargaining association of producers is organized or if marketing firms and producers are regulated by a marketing order.

Both bargaining associations and marketing orders change the nature of the bargaining process. Producers organized in a bargaining association may be able to see their interests in a slightly different light and may be able to wield more power in the bargaining process to the extent that they can control an important share of the product involved. In order to be successful they must be an important influence on the total volume marketed. To increase price they must be able to reduce the quantity moving into the retail channels.

The administrative committees of marketing orders often make decisions with respect to volume moving into different markets. Once these decisions are made the producers may enjoy certain benefits and be in a stronger competitive position relative to the marketing firms buying the product. Decisions with respect to quantity and distribution reduce the area within which the bargaining process takes place and thereby affect the relative competitive position of marketing firms.

Effect on Volume of Business

In addition to the effects of a changed competitive situation, marketing firms may be affected by the volume control activities of marketing orders. Both good and bad implications are present. Since the profits of marketing firms are ordinarily directly related to the volume handled, any action to reduce the quantity marketed in a particular market is likely to reduce the revenue of those marketing firms affected by the action. This means that firms operating in the primary markets are more likely to suffer from efforts to control the distribution of a product than are firms in the secondary markets. In fact the secondary markets which serve as a diversion outlet may actually enjoy increased volumes. A firm operating only in the primary market then would incur some detrimental effects from the volume control activities.

Some firms may actually discontinue marketing certain products with the issuance of marketing orders. The issuance of orders seems to hasten certain structural changes, and with the increased stability and more orderly marketing, certain types of marketing firms may actually discontinue handling the product. During World War II and the years immediately after, auctions were one of the major outlets for Florida tomatoes. With the development of a tomato marketing order in the mid 1950's, auctions were no longer used as a market for the product.[22] Even though the order was terminated after a few years of operation, use of the auction market was not resumed. Some of the changes in the number of firms handling a product are associated with the volume marketed while in other cases it may be more nearly the effect of improved organization within the market and better organization of producers.

Fluctuations in quantities moving through specific types of markets are reduced with the issuance and operation of a marketing order. Again, both favorable and unfavorable implications are present for specific firms. Even though the volume is reduced, the increased stability in marketings and the greater certainty associated with the change can result in improved planning with respect to scale of operation. Better planning of physical facilities and organization of the labor force can result. To the extent that marketing firms earlier found it profitable to assume the risk associated with variation in quantity and price, these marketing firms may have lower net income as a result of the change. Much depends upon the flexibility inherent in the marketing firm and the degree to which it was formerly involved in the role of speculative activity. Stabilization of grade, size, or maturity under quality regulations may be of considerable importance to firms interested in specification buying. A movement in this direction is advantageous for the large retailing firms.

Effect on Price

The extent to which marketing firms have been forced to pay higher prices than would otherwise have been the case is largely associated with the degree to which volume regulation has been exercised. Again, differences exist between the primary and secondary markets. The lemon prorate plan was operated in such a way as to maintain prices in the primary market, but in doing so the production increased to the point that prices declined in the secondary markets to such an extent that the blend price also declined.

In general it may be said that self-help programs have not forced marketing firms to pay prices much higher than would otherwise have been the case. They have resulted in less price fluctuation. Periods of excess supplies and large marketings of low-quality products have been reduced, resulting in more price stability. The situation is well stated in a summary of the history of developments in California:[23]

[22] Black, *op. cit.*, p. 4.
[23] Hoos, *op. cit.*, p. 818.

California experience indicates that volume control as a provision of an order can at times be an effective means of affecting farm price and income. But the temporary or short-run effects can in time be outweighed by the long-run effects. Unless volume control is exercised with care and caution, the marketing problem to be eased can instead be aggravated; production in established areas can be encouraged and production in new areas introduced.

Marketing firms interested in handling large quantities at low prices, or handling lower quality products, may be adversely affected by the marketing order in terms of its effect on price. Similarly the firm interested in speculation or the assumption of price risk may also be adversely affected. Other marketing firms may find it advantageous to operate within the order with its greater price stability and greater certainty. Much depends upon the individual firm and its method of operation.

IMPLICATIONS FOR FARMERS

Marketing orders, bargaining associations, and other programs of this type may be regarded as institutional devices available to farmers. These devices may prove useful in the case of some commodities while in others they may not. Just as in the case of marketing firms some farmers will find the results of these types of programs desirable while other farmers would prefer to operate without the programs. The membership in most cooperatives and bargaining associations is voluntary. As a consequence of the voluntary nature of such programs, regulations of member marketing activities is limited and the nonparticipants may take action to completely offset the efforts of the association or cooperative.

Marketing orders were designed to overcome the problem of nonparticipation. The order is optional with growers and handlers until it is approved and the order is issued. Provisions can then be avoided only through termination of the order by a majority of the producers involved. A few marketing orders have been in existence for over two decades while others have been in existence only a short time and were then terminated. Examination of some of the results from marketing orders and their implications for farmers indicate why this was true.

Impact on Decision Making

In the absence of marketing orders, quantity and quality results for the industry are the sum of individual decisions by farmers. Likewise the quantity and quality moving into different markets is a result of decisions by marketing firms. The issuance of an order places the responsibility for many of these decisions in the hands of an administrative committee. Since farmers are normally well represented in the administrative committee and in fact make up more than a majority of the membership, they become involved in many of the marketing decisions formerly made by marketing firms. As a result, farmers operating within an order quite often become much better informed on the market interrelationships and factors affecting market results.

Marketing orders do not regulate the quantity nor the quality of products farmers produce. However, observance of differences in prices received for the products moving into the primary and secondary markets as well as the blend price may influence the quantity of product farmers produce. Likewise, differences in prices paid to producers for different qualities as a result of the quality regulations in the program may encourage producers to produce a different quality product. The administrative committee ordinarily issues a marketing policy statement prior to the harvest season. This, in addition to the results from previous seasons, gives producers some idea of what to expect from the operation of the marketing order. This statement is often issued early enough to have some impact on decisions of producers and thereby affect the quantity and quality of products marketed.

Effect of Program on Derived Demand

Since the demand at the farm level is a derived demand, it will change as the demand at the retail level changes. Assuming no change in the level of marketing charges, a self-help program which results in increased consumer demand will also result in an increase in the demand at the farm level (see Chapter 16). To the extent that self-help programs emphasizing an advertising or promotion approach are successful in expanding the demand for the product involved, benefits will accrue to the producer of the product. Consideration must of course be given to the rate of increase in marketing margins relative to the rate of increase in demand. An increase in demand achieved through promotional activities might actually be nullified by an increase in the cost of marketing the product involved.

Demand for farm products is dependent upon marketing firms' anticipation of consumer demand. Derived demand may be higher or lower than actually warranted depending upon the extent to which consumer demand is correctly anticipated. It is possible that the operation of marketing orders and agreements will contribute to better anticipation of consumer demand. This statement is made on the basis of increased stability of marketings, less variation in quality, and the increased effort to obtain data and analyze demand for the product in various uses. The problem of anticipating price levels at which varying quantities will move would appear to be much less difficult when there is little variation in quantity. It is also possible that marketing cost might be reduced at the same time because of the greater stability of price, the increased orderliness of flows over time, the absence of poorer qualities, and elimination of cheap products which tend to ruin a market.

To what extent do changes in structure and regulation of conduct under marketing orders provide farmers with power sufficient to obtain a reduction in marketing margins? Empirical evidence to answer this question is not available, but it would appear that the chances are small because marketing orders do not control production of areas not covered by the order, entry into production of the product, nor do they control output of the members. Thus it is doubtful if sufficient monopoly power is acquired to be a threat to marketing margins.

To sum up, marketing orders may provide for increased derived demand to the extent that consumer demand is increased, that marketing margins are reduced as a result of more orderly marketing, or that consumer demand can be more accurately determined.

More Information and Less Uncertainty

During the 1930's, marketing agreements and orders were viewed as a means of reducing supplies by an amount large enough to improve prices considerably. Over time the objective has become more one of stabilizing marketings, and in this way removing much of the price fluctuation characteristic of the commodities involved. More orderly marketing results in much less uncertainty, and producers know more about the quantities that will move into different markets, the quality of product desired, and the general price level likely to exist.

A recent study of marketing orders conducted by the Food Research Institute at Stanford University illustrates the effects of marketing orders on market uncertainty.[24] The authors concluded that the apparent shelter against at least some of the uncertainties of the market offered by the marketing order and the grower bargaining association was a major factor in the entry of additional capital and grower's into cling peach production.

The greater amount of information available to producers and marketing firms and the greater certainty with respect to market conditions contributes to better allocation of resources for those commodities involved. End results conform more closely to expectations at the time decisions are made, and therefore producers are able to plan their operations more efficiently. This does not imply that marketing orders or similar type programs remove all of the instability and uncertainty nor that the information available is always adequate. For instance weather continues to be a disruptive influence and will result in smaller or larger production during particular seasons and subsequent higher or lower prices. Other factors also continue to permit some price variation even though the product is covered by a marketing order.

[24] John A. Jamison and Karl Brandt, *Marketing Orders: Performance, Potential, and Limitations, The Case of California's Cling Peaches and Asparagus* (Stanford: Food Research Institute, 1965), p. 293.

Impact on Returns to Farmers

The impact of marketing orders or other self-help programs on returns to producers must be considered in both the long-run and short-run context. In either case the analysis is quite difficult because of the problems involved in attempting to estimate what conditions would have been without the order. Conditions before and during the order can be compared to give some insight into this question. In addition, estimates of price elasticity of demand can be used to determine the effect of diverting a portion of the total supply to a surplus pool or to secondary markets. It is also possible to observe trends over time in terms of the percentage of the product which is allocated to different markets as well as the price trends in these various markets.

Jamison and Brandt's case studies of the cling peach and asparagus orders compared changes in total revenue from these products with changes in total revenue from other fruit and vegetable crops not subject to marketing orders.[25] The comparison was used as one basis for conclusions as to the effects of the orders. However, this approach is also subject to criticism since it fails to take into account factors other than the orders which may have affected total revenue. The bothersome question of the level of total revenue from cling peaches and asparagus had the orders not been in effect remains unanswered.

As suggested earlier, the results from the adoption of marketing orders vary almost as much as the commodities and orders involved. There are certain general conditions under which orders appear to be more effective than others. Hoos of California suggests that marketing orders are likely to be more successful when the demand for the product at the farm level has a low price elasticity, especially if volume control is to be exercised; where the price elasticity and cross elasticity of supply are not high; in those areas where producers and handlers are able to see that they have mutual interest regarding the marketing problems; where the production is concentrated in areas sufficiently small so that rather homogeneous production and marketing conditions exist; and where some interested organization such as a cooperative or grower association is interested and active in informing growers about the program.[26]

The marketing order which is highly successful in increasing prices to producers in the short run is likely to experience trouble over the long run. The higher prices, especially if they are high relative to other products, will result in increased production over time. This in turn makes operation of the order through diversion of the surplus to either

---

[25] *Ibid.*, pp. 287–88.

[26] Sidney S. Hoos, "Marketing Agreements and Orders," *Farm Policy Forum* 16 (Ames: Iowa State University Press, No.1, 1963–64), p. 7.

secondary markets or a surplus pool much more difficult. The freedom of entry characteristic of most agricultural production is such that higher prices encourage the entry of new producers as well as the expansion of production by existing producers. This is why those orders which have continued to exist over time have not operated with very high price objectives but rather have emphasized a more stable market at more moderate price levels.

The extent to which alternative markets are available for a particular commodity also becomes important in the long run. If there are no outlets other than the primary market, excess supplies must either be held until another time period, or destroyed, if volume regulation is to be effective. This in turn requires that the price elasticity of demand be quite low because the increase in the price for the amount marketed must more than offset the value of product that is destroyed or the cost of storing the product until a later period. This was no doubt one important factor in the defeat of the proposed national turkey marketing order. The price elasticity of demand for turkey meat is very close to unity, and there are few alternative outlets for turkey meat. Therefore the more inelastic the demand in the primary market, the greater the number of secondary markets, and the more elastic the demand in secondary markets the easier it is to operate a marketing order and increase returns by controlled distribution of the product.

Supply conditions have also become important in the operation of the marketing order because of the tendency of individual producers to increase production if price increases. Even with stable prices a decline in the price of alternative products will result in some expansion in production if the supply elasticity is high. This suggests that volume regulation over time and maintenance of orderly marketing conditions will be much easier to facilitate when expansion in production is not likely or when the supply elasticity is low.

A GENERAL SUMMARY

Marketing orders and agreements as well as other types of self-help programs can scarcely be regarded as cure-alls for the problems of a commodity group or for the agricultural economy in total. There are instances when these devices help producers and marketing firms deal with some of the prevalent problems. For such commodities these devices are alternatives to more direct government involvement through price support programs. The term "self-help" might be questioned to the extent that government does become involved in either encouraging the programs or excusing such programs from regulations imposed upon other industries, or through actual assistance and involvement in the administration of such programs. The term "self-help" is fitting in the sense that most of these programs are developed by the industry on their own, are voluntary, and require action by the commodity group in order to effectuate such programs. The appropriateness of such a program for a specific commodity must be examined in terms of the market conditions for the commodity, the characteristics of the commodity, and the interest of producers and handlers in using such a device.

Chapter 22 AGRICULTURE AND ECONOMIC PROGRESS

The subjects of economic progress, economic growth, or economic development are very complex subjects; and a single chapter in a book cannot treat the subjects adequately. Neither can the relationship of agriculture to economic progress or economic development be thoroughly developed. Rather, an attempt will be made to merely sketch the role which agriculture plays and the contributions which it makes to economic development, and attention will be called to the problems economic development poses for agriculture.

One of the objectives of the earlier chapters on the government and the agricultural economy was that of demonstrating how the economic tools of analysis presented in the other sections of the book are useful in understanding some of the problems of agriculture and proposed programs to alleviate these problems. This is less true in this chapter because the same tools of analysis are not as appropriate when considering economic development. In fact the academic world is far from agreement on the appropriate theories to use in explaining economic development and suggesting action which will make the greatest contribution to progress or development. However because of the widespread attention now being given to the subject of economic development and the belief that agriculture plays an important role, some consideration of the subject is deemed desirable. An additional reason for considering the importance of agriculture as it relates to economic progress is the desire to point out some of the more pleasant aspects of the situation in the agricultural economy as contrasted to some of the problems which have been discussed earlier.

Concern over economic development is so widespread that verification of its importance hardly seems necessary. Naturally the less-developed nations are interested in improving their own status. Likewise the more highly developed countries are interested in continued economic growth and development in their own countries as well as progress in the less-developed nations. Both the free world and the communist world have indicated their concern over economic development in the less fortunate nations, with the reasons for this concern no doubt both selfish and humanitarian. Among the reasons which might be classified as selfish are the desire to demonstrate the effectiveness of different forms of government in promoting economic development and the desire to see countries developed so that they will provide greater markets for exports. Perhaps of even greater importance though is the desire to see improved living conditions in the less fortunate nations.

The concern with lack of progress and the commitment to more rapid economic development is indicated by the evolution in terminology used with respect to less-fortunate countries. Countries which at one time were described as "backward nations" are now referred to as "underdeveloped" or "developing nations." This has also led to desire and request for assistance from countries which are more fully developed as well as additional efforts to obtain investment from both internal and external sources. However, the experiences of a number of countries in recent decades indicates that the road to economic development is not an easy one but rather is quite bumpy and has many curves and detours.

The idea of economic growth is a very complex one and has even been called different things at different times in the past. During Adam Smith's time it was referred to as wealth of nations and has even more recently been called economic progress, economic growth, or economic development. All of these terms will be used somewhat synonymously here. Just as there is a disagreement over terminology, there is also disagreement as to the chief ingredients. There is much disagreement as to the necessary conditions for growth and the best means of achieving the necessary conditions. Examination of the experiences of more developed countries provides some insight into conditions which were present in individual situations, but the situations have differed and so the argument rages on as to what conditions are essential.

ROLE AND PLACE OF AGRICULTURE IN ECONOMIC DEVELOPMENT

It is easy to find examples of the importance of agriculture as a factor in economic development. Tremendous increases in efficiency and productivity of agriculture in the United States have contributed much to the economic development of this country. At the other extreme, the lack of a productive agriculture in Communist China became a stumbling block to the "great leap forward." However, these, plus other examples which might be given do not prove the necessity of an efficient agriculture to achieve economic development. Rather than undertake such a proof, an attempt will be made here to outline the role played by agriculture, consider some of its contributions, and indicate some of the problems for agriculture which result when economic development does take place. Economic development results from changes in beliefs, in the institutions present in an economy, in the size of the population and the quality of the labor force, in the ways in which resources are combined, in technology, and in the relative proportions of goods demanded by individuals in the economy. The role of agriculture in development can best be discussed in terms of the stage of development and the rapidity with which these factors are changing.

Stages of Development

Descriptions of the process of economic development are almost as many and varied as there are writers on the subject. There have been differences between countries as to the process of development which was actually involved, and there are also differences between writers as they view the process from different perspectives. One of the more widely accepted analyses of the process of economic development divides it into various stages including the traditional society, preconditions for takeoff, takeoff, maturity, and one of high mass consumption.[1] Although differences in terminology and definition of stages may exist, there is general acceptance of the fact that agriculture plays different roles at different points within the process of development.

The traditional society and the preconditions for takeoff stages are descriptions of countries in the early phases of economic development and are characterized by economies in which agriculture is of prime importance. For example, the proportion of the gross national product contributed by agriculture or the percentage of the labor force employed in agriculture are both normally high during the early stages of development. As indicated in Table 22–1, it is not uncommon for countries to have 60 to 70 percent or more of the labor force engaged in agriculture during the early stages of development. This is in contrast to countries in the takeoff or maturity stages which may have 40 and 20 percent respectively employed in agriculture.[2] It becomes apparent then that in order for a country to move beyond the early stages of development, significant progress must be made in agriculture.

The Importance of Agriculture

A number of conditions are essential to economic growth. Among these would be included natural resources, labor with appropriate skills, capital, technology, and sound public administration. The presence or absence of these essentials to growth is not unrelated to the situation in the agricultural economy. In a country which is just beginning to develop, increased productivity in agriculture characterized by wise use of the resources available, development of appropriate skills in the agricul-

---

[1] W. W. Rostow, *The Stages of Economic Growth, a Non-Communist Manifesto* (New York: Cambridge University Press, 1960), pp. 4–12.

[2] *Ibid.*, p. 71.

TABLE 22-1

INCOME PER CAPITA, COMPOUND ANNUAL GROWTH RATES FOR POPULATION AND PRODUCTION DURING THE 1950's, AND AGRICULTURE'S SHARE OF GROSS NATIONAL PRODUCT AND TOTAL EMPLOYMENT IN 1950's FOR SELECTED COUNTRIES*

Country	Income per Capita 1959–61†	Compound Annual Growth Rates‡			Agriculture's Share	
		Total Population	Gross National Product	Total Food Production	Gross National Product	Total Employment
Developed:§						
United States.......	$2,289	1.7%	3.3%	1.8%	5.1%	12%
Australia...........	1,170	2.2	4.0	3.0	...	13
Denmark..........	1,058	0.7	3.3	2.4	12.4	23
France.............	1,006	0.9	4.3	3.0	11.1	26
Netherlands........	801	1.3	4.9	3.0	11.6	19
Israel..............	763	3.5	10.6	3.9	11.9	17
Italy..............	514	0.6	6.1	2.3	21.9	28
Venezuela..........	729	4.0	7.6	3.8	7.0	41
Developing, Rapid:‖						
Rep. of So. Africa....	397	2.4	(5.1)	3.7	12.7	33
Jamaica............	355	1.4	9.0	. .	15.2	49
Japan.............	346	1.4	8.8	3.9	20.0	40
Greece............	333	1.0	5.7	3.8	32.8	53
Mexico............	312	3.1	(7.0)	7.6	...	58
Spain.............	296	0.9	(7.2)	2.5	25.5	49
Yugoslavia.........	218	1.2	10.0	6.5	29.8	67
Colombia..........	203	2.2	4.5	1.6	37.3	54
Guatemala.........	153	3.0	(5.6)	2.7	34.0	68
Egypt.............	138	2.4	4.9	3.4	36.2	64
Brazil.............	130	3.2	5.7	3.2	38.3	59
Taiwan............	110	3.4	(6.2)	4.6	32.7	50
Korea.............	102	1.9	5.8	2.9	41.6	80
Thailand...........	82	3.6	5.6	3.4	46.2	82
*Developing, Slow:***						
Chile..............	491	2.9	3.4	1.1	14.0	30
Argentina..........	363	1.6	1.6	0.9	20.6	25
Panama............	335	3.1	3.7	3.5	27.3	50
Costa Rica.........	313	3.9	(5.6)	. .	41.0	55
Malaya............	211	3.1	2.2	4.8	46.0	58
Turkey............	176	2.9	(4.2)	3 6	(43.0)	77
Jordan.............	168	3.1	4.3	. .	(20.0)	. .
Tunisia............	157	1.6	3.5	1.3	(34.1)	68
Ecuador...........	145	3.1	4.9	. .	37.5	53
Philippines.........	131	3.2	4.9	3.4	36.2	64
Peru..............	130	1.8	(2.4)	1.9	27.6	. .
Sudan.............	86	3.3	2.0	. .	58.5	. .
Pakistan...........	76	2.1	2.5	1.7	56.7	65
India.............	68	1.9	3.7	3.0	48.4	71

* Data in parentheses are estimates.
† Estimated by Arthur Mackie, DTA, ERS, USDA from United Nations reports.
‡ Computed from beginning and ending points of linear trend for years indicated. Population growth for 1952/53–1961/62, and Gross National Product and agricultural sector output for 1950 to 1960 or other years in this decade from United Nations reports. Total agricultural production and total food production for 1952/53–1961/62, and agriculture's share of Gross National Product from reports of Food and Agriculture Organization.
§ Per capita annual income $500 or more.
‖ Per capita annual income less than $500, and per capita income growth rate 2 percent or more annually.
** Per capita income less than $500 annually, and growth rate less than 2 percent annually.

tural labor force, careful use of the limited amount of capital available, and development of new technology is essential if agriculture is to make the necessary contribution to economic development.

Agriculture can be important to economic development in a number of ways. First, it can provide an expanded food supply for an increased population. If food supplies do not increase, either diets will be inadequate or it will be necessary to use foreign exchange to import food. Neither is a desirable alternative as the problem of inadequate diets is obvious and foreign exchange is usually scarce in the country attempting to move forward with its development program. As development takes place, the urban population usually expands at a greater than proportionate rate, which means the need for increased food supplies is further emphasized. The race between increased food supplies and growth in the population is of major consequence in practically all developing countries.

Agriculture is also important as a source of capital in developing countries. Its magnitude relative to other industries in the early stages of development is such that it must provide a major portion of the revenue obtained by government. Likewise the income generated in agriculture becomes a source of investment funds which can be used in developing other industries.

Just as an increased supply of agricultural products is important, the increase in demand which agriculture provides for the products of other industries may also be important. During the early stages of development, consumer demand as well as demand of other industries is likely to be somewhat weak. To the extent that technological progress in agriculture leads to increased demand for machinery, chemicals, and other nonfarm produced inputs, this may also be a stimulus to the development of other industries and overall development of the economy.

Examples in countries which have moved through the development stages as well as those which are now attempting to begin the take-off stage indicate the crucial importance of agriculture. In some, agriculture has been important in all of the ways mentioned, while in others it has been important in terms of its failure to increase in productivity fast enough so that scarce capital had to be used to import food supplies and development was hindered.

Interrelationships—Agriculture and the General Economy

The interrelationships between agriculture and the general economy which are significant in explaining economic growth and development are many and are quite complex. A few of the more obvious ways in which agriculture is important to economic development have already been suggested. However, it is equally true that agriculture cannot become productive in the absence of certain conditions in the general economy.

Along with the increase in agricultural production there must be a simultaneous increase in effective demand for the products of agriculture. That is, along with an increase in the *willingness* to buy there must also be an increase in the *ability* to buy in the form of greater purchasing power. If there is only an increase in the population without any increase in aggregate economic activity, the benefits from increased production accruing to agriculture are likely to be small because there has been no increase in effective demand.

Many of the technologies required to increase agricultural productivity necessitate some development of industries which can provide these inputs. Almost without exception increases in agricultural productivity require increased nonfarm inputs to combine with the labor and land already in use. Recent emphasis on the development of chemical production in the Soviet Union is an example of recognition of the importance of these inputs to agriculture.

Along with an increased demand for agricultural products and the availability of nonfarm inputs, the development of educational facilities, improved transportation and communication systems, more highly coordinated marketing systems, the presence of a relatively stable and conscientious government are important characteristics. Without attempting to further catalog the important interrelationships between agriculture and the general economy, these should provide some indication of the presence of such interrelationships.

As suggested earlier, a number of conditions are essential to economic growth. It is interesting to note a few of the activities and events which helped provide conditions conducive to development of agriculture in the United States. These activities involved changes in several conditions, namely, natural resources, labor, capital, technology, and government. For example, numerous efforts were made to facilitate the development of the land resource of which the Homestead Act of 1862 was prominent. The Morrill Act of the same year also encouraged the development of educational facilities necessary to the improvement of the labor force and the provisions of the required skills in agriculture as well as in the rest of the economy. Numerous land grants were made to private companies which in addition to encouraging development of the land resource also promoted the establishment of a marketing system and the necessary transportation and communication systems. A lenient immigration policy which helped increase the amount of labor available as well as numerous efforts to provide ample capital were also significant. No attempt will be made to rank the relative importance of these activities, but their combined effect is evident in the contributions which United States agriculture has made to economic growth.

CONTRIBUTIONS OF AGRICULTURE TO ECONOMIC DEVELOPMENT

The record achieved by the agricultural sector in the United States is well known. Its progress in increasing food supplies has more than matched the increases in population, and overall output per unit of input has more than doubled in the past century. Although not quite to the same extent, agricultural productivity has increased rapidly in nearly all of the developed nations of the free world. The record in cereal production is indicated in Figure 22–1. Total production has increased in the

FIGURE 22–1

CHANGES IN WORLD POPULATION AND CEREAL PRODUCTION, 1935–39 TO 1959

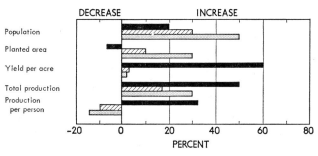

Cereals included are wheat, corn, rice, rye, barley, and oats.
SOURCE: *How the United States Improved Its Agriculture*, Development and Trade Analysis Division, Economic Research Service, U.S. Department of Agriculture.

communist countries and in the less-developed countries, but it has been more than offset by increases in population. This success story about United States agriculture is important within itself, but it is also important as it contributes to economic development in numerous ways.

Increased Food Supplies

Most developing countries have an increasing population and experience an increase in the demand for food. If higher food prices are to be avoided, there must be more food available. The increased supply of food may come from domestic production or from imports, but the alternatives are not equally desirable in most instances. Imports require foreign exchange which could otherwise be used to purchase other kinds of goods needed to further economic development.

United States agriculture certainly met the challenge. The number of persons supplied with food per farm worker increased from 4 in 1830 to 37 in 1965. During the same time period the quality and variety of food consumed also increased with noticeable increases in consumption of meat, citrus fruit, and green and yellow leafy vegetables.

Food production has been adequate to prevent large increases in food prices. Farm prices have moved upward only slightly relative to nonfarm prices since 1800 and have declined significantly relative to disposable income. The percentage of disposable income spent for food has dropped from approximately 28 percent in 1910 to approximately 18 percent in 1966. Thus food supplies have increased fast enough to provide adequate diets at relatively lower cost and have allowed individuals to spend an increased proportion of their income for nonfood items. This in turn encouraged investments in and production of nonagricultural goods with subsequent progress in economic development.

Increased Exports

Agricultural production increased fast enough in the United States to feed the domestic population and also provide sizable export earnings. Prior to 1900 agricultural exports were over half of total exports and were 65 to 90 percent of total exports during the period 1865 to 1900. Meanwhile total exports quadrupled but agricultural exports retained a relatively important position.

Exports of agricultural products continued to increase in value up to 1920. Exports of agricultural products exceeded agricultural imports up to that time and provided a source of foreign exchange during the time the United States was a debtor nation.

Increased Capital

Shortage of capital for the investments necessary to expand manufacturing capacity was a problem in the United States as in all developing countries. Agriculture contributed to an alleviation of this problem in a number of ways. Chief among these were the provision of cheaper food and fiber and the generation of foreign exchange.

The nonfarm labor force expanded rapidly during the late 1800's, increasing from 6.1 million in 1870 to 18.2 million in 1900.[3] During this period agricultural prices declined which allowed manufacturing industries to pay living wages and at the same time use a large portion of their earnings for additional investment in buildings and equipment.

As the domestic production of manufactured goods for consumption increased, the need for imported raw materials and foreign capital increased. Borrowings from foreign investors increased to over $3 billion

---

[3] Harry J. Carman, Harold C. Syrett, and Bernard W. Wishy, *A History of the American People* (2d ed.; New York: Alfred A. Knopf, Inc., 1961), Vol. II., p. 891.

dollars by 1890.[4] Earnings from agricultural exports helped bear the interest burden on the foreign investment and maintain the international balance of payments.

Even during more recent years the favorable balance of trade in agricultural products has helped meet the need overseas for economic, technical, philanthropic, and military aid. In fiscal 1963 exports exceeded imports by over $1 billion and the balance of payments deficit would have been 30 percent more without this contribution from agriculture.[5] During this period surplus agricultural products have been available for use in countries with food deficits and have also contributed foreign currencies to be used in other ways.

Release of Labor

Many of the countries attempting to speed up the rate of economic development have large populations. This is especially true relative to agricultural resources and disposable personal income. This does not mean there is an abundance of skilled, well-trained labor. Rather the situation is usually one of a high proportion of untrained and even illiterate individuals. Such was not the case in the United States as it moved through the stages of economic development. In fact a rather lenient immigration policy was pursued in order to provide the labor needed to develop the country as its frontier moved westward.

The United States depended upon foreign populations for additional labor during much of the late 1800's and early part of the 1900's. The movement of immigrants to this country reached a peak during the decade 1900–1909 and then declined for the next three decades (Table 22–2). Following World War II the entry of workers from other countries dropped off and migration from farms became a more important source of manpower.

The adoption of laborsaving technology on farms permitted a mass exodus from farms during the two decades beginning in 1940. The farm population declined from slightly over 30 million in 1940 to 15.6 million in 1960. The average annual net outmigration from the farm population was 1.6 million in 1940–45, 1.1 million in 1950–55, and near 1 million during the other years since 1940.[6] Thus, agriculture continued to increase production while at the same time releasing labor to be used in nonfarm industries. Of course this was not a one-way relationship as the expanding opportunities for employment in nonfarm jobs helped encour-

---

[4] John M. Brewster, "The Farmer's Role in the Economy," *Journal of Farm Economics,* Vol. XLIV (December, 1962), p. 1305.

[5] Robert L. Tontz and Dewain Rahe, "Our Agricultural Exports," *Farmer's World,* The Yearbook of Agriculture, 1964, p. 365.

[6] *Handbook of Agricultural Charts,* Agricultural Handbook No. 258 (Washington, D.C.: USDA, 1963), p. 178.

TABLE 22–2

The Number of Immigrants into the United States Compared with the Number of Persons Moving Out of Agriculture, 1900–1959
(Thousands)

Decade	Immigrants into the U.S.	Net Migration from Farms
1900–1909	8,202	*
1910–1919	6,347	*
1920–1929	4,296	5,810
1930–1939	699	3,715
1940–1949	857	8,784
1950–1959	2,499	9,761

Source: *Agriculture and Economic Growth*, Agricultural Economic Report 28, Economic Research Service (Washington, D.C., 1963), pp. 20–21.

age movement from farms, which in turn encouraged the adoption of laborsaving technology.

Increased Demand for Nonfarm Inputs

The release of labor from farms would not have been possible in the absence of other inputs to combine with those remaining on farms. The substitution and increased use of other inputs is dramatically portrayed in Figure 22–2. Beginning in 1870 the use of other inputs has practically doubled each 30 years. The use of capital inputs, as contrasted to labor and land inputs, has been increasing at an increasing rate. The annual

FIGURE 22–2

Major Input Groups

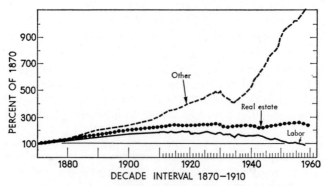

Source: *How the United States Improved Its Agriculture*, Development and Trade Analysis Division, Economic Research Service, U.S. Department of Agriculture.

compound rate of increase in use of capital inputs was 2.7 percent during 1870 to 1930 compared with 4.1 percent for the 1935–60 period.

There has been a rapid rise in the use of purchased inputs as contrasted with nonpurchased inputs (Table 22–3). Use of purchased inputs was fairly stable from 1910 to 1935 but has doubled since 1935. In terms of actual dollars, production expenses in 1965 were six times what they were in 1935 increasing from $5,061 million in 1935 to $30,735 million in 1965. Data on production expenses by major groups indicate that purchases of feed, seed, fertilizer, building materials, machinery, and equipment have all increased and provided substantial markets for products of nonfarm firms.

TABLE 22–3

INDEX NUMBERS OF NONPURCHASED AND PUR-
CHASED INPUTS FOR SELECTED YEARS, UNITED
STATES, 1910–65
(1957–59 = 100)

Year	Nonpurchased*	Purchased†
1910	162	44
1915	166	50
1920	174	55
1925	169	60
1930	170	62
1935	150	56
1940	142	72
1945	140	76
1950	119	91
1955	111	97
1960	96	103
1965	86	113

* Includes operator and unpaid family labor, operator-
owned real estate, and other capital inputs.
† Includes all inputs other than nonpurchased inputs.

Increased purchases of inputs continued during the 1950's and 1960's even though prices of many agricultural products were declining. The rapid development of new technology and the increased awareness of the productivity of numerous purchased inputs were such as to encourage farmers to use an increasing amount of many purchased inputs. The productivity of these inputs was apparently great enough to more than offset output price declines.

FUTURE CONTRIBUTIONS OF AGRICULTURE

The contributions of agriculture to economic development in the United States are well recognized. The role it can play in the future is not so well defined. It is evident that because of changes in its relative importance as an occupation, the nature of demand for farm products, the kinds of inputs now used in production and the highly developed state of our economy, agriculture will not play the same role it has played in the past. It is also equally evident that a productive agriculture will be essential. For example, population projections suggest that the number of domestic consumers will exceed 300 million by the year 2000. In view of these projections, it would appear that one of the major contributions of agriculture will be continued provision for food and fiber needs. The rapid adjustments being made on commercial farms along with the ever increasing flow of new technology into agriculture suggest that domestic food and fiber needs will be met with products as well as "know-how" left over for use in programs concerned with world economic development.

Provision for Food and Fiber Needs

The situation in future years with respect to the adequacy of food and fiber is dependent on relative changes in supply and demand. To evaluate the potential supply and demand, it is necessary to estimate the importance of specific factors affecting supply and demand and estimate the relevant levels for each of the factors. Such an analysis is not easy, and even using the most rigorous of techniques it is subject to sizable errors. However, identification of the more important factors and some indication of their potential effects does provide some insight into what might realistically be expected.

First, as suggested earlier in the chapter on demand and possibilities of demand expansion, changes in demand will primarily result from increases in population, changes in disposable income, and changes in export demand. The latter would not be of much importance if concern is limited to domestic food and fiber needs. Since the level of food consumption is already relatively high in the United States, changes in disposable income will affect food and fiber needs, but the effects will not be of large magnitude. Population growth will increase food and fiber needs considerably with population expected to increase by slightly over 50 percent by the year 2000. Current population and per capita income projections indicate a growth in domestic demand for farm products of approximately 2 percent per year during the next two or three decades.

Supply changes are much more difficult to project. Changes during the 1940's and 1950's were dramatic, and the potential for even greater production was increased. Numerous factors were responsible. These include: new and improved machines which can be substituted for labor; improved seeds; reduction in the real price of fertilizer and greater appreciation of its productivity; new and improved herbicides and insecticides; and improvements in the capabilities of labor and management employed in agriculture. These factors were even more effective because of the enlargement of farms and increased specialization which occurred simultaneously. It is obvious that many of these factors will continue to be effective in the foreseeable future, but the magnitude of the effects is impossible to predict.

An indication of supply conditions can be obtained by merely assuming a continuation of the trends in improvements in farming. A recent study by Iowa State University estimates the amount of farmland which would be needed in 1975 to provide for domestic needs plus a 25 percent increase in grain and soybean exports.[7] This study indicates that surplus capacity would increase from 50 million acres in 1965 to 66 million acres in 1975. The results also indicate a similar outcome if extended another 10 years. This analysis, along with others of a similar nature, suggests that United States agriculture will be more than capable of providing for domestic food and fiber needs in the next few decades plus some increase in exports.

Source of Manpower

Agriculture will not be as important in future years as a source of manpower. This is true both in absolute and relative terms because the farm population now comprises less than 6 percent of the total population and the total number of persons on farms is less than 12 million.

Perhaps of even greater importance is the fact that during the 1960's nearly two thirds of the farm operators were over 45 years of age. Persons in this age group are not likely to move into nonfarm employment in large numbers even with the most favorable conditions for outmigration.

However, this does not mean to suggest that the net movement of labor from agriculture to nonfarm employment has ended. Nearly five million of the total farm population in 1964 were in the age groups 14 to 44. If only one half of these move into nonfarm employment during the remainder of the decade of the 1960's, this would amount to nearly one-half million per year. This is possible without unduly hampering total agricultural production.

The potential for continued outmigration is emphasized by the fact that in 1965 farms with sales of less than $2,500 accounted for 43 percent of all U.S. farm families. In past years the rate of outmigration has been highest from this class of farms as evidenced by the fact that the number of farms in this class in 1965 was only 42 percent of what it was in 1949.

---

[7] Earl O. Heady, "Potential Shifts in Commercial Agriculture Relative to Technological Changes; Policies for Long Run Solutions to Surplus Problems" *Our Stake in Commercial Agriculture, Rural Poverty and World Trade*, Proceedings of the Fifth Annual Farm Policy Review Conference, CAED Report No. 22 (Washington, D.C., January 25–27, 1965).

During the same period the number of farms with total sales exceeding $2,500 remained almost constant so the net decline in farm families was approximately equal to the decline in the class with less than $2,500 sales.

The movement of labor out of agriculture is of course affected by many factors other than the level of total sales. The ease of finding nonfarm employment or the level of unemployment in the nonfarm economy is recognized as being of major importance. Potential mobility is also related to age and nonfarm experience.[8] The highest rate of outmovement then is likely to be from farms with a low level of total sales, and the migrant is more likely to have nonfarm experience or be relatively young. Many efforts are currently underway to provide these potential migrants with the educational training and social background necessary to make them more productive in the nonfarm economy.

Assistance in World Economic Development Programs

United States agriculture is in a position to make a substantial contribution to world economic development. This contribution can be in the form of both products and technical assistance. The capacity to produce an excess over domestic needs is evident, and the technical efficiency of U.S. agriculture is respected throughout the world.

The appropriate mechanics or procedures to use in making this contribution are not nearly so easy to discover. Difficulties which arise in trade negotiations concerning agricultural products are evidence of the problems the more highly developed countries have in determining the appropriate balance between imports and development of their own agricultural economies. In certain instances the relatively low-priced agricultural products available from the United States are helpful to supplement domestic production, but the well-being of their own agricultural producers must also be considered.

Likewise the contribution of agricultural products as a form of economic aid to underdeveloped countries is not without problems. Experience with Public Law 480 demonstrates the difficulties involved. Programs of this type must be worked out carefully with each country involved if the efforts are to promote economic growth. Most of these developing nations face problems of food shortages, but questions must be resolved in each instance as to the appropriate mixture of food donations, technical assistance, or other forms of economic aid.

Projections indicate that even if U.S. agriculture produced at maximum capacity, it would be unable to provide for the increased world

---

[8] H. W. Baumgartner, "Potential Mobility in Agriculture: Some Reasons for the Existence of a Labor-Transfer Problem"; *Journal of Farm Economics,* Vol. XLVII (February, 1965), p. 82.

food aid needs by the late 1980's.[9] This suggests that the developing nations must increase their own production. The need for improved technology and management skills in the agricultures of developing nations is quite evident. However, this is an extremely difficult task because of the hetergeneity in conditions which exist. Development of higher yielding varieties of crops, cheaper sources of plant nutrients, effective insecticides, and appropriate forms of mechanization is needed in most of these countries. Educational programs designed to promote the use of improved techniques is likewise a prerequisite to increasing agricultural productivity. Adaptation of scientific knowledge present in the United States to the needs of individual underdeveloped countries poses a real challenge to those who become involved in providing this technical assistance.

PROBLEMS ECONOMIC GROWTH POSES FOR AGRICULTURE

Economic growth is a value which is very widely held. Questions arise not about the desirability of economic growth but rather about the most appropriate procedures for achieving growth. Agriculture as such is interested in economic growth because it enhances the demand for agricultural products and, perhaps of even greater importance, provides greater opportunities for off-farm employment for those no longer needed in agriculture. People in agriculture also subscribe to the value merely because of its benefits to society as a whole. However, economic growth also poses problems for agriculture because of the industry's unique characteristics.

Impact on Demand and Cost of Production

An increase in per capita disposable income is ordinarily associated with economic growth. This means that products with a positive income elasticity of demand will experience increases in demand as economic growth takes place. Although aggregate demand is increased by economic growth, individual commodities experience a differential impact. The demand for some products increases substantially while the demand for others may increase only slightly or even decline as disposable income increases.

Studies of consumption patterns in different countries indicate considerable differences among countries as to expenditure patterns as well as responses to changes in income. Nations with high levels of economic activity such as the United States respond differently from those nations

[9] Quentin M. West, *World Food Needs*, Foreign Regional Analysis Division, Economic Research Service, U.S. Department of Agriculture (Washington, D.C., 1966), p. 22.

classified as developing nations. Of particular relevance to agriculture is the fact that countries with high levels of income do not increase food consumption nearly so much when incomes increase. This is true because diets are already at a fairly adequate level and increases in income are spent for other types of goods. The net effect is that economic growth results in an increase in demand for agricultural products, but the increase is relatively small compared to the change for many other types of products.

Cost of production is also affected by economic growth. Labor as well as other types of inputs used in agricultural production are also used to produce other kinds of products. As the demand for these other products increases, quite often the price of the labor or the raw materials used in their production is increased. This means that agriculture must bid against other industries for production inputs. Thus, economic growth results in an increase in the cost of producing agricultural products, and in fact there is a tendency for the change to be greater than the increase in demand for these products. This phenomenon is a major factor in the cost-price squeeze prevalent in agriculture during recent years.

Adjustments on Farms and in the Marketing System

The contributions of agriculture to economic growth in the United States have been accompanied by significant changes in the agricultural economy. New technologies and more efficient methods of production have resulted in an increase in the size of the most efficient units of production. Farms have tended to become larger and more specialized. Farmers have been forced to either make adjustments or suffer the consequences in terms of lower returns. Some farms have made the transition to larger, more efficient units quite readily while others have adjusted by moving to nonfarm employment. Others have been unable to make the required adjustments and have had to accept lower returns to the labor resource. In addition, efforts to become more efficient and offset higher prices for inputs have quite often been output increasing which has tended to further emphasize the need for adjustment.

As suggested earlier, economic growth has had a differential impact on the demand for individual agricultural commodities. The demand for some has increased rather rapidly while the demand for others has declined. This has provided a stimulus to farmers to increase the production of some commodities while reducing the production of others. Similarly the marketing system has been forced to make adjustments to the changing consumption patterns of consumers. Not only has the volume of individual products handled been subject to shifts but the kinds of services desired by consumers has also changed. In fact, the effects of economic growth have been such that the demand for services has increased much faster than the demand for the agricultural products involved.

Thus, while agriculture has contributed to economic growth it has also been affected by economic growth. Its contributions in the past have been many and varied, and it is expected to continue to make contributions in the future. Farm firms as well as those firms providing inputs to agriculture and marketing agricultural products have been forced to make adjustments as a result of the changing needs of a growing economy.

Appendix

Appendix

NOTATION AND

GEOMETRIC

CONSIDERATIONS

NOTATION

Functional Notation

The production function relates output, Y, to input, X. The definition of a "function" is: If a variable Y depends upon another variable X so that when each value of X is known, a unique (single) value of Y is determined, then Y is called a function of X. A shorthand expression for a function is

$$Y = f(X) .$$

This notation is called functional notation and is read "Y is a function of X." Y is usually called the dependent variable, and X the independent variable.

Subscripts

Subscripts are useful when symbols are used. Their use adds some additional meaning to the symbol. Consider, for example, the notation for the production function.

$$Y = f(X) ,$$

where X is the amount of input and Y the resulting amount of output. Because there is only one input and one output, there can be no confusion about identification of input or output. In this case, subscripts can be used to denote *amounts:* X_1 is an amount of X, X_2 is a greater amount than X_1, X_3 is a greater amount than X_1 or X_2, etc. Also, subscripts on Y can be used to denote amounts of Y. Thus, amount Y_1 of Y results from the use of X_1 amount of X or

$$Y_1 = f(X_1)$$
$$Y_2 = f(X_2)$$
$$Y_3 = f(X_3) .$$

When more than one input or output is included in a problem, subscripts can be used as a means of identification. For example, when output is a function of three inputs, the production function can be written

$$Y = f(X_1, X_2, X_3) \,,$$

where X_1, X_2, and X_3 are distinct and different inputs. The subscripts identify the inputs. If amounts are to be denoted, additional subscripts must be used. X_{11} is an amount of X_1; X_{12} is a greater amount of X_1; X_{21} is an amount of X_2; X_{22} is a greater amount of X_2; etc. Subscripts can also be used to identify outputs. Thus, Y_1, Y_2, and Y_3 can be distinct outputs; amounts could be shown by adding another subscript.

The "Δ" Notation

When dealing with problems concerning the change in a variable, the following notation is common: The change in any variable is denoted by "Δ" (the Greek letter "delta") placed before the variable. For example, the change in the variable X is denoted by ΔX, the change in Y is ΔY, the change in Z is ΔZ, etc. Note that ΔX does not mean a quantity Δ multiplied by a quantity X, but it denotes a single quantity, the change in X. If ΔX is positive, the change in X is an increase. If ΔX is negative, the change in X is a decrease and similarly for other variables. The change ΔX is called the increment of X.

Discrete and Continuous Data

The difference between discrete data and continuous data is in the divisibility of the inputs (or outputs). An example of a discrete input is a cow. A dairy herd may be composed of two, three, or more cows. However, one and a half, two and an eighth, three and a quarter cows, etc., will not be found in a dairy herd because, at least at the time of this writing, cows come only in units of one. Commercial fertilizer, on the other hand, is an example of a continuous input. Fertilizer can be divided into any size unit, and for each size unit there is a resulting yield.

The production schedules used in this text are an example of discrete data. On a graph, a discrete production function would appear as:

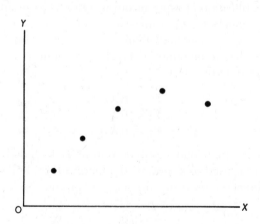

Here, no yield is forthcoming between the dots. One and a half cows give no more milk than one cow. Continuous production functions would appear as:

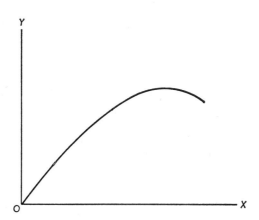

SOME GEOMETRIC CONSIDERATIONS

The Slope of Lines and Curves

Determining the slope of a curve is a problem in applied mathematics. Mathematicians are interested in the slope of a curve because it denotes the rate of change in a variable such as output, Y. Economists are interested in the slope of a curve (production function) because it represents a marginal concept, such as the marginal product of an input, X.

Determining the slope of a curve is easier said than done because, generally speaking, slope differs for each point on the curve. In Figure A–1, the slope of the curve at A is different than the slope at B. Also, the slope at any point between A and B is different than the slope at A or B.

FIGURE A–1

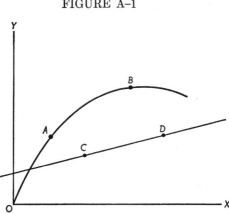

In contrast to a curve, the slope of a straight line is the same for all points on the line and is therefore easily determined. In Figure A–1, the slope of the straight line is the same either at C or D. It is also the same for all points other then C or D. If the slope of a straight line is easily determined but the slope of a curve is difficult to determine, the question might arise: Why not use the straight line to determine the slope of a curve? That is what we will do. First, we will determine how to measure the slope of a straight line and then we will show how a straight line can be used to determine the slope of a curve.

The Slope of a Line. Through any point C on a straight line draw CD parallel to the X axis (Figure A–2). Next, draw line DE parallel to the Y axis. Then,

$$\text{the slope of line } AB = \frac{DE}{CD}.$$

FIGURE A–2

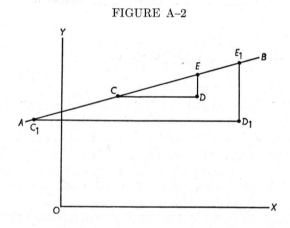

This is the "rise" over the "run" and measures the gradient or slope of the line AB. Notice that in Figure A–2, CED and $C_1E_1D_1$ are similar triangles, therefore

$$\frac{DE}{CD} = \frac{D_1E_1}{C_1D_1}.$$

The slope of the line AB is the same at any point on the line. On a straight line, the size of the triangle CED is immaterial because only the ratio of the sides of the triangle determine the slope.

The following can be said of the slope of a straight line:

1. The slope of a line parallel to the X axis is zero.
2. The slope is the number of units that Y increases (or decreases) when X increases one unit.

3. The slope of a line which falls to the right is negative.
4. The slope of a line which rises to the right is positive.

Figure A–3 is essentially the same as Figure A–2. However, Figure A–3 is labeled differently. Point C is now denoted by the coordinates (X, Y). Point E is now $(X + \Delta X, Y + \Delta Y)$. ΔX is any change in X and ΔY is the corresponding change in Y. Now,

$$\text{the slope of line } AB = \frac{\Delta Y}{\Delta X}.$$

FIGURE A–3

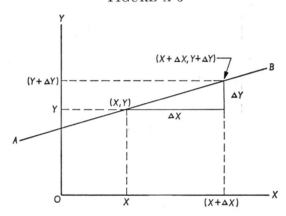

But, when Y is an output and X is an input,

$$\frac{\Delta Y}{\Delta X} = \text{marginal physical product of } X.$$

Because the slope is a measure of MPP_x, MPP_x is a constant for a straight line (linear) production function.

Determining the Slope of a Curve. Figure A–4 illustrates one way a straight line may be used to determine the slope of a curve. Here, points B (X_1, Y_1) and A (X_2, Y_2) are known and we want to measure the slope of the curve between B and A. (The subscripts are used to denote amounts). The slope is

$$\frac{Y_2 - Y_1}{X_2 - X_1} = \frac{\Delta Y}{\Delta X}.$$

$\Delta Y / \Delta X$ does not measure the slope of the curve at A or the slope at B but measures the slope of the line CD. However, the slope of CD can be regarded as an estimate of the slope of the curve between A and B. As the distance between A and B decreases, the slope of the curve is more closely approximated by the slope of the line.

Figure A–4 presents pictorially the situation that occurs when marginal physical products are computed from a production schedule containing only a few values of the continuous input. When used to make graphs, the marginal physical products computed in this manner are

FIGURE A–4

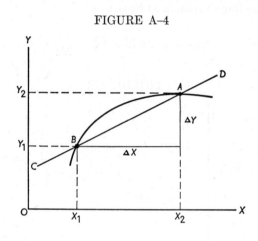

FIGURE A–5

placed halfway between the input levels rather than on either level. That is, in Figure A–4, the MPP_x resulting from adding the input amount $X_2 - X_1$ would be graphed halfway between X_1 and X_2. (Line CD is called a secant.)

A straight line can also be used to determine the exact slope of a curve at any point. In Figure A–5, the slope of the curve and the line AB are equal at C. AB is tangent to the curve at C. By determining the slope of line AB, the exact slope of the curve at C can be determined. Thus,

$$\text{the slope of } AB = \frac{CD}{HD} = \text{slope of curve at } C$$

and

$$\frac{CD}{HD} = \frac{CD}{OE} = \text{.the exact } MPP \text{ of } X \text{ at } C \text{ (for } OE \text{ amount of } X)$$

when the curve represents a production function. Similarly, by drawing a straight line tangent to any other point on the curve in Figure A–5, such as G or F, the MPP_x at that point could be determined.

A Line Passing through the Origin. So far, the straight line has not necessarily gone through the origin (point where $X = 0$ and $Y = 0$). Consider now the special case of a straight line that passes through the origin. The slope of line AB in Figure A–6 is GF/OF. Also,

$$\frac{GF}{OF} = \frac{\Delta Y}{\Delta X} = MPP_x$$

for the line (or production function) AB. When the straight line passes through the origin,

$$GF = OH = Y = \text{an amount of } Y$$

and

$$OF = X = \text{an amount of } X$$

so

$$\frac{GF}{OF} = \frac{OH}{OF} = \frac{Y}{X} = \frac{\text{yield}}{X \text{ used to produce yield}} = APP_x$$

Therefore, the slope of a straight line (production function) passing through the origin is equal to APP_x at any point on the line. And, if the straight line is a production function, $APP_x = MPP_x$ for all amounts of X.

In summary, the following points have been discussed:

1. Determining the slope of any straight line.
2. Use of a straight line (secant) to determine the average slope between two points on a curve.
3. Use of a straight line (tangent) to determine the exact slope at a point on a curve.
4. The special case of a straight line passing through the origin.

Application to the Production Function

Given a graph of the production function, straight lines can be drawn tangent to the production function at any point to measure the exact MPP_x at that point. Also, straight lines can be drawn through the origin to determine the APP_x at the point where the line intersects the production function; the slope of the straight line measures APP_x at the point(s) where the line intersects the production function. However, two uses of straight lines that are of particular interest are shown in Figure A-7.

FIGURE A-6

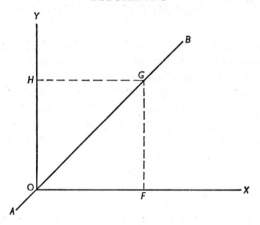

FIGURE A-7

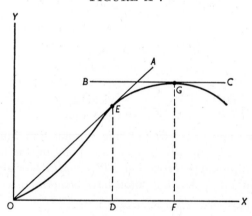

In Figure A-7, the line OA passes through the origin and is tangent to the production function at E. At E

$$\frac{ED}{OD} = \frac{Y}{X} = APP_x = MPP_x.$$

Therefore, the line OA is tangent to the production function at E where marginal and average physical product are equal. OA is used to determine the least amount of X that would be used, the boundary between

Stages I and II. If any X were to be used, OD amount of X would be used. APP_x for this production function must be a maximum at E (for OD amount of X) because any straight line passing through the origin and steeper than OA would not touch the production function.

Line BC in Figure A–7 is parallel to the X axis and tangent to the production function at G. Because the slope of any line tangent to the production function at a point determines the MPP_x at that point, the MPP_x at G (resulting from OF amount of X) is zero. OF is the most X that would be used even if X were a free good. For quantities of X exceeding OF, total product decreases. Thus, the line BC is used to determine the maximum amount of X that would be used, the boundary between Stages II and III.

The values of X between and including OD and OF make up Stage II of the production function, sometimes called the region of "economic relevance." This latter term arises because input and output prices are needed to determine the most profitable amount of X to use *within* Stage II.

Application to Elasticity

When "average" measures of MPP_x are used (such as demonstrated in Figure A–4), then an "average" measure of elasticity is used. This measure, called the arc elasticity formula, is

$$\epsilon_p = \frac{X_1 + X_2}{Y_1 + Y_2} \cdot \frac{Y_2 - Y_1}{X_2 - X_1}$$

or

$$\epsilon_p = \frac{\dfrac{X_1 + X_2}{2}}{\dfrac{Y_1 + Y_2}{2}} \cdot \frac{\Delta Y}{\Delta X} .$$

When $\Delta Y/\Delta X$ is a measure of the "average" slope of the arc (Figure A–4), then $X_1 + X_2 / Y_1 + Y_2$, the average value of X and Y between points B and A, is also used.

When the exact MPP_x is determined by the use of a tangent (Figure A–5), then an exact measure of elasticity is used. This measure, called the point elasticity formula, is

$$\epsilon_p = \frac{X}{Y} \cdot \frac{\Delta Y}{\Delta X} = \frac{MPP_x}{APP_x}$$

Here, $\Delta Y/\Delta X$ must be defined to be the exact MPP_x at C (Figure A–5), and X and Y are the exact amounts of input (OE) and output (EC) at point C.

The names of the two formulas suggest their use. The arc formula is used to measure the elasticity over an arc. The point formula is used to measure the elasticity at a point.

Index

INDEX

This book has been set in 10 and 9 point Caledonia, leaded 2 points. Part numbers and titles and chapter numbers and titles are 18 point Spartan Medium. The size of the type page is 27 by 45½ picas.